Dedicated
to our
Friend and Mentor
Isaäc J. H. Isbrücker

Hans-Georg Evers
Ingo Seidel

Cover Photos:

Title: *Hemiloricaria lanceolata*
                  I. Seidel

Back cover: *Harttia surinamensis*   *Pseudohemiodon apithanos*
                  I. Seidel   H.-G. Evers

                  Otocinclus sp. "Zebra"   *Lampiella gibbosa*
                  I. Seidel   H.-G. Evers

Opposite page: Hypostominae sp. "Rio Jaciparana" on a spectacled caiman
                  (*Caiman crocodilus*).
                  H.-G. Evers

Inside front: The Rio Cipó in southern Brazil.
                  H.-G. Evers

Inside back: The Río Sipapo at Raudal Caldero (upper Orinoco, Venezuela).
                  I. Seidel

The authors of the various photographs are named next to the photos.

1st edition 2005

CATFISH ATLAS Vol. 1:
South American Catfishes of the Families Loricariidae, Cetopsidae, Nematogenyidae
and Trichomycteridae
Hans-Georg Evers; Ingo Seidel
1st edition 2005
ISBN 3-88244-064-3

Layout: Mergus Verlag GmbH, Melle
                             Dr. Gero W. Fischer, Quito, Ecuador
Scans: Mergus Lithoart, Singapore
Printing: MERGUS PRESS, Malaysia
Publisher: Hans A. Baensch
Translated and revised by: Gero W. Fischer, Ph.D.
Proofreading: Heather Johnston

Printed in Malaysia

Hans-Georg Evers   Ingo Seidel

Volume 1

MERGUS

Publishers of Natural History and Pet Books
Hans A. Baensch • Melle • Germany

Preface

It has been several years—it was during the winter of 1995/96, to be exact—that the idea of a CATFISH ATLAS began taking shape in our minds and that we started planing the actual making of such a project. Initially, it was slated to be a work of several volumes, dealing with all the catfishes of the world, but once work started, it became clear that such a giant undertaking was hardly realizable. General tomes on catfishes are a plenty, but as far as we know, there are only a few of the truly more specialized publications. To realize this project for all catfish families is very hard and perhaps close to impossible. Nevertheless, enthusiastically we jumped right in, dealing first with the arguably most important catfish family, the Loricariidae or suckermouth catfishes. Soon we came to realize that even to properly deal with this single, albeit extensive group, the confines of a single "normal" volume would not suffice—two volumes are needed to present in detailed manner all the suckermouth catfishes. Therefore, the volume in your hands represents the first part of the monograph on the Neotropical catfishes. We began our work with the loricariid subfamilies Hypoptopomatinae and Loricariinae. The second volume—meanwhile virtually completed—will deal with the subfamilies Ancistrinae, Hypostominae, and Neoplecostominae exclusively and will be published shortly. Given that our aim is to present all Neotropical catfishes as completely as possible, we included in this first volume also the families Cetopsidae, Nematogeneidae, and Trichomycteridae. That section of the first volume was placed at the end and has its own bibliography in order to present the reader with an easier grouping of resources. The complete bibliography of the suckermouth catfishes can also be found at the end of this volume. A third volume is already in its planing stages. It will contain the Callichthyidae and possibly all other Neotropical catfish families.

The Loricariidae, with over 650 described species, is presently the largest catfish family. Aquaristically, its members only played a secondary role for many years. Still during the mid-eighties, the interested hobbyist only had 20 different species from which to choose from, as they sporadically appeared in the trade. There were one or two *Ancistrus* spp., several *Hypostomus* (commonly under the synonym of "*Plecostomus*"), and *Glyptoperichthys* or *Liposarcus* (back then under the collective term of "*Pterygoplichthys*") which grew excessively large, one species of the genus *Peckoltia*, one or two *Sturisoma* species, and several *Rineloricaria* (usually under the collective term of "*Loricaria parva*") and that was it. It was in the year 1988 when the German aquarium magazine DATZ began to present aquaristically new suckermouth catfishes with a code, the so-called L-numbers. Suddenly, Brazilian suckermouth catfishes with interesting designs appeared everywhere, and the interest of aquarists for the Loricariidae grew immensely. A first climax was reached with the September 1989 edition of the DATZ, where a gorgeous suckermouth catfish—L 46, later described as *Hypancistrus zebra*—was presented. Suddenly, everybody wanted one. Is it possible that this fish triggered the subsequent worldwide boom in catfishes? Many additional suckermouth catfishes followed, several with similarly attractive designs. Nowadays we are close to the L-number 400, and no end is in sight as new, unexplored areas in South America are being combed by commercial fishermen and new jewels reach the aquaristic scene virtually every day. This popularity of suckermouth catfishes is global. Whether it is in Europe, Japan or other countries of the far east, or in the United States, these fishes can be found in aquaria everywhere and are the objects of unbridled popularity.

Our knowledge in regard to maintenance requirements and breeding of suckermouth catfishes has come a long way in recent years, and we have attempted to collect the most up-to-date information and present it in this book. The same applies to the characteristics of the natural habitats of suckermouth catfishes, of which we were able to visit several personally in recent years. Often it can be read that suckermouth catfishes are difficult to unequivocally identify, which is why in the aquarium literature it is common to find that the fishes are only determined to the genus level. As a by-product of our extensive bibliographic research for this book, it was possible to identify numerous aquaristically known fishes to the species level. We were therefore able to identify several species that had been known in the hobby for a long time, and present them here under their presumably correct designation.

The work on this book over the years has been very enjoyable and we hope that our enthusiasm for these fishes has contributed to present the aquarist, and others interested in suckermouth catfishes, with a tome that will help in answering most of their questions.

Hans-Georg Evers
Hamburg

Ingo Seidel
Seefeld

Acknowledgments

Acknowledgments

In writing the acknowledgments, we become aware of how many nice people have helped us over the years in providing not only information, fishes, and photos, but also lodging and meals. A monograph as extensive as this one could never be undertaken alone by one or even several authors, but depends on the help of others. We are proud and happy about the large number of friends and acquaintances who have helped us with this endeavour.

First, our thanks go to our publisher and friend Hans A. BAENSCH, who allowed us the latitude to work and who made the lavish presentation of the first two volumes possible. Without mentioning the good collaboration with our [German] proofreader Gaby NICKSTADT, this acknowledgment would be incomplete. Gero FISCHER and Heather JOHNSTON prepared the english translation.

Certainly we owe many thanks also to our friend Stefan K. HETZ, who unselfishly proofread the entire manuscript, a strenuous undertaking, for sure. Large sections of the manuscript on suckermouth catfishes were proofed by Isaäc ISBRÜCKER (Amsterdam, Holland) and André WERNER (Planegg, Germany). The section on Cetopsidae, Nematogeneidae, and Trichomycteridae was checked graciously by Isaäc ISBRÜCKER (Amsterdam, Holland), parts were also annotated by Richard P. VARI (Washington, United States), Carl FERRARIS (San Francisco, United States), and Mario C. DE PINNA (São Paulo, Brazil). To all of them we owe our sincere thanks for their comments and suggestions for improvement.

We also thank Stanley H. WEITZMAN (Washington) for his contribution about the hearing apparatus in otocinlus.

Although both authors are expert aquarists and have bred many suckermouth catfishes personally, it is impossible to know everything. Therefore, we thank the following persons for their important indications in regard to maintenance and breeding of various catfish species, without which this book would not have been possible [Germany, unless otherwise indicated]:

Gerd and Karin ARNDT (Wiemerstedt), Volker BOHNET (Oldenburg), Raimond BREUER (Oyten), Robert BUDROVCAN (Erlangen), Peter DEBOLD (Stralsund), Klaus-Dieter ELSHOLZ (†, Berlin), Johannes FLÖSSHOLZER (Austria), Haakon HAAGENSEN (Norway), Mike HEMMANN (Gera), Roland KIPPER (Bremen), Joachim KNAACK (Neuglobsow), Christian KUHLMANN (Zirmdorf), Johannes LEUENBERGER (Kaiseraugst, Switzerland), Dani MADÖRIN (Oberwil, Switzerland), Rainer MELZER (Berlin), Raimond NORMANN (Satow), Klaus-Dieter ROHLOFF (Berlin), Erik SCHILLER (Neumarkt/Opf.),

Acknowledgments

Michael Schlüter (Hamburg), Ernst Schmidt (Nürnberg), Mike Schneider (Dülmen), Markus Sommer (Großheide), Andreas Sprenger (Witten), Helmut Wendenburg (Hünfeld), Ulrich Wälti (Frenkendorf, Switzerland), Herbert Windhorst (Harpstedt), Uwe Wolf (Zella-Mehlis).
A very special thank you to our friends of the company Trop-Rio in Rio de Janeiro: Marco Tulio C. Lacerda and Mario Pinheiro have, over the latter years, repeatedly lent their support to us. Over the course of several years, together with Maik Beyer (Maricá, Brazil), the catfishes of southeastern Brazil were tracked down in the farthest corners and sent to Germany. Through the mediation of Aquarium Dietzenbach these fishes in the end reached Hamburg and consequently, our aquaria. Besides the named persons, especially Paulo Valerio da Silva gave us uncalculable aid in our Brazilian trips. To him and his wife Cecilia, as well as to the employees of Peixe Vivo (Aruanã, central Brazil) a heart-felt thank you!

We also want to express our gratitude for the selfless support during our South America trips—which gave us valuable insight into the natural lifestyle of several of the fish species presented here—to the following persons:
Sandra and Juarez Carvalho de Almeida (Rondônia Aquarios, Porto Velho, Brazil), Norbert Flauger (Bejuma, Venezuela), Hans-Jürgen Köpke and Sixto Rodriguez (Valencia, Venezuela), Cecil Persaud (Guyana Aquarium Traders, Georgetown, Guyana), Karsten Augustin and Hans Rieger (Santa Cruz, Bolivia), Carlos Areia Pereira and Marcos Wanderley (D'agua, Recife. Brazil), Erhard Thiemicke (Calabozo, Venezuela), Mario Voyt and Alvaro Carrera (Puerto Ayacucho, Venezuela), Thomas Zirm (Pucallpa, Peru), as well as to the nameless South American fishermen and helpers, who with their friendly attitude and hands-on support have made it possible for us to capture many suckermouth catfishes.

The companies and private persons mentioned here, selflessly supplied us with their fishes for us to photograph them. In part they even called our attention towards new imports, and this way helped us over the years to accumulate a large inventory of rare suckermouth catfish photographs. Many thanks to:
Karin and Gerd Arndt (Wiemerstedt), Volker Bohnet and Jan Olsen (Aqua Design, Oldenburg), the Berthold family (formerly Bertholds Welswelt, Euskirchen), Friedrich Bitter (Bitter Exotics, Geeste), Raimond Breuer (Oyten), Robert Budrovcan (Erlangen), Werner Dinklage (Bremen), Elfriede Ehlers and Herbert Wegner (Karstadt Zooabteilung, Hamburg), Gerold Friede (Zoo & Angelsport Hagenow), the Glaser family and Frank Schäfer (Aquarium Glaser, Rodgau), Jens Gottwald (Aquatarium, Garbsen), Familie Heidbrink (Großhandel G. Höner, Hiddenhausen), Mike Hemmann (Gera), Gerolf Jander (Aqua-Global, Seefeld), Tim Kohnen (Ute's Welskeller, Peine), Christian Kuhlmann (ehemals Z3, Zirmdorf),

Acknowledgments

Herbert NIGL (Aquarium Dietzenbach, Dietzenbach), Roland NUMRICH (Mimbon Aquarium, Köln), Karl-Heinz RECK (Aquariengrotte, Hamburg), Werner and Frank GOTTSCHALK and Horst RICKHOFF (Zierfische Gottschalk, Neu Wulmstorf), Erik SCHILLER (Neumarkt, Opf.), Mike SCHNEIDER (Aquahaus, Dülmen), Sven SEIDEL (Welsladen, Oberlungwitz), Markus SOMMER (Großheide), Andreas SPRENGER (Witten), Arthur and André WERNER (Transfish, Planegg), Herbert WINDHORST (Harpstedt).

The following persons contributed photographs and/or gave us valuable information in regard to the loricariids habitats visited by them, without which these books would never be so informative. We express our gratitude to:
Kai ARENDT (Helmstedt), Jonathan W. ARMBRUSTER (Auburn, USA), Hans A. BAENSCH (Melle), Maik BEYER (Maricá, Brazil), Danny BLUNDELL (Morecambe, England), Peter DEBOLD (Stralsund), Lee FINLEY (Pascoag, USA), Hanns-Joachim (†) and Erika FRANKE (Gera), Johannes FLÖSSHOLZER (Austria), Jens GOTTWALD (Garbsen), Mike HEMMANN (Gera), Stefan K. HETZ (Berlin), Isaäc ISBRÜCKER (Amsterdam, Holland), Michael KEIJMAN (Rhenen, Holland), Bernd KILIAN (Bonn), Stefan KÖRBER (Mülheim), Joachim KNAACK (Neuglobsow), Marco T. C. LACERDA (Rio de Janeiro, Brazil), Johannes LEUENBERGER (Kaiseraugst, Switzerland), Rainer MELZER (Berlin), Birgit and Raimond NORMANN (Satow), Edson PEREIRA (Porto Alegre, Brazil), Sven PLOEGER (Berlin), Torsten PLÖSCH (Leer), Juan REICHERT (†, Montevideo, Uruguay), Rüdiger RIEHL (Düsseldorf), Dietrich RÖSSEL (Königstein-Falkenstein), Frank SCHAEFER (Rodgau), Scott A. SCHAEFER (New York, USA), Erik SCHILLER (Neumarkt/Opfalz), Ingo SCHINDLER (Berlin), Erwin SCHRAML (Augsburg), Rolf SCHRÖDER (Hamburg), Christoph SEIDEL (Bonn), Wolfgang STAECK (Berlin), Rainer STAWIKOWSKI (Gelsenkirchen), Marcos WANDERLEY (Recife, Brazil), Frank WARZEL (Mainz-Kostheim), Helmut WENDENBURG (Hünfeld), André WERNER (Planegg), Uwe WERNER (Ense-Bremen), Mario WILHELM (Kampsdorf)

We also owe a debt of gratitude for the procurement of aquaristic and scientific literature to following people:
Gloria ARRATIA (Berlin), Carl FERRARIS (San Francisco, United States), Lutz FISCHER (Oldenburg), Stefan KÖRBER (Mülheim), Shane LINDER (Caracas, Venezuela), Thomas LITZ (Gau-Algesheim), Mike E. RETZER (Illinois, United States), Stanley H. WEITZMAN (Washington, United States), André WERNER (Planegg), Anja and Thomas Wittauer (Delmenhorst).

Last but not least, our thanks go out to the numerous and not listed members of the working group BSSW, to the catfish group of Mecklenburg, and to all others that have helped us in any way and which have not been mentioned here, due to an involuntary (and unfortunate) omission on our part (please forgive us).

Table of Contents

Table of Contents

Table of Contents

Table of Contents

Symblogy

Symbols Used in the Illustrated Fish Section:

Fam.:	=	Family
Subfam.:	=	Subfamily
F:	=	First describer
Syn.:	=	Synonym
Hab.:	=	Habitat. The original area of distribution of the species.
M.&B.:	=	Maintenance and breeding
S:	=	Special observations
T:	=	Temperature
L:	=	Length of the adult specimen.
A:	=	Aquarium length
WR:	=	Water region:
		t = top
		m = middle
		b = bottom
♂	=	male
♀	=	female

Family Loricariidae   Bonaparte, 1831

Introduction

The family of suckermouth catfishes (Loricariidae) is without a doubt, morphologically speaking, one of the most polyfacetic families of freshwater fishes. With over 90 genera and in excess of 650 described species, this is the largest family of Neotropical catfishes, only bettered by the families Characidae (characins), Cichlidae (cichlids), and Cyprinidae (cyprinids). In contrast to these families, however, the distribution of the suckermouth catfishes is limited to the Central and South American continent. There, according to Schaefer (1998), they comprise approximately 10% of all described piscine species. The area of distribution of loricariids extends from Costa Rica in the north to the southern section of the South American continent (Uruguay and Argentina, with the exception of Chile, Tierra del Fuego, etc.) in the south. The distribution is limited to freshwater, since suckermouth catfishes do not tolerate large fluctuations in salinity.

Suckermouth Catfishes as Research Subjects

In the year 1831 Bonaparte established the "Loricarini" as a subunit of the family Siluridae, a family in use at that time. Today the loricariids represent their own family and the Siluriformes have been established as their own independent order. Due to the immense number of taxons, suckermouth catfishes have always provided for a broad field of activity for ichthyologists. Many generations have dealt with the systematics of this family and as a result, there are several very important publications available. According to Isbrücker (1980), complete or partial overviews of the family Loricariidae have been published by Valenciennes, in Cuvier & Valenciennes (1840), Kner (1854a and 1854b), Bleeker (1858, 1862, and 1863), Günther (1864), Eigenmann & Eigenmann (1888, 1889, 1890, and 1891), Regan (1904), Eigenmann (1910), Gosline (1945, 1947), Fowler (1954), Boeseman (1971), and Isbrücker (1979). The aim of these scientists has been to logically subdivide this family

The dutch ichthyologist Isaäc ISBRÜCKER with an undescribed suckermouth catfish, related to the genus *Panaque*.

further, into smaller systematic units, as a means to better represent the relationships among them.

One of the most important monographs on suckermouth catfishes appeared as early as at the turn of the 20th century. In 1904, the British ichthyologist Charles Tate REGAN published his "Monograph of the Family Loricariidae" where he divided the family into five subfamilies: the Loricariinae, Plecostominae, Hypoptopomatinae, Neoplecostominae, and the Argiinae. In doing so, he added the subfamilies Neoplecostominae and Argiinae to the other three known to EIGENMANN & EIGENMANN (1890), which previously had been given by GILL (1872) the status of independent families. A similar systematic arrangement is also found in GOSLINE (1947), who additionally established the subfamily Lithogeneinae. GOSLINE already dealt with 400 species and subspecies in 49 genera.

Presently, the Dutch ichthyologist Dr. Isaäc J.H. ISBRÜCKER is very involved in the field of suckermouth catfishes. In 1980 he published his suckermouth catfish catalog "Classification and catalogue of the mailed Loricariidae," where he lists approximately 600 species and 70 genera. Practically all modern literature still refers to this publication. In his catalogue, ISBRÜCKER divides the family Loricariidae into the six subfamilies Loricariinae, Ancistrinae, Hypostominae, Hypoptopomatinae, Neoplecostominae, and Lithogeneinae. He based his classification on a division of the family created in 1853 by the Austrian Rudolph KNER (see KNER 1853b, 1854b). There, the loricariids are still called the family Loricata (armored fishes) and the second main group, the "Hypostomids," is subdivided into the subunits Inermes (later the subfamily Hypostominae; interoperculum with little motility, lack of clustered hooks) and Lictores or Ancistri (later the subfamily Ancistrinae; interoperculum raiseable, with clusters of hooks).

Today, the subfamilies Hypostominae and Ancistrinae usually receive the genera previously classified in the Plecostominae. The name Plecostominae has disappeared because *Plecostomus* is now considered a synonym of *Hypostomus*. The argiids were separated from the loricariids and elevated into a family in their own right. However, to complicate matters more, today this family is not called Argiidae anymore, but Astroblepidae, since the genus *Arges* is meanwhile considered a synonym of the genus *Astroblepus,* HUMBOLDT 1805. Although the South American hillstream catfishes share the inferior discoid mouth with the loricariids, they are completely naked. They are species inhabiting the upper courses of streams and have no aquaristic significance. Later, NIJSSEN & ISBRÜCKER (1987) also included the genus *Lithogenes* into the family Astroblepidae, based on its very slight armor (the member species are virtually naked) and hereby dissolved the subfamily Lithogeneinae. Recent research confirmed the validity of the Lithogeneinae and one more subfamily is planned (not published until yet). Here we nowadays talk about 6 subfamilies.

- Loricariinae BONAPARTE, 1831
- Ancistrinae KNER, 1853
- Hypostominae KNER, 1853
- Hypoptopomatinae EIGENMANN & EIGENMANN, 1890
- Neoplecostominae REGAN, 1904
- Lithogeneinae GOSLINE, 1947

With the exception of the subfamily Neoplecostominae, all subfamilies have numerous species that are well known in the aquarium hobby.

Whereas the Neoplecostominae according to GOSLINE (1947) still included 12 genera of suckermouth catfishes primarily found in the southeastern Brazilian area—of which most today are considered part of the Hypostomidae—according to ISBRÜCKER (1980), the Neoplecostominae only comprise the genus *Neoplecostomus*, which after a revision by LANGEANI (1991) consists of six species. However, newest analyses let us expect the inclusion of additional genera—already mentioned by GOSLINE—into the subfamily. A revision of the subfamily has already been announced by the American ichthyologist John ARMBRUSTER on the internet, but it is not yet considered published.

This is the current division of the family Loricariidae, even though in the past, several authors have brought new subfamilies to life. For example, BAILEY & BASKIN established in 1976 the subfamily

Fam.: Loricariidae

A peek at the suckermouth catfish collection of the Zoological Museum in Amsterdam.

Scoloplacinae, but IsBRÜCKER (1980) separated it in his catalogue of loricariids, since in his opinion those fishes have even less in common with the family Loricariidae than the astroblepids. Today, the Scoloplacidae are considered an autonomous family. Furthermore, the additional subfamily Chaetostomatinae established by HOWES (1983) (according to NIJSSEN & ISBRÜCKER, 1987, incorrectly called Chaetostominae by HOWES) is not recognized by most ichthyologists because of excessive difficulties and uncertainties involving the classification of genera into this taxon.

The systematic classification of numerous species into certain groupings in the past was primarily based on externally visible characteristics. The ichthyologists attempted to characterize a fish and to distinguish it from similar species by counting, measuring, and describing particular characteristics. However, the phylogenesis (genealogy) of suckermouth catfishes has only been of recent consideration by ichthyologists. Especially suitable for this approach are the osteological characteristics.

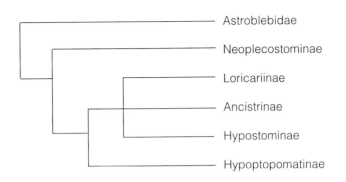

Astroblebidae

Neoplecostominae

Loricariinae

Ancistrinae

Hypostominae

Hypoptopomatinae

Based on such an analysis, for example, the American ichthyologist Scott A. SCHAEFER (1991) revised the subfamily Hypoptopomatinae and arrived at surprising conclusions. SCHAEFER determined in his phylogenetic analysis of the Hypoptopomatinae the following relationships to the other subfamilies of the Loricariidae and the separate Astroblepidae:

Further fundamental changes in the systematics of the Loricariidae must be anticipated in the near future. The American ichthyologist Jonathan W. ARMBRUSTER (pers. comm.), who has worked on the phylogenesis of hypostomid suckermouth catfishes for some time, has already announced several changes. ARMBRUSTER (1997) investigated numerous characteristics of various loricariidae of the subfamily Hypostominae and came to the conclusion that its members are both polyphyletic as well as paraphyletic, i.e., some of its members have different ancestors and there are members of other subfamilies which seem to share the same ancestors as some of the hypostomine genera. Although there has not yet been a taxonomically relevant publication on the matter, ARMBRUSTER expresses that there is one in preparation. The results of ARMBRUSTER's analysis can already be obtained from his internet homepage (see index: ARMBRUSTER, 1999). However, we do not want to anticipate anything, which is why for this book we follow the currently valid systematics of the various genera as given by ISBRÜCKER (1980) and

Nijssen & Isbrücker (1987). In any case, the future changes affect only the subfamilies Ancistrinae, Hypostominae, and Neoplecostominae, all subfamilies dealt with in the second volume of the Catfish Atlas.

Although the Loricariidae have been studied scientifically for more than 200 years, our knowledge of their evolutionary history is rather superficial. It will be interesting to see what future phylogenetic studies will reveal, especially since new procedures, such as DNA sequencing, have hardly been used to date. It is only now that these new techniques are being applied to this fish group, and preliminary results are already available, for example, by Montoya-Burgos et al. (1997; 1998). These results, too, confirm that the present distribution of genera among the five subfamilies cannot be definitive, since apparently only the subfamily Loricariinae seems to represent a monophyletic group. Especially the concept of a larger subfamily Neoplecostominae, as it was already established by Gosline (1947) and taken up by Armbruster, seems to gain force at least in part by the research performed by Montoya-Burgos, Muller, Weber, and Pawlowski. Something similar is happening with the unification of the subfamilies Ancistrinae and Hypostominae as announced by Armbruster, thanks to these same initial genetic analyses. Additionally, these analyses show that probably a part of the Hypostominae, and perhaps the monophyletic Loricariinae, originated from a branch of lower ancistrinids. Of all loricariids studied by Montoya-Burgos et al., *Hemipsilichthys gobio* was determined to be the species that diverged from the family first. The Swiss ichthyologists divided the family into lower and higher Loricariidae. They determined to be the Neoplecostominae *sensu* Armbruster (*Neoplecostomus* plus several southeastern Hypostominae) as well as the Hypoptopomatinae as the more primitive forms. The higher Loricariidae, according to Montoya-Burgos et al., are comprised of the Ancistrinae, the remaining Hypostominae, as well as the Loricariinae.

As we have been able to show in the previous paragraphs, there is a lot of scientific literature that deals with the suckermouth catfishes. However, aquaristic books that treat this family in detail are few and far between. The arguably most complete overview of the family of suckermouth catfishes is given by the Dr. Warren E. BURGESS (1989), who in his "Atlas of Freshwater and Marine Catfishes" lists all species valid at the time, together with their origin, many also including a photograph. Similarly, if not quite as extensive, the English Dr. David D. SANDS (1984) wrote on the subject in the fourth volume of his five-part series "Catfishes of the World." The reference publication in the German language, for a long time, was the book by Dr. Hanns-Joachim FRANKE "Handbuch der Welskunde" [= Handbook of Catfish Science] (1985). For the first time, he presented to German aquarists texts and illustrations of fishes up to then totally unknown. Whereas his book is becoming outdated in regards to nomenclature and systematics in general, it maintains its value for the prospective breeder because of its wealth of information in regard to practical maintenance and breeding conditions. Unfortunately, it is out of print.

Morphological Characteristics

The ludicrous shape of many suckermouth catfishes, which has made them popular among numerous aquarists, is based mostly on some morphological particularities, very unusual within the fish kingdom. Particularly characteristic for this group of fishes is the ventral arrangement of the oral and branchial openings. The discoidal shape of the oral opening is considered a particular adaptation to the benthic lifestyle. The non-closable mouth is surrounded by a relatively narrow upper lip and a usually much broader lower lip, which in many species is covered interiorly by numerous papillae. On the lateral edges of the mouth are so-called rictal barbels, which connect the upper and the lower lip. In most suckermouth catfishes the mouth is shaped in such a way as to allow them to adhere to a substrate even while exposed to a strong current. Their dorsoventrally flattened body aids them by offering little resistance to the current. On the other hand, bottom-dwelling loricariids, which do not have to adhere to a substrate in order to maintain position, have a much smaller mouth which is not suited as well to attach themselves. Especially among this group, there are many where the lips have numerous branched barbels. These "natural works of art" are tactile organs, employed in searching for edibles in the sand. Head shape is another area where suckermouth catfishes differ among the various groups, for some it is even their most notable feature. Especially the rostrum—a distinct elongation of the snout—is something typical for numerous suckermouth catfishes. Especially impressive is the development of this rostrum in members of the genus *Farlowella,* where it may have a length of several centimeters.

There are both dwarf species as well as true giants among the suckermouth catfishes. Some species may readily reach a length of 120 cm (e.g., *Pseudacanthicus hystrix*), whereas others do not exceed 2 cm (such as *Parotocinclus longirostris*). Given that the body of most fishes is covered by scales, a casual observer might assume that a loricariid may also have scales. Nothing could be further from the truth: head and body of loricariids are encased in bony dermal plates (scutes). These bony plates are arranged in longitudinal and cross-rows, covering the body of loricariids with a tough shield reminiscent of medieval knights. Therefore, loricariids are also often called armored catfishes, a source of confusion with the *Corydoras* and another. This body armor, however, allows for sufficient lateral flexibility so as not to interfere excessively in the mobility of these species.

As additional "weapons," loricariids have numerous spinelike protuberances, called odontodes, which may be arranged in great numbers on the scutes of the entire body—with the exception of the unprotected ventral area. All fin rays and the exterior surfaces of the cranial bones are additional sites of extensive aggregates of these odontodes. The surface feels rough to the touch, similar to shark skin. The degree of development of these odontodes varies from species to species. In representatives of the genus *Pseudacanthicus* they are developed to such an extent that these fishes justifiably go under the common name of cactus catfishes. Especially long (hypertrophied) odontodes are displayed by many suckermouth catfishes on the head region, on the pectoral fin rays, and on the dorsum and posterior body. Males of some species

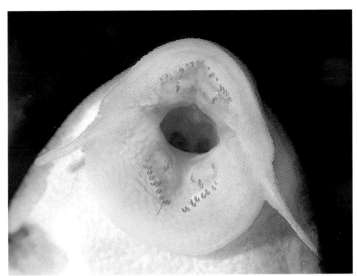

Peckoltia sp., oral disc.

H.-G. Evers

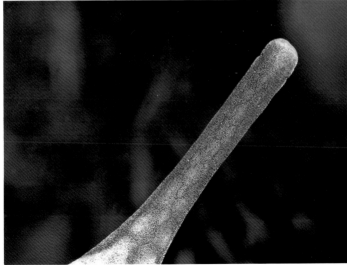

Farlowella sp., rostrum.

H.-G. Evers

Despite the body armor made of bony plates, loricariids are quite nimble.   H.-G. Evers

Odontodes on the pectoral fin spine of *Parancistrus aurantiacus*.   H.-G. Evers

I. Seidel

Male loricariids, in particular, often have their entire body covered by odontodes (here *Rineloricaria* sp. aff. *latirostris*).

develop particularly long odontodes during periods of sexual activity. One group of loricariids—the representatives of the subfamily Ancistrinae—develop odontodes on the interoperculum, which is mobile and may be everted. These odontodes are generally the largest in adult male specimens. The interopercular odontodes may also be used as effective weapons against conspecifics and predators. Interestingly, it has been repeatedly observed how small aquatic fauna take advantage of these defensive structures, remaining preferably among their midst as protection. FREIHOFER & NEIL (1967) and RAPP PY-DANIEL (1991) documented independently cases of commensalism in *Ancistrus* sp. and *Chaetostoma fischeri* from Ecuador, for *Chaetostoma lineopunctatum* from Peru, as well as in *Chaetostoma jegui* from Brazil. In all cases the commensals were chironomid larvae (midge larvae, Diptera) that had adhered to the soft membrane between the hooklets. There is certainly sufficient food in the interopercular region, since organic matter constantly becomes entangled among the spines.

While investigating the odontodes on the body of several lorica-riids, P_EYER (1922) and B_HATTI (1938) determined that they are cal-cified conical structures, very similar to oral teeth. They are there-fore also called dermal teeth, and can also be found on several other Neotropical catfish families, which is why today the loricariids are classified together with members of the families Astroblepidae, Callichthyidae, Nematogenyidae, Scoloplacidae, and Trichomyc-teridae into the suborder Loricarioidei of the order Siluriformes—all families which distinguish themselves for having corporal odon-todes—according to B_ASKIN (1978).

All suckermouth catfishes have a spine on all and every one of their fins. This first ray is unbranched, usually thicker than the fol-lowing soft spines, and heavily ossified. An exception is the anal fin, where in most species the first ray is not much thicker or tougher than the remaining rays. The soft rays are much more delicate and—in contrast to spines—usually branched at their tip. Numer-ous loricariids have a second fin on their dorsum, the adipose fin, which is composed of a small spine and a posterior membrane. It developed from a central bony plate of the dorsum. In some ar-mored catfishes, the spines of the dorsal, caudal, pectoral and/or ventral fins are elongated beyond the edge of the fin, in some cases even forming a filamentous elongation as long as the body itself. Especially common is this characteristic in the subfamily Loricariinae, where most members show at least an upper caudal filament.

As with some other typical nocturnal benthic species (e.g., flat-fishes), the eyes of most suckermouth catfishes have a cover mechanism which during the day protects the eye from excessive illumination. This function is accomplished by a small dermal ap-pendage covering the iris. It expands in bright light and contracts once the illumination is dim.

A characteristic of Amazonian waters are the extensive variations in water levels, accompanied by changes in temperature and dis-solved oxygen concentrations. Especially in lagoons and flood lakes, the dissolved oxygen concentration may even approach zero on many occasions (K_RAMER et. al., 1978). Such conditions are le-

Filament on the upper caudal fin lobe of a *Spatuloricaria* sp.

H.-G. Evers

Typical superior dermal appendage over the iris of a *Hypostomus* sp.

I. Seidel

Oxygen deficiency is a common occurrence in South American waters. Often the loricariids are better adapted to such conditions than most other fishes. This *Hypopto-poma* sp. is breathing atmospheric oxygen.

thal for fishes solely dependent on branchial respiration. However, some species are capable of surviving even under such circumstances by obtaining supplemental oxygen from the air. In order to accomplish this feat, however, they must have an additional breathing organ, which allows them to breathe the air directly. Therefore, many catfishes have accessory breathing organs which may be quite variable in morphology, depending on the catfish family. Basically, any organ having a large surface area covered by a thin, richly-vascularized membrane coming in contact with the air can at least partially contribute to the fishes' gas exchange budget. This works particularly well on the richly-vascularized epithelia of the branchial cavity, the oral cavity, the swim-bladder, and the intestinal tract. Over the course of evolution of the bony fishes (teleosts) it seems that the capacity to utilize atmospheric oxygen has developed independently in the various fish groups.

In the aquarium literature it is frequently stated that the intestine of suckermouth catfishes fulfills the functions of an accessory breathing organ. According to Emmy DORN (1985), who studied the capacity of various species of teleosts to breathe atmospheric oxygen, the stomach also participates in atmospheric breathing. In the studied specimens, it is said to have always been balloonlike inflated with air. The food, as suspected by DORN, seems to be transported through the stomach in small portions without interfering with air breathing. However, as shown by ARMBRUSTER (1998b), this does not apply to all loricariids. He determined an enlarged stomach adapted for breathing among members of the genera *Pterygoplichthys*, *Glyptoperichthys*, *Liposarcus*, and *Lithoxus*, as well as in the species "*Hemiancistrus*" *annectens*, *Hemiancistrus maracaiboensis*, and "*Hemiancistrus*" *panamensis*. In *Pogonopomoides parahybae*, GOSLINE (1947) already noticed an unusual posterior section of the swim-bladder, but did not discern its function. According to ARMBRUSTER, such a U-shaped structure—in addition to the genus *Pogonopomoides*—is also found in the genera *Rhinelepis*, *Pseudorinelepis*, and *Pogonopoma* and probably functions both as a hydrostatic organ and as an accessory breathing organ. *Otocinclus* spp. are said to have a similar, ring-shaped diverticulum. The various morphological characteristics of the breathing organs, according to ARMBRUSTER, provide us with an additional characteristic to define relationships among the various species. Naturally, suckermouth catfishes are only facultative air breathers, i.e., this capability is only used when the dissolved oxygen concentration of the water has become insufficient. After all, it is not without danger to emerge for air in their natural habitat. In doing so, the well-camouflaged benthic catfishes reveal their presence to piscivorous birds, normally unaware of their existence.

Furthermore, their ability to breath atmospheric oxygen should not lead to the (erroneous) conclusion that water quality needs not to be managed properly in an aquarium. Rather, the aquaristic experience has shown that many suckermouth catfishes—the inhabitants of cooler lotic environments in particular—are unable to compensate for oxygen deficits in the aquarium by breathing atmospheric oxygen. These species quickly die in case of filtration pump failure and the associated prompt fall in dissolved oxygen concentrations. The reasons are obvious.

GEE (1976) determined that the ability to breathe atmospheric oxygen depends on the likelihood of a given species being confronted with a decline in dissolved oxygen in its natural habitat. Therefore, stenoic (non-changing) species in regard to oxygen supply, such as those living in raging currents of rivers, (e.g., the close relatives of the loricariids, the astroblebids, or the loricariids of the genus *Lipopterichthys*), would lack any mechanism to breathe air, whereas those of rivers with a moderate current, such as those of the genus *Chaetostoma,* have at least a slight supplemental capacity. Consequently, the most proficient air breathers are the suckermouth catfishes living in euryoic biotopes in regard to dissolved oxygen concentrations, i.e., in the (flood)planes with mostly lentic aquatic conditions. Examples include the sailfin suckermouth catfishes of the genera *Glyptoperichthys* and *Liposarcus,* many species of the genus *Hypostomus*, and some representatives of the genus *Ancistrus.*

Rheophilic catfishes, such as this *Chaetostoma* sp., have only a limited capability to breathe atmospheric oxygen.

Hearing in Catfishes
Especially that of the Family Loricariidae

By Stanley H. WEITZMAN
Division of Fishes, Department of Zoology
Smithsonian Institution, Washington D.C., USA.

Because volumes 1 and 2 of the Catfish Atlas are primarily concerned with loricariid catfishes, presenting a short illustrated discussion of one of the more or less overlooked, but nevertheless remarkable aspects of the sensory systems of these catfishes seemed particularly appropriate for this volume's second printing [German edition], especially because certain aspects of hearing structures of some of these fishes are noticeable externally. One might almost say that certain of these fishes have "bony external ears." It appears that at least the species of the genus *Otocinclus* of the loricariid subfamily Hypoptopomatinae are extreme in this regard and may have augmented hearing ability based on the structure and large size of their "external bony ears."

In order to more clearly discuss this possibility it is desirable to present a brief illustrated discussion of the anatomy associated with sound reception in loricariid and certain related fishes. To do this efficiently it is best to first consider the basic anatomical plan of the hearing apparatus of otophysan fishes. The term Otophysi is a name for a group of mostly freshwater fishes that includes catfishes, the related knifefishes, minnows and carps, characins, suckers, and loaches.

Otophysan fishes are characterized by the possession of a structure known as the Weberian apparatus that was discovered by the German anatomist Ernst Heinrich Weber in 1820 and later named after him. This apparatus consists of a series or chain of movable bones that are modified parts of the anterior vertebra just behind the head. The most posterior of these movable bones, the tripus, is attached to the swimbladder wall where it receives vibrations from sound waves received by the swimbladder wall. These vibrations are then transferred anteriorly via these movable bones to fluid filled tubes that transfer these vibrations to the inner ear where the sound wave information is received by special hair cells and altered into electrical information that is forwarded to the brain via the eighth cranial nerve. See Fig. 1. This anatomical pathway, when compared to sound perception methods in many other fish groups, more efficiently and with a greater sound frequency range transfers sound waves from the swimbladder to the inner ear. For example, non-otophysan fishes so far subject to hearing experimentation react to sounds between 1 to 1000 hertz whereas in the relatively few otophysan fishes that have been subject to such experimentation react to sound waves between 1 to 10,000 hertz. This greater range of sound reception is apparently due to the efficiency of the Weberian apparatus. The physical aspects of sound reception in water are such that hearing can be made more efficient if a structure such as a swimbladder—that has a different density from the remainder of a fish's body—intercepts sound waves and these waves are transmitted to the internal ear via a series of anatomical structures such as the Weberian apparatus. Some other bony fish groups also have various kinds of con-

Fam.: Loricariidae

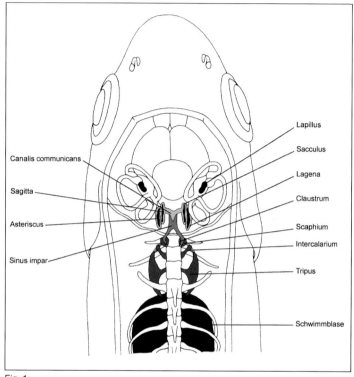

Fig. 1:
Line drawing of the relatively unspecialized Weberian apparatus in an Eurasian dace; dorsal view. The swimbladder, the Weberian ossicles and the modified structures of the inner ear are in gray. Modified representation based on FRISCH (1936).

Labels: Lapillus, Sacculus, Lagena, Claustrum, Scaphium, Intercalarium, Tripus, Schwimmblase, Canalis communicans, Sagitta, Asteriscus, Sinus impar

nections between their swimbladder and their inner ear such as herrings and relatives, but the connection found in the Otophysi is unique in its anatomical structure and efficiency. In members of the Otophysi the sound waves are transmitted from the swimbladder wall via the Weberian ossicles, the tripus, the intercalarium, and the scaphium and claustrum, to the paralymphatic fluid filled sac of the cavum sinus imparis and then to

the endolymphatic fluid filled sac of the canalis communicans all shown diagrammatically in Fig. 1.
From the canalis communicans sound waves proceed to the sacculus and lagena of the fish's inner ear, where special receptor hair cells detect and transduce the sound waves or vibrations into electrical energy and send this electrical information as nerve impulses via afferent nerves of the peripheral nervous system ultimately to

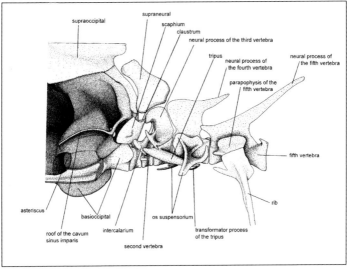

Fig. 2:
Posterior cranial region and first vertebrae of the hatchet fish *Carnegiella strigata*; lateral view, left side. The pectoral girdle is not represented. The Weberian ossicles are still quite unspecialized. The exoccipital, as well as parts of the basioccipital, were removed on the left side of the cranium in order to reveal the lumen below the roof of the cavum sinus imparis of the right side, which contains the sinus impar and the canalis transversus of the right side. Adapted from WEITZMAN (1954).

the hearing area of the brain where the incoming electrical information is perceived by the fish. Fig. 2 of a characiform fish, *Carnegiella strigata* (Gasteropelecidae), depicts the Weberian ossicles and the inner areas of the right side of the cranium associated with auditory nerve paths. The sinus imparis of Fig, 1, where sound waves are transmitted to the inner ear, lies ventral to the roof of the cavum sinus imparis in Fig. 2. The otolith (earstone) labeled the asteriscus in Figure 2 lies within the lagena that is diagrammatically depicted in Figure 1. All the Weberian ossicles are developmentally derived from the vertebrae with which they are associated in the adult as illustrated in Fig. 2. The scaphium, intercalarium, and tripus each pivots or "rocks" against their associated vertebral body as seen in Figs. 1 and 2. The posterior part of the tripus, the transformator process labeled in Figure 2, is attached to the dorsal anterior surface of the swimbladder and transfers swimbladder vibrations to the series of Weberian ossicles. Although not illustrated in Fig. 2, ligaments connect the more or less peripheral parts of the Weberian ossicles to one another. In cyprinids, characins, gymnotoids, suckers, and loaches the basic plan of the vertebrae bearing the Weberian ossicles and their physical relationship to other structures in this

Fam.: Loricariidae

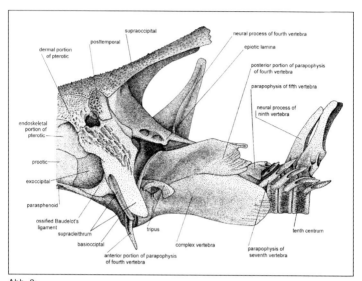

Abb. 3:
Lateral view of the posterior cranial region and first vertebrae on the left side of the marine catfish *Bagre marinus*. Only the upper section of the pectoral girdle is represented. The bony sections of the Weberian apparatus of this species shows the morphology typical of many catfishes and differs by the presence of various specializations from that of characins and cyprinids. Along the same lines, only the posterior-most Weberian ossicle, the tripus, remains visible; all other elements are hidden behind bones. The swimbladder is incompletely divided into a left and a right chamber. The left chamber leans against parts of the Weberian apparatus, designated as compound vertebra and "parapophysis of the fourth vertebra."

region remain relatively simple as illustrated in Figs. 1 and 2, although there are some differences in the details of these supportive structures among these fish groups. In the above fish groups the anterior and posterior portions of the swimbladder are located in the midline of the body just below the vertebrae. In catfishes this arrangement is much modified.

Figures 3 and 4 illustrate some of the bony aspects of the Weberian apparatus of a marine catfish, *Bagre marinus* (Ariidae), and depict the osteology of the rear part of the skull and

anterior vertebrae from both side and ventral views. This region of *Bagre marinus* is more or less typical for that of many of the relatively unspecialized catfish families. The only part of the Weberian ossicle series that can be seen in Figs. 3 and 4 is the middle and posterior section of the tripus. The bone labeled the supracleithrum is the upper part of the shoulder girdle (not illustrated in Figs. 1 or 2). The supracleithrum attaches to the posterior region of the skull and supports the lower part of the pectoral girdle and the pectoral fin. The lower portion

34

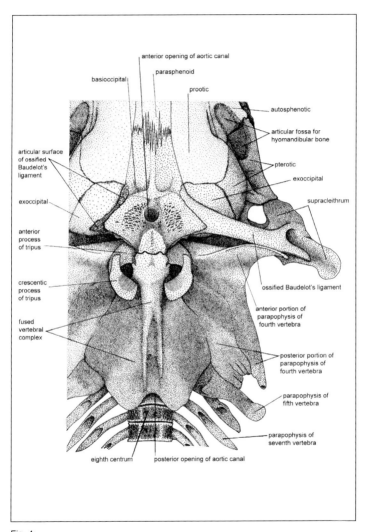

Fig. 4:
Ventral view of the posterior cranial region and first vertebrae of the marine catfish *Bagre marinus*. The structure designated as "compound vertebra" is made up of the fused vertebrae one through four.

Fam.: Loricariidae

of this girdle in *Bagre marinus*, the cleithrum, the largest bone supporting the pectoral fin, is not shown so that more of the modified anterior vertebrae could be illustrated. The supraoccipital, posttemporal, pterotic, prootic, exoccipital, and basioccipital bones as illustrated are all parts of the exterior of the posterior region of the cranium. The anterior part of the swimbladder, the only part remaining, is partly divided into left and right halves and each half is located against the ventral and lateral surfaces of the fused vertebrae numbers two through four of its respective side. The posterior part of each tripus, again one to a side, attaches to that part of the swimbladder located on each side.

The inner ear of each side of the head, each with its sacculus and lagena, are contained within the prootic and exoccipital regions In the most primitive of living catfishes, species of the South American genus Diplomystes, the second through the fourth centra are fused into a complex centrum that supports the Weberian apparatus. However, in other catfishes the complex centrum apparently consists of at least vertebrae two through five and in some catfish groups the first vertebra is also fused with the complex centrum. Depending on the family group of catfish families and also which of the approximately thirty-four different catfish families, the Weberian apparatus may be greatly modified from the condition found in *Bagre marinus*. Also, the posterior part of the cranium, the upper part of the shoulder girdle, and some additional anterior vertebrae can be much modified. In loricarioid catfishes including the families Amphiliidae, Nematogenyidae, Trichomycteridae, Callichthyidae, Scoloplacidae, Astroblepidae, and Loricariidae, the Weberian apparatus, some of the posterior skull bones, the upper part of the shoulder girdle, and the swimbladder

may be modified so much that they appear hardly recognizable as the same structures present in less specialized catfishes such as *Bagre marinus*.

One loricariid catfish genus, *Otocinclus*, of the subfamily Hypoptopomatinae has this region modified in a fascinating and complex way that in effect may further increase the efficiency of the swimbladder as a receptor of sound waves. Figures 5 and 6 show approximately the same region of the skull of *Otocinclus vittatus* as Figures 3 and 4 illustrate for *Bagre marinus*, except that part of the eye socket and surrounding bones are included in the drawing of *Otocinclus vittatus*. Also, the gill cover (opercle) and more of the pectoral girdle bones are illustrated in the *Otocinclus vittatus* drawing. One of the more obvious modifications associated with hearing in the loricariid catfishes is the large complex bone on each side of the head shown here for *Otocinclus vittatus* and labeled the "pterotic + supracleithrum" in Figures 5 and 6. This bone plus various modified parts of the complex vertebra of the head form a bony capsule surrounding the anterior portion of the swimbladder that is here divided into two bladders, one for the right and one for the left side of the head. The composition of the "pterotic + supracleithrum" or the "complex pterotic" as some prefer to call it, remains uncertain and variously interpreted. Certainly its actual composition will only be resolved by developmental studies for each particular genus and species of loricariids. Thus in loricariids each right and left swimbladder chamber is surrounded by the bony capsule whose lateral and dorsal portion form its external surface that usually consists of the bones that form the so-called "pterotic + supracleithrum." The entire swimbladder capsule of each side consists of

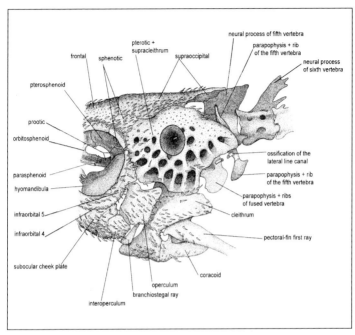

Fig. 5:
Lateral view (left side) of the posterior cranial region and first vertebra of the loricariid *Otocinclus vittatus*. Somewhat more than half of the orbita is visible anteriorly to the compound bone designated as "pterotic + supracleithrum." In the center of the "pterotic + supracleithrum" a circular cutout was drawn to show the posterior section of the tripus well inside the bony capsule, which contains the left chamber of the swimbladder. This bony capsule with the swimbladder and the posterior section of the tripus could be considered an analogous structure to the outer ear of mammals; it is likely to improve the hearing ability of the suckermouth catfishes of the subfamily Hypoptopomatinae. The multitude of windowlike openings (fenenstrae) in the lateral wall of the bony capsule could provide for direct access of the sound waves to the swimbladder and this way allow for a more effective reception and transmission of the sound through the Weberian apparatus, as compared to the conditions present in other otophysan fishes, where the swimbladder is covered by the quite massive side of the body.

the external part just mentioned plus parts of the complex vertebrae that form the internal capsular wall and support the tripus as well as parts of the parapophyses of the fourth verte-brae. In Figure 5 the posterior portion of the tripus can be seen deep within the capsule through a circular hole cut in the capsule's external face. This modification of the bony part of the

Fam.: Loricariidae

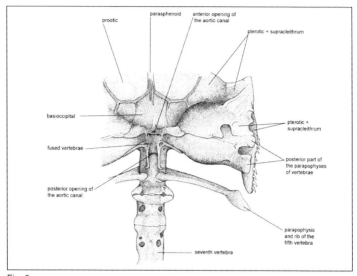

Fig. 6:
Ventral view of the posterior cranial region and initial vertebrae of the loricariid *Otocinclus vittatus*. The extraordinary size of the bony capsule and the swimbladder contained therein in relation to the size of the entire catfish head becomes clear in this view. The fact that the sound reception organ occupies such a large volume in these suckermouth catfishes might indicate that the sense of hearing plays an important role in the social interactions of these fishes. Some *Otocinclus* species occur in great densities in their natural habitat and take their food from littoral submersed grasses and perhaps hearing plays a decisive role to assure the cohesion of the group.

Weberian apparatus and head of *Otocinclus* is different from what is found in *Bagre marinus* in that the swimbladder, now in two separate bladders, one in each side of the head, is in a position more or less at the side of the posterior part of the cranium rather than alongside the modified fused anterior vertebrae. Various lateral processes of these fused anterior vertebrae support and form the inner posterior part of the bony capsule surrounding each swimbladder. Another obvious characteristic of especially the species of *Otocinclus* is the large and numerous fenestrae or "win-

dows" in the lateral face of the "pterotic + supracleithrum." It is to be expected that these openings in the bone allow better penetration of sound waves. At these bony openings, sound waves pass only through the skin, then fluid between the skin and the swimbladder and then to the surface of the swimbladder. Thus the bony capsule with its lateral fenestrae and swimbladder constitute what might be called "external ears." If one examines Figure 5, one can see that these fenestrae are directional in their position, all more or less pointing towards the position of the tripus where it attaches to the

38

swimbladder deep within the bony capsule. As can be seen in Figure 6, this capsule is approximately horn-shaped and the tripus is attached to the swimbladder at the internal apex of the capsule. The swimbladder is not attached to the inner surface of the capsule, but approximately follows its horn-shaped contours allowing it to freely intercept sound vibrations and transfer them to the tripus. Presumably this shape of the swimbladder allows it to magnify the sound as occurs, for example, when one cups their ears with their hands in an attempt to better hear sounds barely heard from a particular direction. Thus, for example, it may work as in previous times when the partly deaf persons used ear horns to hear better.

Thus, loricariids such as *Otocinclus* that have exceptionally large otic capsules, each with many lateral fenestrae, may have a particularly specialized and relatively acute hearing apparatus that may serve to keep them organized in schools. Species of *Otocinclus* that I and Hans-George Evers have independently observed in nature frequently travel and feed together in schools, even in turbid waters where vision may play little or no role in keeping the members of such schools together. What sounds may be made by these fishes for communication are unknown, but perhaps simply scraping the substrate with their teeth provides the sound needed. On the other hand perhaps this hearing apparatus helps detect the approach of predators. There is also the possibility that this hearing apparatus in *Otocinclus* may play a role in courtship. Certainly some loricarioid fishes are known to make sounds with their pectoral-fin spines during courtship. Laboratory experiments and field observations are needed to confirm such hypotheses about hearing in *Otocinclus*.

Thanks:

Thanks and appreciation are extended to

Dr. Ralf Britz and Dipl. Biol. Matthias Hoffmann for critically reading and translating the text into German as well as providing German labeling of the various structures in the plates for the German edition of this contribution.

Dr. Scott Schaefer provided a copy of an unpublished manuscript on the temporal region of the cranium of loricarioid fishes by Dr. Adriana Aquino and himself.

Tamara Clark labeled the drawings for the German edition and prepared Figures 5 and 6. Lisa Palmer labeled the plates for the English edition.

Literature:

Frish, K. von (1936):
Über den Gehörsinn der Fische. - Biological Reviews, 11: 210-246.

Weber, E. H. (1820):
De aure et auditu hominis et animalium. Pars I : De aure animalium aquatilium. Leipzig.

Weitzman, S. H. (1954):
The osteology and the relationships of the South American characid fishes of the subfamily Gasteropelicinae. Stanford Ichthyological Bulletin, 4(4): 212-239.

Fam.: Loricariidae

A new day begins at the Rio Juquiá, State of São Paulo. H.-G. Evers

Habitats

It is not an easy task to present all habitats where suckermouth catfishes can be found within the narrow frame of this book. The various members of the family Loricariidae have colonized most known Neotropical habitats in the course of their evolution. Lentic (subfamilies Hypostominae and Hypoptopomatinae) and especially lotic waters of all types (black-waters, white-waters, and clear-waters) (all subfamilies) are inhabited.

For the practical aquarist it is important to know the characteristics of the natural habitat of his or her charges—e.g., which ecological niches are occupied by various species in a large river—in order to draw conclusions in regard to the suitable decor of their aquarium. In the following pages we present a short selection of the principal biotopes. We attempted hereby to indicate the particular habitats within the aquatic environment where particular species are preferably found. We have omitted a basic discussion on Neotropical zoogeography as well as on the historical evolution of South American waters that lead to their present state. STAWIKOWSKI & WERNER (1998) have just recently done so extensively on the basis of a fundamental publication by GÉRY (1969). Additionally, since that publication deals with the most important river systems and their courses, we felt it unnecessary to repeat such a discussion in another monograph on Neotropical fishes. Those with such a strong interest in South American fishes that they wish to learn more about the hydrological evolution of the region, surely will own both monographs anyway. The opinions of GÈRY (1969) have subsequently been revised by other authors and a good overview of the biogeography and evolutionary diversification of the Neotropical ichthyofauna is given by WEITZMAN & WEITZMAN (1982). In recent years, LUNDBERG et al. (1998) gave quite a detailed description about the development of the present tropical South American waters. To reproduce this work is beyond the scope of this book. Both of these publications are recommended further reading for the interested hobbyist.

The family Loricariidae is distributed over extensive areas in the Neotropics. The northern limit is located approximately in southern Costa Rica, at the border region with Panama, and especially

Fam.: Loricariidae

in southern Panama, where several species of the three subfamilies—Ancistrinae, Hypostominae, and Loricariinae (e.g., *Ancistrus spinosus*, "*Hemiancistrus*" *panamensis*, *Fonchiiichthys uracanthus*, *Sturisoma panamense*)—can be found. Trinidad is also a confirmed area of suckermouth catfishes (e.g., *Hypostomus robinii*). The confirmed sightings of loricariids on Hawaii are based on released aquarium specimens that have survived in the wild. The same is true of various species found in Florida and other southern states of the United States, whose ancestors either escaped from local tropical fish farms or were released by aquarists.

In the western area of the South American continent, suckermouth catfishes inhabit Andean waters even further up than trout regions (genus *Chaetostoma* and relatives). Transandean species, however, are scarce, but several species (e.g., genus *Isorineloricaria*) are known from western Ecuador, which is extremely interesting in reference to the zoogeography of the area. The Guyana Shield, the Orinoco Lowlands, and the entire Amazon Basin are the distribution centers of suckermouth catfishes. Hundreds of species inhabit these areas. On the other hand, the basin of the Rio São Francisco in the east, the Pantanal in the west together with the Bolivian rivers, and the gigantic drainages of the Río Paraná and Río Paraguay are also distribution centers. Further south, various species are only known from Uruguay and northern Argentina—further south it is probably too cold. The latter is likely to also apply to Chile, a region from which there are no confirmed loricariid sightings at present.

Research into the aquatic ecology in relation to ichthyofauna is still rare, although precisely in regard to the hydrology of southeastern Brazil there have been a number of publications in recent years as a result of increased interest by Brazilian ichthyologists. The works by LOWE-MCCONNELL (1964 and 1991) and CASATTI & CASTRO (1998), as well as by CASTRO & CASATTI (1997) report on the composition of piscine communities of selected South American river systems, also mentioning the Loricariidae present. The essays by POWER (1984a, b, and c) or BUCK & SAZIMA (1995) even deal primarily with the suckermouth catfishes of the selected biotopes, their habits, feeding behavior, and reproduction. These reports are especially recommended further reading for interested aquarists.

The Rio Cristalino in central Brazil, a clear-water tributary rich in fishes of the Rio das Mortes.

Vultures are also fond of loricariids, but especially in a "riper" state!

Suckermouth catfishes are considered "poor peoples food" in Amazonia.   H.-G. Evers

A classical grouping of water types, especially of rivers, is based on their external appearance. Basically, they are classified into white-, black-, and clear-waters, i.e., the coloration is the determining characteristic. This "coloration" is the result of the composition of the area of their headwaters. Naturally, there are broad transitional zones between each type, i.e., a so-called clear-water river is quickly made turbid when a white-water-carrying creek flows into it. Similar situations hold true for all types. However, they all will house a very different ichthyofauna, and that is where the interesting part for aquarists comes in! The chemical composition of these water types varies and based on these characteristics, the aquarist can deduce the needs of his or her charges. When rivers of similar size but differing water type meet, their waters will quickly mix and give rise to intermediate water types. At the confluence of the Rio Negro with the Rio Solimões (giving rise to the Amazon), for an

Photo below:
The "Encontro das Aguas" [=meeting of the waters] south of Manaus. The black waters of the Rio Negro meet the white waters of the Rio Solimões. From this point on the river is called the Rio Amazonas.

I. Seidel

H.-G. Evers

With the confluence of smaller rivers, the different coloration of the waters is especially obvious. In this case, it is the Rio Ipixuna (black-water) which flows into the Rio Solimões.

extended stretch both types of water can be encountered side by side, since both waters are slow to mix due to their thermal difference. An impressive spectacle of nature.

The clay-yellow coloration of many rivers is given by the high content of tiny suspended mineral matter which may be carried over many hundreds of kilometers in the current. The headwaters of these rivers are often located in, geologically-speaking, very young mountain ranges. The wind and rain erode these mountain ranges and the top layers are carried by the rivers into the lowlands. The best-known example thereof is the largest river of all, the Amazon. It carries unimaginable large quantities of water and fine suspended matter through its richly branched headwater system from the Andes into the giant Amazon lowland. With the waters at flood level, the banks are breached and much water comes to a halt in lowland lakes. The suspended matter settles out and the water becomes clearer. As the waters recede, the deposited sediments stay behind and form a fertile substrate for exuberant vegetative growth (called "várzea" in Brazil) in an otherwise nutrient-poor environment. Nowadays, the local population takes ever more advantage of this circumstance by clearing the original vegetation and practicing agriculture. This has led to a virtually complete loss of primary várzea in the central and lower Amazon. Jute, rice, and wheat, as well as grazing cattle and everything-trampling-water-buffaloes have beaten the manatees in the search of food. Along the same lines, the fry of fish hardly find sufficient shelter and the typical várzea bird species have retreated into undeveloped, more remote areas. Only the upper courses of the large river are still home to untouched várzea with its immense associated biodiversity.

The flowing white-water precludes an effective penetration of light and therefore does not provide suitable growing conditions for phytoplankton as the foundation of the food chain.

Nevertheless, these waters are home to a rich ichthyofauna. The fishes take advantage of other food sources, such as in-

Photo below:
Areal photograph of the várzea at the central Rio Amazonas during the dry season. Broad sand banks are exposed by the low waters. The sediments in this area serve the plants as a nutrient source.

H.-G. Evers

H.-G. Evers

Grasses cover this small várzea near Manacapuru, the entry lake of the homonymous river shortly before entering the Rio Solimões.

sects falling on the water surface, blooms, nuts, etc. In the large rivers, large fish species are numerously represented, both herbivorous species as well as predators can be found. The weight of biomass a single seine pull can bring to shore is surprising. Most suckermouth catfishes from white-water are unattractively colored: brown and gray hues predominate. The main food source for loricariids in such waters is detritus. Large species in the Hypostominae, species in the genera *Liposarcus* or *Hypostomus*, for example, are typical inhabitants of white-waters. They appear in high densities and are considered "poor people food" in Amazonia. But also many loricariin catfishes, e.g., *Farlowella* or *Sturisoma,* are frequently encountered in white-waters. Due to the low transparency there is very little algae growth. Nevertheless, branches and rocks are colonized by in-

Photo bottom right:
At the fish markets of Amazonia, hypostomins—here *Liposarcus pardalis* at the market of Tefé—are offered bundled and still alive.

Every Brazilian child knows these "cascudos," the suckermouth catfishes!

H.-G. Evers

H.-G. Evers

numerable microorganisms which serve the suckermouth catfishes as a nutritional base.

White-water rivers have a pH of around neutral (7.0). The electrical conductivity is with 30–70 µS/cm clearly higher than that of other water types, due to the high mineral content. Fishes from such environments are quick to adapt to domestic tap water conditions with a neutral pH and medium water hardness. Furthermore, it has become apparent over time that especially suckermouth catfishes from such biotopes readily adapt to captive conditions and can be induced to breed with relative ease. Many of the sand-dwelling species, e.g., *Loricaria* and *Loricariichthys* spp., live on the sand banks of white-water rivers. The aquarist does not need to provide special water characteristics in order to breed catfishes of this type.

Clear-water rivers usually have their headwaters in geologically very old and therefore eroded mountain ranges. These substrates (usually granite) offer very little erodable matter with their structure and hardness. In South America, extensive areas of such substrates can be found in the Guyana Highlands and the highlands of central Brazil. These are the headwater areas of the large clear-water rivers.

It can happen that large rivers carry very clear water. However, the smaller a stream, the more it is influenced by momentary local atmospheric conditions. A strong downpour can greatly increase the turbidity of a small lotic biotope, effectively turning the clear-water stream into white-water. Even large rivers may become occasionally turbid. For example, the previously crystal clear Rio Tapajós in Brazil is turning progressively more turbid. This deplorable condition is caused by gold mining operations established in the jungle at its watershed, where the miners systematically dig up the forest floor and direct the muddy wash waters into the Tapajós. The ecosystem is being sensibly disrupted.

Photo top right:
Over millions of years, the Rio São Francisco has cut its bed into rock while flowing into the Atlantic in eastern Brazil. There are hardly any sediments left to be eroded away. Consequently, the water is crystalline.

Photo bottom right:
One is almost enticed into thinking of standing at the Mediterranean, such is the clarity of the Rio São Francisco here at its inferior central course, near Piranhas (State Pernambuco, Brazil).

H.-G. Evers

H.-G. Evers

The great light transmissiveness of clear-water rivers allows for fertile phytoplankton development in calmer areas. This phytoplankton is the first link of the nutritional chain. However, the low fertility in comparison to white-water is a limiting factor. In the area of influence of groundwater wells rich in carbon dioxide and minerals, aquatic vegetation prospers in extensive stands, and the observer feels as if in a gigantic aquarium. Clear-water is aquaristically the most species-rich and therefore most interesting biotope. Many of our most popular suckermouth catfishes live in these waters. The colorful designs and particular physical characteristics of the fishes have biological significance. However, regardless of its meaning, coloration and morphology are the most important criteria at the time to decide which of the many L-catfishes offered in the aquarium trade to acquire.

South American clear-water rivers are usually somewhat acidic, with a pH between 5 and 6. The electrical conductivity is often around 20 µS/cm, sometimes only at 8–15 µS/cm. Such water values are very difficult to maintain in an aquarium in the long term, but most clear-water fishes are adaptable and live a long and fruitful life in standard tap water with distinctly different chemical characteristics. Even breeding is not contingent upon the availability of soft and acid water, as has been repeatedly demonstrated by the many successes in reproduction reported in recent years. Representatives of all subfamilies can be found in clear-water. For sure, the most notable are the Ancistrinae from the clear-water rivers of the central Brazilian highlands. The rivers Xingú and Tapajós are home to the attractive genera *Hypancistrus* and *Leporacanthicus,* among others.

Black-water, the geologically oldest type of water, although free of suspended matter, is tea-brown to cola-colored. The cause for this are a multitude of dissolved organic compounds, collectively called humic compounds. The typical coloration of black-water is influenced by the particular substrate. Leaf litter decomposes under anaerobic conditions, producing humic

Photo top right:
View from a hill at Alter do Chão onto the Rio Tapajós, one of the large clear-water tributaries of the Rio Amazonas.

Photo bottom right:
A beach of the Rio Tapajós at Alter do Chão; just like a Caribbean paradise, but in the middle of Amazonia!

H.-G. Evers

H.-G. Evers

H.-G. Evers

H.-G. Evers

compounds which color the water. The substrate of this area usually consists of white quartz sand, which does not contribute any water hardeners. Such areas can be very small, producing the common result that in some areas clear- and black-water rivers coexist right next to each other.

When giant rivers flow through the plains, their seasonal fluctuations in water level can be enormous. The Rio Negro, in particular, may rise 12 m over its banks and flood the adjacent forest (we speak of the flooded forests, Brazilians call it the "igapô"). The ichthyofauna in black-waters is comparatively poorer than that of clear- and white-waters, but many of the species living in this biotope are appreciated aquarium charges because of their attractive coloration. Due to the dearth of appropriate food, there are very few suckermouth catfishes. Characins and other fishes of the open water can feed on insects and plant parts drifting on the water surface, something difficult to do for benthic species.

Black-waters are very poor in nutrients, high in humic acids, and have a pH that may even be more acidic than 4.5, since the water lacks any kind of hardeners. Although there is a low total fish biomass because of the lack of nutrients, the number of species is surprisingly high, as has been revealed by studies of the Rio Negro. Approximately 450 species have been identified for this region (GOULDING et. al., 1988). Therefore, no species is represented by a numerous population, especially compared to those in other types of water. The people who have tried to fish their dinner in a blackwater biotope know how long one has to wait for a bite; whereas possibly one fish was captured right after the other previously in a white-water river.

Photo top left:
View of the Rio Agua Preta, a tributary of the Rio das Mortes in central Brazil.

Photo bottom left:
Dense stands of aquatic vegetation indicated the presence of well water rich in carbon dioxide. *Hypostomus* sp. (L 37), *Ancistrus* sp., *Parotocinclus* cf. *longirostris,* and *Hemiloricaria lanceolata* can be found here.

The aquarist interested in the care of suckermouth catfishes from such areas must be aware of the heightened demands these species place on water quality. Especially in the case of wild-caught specimens, extreme caution is advised. For example, the attractive *Hemiloricaria* from the Rio Negro

55

H.-G. Evers

H.-G. Evers

drainage are exacting charges which are particularly sensitive during their acclimation phase. Wild-caught specimens from these areas are true starvation artists in nature. Therefore, the diet of these fishes must not be too fatty, as they quickly become fat and rotund, a circumstance never encountered in the wild.

These few examples should suffice to make one thing clear to the prospective caretaker of a particular loricariid species: Inform yourself prior (!) to the acquisition of a fish as to its origin. The following questions should be answered by the suckermouth catfish hobbyist prior to the acquisition of a new species:

- Do the fish come from white- clear- or black-water?
- Are the desired fish appropriate for my aquarium or even aquarium maintenance in general?
- Am I able to provide sufficient current (e.g., for *Hypancistrus* and similar genera)?
- Do I have fine sand as a substrate suitable for burrowing (for *Loricaria*, *Pseudohemiodon,* and others)?
- Are there sufficient hiding places?
- Are there sufficient roots (for *Panaque*, but also for *Sturisoma* and others)?
- Am I able to maintain the aquarium cool enough throughout the year for the species that require such cool conditions (e.g., species from southeastern Brazil)?

First establish the aquarium, then acquire the fishes (fishes are living creatures, that require highest attention). As examples, we present several suckermouth catfish habitats and hope to provide a small glimpse into the natural environmental conditions of our charges. Additionally, the reading of travel reports and—for those further interested—the study of specialized literature on Neotropical ecology are recommended.

Photo top left:
Sandy beach at the upper Rio Negro. The bright reflection of the white quartz sand in the sun is in contrast to the tea-colored water.

Photo bottom left:
There is a paucity of fishes in the main stream, whereas the small tributaries (Igarapés)—here the Rio Miuá (upper Rio Negro)—support a richer aquatic life.

Bolivia

Arroyo Dolores and Río Surutu – In Search of *Pseudohemiodon thorectes*

One of the most interesting groups among the suckermouth catfishes are certainly the mouthbrooders which, on merit of their unusual reproductive biology alone, have always been among our personal favorites. Therefore, we always made sure on our trips to visit biotopes where we were likely to encounter such species. During a trip to
Bolivia in 1998, at least coauthor I. SEIDEL had the chance to travel to the area of distribution of one of the representatives scientifically known only since 1975. Together with his friends and fellow aquarists Peter DEBOLD, Raimond NORMANN, Carsten SCHADE, and Günter SCHWESINGER, as well as their wives Brigitte DEBOLD and Birgit NORMANN, he traveled to the vicinity of the city of Santa Cruz de la Sierra, in southeastern Bolivia.

From an aquaristic point of view, Bolivia still has a lot of uncharted territory. Only few of its fishes are well-known residents in our aquaria. Of course, the richness of its fauna is by far not as extensive as that known from central Amazonia, for instance. Additionally, there seems to be a dearth of spectacular and colorful species. As a result, only the largest importers in Germany are able to import fishes from Bolivia. Most waters of Bolivia and all major river systems (Río Madre de Dios, Río Beni, Río Marmoré, and Río Guaporé) are affluents of the Brazilian Rio Madeira, which, in turn, is a southern tributary of the Amazon. Still, the piscine fauna of the upper Madeira Basin in Bolivia has nothing to do with the Amazonian section, given that numerous and extensive rapids preclude the exchange of genetic information between the two areas.

Along the same lines, there are clear climatic differences between the upper Madeira drainage and the lower course, which is subject to a more Amazonian climate regime. Although in Bolivia, as in Amazonia, the rainy season coincides with the winter in northern latitudes, the dry season—May to October—is always accompanied by a much more pronounced drop in temperatures. Even in the lowlands, cold southern winds can drop the air temperature for a few days all the way to 3°C (RUDOLPH & RAUER, 1999a; 1999b). Consequently, water temperatures also drop sharply and the fishes in such biotopes need to be very flexible in regard to temperature fluctuations.

Pseudohemiodon thorectes is a whiptail suckermouth catfish species from the surroundings of the town of Buena Vista. ISBRÜCKER (1975) describes the type locality as follows: "Bolivia, Est. Santa Cruz, Buena Vista (17°28' S, 63°37' W), west of the Río Palacios, tributary of the Rio Marmoré." Buena Vista is located northeast of Santa Cruz and may be reached easily by car on a well-built road. I. SEIDEL and cotravellers ventured to the vicinity of this town in August 1998 with the aim to investigate a few days and to capture some *Pseudohemiodon thorectes* and other interesting fishes native to the region. Shortly before reaching Buena Vista, the first promising biotopes were encountered. For example, a small clearwater creek—the Arroyo Dolores—was crossed on the paved road. It appeared to have an extensive sandy substrate in the vicinity of the road. Hobbyists that have maintained flunder whiptails in an aquarium know how they relish to bury themselves in fine sand substrates until only the eyes and the filament on the caudal fin protrude into the open water. However, due to their cryptic coloration, even if not buried, these catfishes are difficult to distinguish resting on the substrate. It was therefore not expected to be easy to find these fishes here; but on the other hand, their presence in this ideal biotope was considered certain. The excitement increased as the biotope was approached on foot. We used a special dipnet, which we had utilized in a modified form in Peru to capture *Crossoloricaria rhami* in a similar biotope. It is a dipnet with prongs on the lower section of its frame to rake the substrate and pull-lines, with which the gear is pulled over the river bed, in a manner similar to a dredge. What had worked splendidly in Peru failed miserably in this instance, due to the "improvements" in construction material (for weight reasons, the frame was built in alu-

Fam.: Loricariidae

minum). The "dredge net" broke in two after a few meters and its builder (I. SEIDEL) became the laughing stock of his companions. Thereafter, theflunder whiptails had to be fished the old fashioned way, i.e., with a seine. This net was pulled in such a way as to allow the lead line to sink a few centimeters into the substrate. However, even after numerous attempts, not a single one of the coveted loricariids was obtained. It was decided to try and capture at least some other loricariids—with better success. In this creek, with a width of only a meters in places, we were able to capture, with a dipnet among overhanging submersed shore grasses, *Otocinclus vestitus*, *Farlowella* sp. (this fish is presented in the species section of this book as *Farlowella* sp. "Rio Urutuca"), and a few *Hemiloricaria lanceolata*. In the middle of the creek, however, there were additional suckermouth catfishes, such as numerous *Hemiloricaria beni* of all sizes. At places where the current was swift and rubble and wood had collected, some *Ancistrus* sp. could be found. They were usually juveniles with a length of only 3–6 cm. The following water values were determined at the Arroyo Dolores (Position 17°25.97 S, 63°38.14 W) (August 7, 1998, 14:00 hrs): water temperature 24.4°C; pH 7.6; conductivity 26 µS/cm.

Arroyo Dolores – Upper Madeira Basin, Bolivia:		
Species	**Biotope**	**Observations**
Ancistrus sp. "Buena Vista"	on wood and among rocks	especially juveniles with a length of 3–6 cm
Farlowella sp. "Río Urucuta"	shore vegetation	few subadults
Hemiloricaria beni	on sand and rubble	numerous
Hemiloricaria lanceolata	shore vegetation	less numerous than *H. beni*
Otocinclus vestitus	shore vegetation	numerous, full-grown

This first failure in our attempt to capture *P. thorectes* did not make us lose our faith. The following day, we continued our quest. However, this time we wanted to focus much more sharply on our target species and therefore tried to find out how to get to the Río Palacios. However, no matter how much we asked, we found no one in Buena Vista or its surroundings who knew of the Río Palacios.

Arroyo Dolores in the vicinity of Buena Vista.

I. Seidel

Arroyo Dolores: with the "dredge net" in search of suckermouth catfishes.

I. Seidel

Otocinclus vestitus, *Farlowella* sp., and *Hemiloricaria lanceolata* can be found among the submersed overhanging shore vegetation.

I. Seidel

I. Seidel

The small *Hemiloricaria beni*: the most common sand dweller of the Arroyo Dolores.

And indeed, on a road map purchased in Santa Cruz, this not so small river was drawn much further north and not close at all to Buena Vista. However, we doubted the accuracy of this map, since the coordinates given in the original description identified a location even to the south of Buena Vista. After spending practically the entire day in search of the river, we asked the owner of our residence in Buena Vista if there wasn't a larger river nearby with primarily a sandy, and not muddy, bed. He sent us to the Río Surutu. The Surutu is a tributary of the Río Yapacani, which, according to the map, is the river into which the Río Palacios is shown to flow. We therefore felt justified in our hope to find the fish there. The trip to the Río Surutu with a Land Rover was very difficult. The road lead for approximately half an hour over sand through a cleared section of forest. Sporadic glimpses of the river through the underbrush were possible at sections where the road passed close to the water. Finally we reached a place that offered an unobstructed access to the river. The path lead directly to the shore and seemed to continue across the river. That arrangement apparently was not designed for a car, although it seemed that the river was never over one meter deep anywhere across. However, we determined later that this river is crossed by the local population on foot or on horseback at this trail.

The Río Surutú was very uniform in this area. The entire width of 50 m had a sandy substrate, was void of any vegetation, and there were no agglomerations of rocks or wood either. Only some sporadic individual tree trunks or branches lied around, and at a great distance one from the other. Consequently, we did not expect a great suckermouth catfish species diversity, but it was just the right kind of biotope for our flunder whiptails. Soon we were in the water amazed at how warm it was. In the burning midday sun, this unshaded, shallow, moderately fast river had warmed to 30°C. We did not expect this, especially during the dry season, but it was particularly hot that day. The measured water values at the site (Pos. 17°29.73 S, 63°43.17 W, August 10, 1998, 15:00 hrs): water temperature 29.7°C; pH 8.3; conductivity 355 µS/cm.

After several unsuccessful passes with our seine, we progressively improved our methodology and finally—in a group effort—obtained our first success. A scream blanketed the group as our first *Pseudohemiodon*—a fully grown holding a clutch of eggs in his mouth—appeared in our net. Without a doubt it was *P. thorectes*. Our continued efforts were very tiresome in the great heat, even though the current was light. It took several hours until we had captured approximately 20 specimens with a length of 10–14 cm. Among them were two additional brooding males. Some of the smallest juveniles passed through the mesh of our seine. With the advent of darkness, seven exhausted, sunburned Bolivia catfish-travelers concluded the capture efforts for the day. As by-catch to the *Pseudohemiodon* there were some *Aphanotorulus unicolor* in the net. Additionally, a single *Cochliodon* was captured on an individual piece of wood. The day was successful, but the night was a purgatory for the "red skins" in the group.

Río Surutu – Upper Madeira Basin, Bolivia:		
Species	**Biotope**	**Observations**
Aphanotorulus unicolor	on sandy substrates	only four half-grown specimens
Cochliodon sp. "Bolivia"	on a single piece of wood	only a single specimen
Pseudohemiodon thorectes	on sandy substrates	most common species, all age groups

The object of desire: *Pseudohemiodon thorectes*.

I. Seidel

The Río Surutu in the Yapacani drainage.   I. Seidel

The home of *P. thorectes*: a seemingly infinite expanse of sand.   I. Seidel

Wood was found only in a few places.

Cochliodon sp. was found at such biotopes.

Brazil

Rio Betari – The Cold River

In reality it all started with the study of the scientific literature on suckermouth catfishes, original descriptions and revisions of various species or species groups in particular. Although several loricariids were aquaristically known back in the late 80's, their numbers in no way approached the quantity of those

known today. Many names were only smoke and could not be assigned to any "face." One group which was of particular interest to one of the coauthors (H.-G. Evers)—and which was plagued by "ghosts"—was the suckermouth catfishes of southeastern Brazil.

The Betari River at Iporanga.

H.-G. Evers

Area of swift current with round river stones as substrate.

H.-G. Evers

Genera like *Hemipsilichthys*, *Harttia*, *Neoplecostomus,* or *Pareiorhina* represented loricariids hardly known even to science in those times. The genus *Kronichthys* A. DE MIRANDA RIBEIRO, 1908 was also such a case. What a strange name for a fish genus. What would be the story behind such a name?

Ricardo KRONE was a Brazilian of German descent, who was very interested in the fauna and flora of his home country and who went on various excursions. He lived in the south of the State of São Paulo, in the coastal city of Iguape, and at the beginning of the 20th century he traveled on donkey back through his homeland, collecting and preserving everything which appeared to be biologically interesting. As part of his activities he also collected fishes in the mountains of the Serra de Paranapiacaba, which drain their waters through the majestic white-water rivers Ribeira de Iguape and Juquiá, which, after their confluence, flow into the Atlantic at Iguape, about 100 km later. These rivers are not connected to the voluminous Paraná drainage system and are therefore home to a totally different ichthyofauna. Especially the crystal clear mountain streams are home to many endemics, which only inhabit this restricted zone. Krone collected, in early 1907, various fish species in the vicinity of the small town of Iporanga in the Betari River, which he sent to a renowned ichthyologist of the time, Alipio DE MIRANDA RIBEIRO, in Rio de Janeiro. The ichthyologist was very impressed by the collection and published a paper that same year. In it, he described various new species and a genus of troglodyte catfishes (*Typhlobagrus*, Fam. Pimelodidae). The result were names like *Typhlobagrus kronei* and *Corydoras kronei* (the latter, today is a synonym of *Scleromystus barbatus*). Only one year later, MIRANDA RIBEIRO (1908) described additional specimens from this collection, among them the genus *Kronichthys*. The latter publication, in particular, could not be obtained by coauthor EVERS. This was especially bothersome, as it contained illustrations of the described species.

The name Iporanga was always synonymous of fishes for both coauthors, and it was not until 1995 that finally H.-G. EVERS, at least, had the opportunity to fish in the basin of the Rio Ribeira de Iguape personally. Together with Maik BEYER and Marco T.C. LACERDA, the trip began in April 1995 with a jeep ride from Rio de Janeiro south-

Capture of loricariids using the technique described in the text.

H.-G. Evers

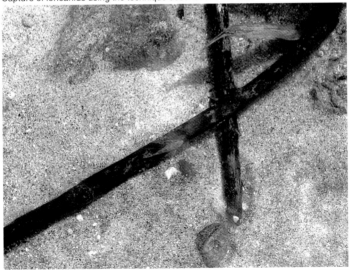

Subadult *Kronichthys subteres* on wood in their natural habitat.

H.-G. Evers

Shore area with root mats, the nursery of loricariids.

H.-G. Evers

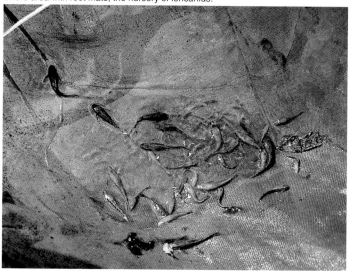

There is good fishing especially among the submersed overhanging shore vegetation!

H.-G. Evers

In the lower courses of the mountain streams, human influence becomes noticeable. The rivers are high in nutrients because of sewage and algae grow wild. The sensitive suckermouth catfish species have disappeared from such river sections!

ward, passing the industrial center São Paulo on the interstate highway BR 116 into the mountains of the Serra de Paranapiacaba. Up to the city of Registro everything was fast and uneventful, but once the detour to the north was taken to enter the mountains, it became painfully obvious what a chore it must have been 100 years earlier to travel these ways on a donkey's back.

The closer Iporanga came, the more inaccessible became the route. In this area, the pitiful remains of a previously majestic Atlantic coastal rain forest, the "Mata Atlantica," can still be admired. On both sides of the dirt road extends the virtually untouched primary forest, to be interrupted only sporadically by a few settlements and, once in a while, by the swift waters of a clear-water creek. The area of the upper Ribeira has meanwhile been declared a protected tourism sanctuary. There are many stalactite caverns and deep canyons which still harbor a cornucopia of unknown ani-

Kronichthys subteres in a photo tank, right after capture.

H.-G. Evers

Ancistrus sp. from Iporanga, just captured.

H.-G. Evers

Rineloricaria latirostris, a net full of subadult specimens. Note the cryptic camouflage coloration, perfectly adapted to its surroundings. There is hardly a difference to the pebbles in the net.

mal and plant species. In a publication by ROCHA & LINSKER (1995) beautiful photographs from the area can be admired.

The Rio Betari and the many other clear-water-carrying streams in the vicinity of Iporanga were intensely fished right upon arrival. The shallow water with a swift current flows over a gravel bed. In certain segments, the bottom is covered with fist- to melon-sized round stones, which, exposed to full sun, are densely covered by algae. For suckermouth catfish enthusiasts, these are the most productive and interesting biotopes. The catfishes are adhered facing the strong current and graze on the algae. The coloration of the catfishes is adapted to the substrate and ranges from various hues of yellow to browns, covered by black design elements. Due to the moving water surface, aerial predators are highly unlikely to detect these cryptically colored suckermouth catfishes on the substrate. Initially, we faced the same problem. But then we crawled

Rineloricaria latirostris, a full-grown specimen in the photo tank.   H.-G. Evers

through the shallow water (depth 30–40 cm) with a diving mask, detecting the catfishes before they nimbly disappeared among the crevices as they were being approached. With a sturdy dipnet shoved under the rocks, the capture of suckermouth catfishes which previously we had only known from scientific descriptions, was successful. The catch included *Harttia kronei* RIBEIRO, 1908, *Lampiella gibbosa* (RIBEIRO, 1908), *Kronichthys subteres* RIBEIRO, 1908, and a beautiful, still unidentifiable *Ancistrus* sp. In areas with a finer substrate—gravel with a granularity of 1–4 cm—*Rineloricaria latirostris* (BOULENGER, 1900) was encountered. Trusting their cryptic coloration, they were easily captured with a net. That is not to say that they had no reason to trust. Even an almost 20 cm long *Rineloricaria latirostris* male is hardly visible from a distance of 1–2 m. Here, *Hypostomus agna* (RIBEIRO, 1907) was relatively common everywhere and in all water zones, although it was only possible to capture subadults of up to 10 cm in total length. Unfortunately, no full-grown specimens could be captured. Aquaristically

Lampiella gibbosa, undoubtedly the most beautiful suckermouth catfish in the area (Rio Betari).

interesting "non-loricariid" were *Scleromystax barbatus* and a member of the bottom-dwelling characin genus *Characidium.*
Unfortunately, snorkeling in this biotope is anything but pleasant. Since the water temperature at the time—at the end of the warm season—was only 20°C, we quickly shivered miserably and had to leave the water to warm up in the sun. There we became prey to billions of flies of the families Simuliidae and Melusinidae which literally blanketed us in hundreds of bites. Experienced South America travelers know that in areas with black- or clear-water only few mosquitoes and other bloodsucking insects must be anticipated, because the nutrient-poor waters do not sustain massive population explosions. Here, however, it was a different story, which was later corroborated by measurements. The pH of the Rio Betari was slightly alkaline at 7.67, its conductivity at 96 μS/cm. Similar values were determined for other rivers in the area with similar piscine fauna. At times of stronger precipitation—June to August—the water levels do not necessarily raise. At this altitude, the water

Rio Betari at Iporanga – Southeastern Brazil		
Species	**Biotope**	**Observations**
Ancistrus sp.	current-swept rubble	relatively common
Harttia kronei	current-swept rubble	rare
Hypostomus agna	all zones	very common
Kronichthys subteres	current-swept rubble	very rare
Lampiella gibbosa	current-swept rubble	rare
Rineloricaria latirostris	calmer areas with gravel	relatively common

level hardly rises, but at the foot of the Serra the rivers swell dramatically and race towards the valley. The water temperatures during that time are only in the order of 15°–18°C, and at higher elevations it may be colder still.

Virtually all fishes captured here at Iporanga are basically unsuitable for aquarium maintenance. Nevertheless, advanced hobbyists may try their hand at keeping these interesting suckermouth catfishes in a cool basement with adequate vegetable fare and a strong current.

Back to Rio de Janeiro, we visited the library of the Museum of Natural History, where old volumes of the magazine Kosmos are stored on microfilm. With great anticipation, we placed the year 1908 into the viewer and suddenly our triumphant yells broke through the distinguished silence of these hallowed halls, making as the focus of angry stares. On the monitor appeared the silhouettes of the fish we had just captured, *Kronichthys subteres* and *Lampiella gibbosa*. Finally, now they had materialized in front of our very eyes, no longer haunting us as ghosts!

Bird's eye view of the upper (Alto) Rio Negro.

I. Seidel

Rio Negro – Species Diversity Despite Nutrient Deficiency

"Rio Negro – Rich Life in Poor Water," is the title of the monograph about the largest blackwater river on Earth, written by GOULDING, CARVALHO, and FERREIRA (1988). Although the Rio Negro is for certain one of the rivers with the lowest nutritional contents in the world, a seemingly endless variety of life has developed in its waters. The black river—as the literal translation of its name would be—has its origins north of the equator in northern South America, and its confluence with the Amazon in the vicinity of Manaus is at 3° southern latitude. Although the Rio Negro is the largest Amazon tributary in regard to water volume, some southern tributaries—such as the rivers Xingú and Tapajós—are longer

The city of Manaus at the mouth of the Rio Negro. The hub of Amazonia.   I. Seidel

The central Rio Negro.

H.-G. Evers

The upper Rio Negro is often framed by overgrown granite rocks.

I. Seidel

then the Negro. The length of the Rio Negro is estimated at 1700 km. It drains approximately one third of the Guyana Highlands and contributes about 15% of the water that the Amazon carries into the Atlantic. That is still more than all European rivers combined.

The Amazon River System is connected to several other drainages through the Rio Negro. The most famous of these connections is without a doubt the Río Casiquiare, which connects the upper Rio Negro System with the Orinoco Basin. Alexander von HUMBOLDT was already very interested in this connecting channel between these two large river systems. When viewed on a map, this connecting course evidently should flow in two directions. According to GOULDING et al., the Casiquiare is a branch of the Orinoco from a geomorphological point of view. However, based on its direction of flow, it is a tributary of the Rio Negro. Changes in the topography of the region have caused the Río Casiquiare to flow against its original direction. The Essequibo Basin of northeastern South America is another drainage system connected to the Amazon Basin through the Rio Negro. The Guiana Highlands are an ancient mountain range which, over long stretches, isolates the coastal waters of the Guyanas from the other South American river systems. However, at the Guyana-Brazil border there is an interruption in this mountain range. At this place the branches of the Rio Negro System (Rio Tacutu, a tributary of the Rio Branco) meet virtually head on with the waters of the eastward-flowing Essequibo system and, at least during the rainy season, they unite. Additionally, it is said that at flood stage, the Rio Negro is in direct connection with the Rio Japurá in the west and the Rio Uatumã in the east.

Whereas the morphology of the large white-water rivers undergoes constant change due to the quantities of carried sediments which settle out and modify their shores, the shorelines of the Rio Negro hardly change at all. A significant variation is brought about only by the seasonal rise and fall of the water level. However, a distinction between upper and lower course has to be made. When the water in the upper course falls during November to February, it is rising in the lower course because it is backed up by the flooding Amazon. The difference between high waters and low waters at

The rapids of São Gabriel da Cachoeira.   I. Seidel

Dekeyseria pulcher, broadly distributed in the Rio Negro.   M. Wilhelm

Manaus is 10 m on average. In line with most black-water rivers, the white beaches and sand banks are also a characteristic of the Rio Negro. Some of these beaches are over 20 km long. The fine quartz sand comes by and large from the Guiana Highlands. Dense rainforest frames extensively the shores of the river and may become extensively flooded during the rainy season. In these flooded forests (igapó), numerous fish species find ideal spawning grounds. It is the nursery for a multitude of fishes, but less so for suckermouth catfishes than for characins and cichlids. Especially the low-lying areas around the central course of the Rio Negro, as well as the numerous tributaries in the region, harbor expansive flooded areas. The lower Rio Negro and the confluences of its numerous tributaries appear like fjords due to the low level of sedimentation. The very deep, lakelike mouths are also called rias. The lower Rio Negro Ria is approximately 15 km wide at its widest site, and at Manaus a depth of approximately 100 m has been measured.

The large South American rivers are characterized by numerous islands, which might be so numerous in places that only local boat drivers know their way around the maze. More so than in virtually any other river, the Rio Negro is home to giant island groups. The arguably best-known is the Anavilhanas Archipelago in the lower Rio Negro. In total, the Rio Negro contains over 1000 of such river islands, the largest of which are over 30 km in length. Rapids are only found in the upper course of the river. The first significant cachoeiras—the Brazilian term for rapids—are encountered approximately 900 km upriver at Tapuruquara, and that is also the end of the line for larger boats during the low water season. The danger to run aground on one of the numerous submersed granite rocks is too big. Another 300 km upriver mark the beginning of the first truly large rapids. These waters are regularly transversed by small motorized boats, but it seems suicidal to do so without an experienced motorist at the helm. Waterfalls are not part of the Rio Negro proper, but numerous tributaries have frequent smaller falls. The further one advances upriver on the Rio Negro, the more frequent become the rock formations that are virtually submersed in the current during the rainy season. These rocks, which frequently have deep crevices, are the habitat of some suckermouth catfishes which also find appropriate spawning substrates in such sites.

During the day these sandbanks are virtually barren. At night they teem with life.

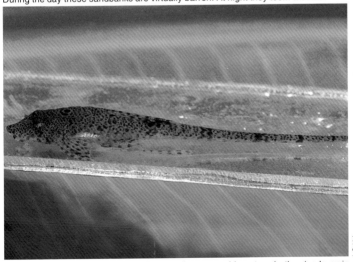

Hemiloricaria formosa, one of the few species we could capture in the river's main channel.

Since the substrate is extremely poor in soluble minerals, the Rio Negro carries extremely soft water. Sıolı (1967) reported about the water chemistry of the Rio Negro, comparing it to that of slightly impure distilled water. The concentrations of the most important elements makes the water comparable to rain water (Gıbbs, 1971). The high acidity, i.e., the low pH, is due to the high acidity of the substrates the tributaries flow over, as well as to the extensive input of acidic organic material. According to Goulding et al. the pH of the river ranges—depending on site and season—between 3.6 and 5.8. Naturally, the values rise right below the confluence of larger clear- and white-water tributaries, such as the Rio Demini or the Rio Branco. The coffee, tea, or cola coloration of the river is the result of the presence of tannins leached from vegetation falling into the water (e.g., leaves, fruits, and tree bark). Although no turbidity-causing agents are present in the water, the visibility under water is only around one meter. Due to the dark coloration of the water, the Rio Negro absorbs more solar radiation than clear-water rivers, and is therefore slightly warmer. This absorptive capacity of black-water can be readily noticed at calm, wind-protected sites. At the upper Rio Negro, we found calm shore areas where a distinct temperature stratification could be observed. The upper, ca. 20 cm, water layer had heated up to such an extent that the layers below felt ice cold. As could be confirmed by our measurements, the water temperatures in the main channel generally exceed 28°C, but only occasionally are warmer than 31°C. The tributaries, which frequently are small forest streams, generally are significantly cooler. Especially during low water levels, the Rio Negro is very shallow at numerous places. In pools and in calm areas the temperature will rise significantly. Due to the heating of the water and the high infusion of plant material, dissolved oxygen concentrations repeatedly diminish severely. In response to this potentially life-threatening situation, many suckermouth catfishes are well-adapted to such environmental conditions thanks to their accessory breathing organs.

Due to the very acidic, nutrient-poor and therefore hostile water of the Rio Negro, hardly any fish food of animal origin can be found. According to Stawıkowskı & Werner (1998) there are only two especially adapted gastropods in the Rio Negro, and the crustacea

Dekeyseria scaphirhyncha seems to inhabit the entire Rio Negro drainage. The pictured specimen was captured in the upper Rio Negro.

are also very poorly represented. Moreover, there is a paucity of aquatic vegetation. However, due to the decay of flooded forest, which is dying due to an ever-increasing amount of submergence time during the last 30 years, the released nutrients are leading to an increase in submerged vegetation. Based on these conditions, it is virtually unbelievable how many fish species, and the suckermouth catfishes are no exception, one can actually find in the Rio Negro. Although there is still a long way to go to match the numerical presence as we know it from white-water and clear-water rivers of the plains, it is still remarkable. The high rate of nutrient input in the form of leaves and fruits, as well as terrestrial insects that fall into the water and serve the fishes as food, has made this possible

During a trip to the upper Rio Negro at São Gabriel da Cachoeira in October 1997, with our companions Maik BEYER, Volker BOHNET, Michael SCHLÜTER, and Paulo VALERIO DA SILVA, we could see for our-

Ancistrus dolichopterus, the big-fin bristlenose, is particularly common in the middle Rio Negro region.

selves just how low the piscine biomass in the main channel really is. Only a few fishes could be observed during the night in the Rio Negro proper. Most were encountered in the mouths of small tributaries as well as among the leaf litter along the shoreline.

During the day, we did not find a single suckermouth catfish in the main stream. It was already a major success to find every once in a while a solitary characin or cichlid while snorkeling over a sand bank. Even the rocky shores did not yield a single loricariid sighting, even though the granite rocks had deep cracks exposed to current—highly appropriate loricariid biotopes. It appeared, however, that all the fishes were in deeper waters.

At night, the situation changed remarkably. We made a successful haul with a seine on a sand bank. Besides numerous characins and geophagine cichlids, we were also able to capture the first loricariid—*Hemiloricaria formosa*. That indeed there are many more species that inhabit the Rio Negro is demonstrated as part of research published by GOULDING, CARVALHO, and FERREIRA (1998). In the context of their studies, they were able to capture and examine 30 different loricariids in the main stream. They estimated the suckermouth catfishes in the Rio Negro to be represented by at least 42 species in 17 genera. That is only slightly less than 10% of the total of fish species suspected to inhabit the river. However, these numbers are only for the Rio Negro proper. The species diversity of the various tributaries, particularly of those carrying white- or clear-water, is expected to be much higher. Typical inhabitants of the Rio Negro itself are the spotted sailfin pleco, *Glyptoperichthys gibbiceps*, the butterfly suckermouth catfish, *Zonancistrus brachyurus*, the flathead suckermouth, *Dekeyseria scaphirhyncha,* as well as the big-fin bristlenose, *Ancistrus dolichopterus*, a species particularly common in the central Rio Negro section. However, all these species are also frequently encountered in the tributaries.

A particular species diversity of loricariids is present in the Rio Demini, a northern tributary of the central Rio Negro that flows into the river at the height of Barcelos. This clear-water river is home to a significant number of suckermouth catfish species exported through Manaus from the Rio Negro region, and is therefore of great interest to the specialized hobbyist. Barcelos is the first holding station of fishes captured in the Demini. From there they are taken to the exporters located in Manaus. The Rio Demini is one of the numerous rivers that drain the Guiana Highlands through the Rio Negro. Its headwaters are located in the Serrana Urucuzeiro, the Serras do Demini, as well as the Serra Gurupira, near the Venezuelan border. WILHELM (pers. comm.) traveled during New Year 2000/2001 for several weeks through the central Rio Negro region, and spent much time in the Rio Demini in search of suckermouth catfishes. His remarks are the basis for the following observations. In extensive sections, the Demini River is a slow-flowing clear-water river with a locally variable coloration and chemistry. The upper course is quite clear, whereas the lower course is very turbid. Additionally, there is the confluence with a large black-water tributary from the West, the Rio Araçá, which consequently changes the chemistry downriver. Whereas upriver of the confluence a pH of approximately 5 is similar to that of most clear-water streams of the central Rio Negro, below, depending on location, it is some-

Fam.: Loricariidae

Lower course of the Rio Demini (central Rio Negro drainage).   M. Wilhelm

The Demini River is the fishing grounds of numerous aquaristically known ancistrine catfishes. These vats are used to transport them to Barcelos.

what lower. The water is extremely soft (conductivity ca. 10 µS/cm). WILHELM determined a temperature of 27°–28°C. The riverbed of the Rio Demini is also highly variable. In extensive areas the substrate is sandy, but especially in its lower course there are extensive sections with mostly rock material, apparently of volcanic origin. It is very holey material, where loricariids find superb shelter. The captors of these loricariids take advantage of this characteristic. Individual rocks are lifted out of the water and the fishes in the numerous caves are simply collected as they wiggle out. Especially frequent catches in such rocks are *Pseudacanthicus* sp. (L 114), *Hypancistrus* sp. (L 136a), as well as *Peckoltia* cf. *braueri* (L 121). *Panaqolus* sp. (LDA 1/L 167) and *Zonancistrus brachyurus* (L 168) were also found, albeit in lesser numbers.

On sandy substrates, various whiptail catfishes can be found. However, *Hemiloricaria melini*, a species broadly distributed in the central Rio Negro region, seems to have an area of distribution limited to the lower Rio Demini. Two additional members of the genus *Hemiloricaria*, *H. fallax* and *H.* sp. "Barcelos," are also found, but much further upriver. *Hemiloricaria* sp. "Amazonia," which has an incredibly broad distribution in the Amazon Basin, can also be captured in the Demini River. However, WILHELM could confirm the species only in its lower course, where it was found during the day on a sand bank. WILHELM also captured a mouthbrooding whiptail catfish. In a small Igarapé flowing into the Demini, with a muddy substrate, he captured several specimens of *Limatulichthys petleyi*. This was the only site within the entire Demini Drainage where this species was found. In a smallish tributary of the Rio Demini, close to the town of Bacabal, WILHELM found two different twig catfishes; however, these were not members of the genus *Farlowella,* but representatives of the genus *Acestridium* in the subfamily Hypoptomatinae. The fishes were adhered to branches in very clear, greenish shimmering water. Syntopically to the brownish *Acestridium martini,* the somewhat broader and greenish-gray *Acestridium dichromum* was encountered. The scientific literature (see RETZER, NICO & PROVENZANO, 1999) confirms that both species may commonly be found together. However, up to that time, these two twig catfishes were only known from the Orinoco Basin and the upper Rio Negro region. It is new to find them this far south—and also together.

The bottom of the lower Rio Demini is covered with volcanic rock. M. Wilhelm

To capture the loricariids, the rocks are simply lifted from the water. In this instance, a small *Pseudacanthicus* is appearing.

The bays and lagoons on the Rio Demini—for example, the Lago Catibuque—were also home to a number of suckermouth catfishes. The substrate of such waters is usually sandy-loamy. The loricariids were adhered to submersed tree trunks and branches. Two Hypoptopomatinae could be found there. Besides a very flattened *Hypoptopoma* sp., WILHELM also captured several *Oxyropsis* sp. In addition to these two, the dense branches also harbored twig catfishes of the genus *Farlowella*. A further inhabitant of lentic biotopes is *Ancistrus* sp. (L 107/L 184). WILHELM captured it numerously in Lake Catibuque on submersed wood. It is said that in the upper Demini drainage *Peckoltia* cf. *braueri* (L 121) is also captured on wood in pools. These specimens differ from those of the lower course by having a more delicate vermiculate design on the head. It is questionable that these two are even independent species.

WILHELM accompanied the commercial fishermen upriver in their quest for ancistrine loricariids. He reported on a surprisingly easy fishing technique, which apparently has a high yield. On land, palm trees are dug up with much of their roots. The earth is removed

Ancistrus sp. (L 107/L 184) from Lago Catibuque.   M. Wilhelm

from among the root web and the root ball is submersed in the river. After some time, these palms are pulled out of the water, and the loricariids, hiding among the roots, are collected. The quantity of fishes captured this way is amazing. According to WILHELM, the collectors removed up to 300 *Pseudacanthicus* sp. (L114) from a single root ball. *Panaqolus* sp. (LDA 1/L 169), which can be encountered anywhere in the Demini, were found among the roots in particularly high numbers. Additionally, WILHELM observed several *Hypancistrus* sp. (L 136b, which have coarser dots than L 136a). The jet-black, blue-eyed *Ancistrus* sp. (L 88) can be found upriver from the confluence of the Rio Araçá, frequently on wood and roots. This relatively large species replaces the big-fin bristlenose *Ancistrus dolichopterus* (L 183), which is encountered in the lower course, exclusively. WILHELM also found an additional white-spotted *Ancistrus* sp., but was unable to identify it further.

Especially noteworthy, however, is the extremely common occurrence of *Pseudacanthicus* sp. (L114), which lives throughout the Demini on rocks and wood. The larger specimens—up to 40 cm in

Rio Demini, above the confluence of the Rio Araçá. Palm roots are placed in the water to capture loricariids.

Peckoltia cf. *braueri* (L 121) from the lower Rio Demini.

M. Wilhelm

Oxyropsis spp. live among submersed branches.

M. Wilhelm

length—are captured for culinary purposes. The smaller individuals are brought to Barcelos for the aquarium trade. WILHELM reports seeing during his trip several thousand specimens with the captors and in the holding stations. The high population rate is not coincidental. It seems this is a very fertile species. As a tree trunk was being lifted from the water, a broodcaring male appeared. Apparently he was sitting on an egg mass on the outer surface of the tree trunk. The spawn consisted of several hundred eggs (4–5 mm in diameter) and filled almost the entire hand (see also the species section in Volume 2).

Pseudacanthicus sp. (L114), extremely common in the Rio Demini.   M. Wilhelm

Hypancistrus sp. (L 136a) is found on rocks and wood.

M. Wilhelm

M. Wilhelm

Further upriver, L 121, with a delicate reticulate design, are captured. The by-catch in this instance is *Cochliodon* sp. (L 167).

Species List of the Rio Demini Central Rio Negro System, Northern Brazil:		
Species	**Biotope**	**Remarks**
Acestridium dichromum	small tributary near Bacabal, on branches and roots	only at one site
Acestridium martini	small tributary near Bacabal, on branches and roots	only at one site
Ancistrus dolichopterus	on wood	only in the lower stream
Ancistrus sp. "Rio Demini"	on wood	only in the upper stream
Ancistrus sp. (L 88)	on wood	only in the upper stream
Ancistrus sp. (L107/L184)	Lago Catibuque, on wood	common
Cochliodon sp. (L167)	on wood	few specimens
Farlowella sp.	in water remnant on branches	only at one site
Hemiloricaria fallax	on sand	broadly distributed
Hemiloricaria melini	on sand	only in the lower stream
Hemiloricaria sp. "Amazonia"	on sand bank	during the day, only in the lower stream
Hemiloricaria sp. "Barcelos"	on sand bank	broadly distributed
Hypancistrus sp. (L136a)	on rocks and wood	small specimens on rocks, larger specimens on wood
Hypancistrus sp. (L 136b)	among roots	low numbers
Hypoptopoma sp.	in water remnant on wood	only at one site
Limatulichthys petleyi	small tributary creek, muddy bottom	few, lower stream
Oxyropsis sp.	in water remnant on branches	only at one site
Panaqolus sp. (LDA 1/L 169)	on wood and roots	widely distributed
Peckoltia cf. *braueri* (L 121)	on rocks and wood	smaller, with coarse reticulate design in the lower stream, larger with delicate design in upper stream
Pseudacanthicus sp. (L114)	on rocks, on wood, and among roots	very numerous
Zonancistrus brachyurus	on rocks and wood	broadly distributed

Rio Pardo – A River of Giants

Large hypostomine suckermouth catfishes have been seen by all South America travellers, be they self-captured giants that are too large to take home, or be it in a fish market, waiting to grace a meal. Members of the genera *Hypostomus*, *Liposarcus,* and/or *Glyptoperichthys* can be encountered in any

larger drainage of the tropics and subtropics of the South American continent. These large suckermouth catfishes are usually inhabitants of white-water biotopes, where they appear in surprisingly high population densities. The nutritional characteristics of white-water foster the broad distribution of these voracious feeders. So it comes as no surprise that in other water types their presence is rather modest. The population skewed towards smaller

In the highlands of São Paulo.

H.-G. Evers

Fam.: Loricariidae

Rio Pardo at Ribeirão Preto.   M.T.C. Lacerda

Hypostominae. An exception is given by the large Hypostominae of the Rio São Francisco (EVERS, 2000c), which are likely to feed on the algae growing in the plentiful rock crevices present. In white-water, detritus is the primary nutritional source of the Hypostominae, and it is completely normal to capture specimens with full stomachs. The large fishes defecate within a few hours and the water in the transport receptacles quickly becomes polluted, turning brown. Those who have tried to transport these giants of 30–40 cm length know how important repeated water exchanges in the transport bags are, even though the fishes have accessory breathing possibilities and are not sensitive at all. The small city of Ribeirão Preto is located on the northern border of the Brazilian State of São Paulo, directly at the central course of the Rio Pardo, an affluent of the large Rio Grande. The Grande River, in Brazil also called Rio Mogi-Guaçu, flows into the giant Rio Paraná, one of the large drainage systems of South America. Hardly a tourist, least of all an aquarium hobbyist, ever makes it into that area,

Hypostomus cf. *roseopunctatus*, a beautiful but rare guest of the Rio Pardo. ^{M.T.C. Lacerda}

Hypostomus cf. *variipictus*, described from the Rio Pardo. M. Beyer

preferring to search for new aquarium fishes in warm Amazonia and not appreciating the relatively cool streams of the highlands of southeastern Brazil.

Nevertheless, Marco T.C. LACERDA of TROP RIO and Maik BEYER of APISTO HEAVEN have repeatedly visited this river. Especially Maik BEYER regularly captures large catfishes in the Rio Pardo for export to all the world. Also co-author H.-G. EVERS visited this place together with M. BEYER in october 2002.

The Rio Pardo is a typical fast-flowing white-water river. During the dry season, approximately from March to October, the conditions are optimal for fishing. At that time the river carries less water, and at some places it can be crossed with the water at chest level—never a great pleasure in the swift current of these cold streams. During the rainy season, the river cannot be crossed in this manner at all. At that time, the river has a raging current and is 2–3 meters deep. Additionally, the IBAMA—the Brazilian office for nature protection—places a general prohibition on fishing in the river from November to January. During that time the fishes are breeding and their season is closed. The water is cold, with an average temperature of 20°C at the most. Additional parameters unfortunately are unknown, but should be in line with typical white-water values.

Fishing is most successful at night. It is best to use a canoe with 2–3 people on board. There is much rubble in the river, but there are also areas with smaller rocks and gravel substrates. The hypostominins adhere to larger rocks and are predominantly captured there. Although capture is difficult, the yield will likely be higher. The fishing tool consists of a large castnet—called "tarrafa" in Brazil—with a coarse mesh and framed by large lead weights. In order to capture the fishes, the net is not simply cast in a round arch into the water, but is dragged on the bottom. One side is lowered into the water, while two people make sure the heavy lead line follows the bottom. After approximately 50 m the other side is lowered into the water and the net is slowly pulled out of the water at shore. Using this rather unorthodox fishing method, great numbers of suckermouth catfishes become entangled in the mesh and can be placed in the prepared transport containers, once untangled carefully, so as not to damage the costly net.

The beautiful *Hypostomus* cf. *lexi* was also described from the Rio Pardo. M.T.C. Lacerda

Hypostomus regani is broadly distributed in southern Brazil. M. Beyer

This method is primarily used to capture the relatively common *Hypostomus regani* (black-brown with indistinct yellowish pink dots) and *Hypostomus margaritifer* (black-brown with small dots, a flatter body, and a very tall dorsal fin). Very commonly captured are also two *Hypostomus* spp. which could not yet be unequivocally identified. According to BEYER (pers. comm. to Evers), one is a species with a distinct reticulate design on the head, and the other has a brown body covered by coarse black dots. Much rarer, an additional *Hypostomus* species can be found in the net which, as far as its body is concerned, is strongly reminiscent of the ancistrine genus *Baryancistrus*. Occasionally, the beautiful *Hypostomus* cf. *lexi* can also be found in the net, as is the case with the tall-finned *Hypostomus* cf. *variipictus* and the beautiful, smaller species *Hypostomus nigromaculatus*. The latter represents a valuable contribution to the aquarium hobby, since it can readily be maintained in an unheated tank and, furthermore, is quite attractive and unusual. Very rarely, a particularly attractive, quite large species might be captured, which has yellow dots on

Hypostomus cf. *strigaticeps* has a less conspicuous design.   M. Beyer

a black body, and which might possibly be *Hypostomus roseopunctatus*. Just as rarely captured with this methodology is *Megalancistrus paranamus*. The *Megalancistrus* usually sit in rock crevices and caves at considerable depth. Being the most sought after by the fishermen, they are captured diving at night, using their bare hands to feel their way in rock caves and pulling them out very laboriously. Since *Megalancistrus paranamus* are very spiny, the activity in not exactly a walk in the park, especially since diving in these cool waters quickly causes hypothermia.

Given the generous mesh size, the captured specimens invariably are large. A small specimen is a rare exception. Two less attractive species—*Hypostomus* sp. "Rio Pardo I" and *Hypostomus* sp. "Rio Pardo II"— as well as *Hypostomus nigromaculatus,* can also be captured with a small seine at shallower areas in large quantities, including small specimens. Hardly ever does a small representative of the other species appear in the net. Strangely, at Ribeirão Preto only very rarely is there ever a small representative of the more colorful *Hypostomus* species captured. However, that would be highly desirable, since usually the younger specimens are much more attractive than the adults, where the distinct dots and vermicular lines fade progressively with age.

To give an indication of the relative populations of the various species, below is a list of the fishes captured by Maik Beyer and his team in the course of one night at the Rio Pardo:

100	*Hypostomus regani* and *Hypostomus margaritifer*
8	*Hypostomus* cf. *lexi*
8	*Megalancistrus paranamus* (4 thereof while diving)
5	*Hypostomus* cf. *variipictus*
2	*Hypostomus* cf. *roseopunctatus*

Additional suckermouth catfishes, which could be of interest to the fans of moutbrooding Loricariinae, call these waters home. They live on coarse sand and gravel substrates *Proloricaria prolixa* (slight design on the head) and *Proloricaria lentiginosa* (with a vermiculate cephalic design) are two species that reach a length of 40 cm and that have been described from the Rio Mogi-Guaçu system. Their appearance is rather reminiscent of the genus

---

Pseudohemiodon because of their broad head, but due to their lip morphology they are unequivocally members of the genus *Loricaria*. However, whether these are indeed two independent species or not needs to be investigated, because according to Maik BEYER only one species is captured exclusively and based on its coloration, it clearly corresponds to the description given for *Proloricaria lentiginosa*. The *Loricaria* are also captured as large specimens exclusively. Never have individuals of just a few centimeters length been captured in the vicinity of the city of Ribeirão Preto. In the course of one night, up to 100 *Proloricaria lentiginosa* may be captured. It seems the species is particularly common in this section of the river.

The distribution and population densities of the named species in the vicinity of Ribeirão Preto are strongly influenced by the season. It is not always that a night is as productive as the numbers given above might lead us to believe. There are nights when hardly anything at all is captured. The large loricariids enter the local market for the food trade, only a very few of these are fished for the export market of aquarium fishes. In that regard, especially Japan and the United States appreciate the robust *Hypostomus* and *Loricaria* for their aquaria. They belong in a correspondingly large aquarium with a length of at least 150 cm fitted with a powerful filtration current. A heater should not be used, these catfishes prefer it cool.

The correct species identification of the specimens mentioned here was a long-term headache. There are many species described from the Rio Mogi-Guaçu System (VON IHERING, 1911; REGAN, 1912; NICHOLS, 1919; SCHUBART, 1964), just a few of which came with a somewhat more elaborate definition, never mind an illustration. Since GOSLINE (1947) the species of southern Brazil have not been revised, and a modern analysis is much needed. The mentioned Hypostominae have in part been described from the Rio Tietê System, a direct Río Paraná tributary in the federal state of São Paulo, but also in part from the Mogi-Guaçu and the Rio Pardo itself. Additionally, these large fishes surely occur in the entire Paraná Drainage, i.e., all the way into Paraguay and Argentina. The Hypostominae from the São Francisco River, pictured in EVERS (2000c), are also strongly reminiscent of those of the Paraná

Hypostomus margaritifer

M. Beyer

Proloricaria lentiginosa

M. Beyer

drainage. There is still a lot of work to be done for dedicated ichthyologists! In any case, it is interesting to note that so many different suckermouth catfish species, and most growing to a very respectable size, inhabit a relatively small river like the Rio Pardo.

Rio Pardo at Ribeirão Preto – Upper Paraná-System, Southeastern Brazil:		
Species	**Biotope**	**Remarks**
Hypostomus cf. *lexi*	rubble substrate	rare
Hypostomus nigromaculatus	gravel substrate, shallow sites	common
Hypostomus regani	rubble substrate	common
Hypostomus cf. *margaritifer*	rubble substrate	common
Hypostomus cf. *roseopunctatus*	rubble substrate	very rare
Hypostomus cf. *strigaticeps*	rubble substrate	common
Hypostomus cf. *variipictus*	rubble substrate	common
Hypostomus sp. "Rio Pardo I"	gravel substrate, shallow sites	very common
Hypostomus sp. "Rio Pardo II"	gravel substrate, shallow sites	very common
Megalancistrus parananus	rubble substrate, rock caves	very rare
Proloricaria lentiginosa	coarse sand, gravel	very common

Rio do Peixe, July 1999.

H.-G. Evers

Fam.: Loricariidae

Where the shore vegetation reaches into the water, many loricariids—such as *Hemiloricaria lanceolata*, *Otocinclus* sp. "Rio do Peixe," and *Farlowella henriquei*—live in the current-swept sections.

Rio do Peixe – Life Among Wood

"Peixe" is Portuguese for fish. The "Rio do Peixe," correspondingly, is the "river of fishes." We hoped that name was given for a good reason. Everywhere in Brazil there are rivers with this name, similarly as there is a seemingly endless supply of Rio Preto (= the black river) or Rio das Aguas (river of the wa-

ters) in all States of that expansive country. "Our" Rio do Peixe flows through the State of Goias in central Brazil, and enters at approximately 14° S into the Araguaia River. We are therefore still in Amazonia, if, as is customarily done, the rivers Araguaia and Tocantins are considered part of the giant basin.

110

View from a bridge onto the Rio do Peixe during the dry season June 1999.   H.-G. Evers

The same view from the same bridge during the rainy season, March 1998. The water level is much higher.

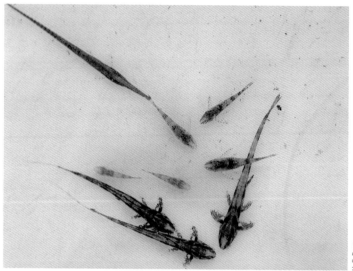

Hemiloricaria lanceolata, Farlowella henriquei, and some *Otocinclus* sp. "Rio do Peixe," all just captured in the Rio do Peixe.

On two trips to this region in March 1998 (end of the rainy season) and in June 1999 (dry season), one of the authors, EVERS, visited the Rio do Peixe each time, to explore the fishes in its waters. His companions each time included Paulo VALERIO DA SILVA and his right hand, Romulo, from the company PEIXE VIVO of Aruanã, a small city at the central Rio Araguaia.

According to the season, the Rio do Peixe each time presented itself differently. In March 1998 the water level was very high and the stream was raging in parts. Limbs and branches of the shore vegetation reached into the clay-turbid waters. As we determined later, many suckermouth catfishes adhere to these current-swept substrates and apparently take advantage of this seasonal source of food. At that time the water temperature was 30.7°C in the shallow shores on sand banks. At steep shores, at ca. 1 m depth, it was only slightly lower (29.8°C). In March, the pH was 6.7, and the conductivity 42 µS/cm.

Most suckermouth catfish species can be found at such wood-rich habitats.

L 37, just "peeled" from a trunk!

Besides huge amounts of characins of all colors and various knifefishes, we also captured several interesting catfish species during the rainy season. For example, there were the tiny *Corydoras cochui* as well as several candirús (parasitic catfish) of the species *Branchoica bertoni,* which were trapped in the mesh of our net. However, the suckermouth catfishes were numerically better represented. We captured *Panaque* sp. (L 27), *Cochliodon* sp. (L 50), *Hemiloricaria lanceolata,* and the beautiful *Hypostomus* sp. (L 37) in areas of wood piles and among the overhanging shore vegetation. A trial run with a seine—no easy feat in the swollen waters and swift current—yielded several *Sturisoma* sp. "Araguaia" and *Loricaria lata*. However, for the professionals of PEIXE VIVO the yield was modest and the comment was "return in the summer, then you will see cascudos!" ("Cascudo" is the common name in Brazil for suckermouth catfishes. Every child knows the term and everywhere where we asked for cascudos we have been helped.)

On the second visit to the area a year later, June 1999, the situation at the Rio Peixe presented itself somewhat different. The water level was much lower and huge quantities of driftwood lay exposed. The now calm waters slowly flowed over a sand bottom. The shore vegetation, which on the previous trip had been hanging into the water, was over one meter above the water surface.

The pH was 7.5 and the conductivity measured 84 µS/cm. The water temperature was uniformly at 27°C and the maximum water depth was 1.5 m in the center of the stream.

With a smile on their faces, Paulo and Romulo began with their fishing. If a year ago it was quite impressive how many fishes they captured with one pass of the seine, now the quantities defied the wildest dreams. The net emerged full of fishes after it had been slowly pulled along the sand bank. The sand substrate is inhabited by *Loricaria lata* and *Hemiodontichthys acipenserinus*, but also *Stegophilus intermedius* was found in the net. Naturally, there are plenty of other fish species that are captured concurrently, such as *Satanoperca* and *Biotodoma* cichlids and the knifefish *Apteronotus albifrons*. *Squaliforma* cf. *annae* is also found here, but only small specimens of approximately 15 cm total length. Adults probably migrate into deeper zones or into the

Panaque sp. (L 27). This beautiful fish is also found here.

Cochliodon sp. (L 50) also prefers wooden substrates.

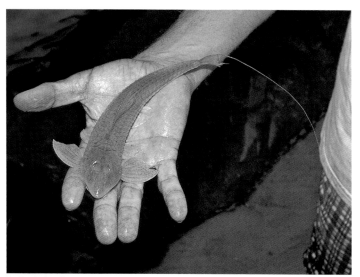

Loricaria lata lives on sand banks.   H.-G. Evers

large Rio Araguaia, where sometimes over 10 specimens of ca. 30 cm length wiggle in the mesh after a single pass with the seine. But the total climax is in the area where driftwood has accumulated. With a divers mask covering one's eyes, the snorkeler immerses him- or herself into the world of suckermouth catfishes. Everywhere on the wood are the fishes adhering, and expertly they scoot to the opposite site of the trunk when the eager hands of the suckermouth catfish fan reach out to catch them. The capture method is invariably the same: One person dives and searches for a promising area. Once a place is found, the companions are called. The wood is lifted and dip nets are placed beneath. Once the wood is lifted out of the water, the loricariids fall into the nets beneath and can then be transferred to awaiting plastic vats. After barely an hour of intensive collecting, almost 100 juveniles of various suckermouth catfish species swam in the vats. Adults inhabit other zones in the deeper water. Here we find the following species: *Lasiancistrus* sp. (L 33), *Cochliodon* sp. (L

With a pass of the seine in the center of the river, large quantities of *Squaliforma* cf. *annae* can be captured as long as the water level is low. However, specimens of this size already live in the Rio Araguaia, the river the Rio do Peixe flows into.

50), the beautiful *Hypostomus* sp. L 37, *Ancistrus* sp. with yellow-white dots, and *Panaque* sp. (L 27). *Hemiloricaria lanceolata* is also common, but is more concentrated in areas with shore vegetation. *Glyptoperichthys joselimaianus* is also quite common among the shore vegetation, a biotope it shares with *Farlowella henriquei*. The *Farlowella* can always be captured at those places where the grass growing from the shore ("capim") is exposed to a stronger current. At such biotopes, *Farlowella henriquei* and *Hemiloricaria lanceolata* adhere with their head facing the current.

The Rio do Peixe is truly a river of fishes, suckermouth catfishes in particular, as these are found in a remarkable species diversity and high population density.

Rio do Peixe at Aruanã – Central Brazil:		
Species	Biotope	Remarks
Ancistrus sp.	wood piles	common
Cochliodon sp. (L 50)	wood piles	very common
Farlowella henriquei	shore vegetation	rare
Glyptoperichthys joselimaianus	shore vegetation, wood	very common
Hemiloricaria lanceolata	wood , shore vegetation	common
Hemiodontichthys acipenserinus	sand banks	rare
Hypostomus sp. (L 37)	wood piles	very common
Lasiancistrus sp. (L 33)	wood piles	very common
Loricaria lata	sand banks	common
Otocinclus sp. "Rio do Peixe"	shore vegetation	rare
Panaque sp. (L 27)	wood piles	common
Squaliforma cf. *annae*	sand banks	very common

Good equipment is essential for successful expeditions!

H.-G. Evers

View of Lago Tefé during the dry season.   H.-G. Evers

Rio Tefé – Night on the Sandbank

During a trip which we under-
took together during October
and November 1997 with our
friends Volker BOHNET and
Michael SCHLÜTER, to Brazil, we
also reached the Rio Tefé, a
small right-side tributary of the
Rio Solimões—as the Amazon
is called prior to its encounter
with the Rio Negro in Brazil. We

had an appointment with Maik BEYER and Paulo VALERIO DA SILVA,
who already had arrived a few days prior to the city of Tefé and
arranged a boat for us all. We therefore wasted no time and skip-
pered with captain TEIXERA and his crew initially 40 km on the Lago
Tefé, and then finally on the Río Tefé proper. During the following

The lower Rio Tefé.   H.-G. Evers

During the dry season, swallows inhabit the caves on the cliffs; during the rainy season, when the water is high, hypostomins reclaim the caves to breed.

H.-G. Evers

Rio Tefé. These sandbanks are home to a plethora of loricariids which are easily captured at night.

days we had the opportunity to fish in the Río Tefé and its tributaries for some 130 km upriver and to get to know the diverse piscine fauna of this region. The Río Tefé is known to aquarists primarily for its green discus. These discus are famous and have been sought for a long time because of their beauty. The situation has changed as of lately with the advent of the popular pigeon-blood and snakeskin bred strains and now hardly anyone is interested in the beautiful wild populations of discus. Beauty truly is in the eye of the beholder.

Unfortunately, the situation at the Río Tefé has also changed as a result of human activity. MAYLAND (1988)—referring to the year 1985—reports about deep tea-brown water and chemical values typical of black-waters. He performed his measurements in early November, i.e., at a similar time of the year as us, who visited the same place 12 years later. However, the Rio Tefé presented itself completely different to us. At this time, the previously tea-colored water was very turbid and more closely resembled coffee with milk.

Fam.: Loricariidae

The reason for this is crude oil. The Brazilian oil company PETROBRAS extracts crude about 250–300 km upriver from the city of Tefé. The obtained crude oil is transported in barges down the river, and especially now, at the height of the dry season, we observe every once in a while dredges keeping the river channel open for these barges. With all this digging, the sediment is whorled up and causes turbidity in what was previously a black-water river. Supposedly, these barges are only allowed to navigate during the daylight hours to help prevent collisions on the narrow river; however, as we slept at night in our hammocks, more than once did we hear the tankers passing. It is a gruesome thought that one of these days such a tanker may spring a leak and release several thousand liters of crude into the Tefé, slowly drifting downward, poisoning everything in their path. Such "accidents" have already occurred repeatedly in Brazil.

The water values determined in late October 1997 in the Rio Tefé by ourselves were the following: pH was very low at 4.8, in contrast, the relatively high conductivity of 38 µS/cm might be explained by the suspended matter. In the clear, truly tea-colored small tributaries, conductivity was significantly lower with 15 µS/cm. A habitat still in a relatively natural state is the Igarapé Piraruaia, approximately 80 km from the city of Tefé. After fishing there an entire day, over 20 catfish species were captured, e.g., *Dekeyseria scaphirhyncha*, numerously found on driftwood.

The water temperature of the Rio Tefé was constantly at 32°C over the course of several days, the ambient temperature often much higher during the day. The water level was extremely low, and shallows often had to be circumnavigated. Since the Tefé supports a fair amount of traffic, rare birds, such as macaws and toucans, have retreated into the depths of the forest. However, many species of egrets and the spectacled caiman have stayed to prey on the high density of fishes. Even botos, the freshwater dolphins of the genus *Inia,* were numerously encountered, which is also a good indication of the plentiful food available. Our diurnal fishing efforts were rewarded accordingly. Large quantities of characins, cichlids, knifefishes, and others were our haul.

Agglomerations of driftwood are found at several places of Lake Tefé and its tributaries. In one of the clear tributaries of the lake,

There is significant traffic on the Rio Tefé.

H.-G. Evers

H.-G. Evers

There is driftwood everywhere in the river. A good place to capture *Ancistrus* sp. (L 181).

Mouth of a small Igarapé into the Tefé.

H.-G. Evers

The Igarapé Piraruaia, an apparently undisturbed habitat for many fish species.

H.-G. Evers

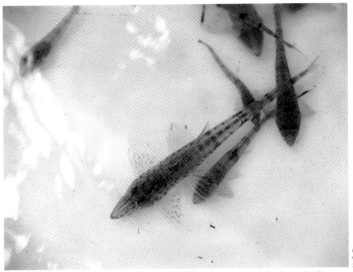

Furcodontichthys novaesi and other sand-dwellers the morning after in a plastic vat.

subadult *Ancistrus* sp. (L 181) could be shaken out of the wood. Large quantities of swallows nested in tubular caves on the cliffs of the river. At the high water season, some of these caves are inhabited by hypostomin suckermouth catfishes as breeding sites. Numerous *Liposarcus pardalis* and *Glyptoperichthys* cf. *gibbiceps* (L 164) with beautiful red upper and lower caudal fin rays were also found, but the most catfishes were captured with a 5 m long seine which we pulled, between four and five people, over the numerous sandbanks.

The crowning of our successes was fishing at night. Everything that hides during the day in the center of the river or in its shelters emerges at night to feed on the sandbanks. It did, however, require some getting used to to step into the lukewarm brew—and always on the lookout for stingrays and electric eels, also common at these sites. We dragged our feet over the sand as we pulled one end of the net in an arc from the shore into the river and back to shore, all while one of us held the other end securely on the

Glyptoperichthys cf. *gibbiceps* (L 164) from the Tefé. Note the gorgeous orange coloration on the fins.

H.-G. Evers

beach. The result was unbelievable. We had never seen so many fishes in one place. Even the species diversity was mind-blowing, as sometimes up to 30 species were captured at once. Besides characins, cichlids, knifefishes, and large osteoglossids, the water boiled from wiggling catfishes. Particularly common were the thorny catfishes of the genus *Hassar*, but also some Auchenipteridae (driftwood catfishes), many Pimelodidae and some other Doradidae were among them. Naturally, our interest was centered on the Loricariidae. Especially the numerous sand-dwelling

Dekeyseria scaphirhyncha, shortly after capture.

H.-G. Evers

loricariids got us excited. Two species of the genus *Hemiloricaria*, *H. phoxocephala,* and *H.* sp. "Amazonia" were among them. The third *Hemiloricaria* species of the Tefé drainage—*H. teffeana*—does not live in the main channel. We could only capture it in the clear water of the small tributaries. Our fancy was particularly struck by the mouthbrooding suckermouth catfishes. The knobnose whiptail catfish, *Hemiodontichthys acipenserinus,* and a form of *Loricaria simillima* could be captured. Furthermore, the catch included an undetermined *Loricariichthys* sp., as well as the enthusiastically received *Pseudoloricaria laeviuscula* and *Limatulichthys petleyi.* The pinnacle was the first *Furcodontichthys novaesi,* which no aquarist had ever seen alive and which we could—unfortunately—only capture during the first night. Whereas during the night all these species were captured with surprising ease, during the day they were hardly ever found in the net. As a catfish fan, it is unavoidable to bite the bullet and fish at night, while ignoring the huffing and puffing caimans nearby. In any case, for us the Tefé was by far the most productive loricariidae site that we have ever fished in.

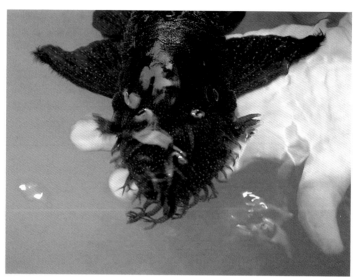

Ancistrus sp. (L 181), a bull from the Igarapé Piraruaia.

H.-G. Evers

Loricariichthys sp., a typical sand-dweller.

H.-G. Evers

Hemiodontichthys acipenserinus is another inhabitant of Rio Tefé sandbanks. H.-G. Evers

Rio Tefé, Amazonia:		
Species	**Biotope**	**Remarks**
Ancistrus sp. (L 181)	wood	only clear-water tributaries
Dekeyseria scaphirhyncha	wood	Igarapés
Furcodontichthys novaesi	sandbank, at night	very rare
Glyptoperichthys cf. *gibbiceps* (L 164)	center of river, cliffs	common
Hemiloricaria phoxocephala	sandbank	rare
Hemiloricaria sp. "Amazonia"	sandbank	common
Hemiloricaria teffeana	sand, leaf litter	only in tributaries
Hemiodontichthys acipenserinus	sandbank	common
Limatulichthys petleyi	sandbank, at night	common
Liposarcus pardalis	deeper areas	very common
Loricaria simillima	sandbank	common
Loricariichthys sp.	sandbank, at night	rare
Pseudoloricaria laeviuscula	sandbank, at night	common

Ore mines gave the state Minas Gerais its name.   H.-G. Evers

Rio das Velhas – In the Footsteps of REINHARDT

A German living in Sweden, the naturalist J. REINHARDT spent several years in central Brazil during the mid 19th century. He established his base camp in the town of Lagoa Santa, still existing today, in the state of Minas Gerais. From there he went on excursions or waited for the locals to sell him interesting

fishes and other animals. This is also the place where the story about the supposed juvenile shovelnose catfish—told in the chapter of the subfamily Stegophiliinae of the Trichomycteridae—unfolds. Like most naturalists at the time, REINHARDT collected all animals that appeared peculiar to him. Especially in the field of ornithol-

Another day begins in Minas Gerais.

H.-G. Evers

The Rio das Velhas at the BR 259: After hard rains the water turns clay-red.

H.-G. Evers

H.-G. Evers

The Rio das Velhas at Nova Lima after several rainless days. Its waters are almost clear.

ogy REINHARDT was very active. In regard to fishes, he visited the drainage of the Rio das Velhas. There he collected in the large river proper as well as in the numerous small clear-water tributaries and sent most of the material to Stockholm, where, among others, LÜTKEN analyzed and published the material. REINHARDT described in one of these publications a *Plecostomus* (today *Hypostomus*) *lima* (REINHARDT in LÜTKEN, 1874), which he had captured himself in the Ribeirão do Mato near Lagoa. The Rio das Velhas is a large river that is born north of Belo Horizonte and flows through the valleys of the mountain ranges of Serra da Moeda, Serra do Cipó (at its end the Rio Cipó flows into the Rio das Velhas), and the Serra do Cabral. It later flows into the headwaters of the Rio São Francisco, the gigantic east Brazilian clear-water river that flows into the Atlantic. The piscine fauna of the upper Rio São Francisco is barely known. Aquaristically there is virtually no known species from this area with the exception of the silver-tipped tetra, *Hasemania nana* (see EVERS, 1998b), which for the longest time

The Rio Cipó is a large clear-water tributary of the Rio das Velhas and is home to a very similar piscine community. The waterfall is a popular destination for local tourism.

was of unknown origin. Along the same lines, there was hardly ever an aquaristic report dealing with the upper Rio São Francisco. Some interesting characins were briefly presented (EVERS, 1997a) and only two *Hypostomus* species have reached us in Germany via Bahia as new imports (EVERS, 1997d).

In October 1996, EVERS made a trip to that area. Together with Marco T.C. LACERDA and Maik BEYER, the trip started by jeep from Rio de Janeiro northeastward into the giant State of Minas Gerais. There they hooked up with Paulo VALERIO DA SILVA and his crew from PEIXE VIVO, who had taken the long road of Aruanã at the Rio Araguaia. The first days were spent investigating small tributaries of the Rio das Velhas and its piscine fauna. A first target was the town of Lagoa Santa with its large lake—today, unfortunately, a polluted puddle with guppies and tilapias. It turned out to be utterly uninteresting. The trip continued on the BR 135 north in direction of Curvelo and later on the BR 259 in direction of Diamantina. Every promising creek was fished in search of inter-

H.-G. Evers

The Rio Vermelho, a direct tributary of the Rio das Velhas, is a suckermouth catfish biotope with swift current.

esting species. The Rio das Velhas was investigated in more detail, both at the bridge of BR 259 as well as at the city of Nova Lima further south. The Rio das Velhas appears to be a typical white-water river with a pH of 7.2 and a conductivity between 50 and 70 µS/cm. The water temperature was 25.5°C. The water was clay-laden turbid with a reddish hue. Fishing was not very successful in the Rio das Velhas proper—only one *Hypostomus* species was captured. However, the tributaries were much more interesting. These creeks are all very similar in appearance. The shallow water flows with relative speed over a substrate that consists mostly of coarse sand. At several places with a particularly swift current, the bottom consists of gravel with a granulometry of 2–5 cm. Occasionally, the water was only 15–20 cm deep and a large quantity of leaf litter and twigs had become lodged among the gravel. Such places were always very productive when fished with a seine against the current and helpers chasing the fishes downstream into the waiting mesh. This is a biotope inhabited by rheophilic species, the rare *Harttia torrenticola* and the even rarer *Parotocinclus* sp. "Minas Gerais" among them. However, the majority of the fishes captured in these creeks and small rivers were always characins of the family characidae, usually in groups of up to 10 different species, whereas catfishes were a rarer catch. These clear waters always had a pH around neutral (7.0) and a conductivity of 40–60 µS/cm. Following heavy rains, these creeks and rivers are always turbid and appear like white-water rivers. Typical white-water rivers, which always show this coloration and at a conductivity of around 100 µS/

Ribeirão Jaboticatuba, another tributary of the Rio das Velhas. This is the home of large quantities of *Rineloricaria* sp. "Rio Cipó."

cm carry significantly more hardeners, are the Rio Vermelho and Rio Jaboticatuba, also visited by us. At a maximum width of 25–30 m and a common depth of 1–2 m, both of these rivers flow into the Rio das Velhas. Here, the *Hypostomus* sp. from the Rio das Velhas and an additional congener could be found—of the latter only specimens up to 10 cm long. Typical is the short caudal peduncle of these quite attractive animals. While attempting to determine the *Hypostomus* from this region, we were faced with major riddles. A total of three names are applicable to fishes of this area. All three taxons, however, are 100 years old or older. One is described in Swedish (*Hypostomus lima*), and the descriptions of the other two species (*Hypostomus garmani* and *Hypostomus macrops*) are very basic and describe the coloration as uniformly olive green, which might be a consequence of the preservation methods employed at the time. Even sending preserved specimens to Dr. Claude WEBER in Geneva did not resolve the puzzle, which is why

Hypostomus sp. "Rio das Velhas I," shortly after capture.

H.-G. Evers

Hypostomus sp. "Rio das Velhas II" from the Rio Vermelho. It has a short caudal peduncle.

Hypostomus sp. "Rio das Velhas II." A handful of this relatively common species.

Rineloricaria sp. "Rio Cipo" can be found in all shown biotopes.

H.-G. Evers

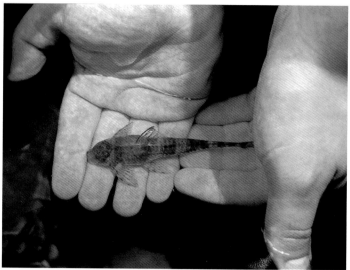

H.-G. Evers

Harttia torrenticola, a ripe female from the Rio Vermelho. October is apparently part of the spawning season.

we chose to designate these fishes as *Hypostomus* sp. "Rio das Velhas I and II." An additional interesting find was *Rineloricaria* sp. "Rio Cipó," which was found numerously both in the Rio Cipó and here. The Rio Cipó is a large tributary of the Rio das Velhas, and represents an exception in regard to water chemistry. At a site below an impressive waterfall the following water values were determined: pH 5.0 and conductivity 8 µS/cm. The water was quite cool in the upper areas of the Serra do Cipó (19.5°C), but towards the lowlands the temperature rose to approximately 22°C. Here, too, we found *Harttia torrenticola,* always in swiftly flowing sections.

All suckermouth catfishes captured during this trip were aquaristically unknown at the time and could, fortunately, be brought back to Germany alive. These catfishes should all be maintained in an unheated aquarium, as they hail from cool waters. For long-term care, *Harttia* surely require strong water movement, whereas, the others will be less dependant on such extreme currents.

It has definitively been worth it to follow in REINHARDT´s tracts and to collect information on the piscine biotopes of this region.

Rio das Velhas-Drainage – Eastern Central Brazil:		
Species	**Biotope**	**Remarks**
Harttia torrenticola	current	small clear tributaries
Hypostomus sp. "Rio das Velhas I"	middle of the river, littoral zone	main stream, tributaries
Hypostomus sp. "Rio das Velhas II"	current	tributaries, common
Parotocinclus sp. "Minas Gerais"	shore vegetation, current	very rare
Rineloricaria sp. "Rio Cipó"	sand substrates	tributaries, common

H.-G. Evers

Harttia torrenticola; a fry captured in leaf litter amidst the current. The dwarf is only a few days old and in a surprisingly poor state of nutrition.

Rio Xingú – Cachoeira Biotope

By far the greatest species diversity of suckermouth catfishes
is encountered in the lotic environments of the South American continent. Already the dorsoventrally flattened body shape
and their inferior mouth—frequently modified into a suctorial disc—give a clear indication that these are mostly rheo-

phylic fishes. Especially the numerous rapids in areas of swift
current—which can only be colonized by similarly well-adapted
organisms—were conquered in the course of evolution by an
unimaginable species diversity. The loricariids hardly face com-
petition that would threaten them in this ecological niche.
On the other hand, the fact that many rivers in central Amazonia
are still paradises in their natural state can especially be attrib-
uted to the presence of rapids (called cachoeiras in Brazil). These
rapids preclude unobstructed shipping and keep a vast proportion of civilization away. But also the incredible species diversity
in South American rivers has to thank the presence of these
rapids. Besides chemical barriers (transitions between white-,
clear- and black-waters), the larger rapids or waterfalls are insur-
mountable dispersal barriers for many fishes, as a result giving
rise to many isolated regions (on occasion only a section of river)
with endemic ichthyofauna.
Whereas up to 15 years ago relatively few suckermouth catfish
species were known aquaristically, the appearance of several
unusual species from the Brazilian Rio Xingú in the late 80's
ignited a downright loricariid bonanza. Quickly, the commercial
value of these fishes was recognized and a continued quest for
new treasures hasn't relented since. New biotopes are fished,
such as the depths of rivers and the immediate vicinity of rapids.
The finds of commercial fishermen are virtually unbelievable. Nobody expected to find so many beautiful and even colorful
loricariids. This resulted in the numerous L- and LDA-catfishes,

One of innumerable cachoeiras of the Rio Xingú: the Cachoeira Cutuvelo.   J. Gottwald

which since then have received code numbers in the aquarium trade magazines. At first it was primarily the Rio Xingú and the Rio Tocantins which were targeted in the search for new suckermouth catfishes, but later it was determined that other Amazon tributaries house a similarly endemic loricariid fauna. Consequently, there have meanwhile been numerous new catfish discoveries and imports to Germany from rivers such as the Tapajós and the Trombetas. It is virtually certain that in the future other rivers will follow. We may already now begin to anticipate the next coming attraction.

Without a doubt, the greatest species diversity of endemic suckermouth catfishes has so far been discovered in the Rio Xingú. This river is one of the large southern Amazon tributaries in Brazil. Its waters travel almost 2000 km from its several headwaters in the central Brazilian highlands of the northern section of the State of Mato Grosso to its confluence with the Amazon near the town of Gurupá. At its mouth it is divided into several streams by the presence of several large islands (e.g., Ilha Urucuricaia and Ilha Grande de Gurupá). Along its course, the river is fed by numerous smallish tributaries, mostly called igarapés in Brazil. Whereas—according to BERGLEITER (1999)— in the lower course of the Xingú the Atlantic tidal rhythm still influences the water level of the river with a fluctuation of up to 40 cm because of the rise in the Amazon, this phenomenon disappears above the lowermost large rapids. The clear-water river flows northward over innumerable rapids (the arguably best known being the Cachoeira von Martius), which makes the river navigable only in sections. The Xingú is home to several remarkable endemics, of which quite a few have been made available to the aquarium hobby.

In September 1988, KILIAN, SCHLIEWEN, and Stawikowski fished the Xingú close to the city of Altamira (see SCHLIEWEN & STAWIKOWSKI, 1989; STAWIKOWSKI, 1989). Altamira is a city with over 150,000 inhabitants, which may also be reached by means of the Transamazonian Highway. It is said that at Altamira the Xingú is approximately one kilometer wide, even during the dry season. The local shore and the river bed consist mostly of dark brown to black rock of volcanic origin, which gives the river a very characteristic appearance. In extensive areas, the substrate reveals a honeycomb structure. Individual cells often have a diameter between 20 and 50 cm and are framed by narrow, vertical walls. Whereas in the shallow water (during the dry season) the walls appear only a few centimeters tall and seem ground down, in deeper waters they may be 20–40 cm tall and have sharp edges where one can easily injure oneself. Additionally, there are tower-like rocks that extend up to two meters above the water's surface and have a surface riddled with crevices. There are numerous hiding places for suckermouth catfishes. They find shelter in the crevices which often are up to one meter deep, or in the numerous holes in the rocks or beneath rocks. There are said to be regular "freshwater reefs" in deeper sections, complete with fishes, sponges, crustacea, and mollusks.

Water temperatures are warm in extensive areas of the Amazon. KILIAN, SCHLIEWEN, and STAWIKOWSKI measured on September 25th, 1988 at around 14:00 hours a water temperature of 32.2°C in a section of the main stream; in the extreme shallows it was even

Balneario Pedral am Xingú, typical rock formations. J. Gottwald

Xingú River; hardly any loricariids are found in such warm and calm shore areas.

35°C. The aerial temperature was 34.5°C. Additional water values: pH 6.5; hardness approximately 1°KH and ca. 1°dGH; electrical conductivity 120 µS/cm; Fe less than 0.05 mg/l. The current was not particularly swift at the time (end of the dry season). It is reportedly much faster during the rainy season.

KILIAN, SCHLIEWEN, and STAWIKOWSKI encountered suckermouth catfishes in the Xingú virtually exclusively in areas with a rocky bottom. In contrast, in a section of shore littered with numerous dead and fallen trees—certainly a select habitat for various loricariids in other South American rivers—they hardly found any loricariids at all. Likewise, in a somewhat downriver-located section with shallow sand substrate there were no suckermouth catfishes found (however, that could have been a consequence of the time of day). In contrast, the species diversity of rock-dwelling loricariids was found to be much greater than elsewhere. Over the course of the latter years, over 30 different species have been imported to Germany from various areas of the Rio Xingú. These fishes received the so-called L-numbers as identifiers. However, not all of these fishes come from the vicinity of the city. Many species have a highly localized area of distribution or only occur in sufficient numbers at certain sites as to make commercial fishing feasible. Along these lines, virtually at every larger cachoiera there are specific species being captured for export. Significant cachoeiras even define the areas of distribution of certain species, so that there is a different fauna upriver from these barriers than downriver. The best time to capture suckermouth catfishes in the Rio Xingú are the driest months of August and September. During the rainy season, and especially in the months of February and March, the water is so high that even shallow-water species are difficult to capture.

Due to the high commercial value of several Xingú loricariids , it is difficult to obtain correct habitat information, as the captors prefer to maintain their sources a secret. As a consequence, Altamira is a common designation of origin, given that the city is a collection point for transshipment. But also here, numerous interesting loricariids can be found. STAWIKOWSKI (1989) reports about the habits of several species in the direct vicinity of Altamira. STAWIKOWSKI and his companions captured, for example, the "delta-tail

Squaliforma cf. *emarginata* (L 11) is very tolerant of elevated temperatures. It is therefore found even in calm shore areas.

catfish" *Squaliforma* cf. *emarginata* (L 11) frequently in the high-temperature shallows where it searched for shelter among roots and under rocks. According to STAWIKOWSKI, the ancistrine L 12 and L 13 were more difficult to capture. These species prevailed at a depth of one to two meters, where they sought shelter among rocks and darted away extensive distances when feeling threatened. The suckermouth catfish *Scobinancistrus aureatus* (L 14), which may reach a length in excess of 30 cm, was encountered singly at depths of two to three meters beneath large rocks or in rock caves. On occasion, these caves were shared with other species of fishes. The "striped peckoltia" *Peckoltia* cf. *vittata* (L 15) were found by STAWIKOWSKI and friends close to shore (depth 1–3 m) where often several huddled under rocks and in caves. According to STAWIKOWSKI, tiny young Ancistrinae sp. (L 16), with a total length not reaching one centimeter, were often encountered in groups of two, three, or four individuals, especially under rocks

J. Gottwald

Baryancistrus sp. (L 18) (orange-fringed suckermouth catfish) is a common presence in shallow waters with a swift current.

where the current had carried gravel into indentions of the rocks. Larger specimens were found in caves. However, it is doubtful that all these fishes were indeed L 16, since the more commonly iesported Ancistrinae sp. (L 30) and *Parancistrus* sp. (L 31) occur syntopically with L 16 and are extremely similar in appearance (GOTTWALD, pers. comm.). *Pseudancistrus* sp. (L 17/L 67) is another inhabitant of the immediate vicinity of Altamira. This species, too, was encountered at depths of one to three meters in caves and beneath rocks. One of the most beautiful Altamira species is the "golden nugget pleco," L 18, a representative of the genus *Baryancistrus*. STAWIKOWSKI could frequently observe this attractive species while snorkeling. As stones were turned, groups of up to six specimens of assorted sizes suddenly darted away in search of new shelter. L 18 is a popular table fish along the Xingú River; it grows to a respectable size and is a numerous find in shallow waters. GOTTWALD reports that experienced fishermen may

Peckoltia cf. *vittata* (L 15) is commonly found under rocks at Altamira.   J. Gottwald

capture with a cast net a respectable quantity in a short period of time, but these fish all end up in a cooking pot. Besides L 18 and its adult form L 85, L 19 is an additional *Baryancistrus* species which is captured in this manner for the food market. Another appreciated food fish is *Panaque* sp. "Rio Xingú," a striped suckermouth catfish of the *P. nigrolineatus* type. STAWIKOWSKI discovered, in the basket of a fishermen, a specimen of approximately lower arm's length.

An amusing episode happened to STAWIKOWSKI with the suckermouth catfish L 20, a representative of the genus *Oligancistrus*. While snorkeling among rocks, numerous small holes, where various fish species found shelter and probably also suitable breeding substrates, caught his eye. STAWIKOWSKI almost always found suckermouth catfishes in these small caves, mostly L 20. Once they were dislodged from their caves where they fastened themselves by spreading their pectoral fin rays, they quickly sought a new shelter. A fleeing specimen headed straight into STAWIKOWSKI'S sports sneakers and attempted to hide therein. Given the scarcity of suitable shelter, another specimen even swam under his shirt and adhered to his stomach.

In light of the presence of these many exciting ancistrines and hypostomines, the other suckermouth catfishes of the Rio Xingú— of which there is hardly ever a report published, and which, of

Species List Río Xingú at Altamira (Amazonia):		
Species	**Biotope**	**Remarks**
Ancistrinae sp. (L 12) and (L 13)	at 1–2 m depth	under individual rocks
Ancistrinae sp. 16) and (L 30)	in stone caves, juveniles among gravel in rock indentions	occur next to each other(L
Baryancistrus sp. (L 18/L 85)	in shallow water, on and beneath rocks	very common species
Baryancistrus sp. (L 19)	in shallow water, on and beneath stones	not as common as L 18
Hemiloricaria sp. "Amazonia"	sandy areas	
Hypoptopoma sp. "Rio Xingú"	on sandbanks	
Loricaria lata (L 10)	sandy areas with detritus and mud	
Oligancistrus sp. (L 20)	in small holes of rocks in shallow water	common species
Panaque sp. "Rio Xingú"	on wood and rocks	
Parancistrus sp. (L 31)	on and beneath rocks in swift current	L 30
Peckoltia cf. *vittata* (L 15)	at 1–3 m depth in caves and beneath rocks	often several in one cave
Pseudancistrus sp. (L 17/L 67)	at 1–3 m depth in caves and beneath rocks	common species
Pseudoloricaria laeviuscula	sandy areas	
Scobinancistrus aureatus (L 14)	at a depth of 2–3 m beneath large rocks or in caves.	individually, but often mixed with other species.
Squaliforma cf. *emarginata* (L 11)	in shallows, under stones and wood	very heat tolerant

Hypoptopoma sp. from Altamira.

J. Gottwald

Pseudoloricaria laeviuscula lives on sandy substrates.

J. Gottwald

149

course, are only rarely imported—play a rather secondary role. Although STAWIKOWSKI also confirms the presence of L 10 at Altamira, this *Loricaria* sp.—probably *Loricaria lata,* has never been imported to Germany except by GOTTWALD (Aquatarium). STAWIKOWSKI captured it at all those places where sand or detritus created a soft substrate in an otherwise hard rock bottom. Additional loricariids inhabiting the vicinity of Altamira are *Pseudoloricaria laeviuscula* and *Hemiloricaria* sp. "Amazonia," which has also been already imported by GOTTWALD. The only hypoptopomatine whose presence could be determined is *Hypoptopoma* sp., pictured on the previous page, top, which can be found on sand banks. However, many of the Xingú loricariids known to us from the literature and the aquarium stores do not hail from the vicinity of Altamira. Some of the most beautiful species are captured exclusively at specific sites either upriver or downriver, and then in part only at greater depth. The American FORSHEY (1996) observed the Xingú suckermouth catfish fishermen during their activities and made a report. According to FORSHEY, the fishermen employ various methods to capture the loricariids in the Xingú River. To capture the loricariids at greater depths, they employ an air supply system similar to the one employed by people prospecting for gold. A small compressor supplies a pressurized air tank, which has two hoses connected to it. Both have a valve to regulate the air flow. The air hose is wrapped around the body because of the strong current. An additional 10 pound weight is carried by the fishermen, so as not to be swept downriver by the current. Besides their hands, the suckermouth catfish fishermen also employ two sticks called "vaqueta." These sticks are used to flush the fish out of their hiding place and into the fishermen's hands or net. Despite the crudeness of the method, only rarely are the fishes harmed. However, the fishermen operate very patiently and manipulate the animals with great care. After all, they are their livelihood. The captured specimens are provisionally stored in the pants pockets, the diving mask, or similar improvised locations. According to FORSHEY, a good fishermen earns approximately US$ 200 per week—an extremely handsome income in that part of the world.

One of the most difficult suckermouth catfishes to capture is the ever popular zebra catfish (*Hypancistrus zebra*), given that this species is virtually exclusively at home at great depth. *H. zebra* (L 46) is said to be captured at a depth of three to nine meters during the dry season, and even at 9–18 meters or more during the rainy season. The capture of this species requires great ability. LUCANUS (written comm.) told us that he almost drowned during an attempt to capture these fishes. It is likely that given this type of fishing method and the presence of cross currents even at great depth there are repeated fatalities among the less experienced fishermen. That is an unfortunate side effect of the rising popularity of suckermouth catfishes, not to mention the bodily harm that is likely to occur over time as the captors repeatedly subject themselves to significant changes in pressure during their diving endeavors. However, most ancistrine loricariids are found in shallow waters with a strong current. Most of them are at least partially feeders of aufwuchs, and such a diet can only be satisfied in the sunbathed shallows near shore. During the dry season, these species may also be found in calm sections of water and water remnants. FORSHEY noted that the suckermouth catfishes, captured by him during September 1991 (dry season) in the Rio Xingú, all had a length between 12 and 22 cm. The fishermen explained that smaller specimens can only be captured at particular times of the year. Therefore, these fishes are subjects of a strong reproductive periodicity which, depending on species, is regulated to a greater or lesser degree by the onset of significant rain showers and their associated chemical and physical changes in the biotope.

Guyana

Potaro River and Konawaruk Creek – Species Paucity in the Guyana Highlands

To follow in the footsteps of renowned ichthyologists and to
visit places in South America
which they had visited many
years before, is—as you could
already deduce from reading
several pages before—a very
exciting activity. That is exactly
what happened to one of the
coauthors (SEIDEL) during his trip

to the South American country of Guyana. He was able to under-
take this tour in the year 2000, in the months of August and September, together with Peter DEBOLD, Gerolf JANDER, Günther SCHWE-
SINGER, and Andreas SPRENGER.

This small country (by South American standards) in the northeastern section of the continent has an area equivalent to 60% of
Germany, and by no means is a typical travel destination. Due to
an extended period of political instability, this former British colony
previously known as British Gyana, was considered somewhat un-
safe and was therefore usually avoided by European travellers.
However, in the mean time, this country has turned into the ideal
destination for those who want to experience unspoiled nature and
can do without the latest comforts of civilization.

What today can be achieved by any Guyana traveler with a modest amount of money, was only possible with the greatest eco-
nomic sacrifice at the turn of the century for the American Naturalist Carl H. EIGENMANN. For the longest time, his dream of a collecting expedition to Guyana was just that, a dream, until financing
was arranged by the CARNEGIE MUSEUM in Pittsburgh. EIGENMANN em-
barked on September 6th 1908 from New York on a two-and-a-half-
month Guyana expedition which led him through various areas of
the country. His goal was to collect and photograph the greatest

Rapids and rocks dominate the view of the Potaro River at many places.   I. Seidel

quantity possible of fishes for his later to be published characin monograph. Additionally, he intended to determine the relationship, if any, between the piscine fauna of the Guyana Highlands and the lowlands, by emphasizing the analysis of the fauna of the upper and lower Potaro River. This region is particularly interesting because along the river's course are numerous waterfalls where an endemic ichthyofauna could have developed upstream. The Potaro River is one of many tributaries of the Essequibo River, the largest river of Guyana. EIGENMANN's expedition must be termed a full success, since in a short period thereafter it produced 25 descriptions of new genera and 128 new species descriptions. In total, EIGENMANN and his entourage collected 25,000 fish specimens for the museum. In his publication, "The Freshwater Fishes of British Guyana" (1912), he described in detail the trajectory of his expedition.

The headwaters of the Potaro River are located at an altitude of over 2000 m in the Ayanganna Massive, which reaches north to

During the dry season, the Tumatumari Falls all but disappear.

I. Seidel

The Potaro River below the falls.

I. Seidel

I. Seidel

Besides characins and *Corydoras*, suckermouth catfishes call these sandbanks their home.

the Rupununi Savanna. Until its confluence with the Essequibo River (at an elevation of approximately only 20 m) it covers a distance of 225 kilometers. The river spills over several impressive waterfalls into the plains. The best-known are the Tumatumari Falls and the giant Kaieteur Falls. The latter are the attraction of Guyana, as they are about twice as tall as the Victoria Falls and even fivefold the height of the Niagara Falls. With the seasons, their height varies between 75 and 120 m, and at one place the water even falls over 250 m onto the land below.

On October 5th, 1908, EIGENMANN began his journey to the Potaro. Initially, he wanted to fish at Tumatumari, both above and below the falls, and then proceed, on October 15th, further upriver to the Kaieteur Falls. Whereas in those days EIGENMANN had to reach Tumatumari by boat—which included several accidents—today it is relatively straightforward to reach the town by car. The town of Tumatumari has to thank the cataracts on the Potaro River for its existence. At the turn of the century, any goods traveling along the river had to be unloaded here to be transported on land upriver, in order to proceed with the river trip on new boats above the falls. This transfer activity gave work to all inhabitants in town. Of course, with the opening of the first road in the area, all that changed radically, and today virtually all goods are transported on land only.

The Potaro region continues to be a sparsely populated area today. It is controlled by mining companies, as its land is rich in metals and minerals. Gold and diamonds are panned for in camps along the rivers. The few existing roads have been established by the mining companies to transport their goods. It has only been since April 6th, 1998 that there is an important road connecting the Georgetown-Mabura Hill section with the road from Tumatumari to Mahdia. It was constructed by the MAZDA MINING COMPANY. However, it may not be simply used by travelers. Since all roads have been financed by private investors, a permit must be secured at the companies. An additional permit is required anyway if, as a foreigner, one desires to travel to the interior of Guyana. Until all papers are secured for such a trip, a significant amount of time is wasted—the wheels of bureaucracy turn very slowly in Guyana, too.

Hemiloricaria fallax, in its natural biotope. A typical sand-dweller.

R. Stawikowski

After obtaining all necessary permits, we (SEIDEL and travel companions) started at the end of August 2000 with a vehicle for a three-day trip to the Potaro River. Our driver Ernie and his helper Percy picked us up early in the morning from our hotel in Georgetown. For several hours we rode in his pickup truck to the interior of the country. After the fairly well-built road from Georgetown to Linden came to an end, a seemingly infinitely long laterite strip began. Only every once in a while small settlements came into view. The vegetation became progressively thicker and more primal to the degree that we left the thin, densely-populated coastal strip behind us. Behind Mabura Hill we reached one of the few road crossings, from where the road was to take us northwest to the Potaro Basin. But already after approximately half an hour the road ended abruptly on the Essequibo River, where we had to stand in line with cars that were already waiting. The ferry needed another half hour until we finally could drive on it. Since the Essequibo at this place is by far not as broad as in its lower course,

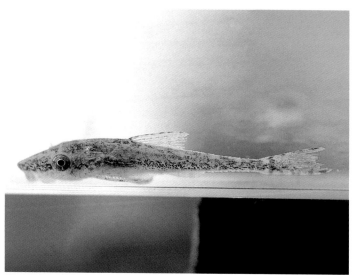

Oxyropsis sp. "Rio Potaro" from Tumatumari.   I. Seidel

the trip across only took fifteen minutes. Once on the other side, we were able to continue our trip on a narrow, but readily usable, forest trail. The road became much more winding and steeper than before. We constantly crossed small creeks carrying completely clear water with a swift current. Half an hour later we arrived at Tumatumari, our momentary goal of the trip. However, we continued on further to admire the falls. We were somewhat disappointed from nature's spectacle, as at the time of our visit—with severe low water—the falls were not recognizable as such. Only a few rock ledges gave a hint in regard to what this section of the river must look like during the rainy season. A dam and the pitiful rusty remains of a hydroelectric generator installation were also visible. Unbelievable was the quantity of fishes which had assembled at the foot of this dam. The connection upstream was cut off and the local population made good captures of small fishes with their synthetic nets. All were characins. To be sure, there must also be suckermouth catfishes, but unfortunately, they were unattainable for us.

We were specifically warned not to camp outdoors in the vicinity of Tumatumari. The riches of gold and diamond mines attract their share of lawlessness, and at night this area is not safe. We were therefore very happy to get the permission of the owner of a restaurant to pass the night in a wooden barn next door. Nevertheless, the night proved no less adventurous, though for different reasons. In the middle of the night, our helper yelled out. The sand below his hammock was drenched in blood. A vampire bat had bitten off a piece of his large toe and had drank his blood to satiation. Fortunately, it wasn't too serious, but to our amazement, he told us that such occurrences are a daily occurrence in the gold digger camps. How fortunate that our hammocks were covered with mosquito netting!

Much less ecxiting was our fishing the following day on the Potaro River. After initially fishing along the muddy shores with a seine, we entered small tributaries with a small boat to fish there on the sandbanks. We captured many fishes, but the majority were characins and cichlids. We only found two suckermouth catfish species. Relatively often we had individual *Hemiloricaria fallax* in our net, a widely-distributed, common whiptail catfish of Guyana and Amazonia. The second species we captured among plant litter along the shores. These were relatively young specimens of a probably still undescribed Hypoptopomatinae species close to the genus *Oxyropsis* sp. "Rio Potaro".

By the way, EIGENMANN was also not particularly successful in this area in regard to the capture of suckermouth catfishes. He, too, fished on sandbanks above and below the falls and was able to capture only one species: *Loricariichthys brunneus*. Unfortunately, we were unable to capture this mouthbrooding suckermouth catfish.

River at Tumatumari – Essequibo River System, Guyana:		
Species	**Biotope**	**Remarks**
Loricariichthys brunneus	on sand	source (EIGENMANN, 1912)
Hemiloricaria fallax	on the sandy shore	more common, but also singly
Oxyropsis sp. "Rio Potaro"	on the sandy shore	singly

Konawaruk Creek, a tributary of the Essequibo River.

I. Seidel

The suckermouth catfishes live among the rocks.

I. Seidel

The Potaro River surely has significantly more to offer in regard to suckermouth catfishes than the two species that we were able to capture on our trip. *Lithoxus lithoides*, described from the Potaro Basin, was of particular interest to us. We knew to search for *Lithoxus* species especially in fast-flowing creeks. That is why we searched in the surroundings of Tumatumari for suitable streams. On our way there, we already had crossed several fast-flowing clear-waters which were definitively worth investigating further. We therefore returned a short distance from Tumatumari back in direction to the Essequibo River. In the end we reached a biotope that was just ideal, a five meter wide creek with crystal clear, fast-flowing water flowing over a rocky river bed. About 50 m from the creek there was a large wooden house on a turn. To our question as to the name of the creek, the answer seemed to be something along the lines of "Kanaruk." Only later were we able to confirm that it must have been the Konawaruk Creek, a stream already mentioned in EIGENMANN's publication of 1912. However, he had only fished in its area of confluence, since obviously he could not

The much flattened *Lithoxus lithoides*.

I. Seidel

I. Seidel

Ancistrus sp. "Konawaruk Creek," the most common of the two loricariids that were found.

reach the place we were at by boat. However, we found out that this creek—although not far from Tumatumari—doesn't flow into the Potaro River at all, but into the Essequibo. Although the type locality EIGENMANN listed was the Potaro River, he was able to confirm the existence of *Lithoxus lithoides* at the mouth of this creek, and that gave us hope.

This creek, at most places close to the road not deeper than half a meter and exceptionally one meter, was similar in appearance to the creeks we knew from the Peruvian Andes and Venezuela. In such biotopes, and at the same general elevation, especially *Chaetostoma* spp. can be found. However, that genus does not inhabit Guyana. In their stead, *Lithoxus* and *Ancistrus* species, both genera present in Andean rivers, are found. We expected suckermouth catfishes especially in the zones with the strongest current, where numerous large and small rocks and pieces of wood were piled up. Armed with a dipnet we proceeded to the knee-deep middle of the creek, always watchful not to loose our balance on the very slippery rocks. Follow-

Konawaruk Creek Essequibo River System, Guyana:		
Species	Biotope	Remarks
Ancistrus sp. "Konawaruk Creek"	on, among, and below rocks	very common
Lithoxus lithoides	on, among, and below rocks	much rarer and occurring next to *Ancistrus*

ing proven procedure, we lifted the rocks over the dipnet and then out of the water. Soon the first loricariids were wiggling in our net. Still, we kept capturing one and the same species. It was a dark gray *Ancistrus* with a black reticulated pattern on head and body. The specimens had a maximum length of ca. 10 cm, and both adult males, with well-developed cephalic "tentacles," as well as numerous small juveniles could be captured. Apparently this is an undescribed species, since its appearance does not coincide with any representative of the genus described from Guyana. After uncountable tries we finally managed to have the next loricariid in our net. It had a similar design but an obviously differing body shape. Without a doubt, this was a *Lithoxus*. Indeed, we were successful, and were able to determine the presence of *Lithoxus lithoides* at this site. Although we spent half a day at the Konawaruk Creek, besides numerous *Ancistrus* of all sizes, we only captured eight *Lithoxus lithoides*. Obviously they were much rarer. The largest specimens had a length of 5 cm, and males and females could be readily distinguished. Besides a whale catfish (family Cetopsidae)—captured in low numbers—there were no further catfishes captured by us. Nevertheless, since we were able to capture the suckermouth catfish that was the most important to us, we felt more than satisfied. Noteworthy is the great similarity existing between newly captured *Ancistrus* sp. "Konawaruk Creek" and *Lithoxus lithoides*. In the aquarium, by contrast, their coloration is completely different and they are readily told apart. It is likely that the specific substrate is the source of this color adaptation, something absent under aquarium conditions.

The water values of the Konawaruk Creek measured on August 28th 2000 at noon were: temperature 25°C, pH 7.6, and electrical conductivity 30 μS/cm.

The Río San Alejandro at the town of the same name.   I. Seidel

Peru

Río San Alejandro – Home of the "Ringed Clown Pleco"

During a meeting of the regional group North of the working group BSSW [Barben, Salmler, Schmerlen, Welse = barbs, characins, loaches, catfishes] during the winter of 1994 in Hamburg, our colleague Bernd Schmitt presented a bucket with fishes he had just brought back to Germany from Peru. Therein swam

several interesting loricariids from the Río San Alejandro, which he really wanted to show us. We couldn't believe our eyes, as we

I. Seidel

Extensive areas of the Río San Alejandro are shallow and have a gravel substrate.

The "ringed clown pleco" *Panaqolus* sp. (L 204) just after capture.   I. Seidel

saw gorgeous, virtually black ancistrines with a conspicuous line design covering their body and fins, and with elongations on the upper and lower caudal fin lobes. We called these fishes—today known as *Panaqolus* sp. (L 204) and regularly offered in the trade— "Ringelsocken-Welse" [ring-sock catfish] because of their conspicuous design.

Naturally, we felt the desire to travel to their home range and capture these fishes ourselves. One of the coauthors (SEIDEL) was able to turn this dream into reality. In the years 1995 and 1996 he was able to travel to Peru with several companions. Among other areas, the Río San Alejandro was one of the sites on the list to visit. The city of Pucallpa in the Peruvian State of Ucayali was chosen as the starting point of this trip. The city is easily reached by plane from Lima. In Pucallpa, the "La Perla Lodge", of the German Thomas ZIRM, was chosen as the hostel. It is located directly on the Yarina Cocha, a dead river arm of the Rio Ucayali. From there, the Río San Alejandro can be reached by the Carretera Federico

Basadre, the only road in western direction towards Lima. Just a few years ago this region was considered extremely dangerous due to the presence of the Maoist "Shining Path" guerilla organization which was active in the area for many years. Then, however, this group was mostly eradicated and the Peruvian president Fujimori sent armed forces into the region to secure the vicinity of the cities. Since then it is possible—at least during the day—to travel on these roads. At certain intervals, military checkpoints have to be passed, and personal data are registered. This may extend the travel time significantly. On a gravel road in bad condition, approximately 3–4 hours are required to cover the 110 km from Pucallpa to the town of San Alejandro on the banks of the homonymous river.

San Alejandro is always ready to surprise. At our arrival in 1995, a drowning victim was carried past us (Peter DEBOLD, Günter SCHWESINGER, Sven VLACH, and Ingo SEIDEL) readily visible in a blanket. He seemed to have drowned while bathing in the vicinity of town. In 1996 the reception was no less surprising (the travel group augmented by Carsten SCHADE, Herbert WINDHORST, and Axel ZARSKE). The inhabitants had congregated on the riverbank to honor the dead from the night before, occurred during the shoot-out between the military and the guerilleros. We made an effort not to remain longer than necessary in this somewhat uninviting town. A fisherman was hired to take us with his small boat downriver to the desired fishes.

The Río San Alejandro is a slightly turbid white-water river which starts in the eastern Andes and flows into the Río Ucayali through the Río Aguaytia. The river was studied in both directions from the town of San Alejandro. In extensive areas in the vicinity of the town it is a very shallow (50–100 cm depth), but swiftly moving stream with a width of 30–50 m. In the center, the river bed usually consisted of coarse gravel. In contrast, the calmer shores often had sandy substrates. It seems that the San Alejandro is void of vegetation in this area. The following water values could be determined on September 25th 1995, at 14:00 hrs: pH 8.4; electric conductivity 190µS/cm; temperature 30°C (measured in shallow water).

Fam.: Loricariidae

Such wood piles are home to many suckermouth catfishes.   I. Seidel

Especially along the river banks there were numerous areas where
large quantities of wood had piled up. Wood-dwelling suckermouth
catfishes were ubiquitous at places where the current was somewhat swifter. In contrast, at sites with moderate current, where there
was a thick layer of sediment on the wood, hardly any loricariids
could be discovered. Many pieces of wood had a holey structure.
Especially fry and insect larvae were found in these numerous
holes. Larger specimens scooted along the outside of tree trunks
or hid in larger cavities of the wood. Right at the onset, three different species of the genus *Panaqolus* were determined to inhabit
the Río San Alejandro. A fourth species, *Panaqolus albomaculatus*,
is said by SCHAEFER & STEWART (1993) to also inhabit this river. Besides *Panaqolus* sp. (L 204) and *Panaqolus* sp. (L 206), the coauthor SEIDEL and cotravellers also netted two specimens of a probably still undescribed *Panaqolus* species. These two animals,
seemingly a pair, had a length of 18–19 cm and were most similar
to *Panaqolus nocturnus* from the Río Marañon Basin. Of all de-

Panaqolus sp. (L 206) and L 204 are syntopic species.
I. Seidel

Adult female of an additional undescribed *Panaqolus* species.   I. Seidel

Panaqolus sp. "Rio San Alejandro" ♂ with distinct odontodes.   I. Seidel

scribed species in this group, only *P. nocturnus* and *P. purusiensis* from the Brazilian Rio Purus achieve such a length. The female was covered by an inconspicuous design based on brown hues. The male specimen was darker still, his body covered throughout with delicate odontodes. Whereas the capture of these two specimens was fortuitous, the capture of L 204 and L 206 was relatively easy with a small net. Just a few pieces of wood had to be lifted out of the water and several suckermouth catfishes fell into the net held beneath. Especially the smaller specimens required some time to come out of the numerous small holes and caves of the wood. Besides the *Panaqolus* species, additional wood-dwellers were found. The beautiful representatives of the genus *Lasiancistrus,* with their long caudal fin filaments that develop with age, merit special mention, the type-species of the genus, *Lasiancistrus heteracanthus*, in particular. Additional loricariids were *Squaliforma emarginata,* an undetermined *Hypostomus* species, an as adult uniformly brown *Cochliodon,* as well as a small, also extensively brown *Ancistrus* sp.

It stands to reason that the wood-dwelling suckermouth catfishes also breed in the holes where they were captured. However, although numerous relatively small juveniles were captured, no brood-caring *Panaqolus* males were identified. However, as a tree trunk was lifted, a male *Lasiancistrus heteracanthus* appeared, which was guarding a large spawn. He had chosen a very large cave, but could close it up with his dorsum in order to protect the eggs. The spawn consisted—in a manner typical for the genus *Lasiancistrus*—of approximately 200, comparatively small (ca. 2.5 mm) eggs. Since at that time of the year (dry season) numerous juvenile *Ancistrus*, *Panaqolus*, *Lasiancistrus,* and *Hypostomus* were found, the question arises if the reproductive cycle of these San Alejandro suckermouth catfishes does not depend on a specific season or if they really only breed during the dry season. Based on the composition of their biotope, there is nothing that would indicate why this season would be particularly beneficial for reproduction. The water was not particularly clear, which means that there was no boost in available food (aufwuchs). Unfortunately, we are still mostly ignorant about these fishes.

After we had fished extensively and successfully among the wood piles, we shifted our attention to the shallower, rocky zones of the water, where we suspected the presence of numerous loricariids among the pebbles. In the calmer shore areas we were able to capture on rocks the chocolate-brown lanceolate whiptail catfish, *Hemiloricaria lanceolata*. In surrounding water bodies we captured the species especially among overhanging submersed shore vegetation, which, however, is absent here. An additional Loricariinae was captured in swifter current on rocks and the moment was cause of celebration. It was *Lamontichthys filamentosus*, which is quite a sight with its long fin filaments. A great surprise for these warm waters was a mountain loricariid also captured among the rocks. The species, in all likelihood *Chaetostoma lineopunctatum,* had bright orange fins upon capture and was only found in zones with swift current.

Whereas the travel group concentrated its fishing efforts on the wood piles and the rocky edges, the captain produced his cast net and began to throw it into swift sections in the center of the river as well as into sandy zones. Soon the first fishes were wiggling in his net. Initially, there were

Cochliodon spp. (here an undescribed species) are typical wood-dwellers. I. Seidel

Hypostomus sp. "Río San Alejandro" lives on wood and gravel substrates. I. Seidel

At calm, sandy shores, loricariids such as *Aphanotorulus unicolor* may be found. I. Seidel

Capturing large characins and loricariids with a castnet. I. Seidel

Fam.: Loricariidae

Spatuloricaria sp., this hunk was captured with a castnet.

I. Seidel

mostly larger characins of the genera *Salminus* and *Prochilodus*, which he removed from the mesh. Soon thereafter he captured his first catfish, a giant loricariin catfish. It was a 35 cm specimen of a *Spatuloricaria* species. Apparently the species was common on the gravel substrate in the current, as the captain captured three additional specimens soon thereafter. His throws on sandy substrates were also successful. Soon he had captured the first mouthbrooding suckermouth catfish, obviously a male *Pseudoloricaria laeviuscula*, as was apparent by the enlarged lower lip. An additional victim of the captain's castnet was a small, aquaristically well-known leopard suckermouth catfish, which used to be known as *Aphanotorulus frankei*. Today, this specialized sand-dweller is called *Aphantorulus unicolor*. Later, additional specimens of the two species were also captured by us with a seine on a sandbank.

Río San Alejandro – Central Ucayali Drainage, Peru:		
Species	**Biotope**	**Remarks**
Ancistrus sp. "Río San Alejandro"	on wood	numerous juveniles and subadults
Aphanotorulus unicolor	in zones with sandy substrates	few large specimens
Chaetostoma lineopunctatum	among rocks	in current-swept areas
Cochliodon sp. "Río San Alejandro"	on wood	only a single, adult specimen
Hemiloricaria lanceolata	only at the edge on rocks	few specimens
Hypostomus sp. "Río San Alejandro"	on wood and rocks	in all sizes
Lamontichthys filamentosus	on gravel substrates	rare, only individual juveniles
Lasiancistrus heteracanthus	on wood	very common, one spawn in a tree trunk
Panaqolus sp. (L 204)	on wood	half as common as L 206
Panaqolus sp. (L 206)	on wood	one of the most common species, in all sizes
Panaqolus sp. "Río San Alejandro"	on wood	only one adult pair
Pseudoloricaria laeviuscula	in zones with sandy substrates	individual specimens with castnet and seine
Spatuloricaria sp. "Río San Alejandro"	on gravel and rock substrates	few, very large specimens
Squaliforma emarginata	on wood	only a few juveniles

View of the Río Previsto in the Boquerón del Padre Abad.   I. Seidel

Río Tulumayo – In the Rough Climate of the Andes

Following the road from Pucallpa westwards towards Lima, at
the preandean lowlands, this
road first crosses the Aguaytia
drainage in the vicinity of the
homonymous city. The gradual
ascend into the Andes begins
after that. Our (the coauthor
SEIDEL and travel companions)
aim was to travel by car to Tingo

María, an Andean city at an elevation of approximately 670 m.
LÜLING visited the city in 1966 and published a report on his trip
(LÜLING, 1971).
On the way to Tingo María, areas of virtually untouched nature are
still commonly seen. Especially the Boquerón del Padre Abad, a
canyon in the Cordillera Azul, a mountain range at the foot of the

The raging waters of the Río Previsto after a downpour.   I. Seidel

Andes proper, through which the Río Previsto flows, presents a gorgeous scenery. The road follows for many kilometers this crystal clear river with greenish iridescent water. On both sides tower steep walls covered by dense vegetation. Numerous small waterfalls frame the road on both sides, the water falling down rock walls. Poison arrow frogs can be heard as they call from shaded damp areas, hummingbirds and butterflies swarm through the air. The cicadas, with their penetrating chirping, remotely similar to the screeching of chain saws, provide for an original and exotic background music. However, the appearance of some clouds quickly brings this paradise back to earth. The ensuing heavy rain converts the previously crystalline river into a raging, reddish-turbid torrent. The fishes native to these waters must be well-adapted to these repeated drastic back-and-forth changes. After the rains, vapor rises from the walls. The river, however, only calms down several hours later, as it still seemed to rain further upriver.

The trip through the Cordillera Azul is very entertaining thanks to the geographic variability. This mountain range, running along the Andes to the east, reaches elevations in excess of 2000 m at some places. Originally it was densely covered by rain forest, but here, too, the advance of civilization has not gone unnoticed. After rainfalls, the road becomes difficult to travel given the occasional land slides which may block traffic for hours. We became first hand witnesses of this circumstance as all of a sudden a huge rock blocked the road ahead of us. Fortunately, other drivers, which had arrived earlier, were already busy with a united effort to clear the road. Just half an hour later we could pass and continue our journey. The Cordillera Azul represents the watershed between the systems of the Río Ucayali and the Río Huallaga. The latter is a considerable stream, even already at its head waters in the vicinity of Tingo María. Lüling (1971) noted, however, that this river, in comparison to typical white-water lowland rivers, is very poor in ichthyofauna. The same surely applies to its tributaries, where we wanted to fish. By the way, the river, since it flows from the nearby highlands, is very cool. Lüling measured on June 12, 1966 at 10:45 a water temperature of 18°C (pH 7.5)—despite an air temperature of 31°C.

Tingo María, the capital of the Province Leoncio Prado in the Peruvian state of Huánuco, is located in the west of the upper Huallaga River valley.

Tingo María is one of the centers of coca cultivation in Peru.   I. Seidel

Those who want to travel to this area should be aware of the fact that this region in Peru is one of the largest producers of coca leaf, the raw material for the elaboration of cocaine. Even as a traveling aquarist one becomes quickly aware of this circumstance. Since the growing of coca in small quantities (e.g., to make tea) is allowed, the road to Tingo María repeatedly leads past great expanses of spread-out coca leaves, drying in the sun. And also at the city's market, coca leaves are offered for sale by the sackful. Still, in

Río Huallaga at Tingo María.   I. Seidel

Fam.: Loricariidae

recent years coca planting has diminished, drastically in places. According to the US Government, the planted area dedicated to the cultivation of coca is said to have diminished between 1992 and 1994, by actions of the antidrug campaign, from 61,000 to 28,900 hectares. New coca plantations, however, have appeared elsewhere, in other river valleys, e.g., the lower Huallaga, Aguaytia, Pachitea, and Apurimac. And meanwhile, the coca growers are returning to the vicinity of Tingo María and the production is rising rapidly again.

After establishing ourselves at a hotel in Tingo María, we went on recognizance by car. One of the most prominent destinations of this trip was the Río Tulumayo, a tributary of the Río Huallaga. The Swiss Johann Jakob VON TSCHUDI, who had already traveled through extensive areas of Peru in the years 1838–1842, captured a fish species, which he described in 1845 in his "Untersuchungen über die Fauna peruana" [= Studies on the Peruvian Fauna] as *Chaetostoma loborhynchos*. The species was of great interest to us, because it is the type species of *Chaetostoma*, a genus which has many representatives.

On a cloudy morning we traveled to the Río Tulumayo. It had rained over night and all streams we crossed were therefore very turbid, despite the fact that they are actually clear mountain rivers. Already from the bridge we could see that the substrate of the river consisted of rocks and small stones over extensive areas. Numerous boulders were visible above the surface and at some parts driftwood piles could be discerned. Aquatic vegetation, however, seemed to be completely lacking. At points of access to the river, its substrate was sandy-muddy. The shore, highly variable in height, seemed to consist of a reddish sand/clay mixture. At the time of our visit, it was a river with partially very swift current and hard, alkaline water (Sep. 10th, 1996: pH 8.5, conductivity 620 µS/cm, temperature 24°C). Especially at areas with swift current, the river bed was covered with numerous flat stones a little larger than fist-sized. These stones were covered by a slippery coating, apparently consisting of algae, detritus, and microorganisms. On many rocks, insect larvae could also be observed. These surely were also part of the fishes' diet. It was in such areas where, after a relatively short time, we also captured the first suckermouth cat-

Río Tulumayo, a tributary of the Río Huallaga.

I. Seidel

Such river sections are the preferred biotope of mountain suckermouth catfishes.

I. Seidel

fishes. The capture of loricariids in such relatively shallow waters is not particularly difficult as long as a team effort can be organized. The flat stones are lifted swiftly over a submersed-held net beneath. The loricariids, usually adhered to the stone, fall a short time later into the net and can be collected. Nevertheless, our success quota was nothing to brag about, since the population density did not appear particularly high and we continuously lifted "empty" stones out of the water. After "weight lifting" for several hours, we were all quite exhausted and needed a break. Our haul was nothing to be proud of. Approximately 30 mountain suckermouth catfishes of various sizes were swimming in our buckets. Additionally, only some loach catfishes (*Trichomycterus* sp.) and darter tetras (*Characidium* sp.) could be captured from among the rocks. There was no remarkable species diversity—about par for this type of mountain river. Surprisingly, however, two different species of mountain suckermouth catfishes could be captured. Besides a plainly colored species with black bone plate edges, which apparently is the above-mentioned *Chaetostoma loborhynchos,* syntopically there was a second species, in this case with black spots and probably still undescribed. Additional loricariids could only be found close to shore on the sparsely present wood there. Primarily these were various age groups of a brown *Ancistrus* sp. with delicate white spots. Additionally, a single specimen of a hereto undetermined *Hypostomus* sp. could also be captured.

Interestingly, there are limnological data available for both the Río Tulumayo as well as for the Quebrada de Puente Pérez nearby (Patrick et al., 1966). We also fished in the latter creek and were able to find only one of the two *Chaetostoma* species (*C. loborhynchos*). Both lotic bodies of water have similar physical and chemical characteristics. The Quebrada de Puente Pérez can also be reached from the road that leads from Pucallpa to Tingo María. The creek is crossed a few kilometers before reaching the city limits of Tingo María. On Sept. 10th, 1996 we were able to determine the following water values: pH 9.0; conductivity 260 µS/cm; temperature 24.0°C. Patrick et al. (1966) determined that the water temperature of the Quebrada de Puente Pérez usually rises during the day from 22°C (in the early morning hours) to 26°C (afternoon). Oxygen saturation of the water fluctuated between 73.1% (at 22:30) and 107.5% (12:30). Comparable values should apply to the Río Tulumayo. Noteworthy among these values is especially the high oxygen concentration of these Andean waters. Comparatively, PATRICK et al. indicate for the Peruvian part of the Amazon River a water temperature of 28°–29°C and an oxygen saturation of only 68.5–76.4%.

Unfortunately, at this time we cannot recommend to the interested

aquarist a trip into this region. We only learned a good time later that Tingo María had again become the site for repeated armed confrontations since the end of 1996, i.e., a short time after our second trip, described above. Unfortunately, this region is also a preferred theater for the activities of the Maoist

The "living room" of *Chaetostoma* species.

Chaetostoma loborhynchos, just captured.

guerilla organization "Shining Path." The terrorists have numerous sympathizers among the impoverished rural population. Since that time, the Peruvian press has regularly reported on confrontations between the guerillas and the military in the upper Huallaga region, with numerous casualties.

Río Tulumayo – Río Huallaga-Drainage, Peru:		
Species	Biotope	Remarks
Ancistrus sp. "Río Tulumayo"	on wood	only few specimens
Chaetostoma loborhynchos	among stones	most common species
Chaetostoma sp. "Río Tulumayo"	among stones	almost as common as C. loborhynchos
Hypostomus sp. "Río Tulumayo"	on wood	only a single specimen

Hypostomus sp. from the Río Tulumayo.

I. Seidel

Aereal view of Yarina Cocha; the Río Ucayali in the background.   I. Seidel

Yarina Cocha – the Jungle Lagoon

Hardly any other South American biotope has been the subject of so many reports lately as Yarina Cocha. Presenting a summary of all publications to date would exceed by far the scope of this book. Therefore, only a small selection will be mentioned here (e.g., LÜLING, 1975, 1979, 1980; VIERKE, 1983). This jungle lagoon was a common destination for scientific expeditions, and numerous travelling aquarists have searched for fishes in its waters. It would seem logical to assume that the lake is so well-known that it would not be worth it to fish in it in search of surprises. However, nothing could be further from the truth. This biotope is home to such a plethora of piscine fauna that every visitor only bears witness to a small segment of its riches. In any case, for us at least (SEIDEL and cotravellers) not one day went by that we did not get to see something new.

Yarina Cocha is a virtually horseshoe-shaped, old river arm cut off from the Río Ucayali main channel. The Río Ucayali is one of the largest Peruvian rivers, a giant white-water stream coming from the south which, at the confluence with the Río Marañón, forms the mighty Amazon River itself. There are many of these dead river arm lagoons (cochas) along the pronouncedly meandering stream. However, at a length of 17 km and a width during the dry season of 800–900 m, Yarina Cocha is one of the largest.

Yarina Cocha is located north of the city of Pucallpa in the lowland rain forest (hylaea). Of course, due to numerous settlements, the forest at many places around the immediate vicinity of the lagoon is not primordial any more. Nevertheless, even the relatively young secondary forest growth conveys to the observer a sense of a complete and pristine jungle lagoon. Yarina Cocha is best approached from Pucallpa by taxi or bus, a trip of just a few kilometers to Puerto Callao, a harbor on the southern end of the lake. During the rainy season, several channels connect the lake to the Río Ucayali (e.g., Lobo Caño and Caño de Paca) and other surrounding lagoons. The waters of the Ucayali flow through the flooded forests, pushing into Yarina Cocha and carrying among them numerous fishes. The shores of Yarina Cocha consist of clay bottoms. At many places packed underwood frames the shore, at others grows a broad fringe of aquatic grasses. Additionally, broad bands of water hyacinths densely cover some areas, floating islands that offer shelter to numerous fishes in this otherwise relatively exposed cocha. A few years ago, these water hyacinths (*Eichhornia*) were a big problem, given that their explosive propagation severely hindered navigation on the lake. At the time of our trip, their population had been brought under control.

Our trip had been purposely planned to take us there during the low-water season in August and September, given that during the high water levels prevalent in the lowlands during the rainy season, the capture of fishes turns into a virtually impossible endeavor. Some species practically disappear altogether. Hardly any fishes

Yarina Cocha seen from Puerto Callao.

I. Seidel

Floating meadows frame Yarina Cocha at many places.

I. Seidel

Such tree trunks are the habitat of many species.

I. Seidel

This algae growth is grazed particularly at night by the loricariids.

I. Seidel

Hypoptopoma sp. "Yarina Cocha" is one of the most common inhabitants.

I. Seidel

Liposarcus pardalis, an appreciated table fish, is ubiquitous.

I. Seidel

were visible in the turbid, clay-gray waters along the shore. Since these sections close to shore—usually shallow and muddy—heat up considerably during the day (a temperature of up to 34°C was determined), fishes avoid these life-threatening areas during that time. Entering the waters, however, it became clear that only shallow areas were thus heated by the sun. With increasing depth the water temperature diminished considerably.

During the evening hours, angelfishes, festivums, talking or thorny catfishes, and numerous characins of various species could be discerned with a flashlight. During these hours, there was productive fishing with a seine. The numerous *Hypoptopoma* turned into a virtual nuisance as they numerously became entangled in the net. Occasionally, several larger sailfin plecos were also netted. It was usually *Liposarcus pardalis*, which we captured up to a length of 50 cm. However, individual rhinoceros sailfin plecos (*Glyptoperichthys scrophus*) could also be captured. Additional loricariids netted in the muddy littoral zone were *Hypostomus* sp. and *Loricaria simillima*. The shore was littered with dead tree trunks which over the years had become blanketed by holes and, in part, were hollowed out. These had a copious algae cover on top and offered hiding places and shelter for numerous fish species. Reaching under water into the numerous small holes, virtually without exception each cave was being claimed by a fish. However, these were mostly doradids, a commonly painful experience when carelessly poking around in these holes with bare hands. Repeatedly something darted out along our hands, loricariids, for sure. And indeed, after a short time we were able to capture the first wood-dweller with a dip net: a full-grown *Ancistrus* male. Identified as a male based on the copious presence of dense tentacles, this white-dotted *Ancistrus* sp. was approximately 20 cm long. Additional specimens of the same species soon followed. On the other hand, the constant capture of *Hypoptopoma* was beginning to bug us and we started to throw them with disdain back into the stream.

However, the suckermouth catfish species diversity was much greater in the small tributaries of Yarina Cocha than in the lagoon proper. Furthermore, these tributaries were usually quite shallow and easily fished. Special mention deserves the Caño de Paca, where we captured most species also encountered in the lagoon

I. Seidel

Liposarcus pardalis is much more common than this *Glyptoperichthys scrophus.*

I. Seidel

In Yarina Cocha, *Loricaria simillima* is found on muddy substrates.

itself, but also several species which we found only here. The Caño de Paca enters the lagoon exactly opposite the La Perla Lodge. This channel, with only slight flow, has a chemical makeup very similar to the lagoon proper, and at shallow zones it was so hot and deficient in dissolved oxygen that numerous fishes were breathing on the surface to gain access to atmospheric oxygen.

Innumerable caves could be discerned on the steep muddy shores of the Caño de Paca. These deep tunnels serve the large loricariids of the lagoon as breeding caves during the rainy season. But at that moment, during the dry season, they were high and dry. We were told that the local population pillages these caves during the breeding season to get to the spawn of the catfishes, which is said to be quite tasty. *Liposarcus pardalis*, a common catfish of Yarina Cocha, was also numerously encountered in all sizes in the Caño de Paca. Larger specimens repeatedly broke the water surface under warm conditions to "ingest air". Additional suckermouth catfishes of the Caño de Paca—without exception encountered on very muddy substrates—were the "long-nosed" *Hemiodontichthys acipenserinus*, the also mouthbrooding *Loricaria simillima*, *Sturisoma nigrirostrum* and, naturally, the omnipresent *Hypoptopoma* sp. "Yarina Cocha." The Caño Lobo enters the lake in the northeast, but at the time of our visit the water level was too low and the channel weed-choked, making it impossible for us to pass. Although the caño was easily reached over land after a ten minute walk, fishing there was not a particularly enjoyable affair. After just a few steps we sank into the mud to our waists, and every step was a chore. The section we tried was densely covered, mostly by *Eichhornia,* but was home to several species we had not found in the lake. Especially the callichthyids were represented by several species, but some twig catfishes and whiptail catfishes were also numerous, specifically members of the species *Farlowella platorhynchus* and *Hemiloricaria wolfei.*

The following water values were determined by us on September 10th, 1995, 11 o'clock a.m., in the Caño Lobo: water temperature 28°C; pH 7.0; 74 µS/cm conductivity.

Caño de Paca, a tributary of Yarina Cocha.   I. Seidel

Sturisoma nigrirostrum primarily inhabits the tributaries of the lagoon.   I. Seidel

Fam.: Loricariidae

Farlowella platorynchus, Yarina Cocha is the type locality.

I. Seidel

Hemiloricaria wolfei is another species that lives on muddy substrates.

I. Seidel

194

Yarina Cocha and Tributaries – Rio Ucayali Drainage, Peru:		
Species	**Biotope**	**Remarks**
Ancistrus sp. "Yarina Cocha I"	on wood	only few specimens
Ancistrus sp. "Yarina Cocha II"	on wood	only few specimens
Farlowella platorynchus	among branches and on submersed vegetation	few specimens
Glyptoperichthys scrophus	on muddy substrates	only one specimen
Hemiloricaria wolfei	on muddy substrates	only in tributaries
Hemiodontichthys acipenserinus	on muddy substrates	only found in the Caño de Paca
Hypostomus sp.	on muddy substrates	common
Hypoptopoma sp.	on wood and muddy substrates	most common species in the lake and its tributaries
Loricaria simillima	on muddy substrates	not common, but everywhere
Liposarcus pardalis	on muddy substrates	very common species
Sophiancistrus ucayalensis	in the boat of a fisherman	only one specimen
Sturisoma nigrirostrum	on muddy substrates	only a few large specimens in the Caño de Paca

Fam.: Loricariidae

Black/brown, the Río Kavac snakes through the rain forest at the foot of the Auyán-Tepuis.

Flat on top, the Table Mountains look like a table.   H.-G. Evers

Venezuela
Río Kavac – At the Foot of the Table Mountains

Hardly any place on Earth can offer such outrageously shaped mountains as is the case with the southern Guiana Highlands, at the border between Venezuela and Brazil. As if cut-off, the massive table mountains tower over the luscious green vegetation of the Gran Sabana below. Locally, the people speak of the

"mesa" (spa. = table) and that is what they look like—tables all set for a giant to sit down at. Up to 3000 m is the elevation of some of these tepuis, another local name for these formations, and the platforms of these unaccessible mountain "islands in time" (GEORGE,

Virtually every day, the Auyán Tepui is shrouded in clouds. Temporary waterfalls form on the edges after rain.

1991) still haven't been completely explored. Many endemic plants and animals—isolated for millions of years—are totally unknown to science, and teams of experts have only in recent years begun to study the tepuis.

The peaks are mostly shrouded in fog, the atmospheric humidity is high and rain is virtually a daily occurrence. All this water must drain somehow; consequently, there are temporary waterfalls at the edge of the table mountains after heavy rains. The most impressive and at the same time probably the highest waterfall of the world is the Salto Angel, which drains the rainwater over the edge of the Auyan Tepuis with a fall of almost 1000 m.

In this region, at the foot of the Auyán Tepui, in the town of Kavac, next to the river of the same name, EVERS spent a few days during August 1994. The actual (successfully achieved) purpose of the trip was to hike on the tepui. While doing so, it was possible to observe, and on occasion also capture, some fishes. The water of the Río Kavac is almost pure, lacking water hardeners. A pH of

H.-G. Evers

Waterfall in the vicinity of Kavac. At the foot of this tourist attraction, in the boiling waters, lives *Ancistrus* sp.

The water thunders into the valley, flowing over rounded rock plates. H.-G. Evers

Numerous small creeks feed the Río Kavac. H.-G. Evers

4.5 was measured at a conductivity of only 3 µS/cm. The water temperature at noon was 24°C in the entire river and also further upstream, in the many small tributaries which hail down from the mountain and unite into the Río Kavac below. The water is tea-colored because of the large quantities of humic acids leached from the decaying plant matter on top of the tepui. While climbing up the table mountain to the first and second levels—approximately to an elevation of 800 m—everywhere small creeks and water courses are encountered, which occasionally widen into pools. That is home to the red form of the lyretail rivulus *Rivulus lyricauda,* and also the loach catfish *Trichomycterus* sp. "Kavac" can be found here, although usually in the currents, below small drops.

The water is extremely nutrient-poor, and the fishes of the Río Kavac are true feeding artists. Snorkeling in the river revealed a low population of fishes. Some *Leporinus* sp. fled already at a distance of several meters, as did large *Crenicichla* sp. Below the well-known Kavac Falls a significant population of a darter tetra, *Characidium* sp., could be observed with a diving mask as it swam seemingly effortlessly against the raging current. Only with the greatest effort was it possible to swim behind a waterfall. There, directly in the roiling waters, sat countless *Ancistrus* sp. in the sunlight and rasped from the rocks the few algae present. This type of environmental conditions (such strong current and extremely soft and acid water) cannot be readily replicated by the aquarist. Therefore, the suckermouth catfishes were left where they were, lest they all died in an attempt to acclimate them to transport and to standard aquarium conditions.

Although this small trip to the table mountains did not reveal any spectacular new suckermouth catfishes, it did broaden significantly our knowledge of loricariids from that part of the world. Spectacular species, such as those contained in the genera *Neblinichthys* or *Niobichthys,* originate precisely from such waters at the foot of table mountains. Especially *Neblinichthys* would be a gem for any catfish hobbyist with its crazy upward-pointed cephalic bristles. However, fishes from such extreme biotopes do not really belong into a "normal" aquarium. Even a specialist and experienced hobbyist often has to throw in the towel. But that shouldn't be too much of a sacrifice, given the large quantity of catfish species better suited for captive environments that are readily available.

This is the home of the poison-arrow frog *Dendrobates leucomelas*.

H.-G. Evers

Snorkeling in the Río Kavac. The visibility is good, but the fish population is low.

H.-G. Evers

Bird's eye view of a smaller table mountain.

H.-G. Evers

Río Orituco, August 1992. H.-G. Evers

Río Orituco – Species Diversity in the Llanos

In August 1992, both coauthors had the opportunity to travel together to the Venezuelan Llanos and get to know interesting fish biotopes in this unusual geography. Especially the vicinity of the City of Calabozo, in the state of Guarico could be studied in greater detail. Among others, many suckermouth cat-

fishes were netted. Since then, virtual hordes of aquarists have descended onto the area and reported about it. One of the most interesting rivers in the aquaristic sense is the Río Guarico, which gave the name to the state. The Guarico River is an affluent of the Río Apure, which together with the Río Meta, is one of the two large

A section of shore in August: the trees have their "feet" wet. H.-G. Evers

The same section in January: the water level of the river has fallen sharply. R. Normann

rivers that drain the region and flow into the all-encompassing Orinoco. The Llanos, a prairielike landscape framed by mountain ranges form the north and west, and from the south by the majestic Orinoco, is a giant area including Colombian and Venezuelan territories. The absolute dry season occurs during the months of December to April, more or less reliably, but shortened or prolonged by the sudden onset of rain showers. However, during January and February the earth is bone-dry, the grass scorched by the Sun. With the first rains, the rock-hard ground turns to mud, and soon thereafter the dry gullies fill with raging water masses. Soon the prairie floods and one must wade through. No wonder, then, that agriculture is not an option in these lands. Only rice grows in enormous quantities. The fields are watered with the Guarico Reservoir, and some skinny cattle feed on meager pastures extensively. A world of extremes—a dust bowl and then flooding from May to August. The rivers, too, rise at this time. The eroded sediments color the water muddy gray, the entire area is a typical whitewater region. There are some clear-water and even black-water biotopes, but our eyes are on the Río Orituco, a textbook whitewater biotope.

We traveled at the end of the rainy season, whereas most other aquarists have gone during the dry season. Therefore, we list below some selected water values which were obtained either by ourselves or by WENDENBURG (1996) or MORENO & FRANKE (1996):

Water Values of the Río Orituco at Calabozo			
Source:	EVERS, SEIDEL	WENDENBURG (1996)	MORENO & FRANKE (1996)
Season:	rainy season	dry season	no indication
Date:	7 Aug. 1992	8 Jan. 1994	no indication
Time:	morning	noon	no indication
pH:	7.0	7.8	7.0 – 7.4
Conductivity:	80 µS/cm	270 µS/cm	not determined
Water temperature:	26°C	27°C	27° – 30 °C

In all cases, the water of the Río Orituco was clay-gray in color, with a maximum visibility of 15–30 cm. These water values correspond to that of "standard" white-water. At the time of our visit, at

From the airplane, the extent of rainy season flooding can be readily distinguished.

During the rainy season the Llanos are green. During the summer the pastures wither and turn into a prairie.

Most small rivers of the llanos are shallow and can be traversed by jeep on suitable passage ways (fords).

the closing of the rainy season, the water level was still very high. The adjacent forest was flooded in extensive areas and our fishing efforts were correspondingly laborious and low-yielding. During the dry season the situation is totally different (MORENO & FRANKE, 1996). The vertical shores tower up to 5 m over the water surface. The waters move leisurely along their channel and, on occasion, form deeper and wider pools. During the rainy season, the river banks are flooded and the luxuriant vegetation serves the fish fry as nursery, protection, and feeding area. The nutrient-rich sediments are the basis for a well-developed microfauna and -flora, the first link in the food chain. The Río Orituco, in particular, is enormously rich in ichthyofauna, both in regards to the number of species, as well as to the population representing each. MACHADO-ALLISON & MORENO (1993) list no fewer than 157 fish species, which they captured during the course of their 2-year investigation, performed at different seasons of the year. Of the collected fishes,

Dense stands of aquatic vegetation are the home for many suckermouth catfishes, especially juveniles grow among their protection. *Farlowella vittata, Hypoptopoma gulare, Hemiloricaria eigenmanni,* and juvenile *Hypostomus* sp. (L 192) were found there.

45% are members of the order Siluriformes—the catfishes—many suckermouth catfishes among them. Unfortunately, many of the species names mentioned in their publication are questionable at best, a correct identification is probably often not given. The same applies to the work by MORENO & FRANKE (1996). Therefore, we mention here the species names we think that apply, but must admit that the fishing efforts by aquarists during the dry season were much more successful, both in quantity as well as quality. We simply base ourselves on our own experiences with the same species, which we captured in much smaller numbers during the rainy season.

Many of the 71 (!) catfish species found in the Río Orituco (see MACHADO-ALLISON & MORENO, 1993; and MORENO & FRANKE, 1996) belong to the family Loricariidae. Among the subfamily Hypostominae, particularly the greenish *Squaliforma* cf. *watwata* (L 195), with its beautiful design, deserves special mention. Others that are found here

Loricariichthys platymetopon, a large specimen, captured with a cast net.

inhabiting similar biotopes are *Liposarcus multiradiatus*, *Aphanotorulus ammophilus*, an additional *Hypostomus* sp. (L 192), and *Cochliodon plecostomoides*. For adults, that biotope is the center of the river and, during the night, shallower areas. Juveniles (with the exception of *Aphanotorulus*) are often found together with other loricariids on wood and, during the rainy season, on shore vegetation hanging into the water. At these biotopes of submerged branches and grasses from shore, as representatives of the Hypoptopomatinae, the small *Otocinclus vittatus* and, in certain areas, *Hypoptopoma gulare*, can be found. At selected areas they can be collected in huge quantities.

Branches fallen into the water and large sections of trees uprooted during the rainy season have intertwined themselves into structures that are stuck at river bends and narrow passages, providing an optimal substrate for many suckermouth catfishes. Besides the already mentioned *Hypoptopoma gulare*, especially suckermouth catfishes from the subfamily Loricariinae are the inhabit-

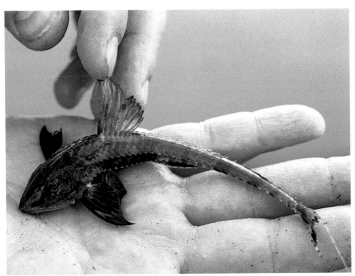

Loricaria sp. "Río Orituco" after its capture.

R. Normann

Aphanotorulus ammophilus, another species in the Río Orituco.

R. Normann

Squaliforma cf. *watwata* (L 195), a beautiful fish that grows quite large.   R. Normann

Hypostomus sp. (L 192), appears in huge numbers at some places.   H.-G. Evers

Río Orituco at Calabozo – Llanos, Venezuela:		
Species	**Biotope**	**Observations**
Acanthicus sp. (L 193)	wood	very rare
Aphanotorulus ammophilus	sand, wood	common
Cochliodon plecostomoides	deep areas, wood	common
Farlowella vittata	wood, shore vegetation	very common
Hemiloricaria eigenmanni	shore vegetation, wood	very common
Hypoptopoma gulare	shore vegetation, grasses	very common
Hypostomus sp. (L 192)	deep areas, wood	very common
Hypostomus cf *watwata* (L 195)	deep areas, wood	common
Lamontichthys llanero	wood	very rare
Lasiancistrus sp. (L 92/L 194)	wood	common
Liposarcus multiradiatus	sand, mud	common
Loricaria sp. "Río Orituco"	sand	very rare
Loricariichthys platymetopon	sand, mud	common
Panaque nigrolineatus	deep areas, wood	common
Panaqolus cf. *maccus* (L162)	wood	common
Sturisoma tenuirostre	sand, wood	rare

ants of these biotopes. *Hemiloricaria eigenmanni* and *Farlowella vittata* are present in great numbers. *Lamontichthys llanero* is particularly beautiful, and has been collected in small quantities by various aquarists in the Río Orituco at such sites. Other loricariids live over sand substrates of the Orituco and other sizeable rivers of the Llanos. We are talking about *Sturisoma tenuirostre* and *Loricariichthys platymetopon,* as well as the beautiful *Loricaria* sp. "Río Orituco," a *Loricaria* species with a particularly interesting design. Given that the Orituco maintains a certain minimal current, even during the extreme dry season, there is an optimal habitat with sufficient oxygen concentration lasting the entire year. Among the wood mentioned above, there are an additional four species of ancistrine loricariids that can be found. *Panaque nigrolineatus* has been described from the vicinity of Calabozo and can be found locally in large quantities. *Panaqolus maccus*—a beautiful species with a ringed design—appears to be rarer. Repeatedly, large specimens of *Acanthicus* sp. (L 193) have been confirmed in the

Río Orituco, an impressive find (see WEIDNER, 1994). *Lasiancistrus* sp. (L 92/L 194) is another frequent capture in the Orituco and completes the listing of the confirmed suckermouth catfishes in this—for catfish lovers—very prolific habitat.

It is of incalculable value that so many aquarist groups have already visited this river. We, therefore, have the results of many excursions, which, taken together, paint a relatively complete picture of the ichthyofauna of this region. Nevertheless, we are convinced that it may be possible to "unearth" one or more additional new species. In nature, there are many migratory species which do not always stay at the same place at various times. It requires quite a bit of luck to identify, at a later time, the fishes found by previous groups—especially in regard to rare species. Conversely, it is possible for beginners luck to strike, and then some inexperienced hobbyist ends up capturing a completely new species. That is only one of the many good reasons to return to a biotope, even after a few years, especially if one is dealing with a rich area such as the unforgettable Río Orituco.

Panaqolus cf. *maccus*, a frequent find in the Rio Orituco.   I. Seidel

Nutrition

There seems to be the general impression among aquarists that suckermouth catfishes, by and large, feed on algae aufwuchs. However, if this varied and extensive family is studied in greater detail, it becomes clear that the group is made up of very different species which inhabit very particular ecological niches in nature. If this would not be the case, the simultaneous presence of numerous loricariid species in the same biotope, as is often the case, would not be possible, or at least far less prevalent.

There are various morphological characteristics among suckermouth catfishes which allow us to infer their lifestyle and diet. Those loricariids, which in nature primarily feed on vegetable matter, have a relatively small stomach and a very long intestinal tract. In predominantly carnivorous species the anatomical characteristics are the opposite, i.e., the stomach is relatively large and the intestine short. But even without having to refer to an autopsy, there are sufficient external characteristics which allow us to make inferences about the lifestyle of the fish. Loricariids, which have a strongly suction-cuplike mouth, at the very least, have a lifestyle that is highly substrate-oriented. They are virtually always found on wood or rocky substrates. The edges of the upper and lower lips are smooth in these species. Adapted to live on smooth surfaces, these species mostly feed on aufwuchs (periphyton) which they scrape from the substrate with the aid of comblike rows of teeth. Aquarists are particularly fond of these species, since they keep the aquarium decoration and glass panes free of undesired algae growth. The dentition of these aufwuchs-feeding loricariids usually consists of a multitude of small, bicuspid teeth arranged in very dense rows.

However, quite a few suckermouth catfishes have become known in recent years which also have a circular mouth, but which have a dentition unsuitable for grazing algae covers. These species usually do not have such a large and strong suction mouth, and in strong currents they have a hard time holding on to a substrate to hold their position. Fortunately, that is not required of them, since these are benthic loricariids which live on sandy, gravely, or rocky substrates. The lips of these species often have barbels devel-

Hypostomus latifrons; with the dentition typical of an aufwuchs-feeder. I. Seidel

This *Hemiloricaria* sp. appears to be an omnivore. I. Seidel

Whiptail catfish with markedly reduced dentition: *Dasyloricaria* sp. "Orinoco"

I. Seidel

L 82 is an example of an entirely carnivorous ancistrine.

I. Seidel

Cochliodon cochliodon; *Panaque* and *Cochliodon* species occupy a special nutritional niche with their spoon-shaped teeth and wood-centered diet.

oped to a greater or lesser degree, and often the inside of their lips is blanketed by papillae. The dentition of their jaws is more or less degenerate, and they have specialized to feed on a totally different diet (e.g., detritus, insect larvae, molluscs, etc.).

However, the distinction between aufwuchs feeders and complete carnivores is not as distinct as might be assumed, but rather there are all kinds of intermediate forms. In nature, most aufwuchs feeders ingest all kinds of animal fare besides plant parts and algae, whereas the "carnivores" ingest vegetable matter every once in a while. The solution is an appropriately balanced diet. In that regard, fish are not much different from humans.

A certain special situation in regard to diet is present among the members of the genera *Cochliodon* and *Panaque*. Both these genera have a highly reduced dentition on their jaws, and the teeth are—in contrast to the bicuspid teeth found in most loricariids—unicuspid, large, and spoon-shaped. This type of dentition seems particularly appropriate to rasp wood, given that in the aquarium

Panaque sp., portrait. Wood is an obligatory ingredient in the aquarium decor for these wood eating suckermouth catfish!

the presence of wood in the decoration is drastically reduced in due time. However, that this also constitutes normal behavior in nature is corroborated by gastrointestinal analyses performed by SCHAEFER & STEWART (1993) on various suckermouth catfishes of the genera *Panaque* and on a *Cochliodon* sp. All analyzed specimens had small pieces of wood as the only macroscopic material in their gastrointestinal tract. Recent research by NELSON et al. (1999) has determined that these fishes are indeed capable of digesting this relatively indigestible food with the help of a range of the most varied symbiotic microbial fauna in their gut.

However, what suckermouth catfishes actually feed on in nature has been determined for only a very few species. Already in the '50s, GEISLER & BOLLE (1956) published the results of stomach contents analyses performed on wild specimens captured in northern Argentina. They studied a typical, aufwuchs-feeding loricariid as well as a species with reduced dentition. In the case of the *Hypostomus* sp., already the significant length of the intestine (approximately 6 times the body length) clearly indicated a primarily vegetarian diet. And, indeed, the gastrointestinal tract was filled with a greenish mud, very rich in plant components. Besides the remains of higher aquatic vegetation and filamentous algae, it contained very numerous diatoms. In the intestine of a larger loricariid specimen of the subfamily Loricariinae, which they surely misidentified as *Loricariichthys brunneus* (that species is native to Guyana), GEISLER and BOLLE found numerous benthic copepods (harpacticids) which had been ingested together with many grains of sand. Somewhat deviant were the stomach contents of young whiptail catfishes, which revealed a high proportion of *Bosmina*, which determined the presence of a greater animal component overall.

Research in regards to stomach contents by GOULDING et al. (1988) on several suckermouth catfishes—among others—of the Rio Negro drainage, revealed that the members of the genera listed in the table below had the following food as a constituent of 25% or more of the total stomach contents:

Genus	Food Present by More Than 25%
Ancistrus	autochthonous vegetable components, detritus
Acestridium	autochthonous vegetable components
Cochliodon	detritus
Dekeyseria	allochthonous and autochthonous vegetable components, detritus
Hemiodontichthys	autochthonous invertebrates
Hypostomus	detritus
Loricariichthys	autochthonous invertebrates
Oxyropsis	autochthonous vegetable components, detritus
Pseudoloricaria	autochthonous invertebrates
Pterygoplichthys (sensu lato)	autochthonous invertebrates, detritus

In the process of the analyses it was discovered that the autochthonous (aquatic) vegetable matter ingested was primarily composed of microalgae. The autochthonous plant components in *Dekeyseria* were parts of blooms and leaves. The presence of a plethora of aquatic invertebrates could be determined in the stomach of the loricariids. In the whiptail catfishes these were mostly

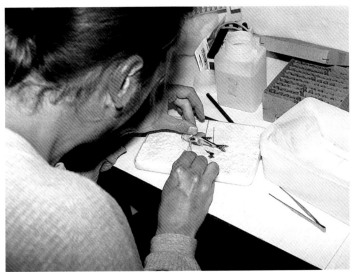

Stomach contents analyses on wild-caught specimens are very laborious. M.T.C. Lacerda

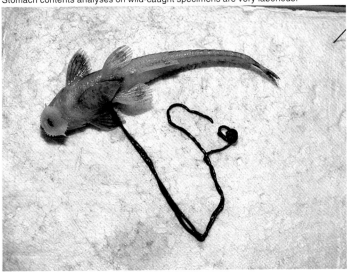

Rineloricaria sp. aff. *latirostris* with dissected intestinal tract. H.-G. Evers

bloodworms (fam. Chironomidae), caddisflies (Trichoptera), water fleas (fam. Chydoridae), and members of the family Macrothricidae. In the stomach of sailfin plecos, copepods of the family Calanoidae could be determined.

Naturally, the composition of the food ingested by certain fish species is also strongly influenced by what is currently available in their habitat, even on a seasonal basis. Food organisms are also subject to populational cycles that, by and large, are determined by season. That is the reason why stomach contents analyses represent just a snapshot for a given moment in time. In times of restricted food availability, the fishes must do with what is available, and that, sometimes, is not much at all. Additionally, food availability and makeup are also influenced by geographic area and type of water. For example, the black-water of the Rio Negro, mentioned earlier, harbors an entirely different flora and fauna than the clear- or even white-water habitats elsewhere. As contrast to the results obtained by GOULDING et al. in their work with Rio Negro fishes, we want to show the results of stomach contents analyses

Unfortunately, loricariids frequently satisfy their need for vegetable fare with a "self serve" system. "Lattice" plants are the consequence.

performed on several loricariids from southeastern Brazil, published by DITTMAR & EVERS (2000). The listed fish species were captured by one of the authors (EVERS) in 1995 and 1996 in several river systems along the southeastern coast of Brazil, where they mostly inhabited rivers of the clear-water type:

Species (n=number of specimens)	Presence	Dietary Composition
Lampiella gibbosa (n = 3)	massive (> 50%)	filamentous bacteria
	very numerous (> 25%)	organic detritus
	numerous (ca. 10%)	diatoms, anorganic detritus
Parotocinclus maculicauda (n = 5)	massive (> 50%)	anorganic detritus (sand, clay, minerals)
	very numerous (> 25%)	blue algae
	frequent (> 5%)	green algae, organic detritus (animal, vegetable)
Schizolecis guntheri (n = 3)	massive (> 50%)	anorganic detritus
	numerous (ca. 10%)	freshwater sponges, plant remains
	frequent (> 5%)	diatoms, fungi, organic detritus
Rineloricaria sp. aff. *latirostris* TL > 110 mm (n = 2)	massive (> 50%)	green algae
	very numerous (> 25%)	organic detritus
	numerous (ca. 10%)	plant remains
	frequent (> 5%)	filamentous bacteria, chironomid larvae, anorganic detritus
Rineloricaria sp. aff. *latirostris* TL < 70 mm (n = 3)	massive (> 50%)	anorganic detritus
	very numerous (> 25%)	green algae
	numerous (ca. 10%)	blue algae
	frequent (> 5%)	ciliates, organic detritus

Sturisomatichthys sp. and *Leliella* sp. "red." Zucchini is an appreciated dietary constituent.

Regardless of which foods the various suckermouth catfishes prefer in nature, under aquarium conditions most of these fishes are quite flexible in regard to diet, accepting virtually anything that is offered to them. For example, suckermouth catfishes of the genus *Leporacanthicus*—reputedly strictly carnivorous in nature—in the aquarium will accept the occasional vegetable fare, and *Panaque* spp. will feed without further ado on bloodworms. However, an excess in these captive feeding practices will lead over time to malnutrition, since the morphology of the entire gastrointestinal tract is necessarily adapted to their natural diet. Therefore, it is always important to take into account the special requirements of individual species for successful long-term captive care. Loricariids feeding on aufwuchs should therefore not be provided with an exclusively animal diet; they require vegetable supplementation. Suitable vegetable fare is collected in nature or purchased in the supermarket. Especially appropriate are various greens, such as cucumbers, cauliflower, peas, potatoes, etc. But also vegetation

However, the same fishes appreciate bloodworms just the same!   H.-G. Evers

growing in the wild (in the yard?), such as dandelion, chickweed, and sunflower leaves are readily suitable aquarium fare. If the vegetable fare is not readily accepted by the fishes in a raw state, blanching with hot water or short-term freezing are appropriate methods used to break the superficial cell membranes, making the food more readily accessible to the fishes.

Additionally, virtually all suckermouth catfishes are fond of zooplankton in the aquarium. Cyclops, daphnia, brine shrimp, mosquito larvae (a caution for allergic persons, be careful with bloodworms) and others are quality options both in live and frozen presentations. Worms are usually too fatty and should therefore be fed sparingly. However, for the rearing of young and the acclimation of newly acquired, usually malnourished specimens, these are highly appropriate. Some species of loricariids might be specialized in nature in capturing crustacea. For such species, *Mysis*, krill, and other crustacea are just right. Molluscivores can be readily fed with gastropod meat and mussels. Especially for the large suckermouth catfishes (e.g., cactus cats), which in nature are likely to feed on carrion, among other things, fish meat will be a welcome morsel. The same way as aufwuchs feeders will consume larger animal organisms, it occurs repeatedly that loricariids with a reduced maxillary dentition will feed on vegetable fare. The diet should therefore always be varied and include some new options occasionally.

However, not even those hobbyists who have no time (or desire) to capture live foods, or are not willing to store frozen foods in their freezer, must renounce their desire to keep loricariids. The pet industry offers such a wealth of choices of all kinds of products on an animal and vegetable basis that, by and large, these commercial diets are even suitable as the sole source of nutrition for our fishes. However, it is preferable to provide sinking foods in the form of tablets, granules, or pellet formulations. Flakes and floating (extruded) pellets are unsuitable, as they often just spoil after drifting undiscovered on the surface.

It is a commonly observable phenomenon among aquarists that a lot of money is spent during the acquisition of the fishes, but that afterwards there is an attempt at saving some of the money in maintenance—the cheapest feeds are purchased and the lack in quality is thought to be compensated by an increase in quantity. Never should there be a feed purchased which does not come in a presentation that is hermetically sealed and protected from excessive light. Additionally, the expiration date and the feed's ingredients should be clearly listed. Fish foods should never be stored warm and moist (on the aquarium cover or in the base cabinet), but ideally cool and dry. Although brand name feeds cost a little more, research for the benefit of our fishes is worth paying for.

In recent years appeared a particular microalgal supplement everybody is talking about: *Spirulina*. This is a type of blue alga which, thanks to its chemical composition, has also achieved a prominent position in human medicine. *Spirulina* is particularly rich in vitamins and minerals, high in protein (60–70%), and contains the important gamma-linolenic-fatty acids (vitamin F). Additionally, *Spirulina* is high in beta-carotene, zeaxanthin, and myxoxanthophyll, which helps intensifying the colors of our aquarium fishes. Still, *Spirulina* is not without its detractors, and warnings in front of these algae are repeatedly voiced. After all, blue algae are not algae *per se*, but rather cyanobacteria, most of which are capable of synthesizing toxic components. *Spirulina* is surely a good and valuable nutritional supplement for commercially produced diets. However, whether or not it is a sensible substitute for other vegetable matter in the diet has not yet been studied in sufficient detail. In relation to that, other algae, such as *Chlorella*, would be a better choice. However, it seems those algae cannot be cultivated at the rate that *Spirulina* is. In contrast, *Spirulina* can be very high-yielding in tropical regions with waters rich in minerals (e.g. in soda lakes).

Maintenance Requirements

The question about the maintenance requirements of loricariids can hardly be answered in a general manner. As already indicated, suckermouth catfishes are encountered in practically all biotopes

H.-G. Evers

Caves and roots are necessary components of the decoration of aquaria dedicated to the maintenance of many suckermouth catfishes.

When caring for sand-dwelling species, that type of substrate is a must. I. Seidel

at various altitudes. Additionally, they fill ecological niches in various manners, feed during the day or night, live on rocks or wood, bury in the sand, or adhere to plant stalks.

The aquarium hobby has known for many years several species which are very undemanding in their care and even in breeding— all recommendable to beginners. On the other hand, there are also numerous loricariids which should not be bothered even by specialists; they should remain where they are, in their natural biotope. Nevertheless, the vast majority of species is readily suitable for aquarium maintenance and when a few peculiarities are respected, suckermouth catfishes are grateful and longevous charges, which may bring joy for over ten years to the hobbyist. Despite the sometimes highly developed specialization for a particular natural habitat, many species adapt without major problems to the conditions prevailing in an aquarium. Often captive aquarium specimens grow older and larger than they would in nature, because the availability of a balanced diet is constant and there are no predators to worry about.

Besides the already discussed need for appropriate nutrition, there are only a few additional factors that must be considered for successful aquarium maintenance. Suckermouth catfishes should only be associated with fishes that allow them proper access to food and to express, unrestrictedly, their normal behavior. A *Hypancistrus zebra* just isn't a good choice in the presence of African mbuna-cichlids. The little food reaching the bottom would hardly be enough to feed the zebra catfish appropriately. Other tankmates turn territorial during the breeding season and claim the caves and hideouts of the suckermouth catfishes. In this case, too, it is difficult to establish a harmonious community in the long run. Fishes of the open water column—the central and upper zones in particular—such as characins, are suitable associates, as are the *Corydoras*. With the boom in L-number species, it has become fashionable to add the colorful catfishes into the community aquarium. Usually only one or two specimens of a species are added, or even better, several species, as that is "more colorful." However, despite their beauty, suckermouth catfishes are no "standard decorative fishes" (if there is such a thing). Precisely because of their beauty, we should make certain that we provide the optimal conditions for our charges. Therefore, it is preferable to acquire a group of 4–6 specimens of a single species and the aquarium conditions can then be adapted to satisfy their particular requirements.

Roots serve as shelter and some species even need them as part of their menu (*Panaque* and *Cochliodon*, see previous section, Nutrition). The popular ancistrine catfishes of the Rio Xingú and other Brazilian rivers require rock edifications as shelters. Fine-grained sand is a must for the inhabitants of sand banks, some species will even bury themselves within the substrate (*Pseudohemiodon* and others).

Many species appreciate to rest at a location exposed to a strong current—for some species it is even a prerequisite for breeding. Fortunately, nowadays it is relatively easy to provide a suitable current in the aquarium with one of the powerful pumps available in the trade. Adult males appreciate current-swept caves as a site of future breeding. It is preferable to turn these pumps off for approximately 30 minutes during feeding time to allow the feed to collect on the bottom, from where it will be consumed (but do not

forget to turn the pump back on). The fishes learn quickly to interpret the moment of calmness and eagerly emerge from their shelters in anticipation of food.

Regular partial water exchanges are a prerequisite for successful
care. Suckermouth catfishes consume large quantities of food
which quickly will increase the concentrations of nitrogenous
wastes in the aquarium water. It is recommended to exchange at
least one third of the water every week, in the presence of particular gluttons, better to exchange even more often.

Diseases

Although suckermouth catfishes are very robust by nature, they
may—naturally—encounter health problems. Fortunately, once acclimated and well maintained in our aquaria, cases of illness are
few and far between. If there is disease, then its cause is likely to
be an error in maintenance. The most common mistakes made in
the care of loricariids are an inappropriate maintenance temperature—either too low or too high, depending on species—and an
excessive level of metabolites in the aquarium water. And, of
course, there are among the loricariids species that require very
soft, acidic water and, if such is not provided, they become prone
to disease due to environmental stress. Fortunately, those are an
exception. Most suckermouth catfishes can be maintained without problem in basically "normal" tap water and even bred there if
a few additional criteria are also met. The greatest danger faced
by our fishes, however, comes from newly acquired and introduced,
diseased, or possibly debilitated specimens due to the stress of
transport. Such fishes must remain under close observation.

The chapter on diseases of suckermouth catfishes is such a complex subject that it would be easy to write a complete book on the
matter. Since that is not within the scope of this work, on the following pages we describe only the most common diseases affect-
ing loricariids. For a detailed report on the subject, the reader is
advised to consult the standard specialized literature (e.g.,
ANDREWS, EXELL & CARRINGTON, 1990; BASSLEER, 1983; BAUER, 1991;
REICHENBACH-KLINKE & KÖRTING, 1993; UNTERGASSER, 1989).

I. Seidel

The true state of health of a fish is not always manifest from the outside. Frayed fins may occasionally occur also in healthy fishes. Quarantine is therefore always the first line of defense in our fight against disease in our aquaria.

Quarantine Procedures

Properly maintained fishes will only in exceptional cases be subject to disease. However, the hobbyist is tempted from time to time to augment his fish population by adding another purchased animal. We must always be aware of the fact that every animal (and even plant, for that matter) added to our healthy stock is a potential vector of disease. It is of little advantage to add prophylactically several drops of our favorite medicine to the aquarium water. The outbreak of disease is avoided only in the rarest of cases, if the introduced fish harbors active disease agents. Since these pathogens multiply geometrically in the narrow confines of an aquarium world and may infect also healthy fishes, the loss of the entire aquarium population is a real possibility. This tragedy may be avoided, especially by the use of quarantine measures. Unfortunately, it is still an exceptional case where the newly acquired

Ancistrus sp. "Rio Araguaia;" obviously in bad shape. Folded fins and light spots are clear warning signals.

fishes are first placed in a separate quarantine tank in order to avoid spreading the disease to our established population and to allow for the close observation of any possible symptoms displayed by the newcomers.

A quarantine is also a financially sound decision. The trade offers for under $50,– a complete aquarium set (ca. 60 liters) with cover, heater, and filter which can well be used as a quarantine setup. Even for fishes where such a small aquarium would be out of the question for normal maintenance, the size is appropriate for the limited quarantine time spent therein, as long as all other conditions are appropriate. For the times the quarantine tank is not needed, it can easily be stored in the closet until the next acquisition. Putting this setup to use does not require a major effort and is done in little time. During periods of nonuse, the filter substrate of a quarantine tank should be integrated into the cycle of a functioning aquarium so as to have a biologically active medium quickly available the next time a new quarantine is established. A protracted maturation cycle becomes unnecessary and there would usually be no time for such a cycle to complete "cold turkey." However, it must be remembered that the filtration medium was in close contact with any possibly disease vector. If a disease appeared during the quarantine period, it is best to disinfect the filter medium or to discard it altogether and to use a fresh medium which should be "matured in advance" in the display tank's filtration cycle prior to use in the next quarantine.

The decor of the tank should be sparse in order to allow for close observation of our new charges. Two or three rock plates and a small root, however, are recommended additions to allow the fishes some shelter, hereby reducing stress. A substrate may be omitted as long as we are not specifically keeping sand-dwelling species such as the mouthbrooding loricariids. Otherwise, a one centimeter layer of river sand should be provided. The advantage of a quarantine tank is that the fish may be readily observed and that we will not damage any plants should medication be necessary. It can be determined, if the fish behaves normally, what and how much it is eating, and also if the feed provided is being digested normally. And if indeed a disease becomes apparent, it is much easier and economical to apply the therapy in the reduced confines of a quarantine tank (some medications are expensive).

During the quarantine period, which should extend for a period of three—or better, four to six—weeks, close attention must be given to the possibility of transferring disease agents from that tank into our established aquaria. After any manipulation in the quarantine tank, our hands must be carefully washed and all utensils used, i.e., nets, buckets, etc., thoroughly disinfected before coming in contact with other aquaria. To disinfect the quarantine tank itself after use, various chemicals are suitable. Strong oxidizers like diluted hydrogen peroxide or potassium permanganate, but also strong saline solutions or simple boiling or scalding are suitable to kill potentially remaining pathogens.

In the aquarium hobby, unfortunately, it is a common practice to use medications with excessive ease, without even knowing what the source of the disease may be. Unfortunately, there are no "silver bullets" to treat all types of disease at once, so one should not just go to the closet to get whatever is left from the time before and try it out. Especially antibiotics should be treated with respect. Their unnecessary use and incomplete treatment regime can easily lead to the appearance of resistant bacterial strains. If fish diseases are unfamiliar to us, knowledgeable help should be sought. Experienced people who are glad to help unexperienced, beginning hobbyists can usually be found in aquarium clubs or in reputable pet shops. If all else fails, veterinarians and veterinary schools at universities are the last line of defense. For a fee, live or very recently deceased fishes can be brought in for a professional diagnosis.

Especially in the case of newly acquired fishes it is extremely important to observe them as closely as possible. If their external appearance and behavior seem normal, we may initially be satisfied. However, if suddenly they turn unusually tame, stay in plain sight at the front or side panes of the aquarium, possibly fanning vigorously with their fins, or are agitated, an illness must be assumed. Now the skin and fins of the fish must be studied in detail, in search of visible signs of disease, especially ectoparasites. In case of need, the fish must be captured and observed from all sides, since some pathogens are not obvious at first glance. Once the coloration of the suckermouth catfish has turned somewhat paler, the eyes are deeply recessed in their sockets, and the fish has lost its normal mobility, any help will usually come too late.

Many diseases of suckermouth catfishes are curable by means other than medication. Large parasites, such a carp lice or isopods, can be removed manually due to their size. In order to control ectoparasitic infestations, in many cases a shift of the water temperature out of the agents' tolerance range may be all that is needed. In the case of suckermouth catfishes from the central Amazon basin in particular, these fishes tolerate a rise in temperature to over 30°C very well, whereas for many ectoparasites such warmth is lethal. However, the temperature has to be raised with caution, making sure that the water is of optimal quality and that dissolved oxygen concentrations can be maintained close to saturation (a low value anyway at such high temperatures). Further details on the matter are mentioned in the following pages for the various specific diseases.

Injuries and Fungal Infections

Thanks to the dense armor of bony plates covering the body of suckermouth catfishes, physical injury is rarely observed in this group of fishes. However, since their interaction is often quite rough and they are always trying to pry their way into all kinds of crevices, occasional abrasions, cuts, and puncture wounds do occur. Sometimes these wounds are self-inflicted by startled individuals hitting the aquarium pane or decoration with respectable force. The mucous layer covering suckermouth catfishes protects them very well against disease agents, but in the case of injuries this layer is locally compromised and the agent may penetrate and cause an infection or fungal attack on the wound. If such a state is determined, the fish should be quarantined in order to facilitate its treatment and to protect it from its habitual tankmates (and vice versa). Particularly sensitive are the suckermouth catfishes of the subfamily Loricariinae, which commonly trust their good camouflage and do not flee as a basic defensive response. It can occur that other species (e.g., *Otocinclus* spp.) adhere to them and rasp

Damage to the mucous membranes is easy to diagnose based on the pale coloration adopted by the compromised body sections (fish to the right).

away their protective mucous layer. Such an injury can be so extensive as to cause irremediable death. In any case, the victim needs to be saved immediately from such "cleaners."

To heal thus injured fishes, several treatment options are available. To prevent infections, for example, UNTERGASSER (1989) recommends acriflavine (trypaflavine) at a concentration of 1 mg/liter aquarium water as a good choice. Alternatively, methylene blue at a concentration of 50 mg/100 liters can also be attempted (a quarantine tank must be used in this case). During the initial stages of an actual infection, a dose of 3 ml/liter of acriflavine should bring about a cure in four days. In the case of extensive injuries, the application of a dermatological antibiotic ointment from human medicine is also recommended. It prevents bacterial infections and accelerates the healing process. For treatment, the fish is initially removed daily from the water and placed on a wet rag. The wound is carefully dried with a paper towel and subsequently the ointment is applied. Once the edges of the wound close—according to UNTERGASSER—the ointment will only have to be applied every second or third day. BAUER (1991) alternatively recommends mercurochrome, an external disinfectant from human medicine, which is simply brushed on the wound. In all cases it has to be observed that the applied medicine does not come in contact with the gills, which could have fatal consequences. If injuries remain untreated, zygotes or fungal spores are most likely to colonize the site. According to BAUER (1991), the cysts first form a hypha and than a so-called mycelium which spreads among the dermal cells, causing their degeneration. Later, this mycelium also breaks through the surface and produces numerous sporangia on the surface. These can be readily seen as white, cottonlike fuzz. In extreme cases, the fungus can break through the dermal layer and infest the musculature and even the skeleton of the fishes. To treat fungal infections, again it is best to remove the patient from the water and wrap him in a wet rag. The white, cottonlike growths are carefully removed with tweezers and the fish is treated with dermal disinfectants as described above. UNTERGASSER recommends a fungicidal ointment (like those used for athlete's foot). In this case, the hyphae need not be removed, since the creamy ointment adheres well, and after a few days of one to two daily appli-

Ancistrus sp. (L 144) with "ich" in the beginning stages.

I. Seidel

cations they will be under control. In slight cases, the fungal infection can also be treated in a continuous bath (in a quarantine
tank) by adding 0.04 mg/l of malachite green (zinc-free).

White-Spot Disease (Ich)

The ciliated protozoan *Ichthyophthirius multifiliis*—commonly called
"ich" for short—is one of the most commonly appearing pathogens
in the aquarium hobby. Most aquarists are well acquainted with
the parasite already. An infestation may get started when a new
fish is added to the aquarium, but the pathogen may also be inadvertently introduced when cysts are adhering to newly planted
aquatic vegetation. However, the agent is frequently present in
the aquarium in a latent state. An outbreak may present itself as
soon as the fishes find their defenses compromised due to general stress, water contaminants, inadequate temperature regime,
or other debilitating factors which allow the pathogen to multiply.

"Ich" has the advantage of being a disease easy to diagnose, even by beginning aquarists. In the initial stages, however, there may be a possibility to confuse the disease with others of similar characteristics (e.g., freshwater *Oodinium*). First the infestation manifests itself by the appearance of individual small white dots which can readily be seen with the naked eye on fin membranes or anywhere else on the body of the fish. As the disease progresses, so does the number of dots. As a matter of fact, it is not an easy condition to diagnose on those suckermouth catfishes which include light dots as part of their normal coloration pattern. A more purposeful observation of these species is in order, so as to distinguish the normal from the disease-induced.

The pathogen of white-spot disease passes through specific developmental stages which, according to Bauer (1991), last 5–6 days at a temperature of 26°–27°C, and correspondingly longer at lower temperatures. Most medication available in the trade is based on malachite green oxalate. However, this active ingredient will only control with certainty the free-swimming stage of *Ichthyophthirius* (tomites). These must find a host within 55 hours or they will die. The trophozoites, which have adhered under the mucous membrane of the fish will not be killed with efficacy during the 4–5 days that they require to mature and fall off anew. In the aquarium, the ripe trophonts fall onto the substrate. The resulting cysts initially divide into four partial cysts which then, through subsequent division, may divide into up to 1024 tomites. Every tomite is the origin of a new vagrant body. The process requires 18–20 hours at 27°C. This predetermined lifecycle of the pathogen should be kept in mind in order to repeat treatment after six days to control the newly developed tomites. Besides chemical control, the addition of an UV-sterilizer in the filtration circuit or the raising of the water temperature to 30°C for 10 days (if the fish can tolerate this—assure optimum aeration) are other ways to control the parasite.

Freshwater-*Oodinium* (Velvet)

Another one among the most common diseases of loricariids— and one which can very quickly turn deadly—is a disease commonly called freshwater-*Oodinium* or velvet in the aquarium hobby.

Freshwater-*Oodinium* is one of the most common loricariid diseases. ¹ Seidel

Up close the parasites are readily visible with the naked eye. ¹ Seidel

It is caused by a parasitic unicellular alga. Especially among anabantids and killifishes, freshwater-*Oodinium* is a frequently observed ciliate. But also suckermouth catfishes are becoming victims more and more often. Much contradictory information can be
read in the specialized aquarium fish literature commonly available. Even the name of the pathogen is still a matter of discussion. Usually called *Oodinium pillularis*, BAUER (1991) lists the species as *Piscinoodinium pillularis*. But even the size of the individual
parasites is not a settled matter. According to BAUER, the parasitiz-
ing, nonmotile, non-ciliated parasites (dinospores) have a size between 0.005 and 0.1 mm and are not visible to the naked eye.
However, according to UNTERGASSER, (1989) they are still barely visible with the unaided eye. On the other hand, ANDREWS, EXELL, and
CARRINGTON (1990) even indicate a size of 1 mm for this pathogen.
We have the feeling that the various authors understand different
things when talking about *O. pillularis*. And indeed, it seems that
the symptomatology of the disease is somewhat different in
loricariids than that displayed by anabantids and killifishes. The
individual parasites are much larger and correspond more to the
description given by ANDREWS, EXELL, and CARRINGTON.
Infested fishes initially display individual yellowish dots on the body.
As the infestation progresses, the parasites are so close together
that in lieu of individual dots, now only a yellowish-gray cover can
be distinguished. However, the parasites also enter through the
oral cavity into the throat, stomach, and intestine and adhere there.
Likewise, the gills are quickly attacked, and this can lead to the
asphyxiation of the fishes, given that the epithelium where the gas-
eous exchange occurs will be severely damaged. Some species
which normally have yellow dots or spots (e.g., *Baryancistrus* sp.
L 18) are very difficult to diagnose during the initial stages of the
disease. However, the attentive observer will virtually always notice a slightly abnormal behavior among his or her loricariids.
Whereas most suckermouth catfishes are normally rather shy
charges which spend much of the daytime hours in hiding, specimens infested with *Oodinium* regularly turn "tame" and prefer to
adhere themselves to the aquarium pane at a place close to the
filter's effluent current. They appear lethargic, fold their fins, or fan
continuously with their paired fins. The fanning of the fins is reminis-

cent of the behavior displayed by the males of several suckermouth catfish species shortly before reproduction, but should not be confused with such, given that the situation is very serious. If nothing is done, the fish will surely die after a few days.

BAUER (1991) describes in great detail the lifecycle of *P. pillularis*. The parasites—round to pear-shaped—develop an attachment disc with rootlike appendages (rhizoids) which they use to firmly fasten themselves to the fish. Given that this is an alga, nutritional requirements may be met through photosynthesis in the chloroplasts. Additionally however, the pathogen also feeds off the host. But in what way that is accomplished is not quite clear at present. Whereas the pathogens of the very similar marine *Oodinium* ingest cellular particles of their host by means of feeding vacuoles through their rhizoid, which are then digested, BAUER suspects that in the case of *P. pillularis* only osmotic processes are involved in the procurement of nutrients from the host. Furthermore, he suspects that fish cells damaged by the rhizoid release chemicals which attract new parasites. This would explain why the parasite appears in such dense clusters. Once extensive tissue damage has been sustained, the debilitated fish is prone to secondary infections due to bacteria, which now can also easily penetrate into the host's body through the damaged area. The multiplication of this serious pathogen occurs without intermediate hosts during cyst stage, which happens on the bottom after the parasite has fallen off its host. Multiple divisions occur within the gelatinous cover of the cysts. After several days, 32–64, flagellated dinospores abandon each cyst and actively seek and infest new hosts. There they adhere and abscise their flagellum. The dinospores must find a host within 24 hours or face death.

The trade offers numerous medications to control freshwater-*Oodinium,* most of which are based on copper sulphate. However, those who expect quick relief in their well-established aquaria from these preparations will be disappointed, because the active ingredient will quickly disappear. Copper has the unpleasant characteristic to quickly bind with organic compounds (so-called chelating agents) and form a hardly soluble complex as well as to be precipitated as insoluble copper carbonate, even under low carbonate hardness conditions. The treatment, therefore, is best performed in a bare aquarium (no decoration or filtration) in order to extend the half-life of the therapeutic concentration. Given that the parasite requires light, treatment efficiency should be boosted by darkening the aquarium. Besides the commercial presentations, copper sulfate can also be administered pure at a rate of 1.5 mg/l. In order to maintain the concentration relatively stable, after both two and four days the water should be exchanged and the prescribed copper concentration administered anew. After treatment is concluded, perform a final water exchange. Possible copper residues can be eliminated by using a water conditioner. The fish should remain in quarantine for at least one week after treatment, better longer. BAUER recommends to disinfect the aquarium where the disease appeared, in order to destroy any possible cysts with certainty.

So much for the theory, in the real world, however, it has been shown that many aquarium fishes are very sensitive to copper, including, unfortunately, many catfishes. The same applies to quinine, which, according to UNTERGASSER, may be used in the form of quinine sulfate or quinine hydrochloride (the latter to be preferred, 1 g quinine in 100 liters of water in a continuous bath for 3 days), but which is also quite toxic to sensitive fishes. It is likely that the most appropriate treatment for suckermouth catfishes is the one also described by UNTERGASSER, and which is based on a continuous bath with malachite green oxalate. A concentration of 0.04 mg/l needs to be maintained over a period of at least 14 days. Treatment is, as before, preferably administered in a bare and darkened tank. Every three days half the water is replaced and the medication added. However, the handling of malachite green demands great care. The dye is suspected of being a teratogenetic (cancer-causing) agent.

UNTERGASSER presents in his book an additional treatment regime, which we consider the best and which we have applied successfully for some time now. Given that the tolerance of most suckermouth catfishes in front of elevated water temperatures exceeds that of the parasite, an elevating of the aquarium water temperature will kill the parasites with certainty. Nevertheless, great care has to be excised while using this method, after all, we are operating within a few degrees of the lethal tolerance of the catfishes themselves. Do not raise the temperature abruptly but gradually, so as not to unduly stress the fishes. However, since time is at a premium, the raise should be accomplished within one day. The target temperature is 33°–34°C. Most loricariids from central Amazonia must endure similar temperatures in nature and will have no problem with such a treatment. However, when treating species from mountain streams or from cooler areas of South America, such temperatures might become lethal. Carefully ascertain the situation prior to initiating treatment. Nevertheless, one of the co-authors (SEIDEL) was able to treat even newly imported, *Oodinium*-infested, mountain loricariids from the genus *Chaetostoma* using this method. However, if in doubt, perhaps a medicated solution should be applied. The advantage of the temperature treatment lies especially in the fact that no chemicals are being used and that treatment can be carried out in the normal maintenance aquarium. Additionally, a subsequent general disinfection of the aquarium becomes unnecessary. A disadvantage is the possibility that sensitive aquatic vegetation might suffer and succumb to such high treatment temperatures. However, we were unable to discern any detriment to our, usually very robust, plants (*Anubias* spp., *Cryptocoryne* spp., etc.).

For the treatment to be as little stressful as possible for the fishes, the water in the aquarium should be absolutely clean and have an optimal concentration of dissolved oxygen. It is therefore recommended to make a final water exchange and a complete maintenance of the filter prior to treatment. During treatment, optimal aeration of the water is essential (diffuser or air stone). When everything has been properly prepared, treatment in all likelihood will be uneventful. In order to maintain the pollution levels at a minimum, none or only very frugal feeding should occur during the treatment period. UNTERGASSER recommends a treatment duration of 24–36 hours, but in our experience we were unable to ever observe a complete die-off of the parasites in loricariids after such a short time. Even when we regulated the thermostat back to normal as soon as we were unable to observe any parasites on our fishes, frequently the disease recurred after a short time. We therefore kept the temperature for an additional 24 hours at 33°–34°C and this way we have had no relapses whatsoever. The entire treat-

Pseudacanthicus sp. (L 25) with a strong vorticella infestation.   I. Seidel

ment, therefore, requires between three and six days, depending on the severity of the infestation.

To avoid a spreading of the disease, all utensils and the hands that came in contact with the water from the affected aquarium should be disinfected. The fishes should be observed for a few additional days prior to them being transferred to another aquarium. If these recommendations are followed and any newly acquired fishes are first placed into a quarantine aquarium for initial observation, much trouble can be averted. Freshwater-*Oodinium* is—at least in regard to catfishes—a disease that is usually introduced with newly acquired fishes (or plants).

Epystyliasis ("White-Speck Disease")

This symptomatology has recently made a more and more common appearance in newly imported Brazilian loricariids. There was no problem with this disease until now. We have christened the disease white-speck disease [Weißstippenkrankheit], because it produces in loricariids a whitish, woollike cover, especially on the head, the spines, and around the opercula—but it may also appear anywhere on the body. This covering is somewhat reminiscent of a fungal attack, but the typical hairlike structures are lacking. GOTTWALD (AQUATARIUM, Garbsen, Germany), who, during the quarantine period, frequently determined this symptomatology on newly imported L-catfishes from northeastern Brazil, sent one affected specimen for diagnosis to the University for Veterinary Medicine in Hannover [Germany]. There it was determined that the causative agent of these white covers was a member of the family Vorticellidae in the genus *Heteropolaria* (also known as *Epistylis*). *Heteropolaria* belongs to the order Peritrichida, a group of ciliated, vase-shaped protozoans. Many species in this genus are sessile, according to REED & FRANCIS-FLOYD (1993) and form branched colonies. The organisms multiply through division and the resulting "offspring" are said to initially swim in the open water. Only as adults do they seek a site to colonize. For these ciliated protozoans, even the fishes are just another substrate to settle on. They do not feed on their host (=substrate), but rather on free-swimming bacteria and other microorganisms that pass them by. However, they release an enzyme at the site of attachment. This enzyme promotes tissue growth. If the parasite is later removed (e.g., by the fish scratching against the decoration) a wound is left behind which easily becomes the point of origin for a bacterial or fungal infection. Whereas the protozoans of the genus *Heteropolaria* or *Epistylis* were hardly known in the aquarium hobby, they are identified in cold-water aquaculture to be one of the pathogens responsible for the dreaded red sore disease (Ger.: Rotwundenkrankheit). However, this disease neither is caused exclusively by the protozoans. The infestation with the protozoans is combined in fishes afflicted with red sore disease with the presence of *Aeromonas hydrophila* bacteria. The protozoans are organisms which are ubiquitous in the habitat of the fishes, but only under certain specific conditions a disease is caused. According to MOELLER (1996), these pathogens are commonly found among the wild populations of scaled fishes. A massive outbreak of the disease occurs primarily in waters strongly polluted with organics (eutrophic waters).

The situation is likely to be similar with the newly imported loricariids. These are so debilitated by transport stress and the suboptimal maintenance conditions during transit, that few defenses are left. Since the water quality in the holding facilities of exporters are surely not the best, the protozoans are likely to find optimal reproductive conditions in these polluted tanks. As long as the infestation is slight, a medicated treatment regime is, in all likelihood, unnecessary. As long as the defenses of the fish are not too compromised, it is likely to be able to deal with the disease on its own. Unfortunately, it is especially in heavily infested fishes that the immune system needs help. With a raise in water temperature, as the one described for ich, the authors were able to induce a distinct reduction in pathogen population, but even at times when absolutely no white dots remained visible, once the temperature was normalized, these dots quickly reappeared. However, this method can surely be used to bolster the fish's immune system. Fortunately, a medicated treatment may follow the same protocol given for "ich," i.e., malachite green. Either a commercial preparation is acquired, or a concentration of 0.04 mg/l malachite green oxalate is used. After about two days the pathogens have disappeared. The possible presence of a secondary bacterial infection must be addressed separately.

Bacterial Infections

Whereas many of the listed ectoparasitic infestations present only a moderate difficulty in regard to diagnosis with the naked eye by the aquarist, bacterial infections are an entirely different matter. That is an area where only few of us are able to determine the specific causative agent. Bacteria are unicellular, unnucleated organisms which multiply by division.

Following BAUER (1991), bacteria are initially classified according to their external shape: there are cocci (spherical), bacilli (rods), vibrios (comma-shaped), and spirilla (spirals). Further classification is based, for example, on biochemical properties such as the acceptance or not a of Gram-stain (= Gram-positive or -negative), propagation in various growth media, as well as the metabolization or synthesis of specific compounds. It can be imagined how the

Whiptail catfish with a bacterial infection.

I. Seidel

multitude of known bacterial fish pathogens makes a positive diagnosis by the average aquarist a very complicated affair. What "normal" hobbyist will be able to afford a small laboratory to find out through stains and microscopy evaluation if he or she is dealing with a gram-positive or gram-negative strain, or to analyze the synthesis or metabolism of specific compounds. In the practical area, in consequence, the usual chain of events—unfortunately—involves in case of a disease the trial and error of sequential usage of various medicines until either the pathogen is controlled or the affected fish has died. This procedure is highly questionable in the best of cases, and may be downright dangerous, given that the fishes are weakened through erroneous medication and that the creation of resistant strains is promoted. We were repeatedly witness to how carelessly antibiotics were administered at export holding stations and in part also in the trade, even in a prophylactic manner. We want to ask you insistently to promptly seek the advice of knowledgeable persons in case of bacterial diseases and to provide him or her with a live diseased specimen for diagnosis. Prompt help may be obtained from some veterinarians or university veterinary departments. But also in the various aquarium societies there are specialists that are able to perform such a diagnosis for a fee. The money that otherwise would be spent on the numerous, unnecessarily administered medications is, in any case, much better spent on such a professional diagnosis, especially since most over the counter medications available in the trade promise little success. Generally, a prescription-requiring antibiotic is needed, a trip to the veterinarian therefore usually becomes unavoidable anyway.

According to Bauer, most piscine pathogens are rods (i.e., bacilli). Round or comma-shaped agents are rarer, screw or spiral-shaped organisms do not play a role in fish diseases at all.

Motility may be accomplished by means of flagella or, if these are absent, through creeping or gliding. However, many bacteria lack active locomotion altogether. Bacteria are amazingly resistent in front of external factors. They are extremely tolerant in regard to changes in osmotic pressure, pH, or temperature. With few exceptions, bacteria live both aerobically as well as facultatively anaerobically, i.e., they can deal with both oxygen-rich as well as oxygen-deficient conditions. One can imagine, based on this resilience, that very precise medication is needed in order to thoroughly control these very adaptive pathogens with effectiveness. Many of the bacteria dangerous to fishes normally live from organics in the water (e.g., detritus or mud) and are only facultatively pathogenic. Only when maintenance conditions of the fishes are substandard (e.g., deficient hygiene, poor filtration, wrong diet, maintenance temperatures outside the appropriate range, inappropriate water chemistry) or the fishes are injured or are in an otherwise weakened immunological state, do these bacteria become dangerous to our charges. A spreading of these disease agents can be averted by providing optimal conditions for one's fishes. They unwittingly become an indicator for the quality of the maintenance provided by us. A different situation involves newly acquired fishes, which are always potential disease vectors. In other words, those who offer the appropriate maintenance conditions and place newly acquired fishes for some time into quarantine, will hardly ever have to face bacterial diseases in their aquarium.

Often a bacterial infection accompanies red dermal zones.

I. Seidel

Distended ventral areas can also have a bacterial origin.

I. Seidel

At this point we do not want to present all possible bacterial diseases in detail, but rather invite the reader to seek the appropriate specialized literature mentioned above. One symptomatology, however, we do want to present, since it is widely encountered, especially among the mouthbrooding suckermouth catfishes of the subfamily Loricariinae. The disease is easily diagnosed and treated by any aquarist. We are dealing with a form of bacterial fin rot. Especially the strongly bottom-oriented twig catfishes are very sensitive to suboptimal maintenance conditions. Often it is not even necessary for the water conditions to deteriorate drastically for the disease to appear. It might already be enough that the sand and gravel substrate necessary to maintain these species presents pockets of anaerobic conditions (putrefaction). If economically feasible, a substratum heater should be used. This type of heater will promote a positive irrigation of the substrate, counteracting anaerobic conditions. In the course of the disease, the fins deteriorate progressively. The edges become distinctly reddish and, naturally, the motility of the fish is compromised to the degree that the fish loses its fins. It usually takes a long time until the life of the affected fish is actually threatened. However, the overall condition of the fish deteriorates day by day until this disease, too, turns lethal. For some suckermouth catfish species (e.g., *Hemiodontichthys acipenserinus*) bacterial fin rot might even be the number one killer. According to BAUER, the symptomatology might be caused by various representatives of the genera *Aeromonas*, *Pseudomonas*, and *Vibrio*. The resulting pathogenicity of these—under optimal maintenance conditions innocuous—bacteria should be a sign of alarm for the aquarist. Now he or she must quickly identify the source of the outbreak and eliminate the culprit. Often the fishes are already helped by a timely transfer into another aquarium, e.g., a quarantine tank with optimal water conditions, naturally! As long as the disease has not progressed to the base of the fin and compromised the musculature, there is a very favorable prognosis just by improving the maintenance conditions. Frequent water exchanges will promote a prompt regeneration of the fins, but some time will have to pass until the fins recuperate to their original glory. In severe cases, the use of antibiotics becomes unavoidable; sulfonamides and nitrofurans are the agents of choice. However, those who pay good attention to their fishes will not ever let the disease get that far.

Parotocinclus jumbo with red sore disease.

E. Schraml

Red Sore Disease

In the years 1995/96 a new, small suckermouth catfish species was imported from the Brazilian state of Pernambuco for the first time [to Germany]. It later received the code number LDA 25 and was recently described as *Parotocinclus jumbo*. It confronted us with a completely new disease. On occasion, among the imported specimens, there are some which show extensive rust-colored sections on their body. Affected specimens initially show no behavioral changes and continue to feed normally. As the disease progresses, the afflicted areas are framed by tumors, the fish looks as if it is going to burst and there are curvatures of the spine. Although the fishes may live for a long time with this disease, they do succumb sooner or later. The disease is, unfortunately, not mentioned in the standard literature dealing with fish diseases, which is why it may be assumed that the pathogen was introduced for the first time with the initial import of LDA 25. If diseased specimens are kept together with other loricariids, it seems that a transmission of the disease only occurs with great difficulty. To our knowledge, so far the red sore disease—as the disease is called very appropriately—could only be diagnosed on a single specimen of a hypostomin species, i.e., *Liposarcus pardalis.*

We have to thank the dedication and perseverance of R. HUSMANN, an aquarist from northern Germany, that some details about the disease have become known to us. Through research on the internet and numerous analyses of tissue samples of a diseased fish at her veterinary clinic by Dr. MERGENTHAL, as well as at the college of veterinary medicine in Hannover, she possibly identified the pathogen and published the results on her home page (see bibliography). These results, however, have to be considered preliminary, since due to a lack of infected LDA 25 she had to study the infected *Liposarcus pardalis* mentioned above. Nevertheless, this specimen evidently presented the same symptomatology—a distinct, rust-red spot. The analysis of a smear taken from the affected area revealed that the rust-red spots are caused by tiny, spore-forming unicellular parasites, so-called microsporidia. The causative agent could be identified as an as of yet unclassified species in the genus *Glugea.*

Microsporidia are intracellular parasites with a presence in all animal groups, from unicellular organisms to mammals, but they are most common in arthropods and fishes. They are usually host-specific and may attack various organs and multiply therein. According to BAUER (1991), the infectious stage is made up of spores with simple morphology which contain a polar pile and an ameboid nucleus. They are ingested with the food and adhere to the intestinal wall. The ameboid nucleus penetrates the intestinal wall and is transported by the circulatory system to a tissue specific to that infectious agent. At the target site the pathogens multiply by division. In the specific case of the red sore disease, the pink-red coloration of the spots is said to occur, according to HUSMANN, because the pathogenic agent penetrates into the fifth dermal layer, the *stratum germinativum*, where pigments are formed. This cellular layer is activated and consequently produces an excess of pigmentation. The control of microsporidia is very difficult. The college of veterinary medicine in Hannover suggests a treatment with Toltrazonil (as Baycox® from BAYER in the trade) in a separate aquarium. This medication has already proven successful in Hannover in the treatment of *Glugea* in some fishes (e.g., carp). The patient is exposed in a 4-hour-bath to a solution of 5–20 mg/l. During the following days, this treatment is to be repeated for one hour each day. Furthermore, the college of veterinary medicine suggests that the entire aquarium where the disease was initially detected to be reset to avoid a reinfection. This is probably sufficient deterrent and an incentive to leave everything as is and make no treatment at all, especially since there is hardly any danger of a contagion to tankmates.

The experience with the disease so far admits the conclusion that the microsporidia represent a secondary infection which may only spread if the potential host is weakened by other factors. However, in that case, an epidemic spreading of the disease becomes a real possibility. According to HUSMAN, there has been at least one wholesaler where in one holding tank with an infected specimen in the end all the *Parotocinclus jumbo* therein became infected. Of course, it is specifically in newly imported fishes, where their immune system is likely to have been stressed due to periodic starvation, changes in water chemistry, use of medications, etc. that the pathogen encounters ideal infective conditions. Nevertheless, the import itself is not the source of infection for the fishes. And as shown by observations in the fish's natural habitat—despite of what is frequently suspected—the problem surely does not lie in excessively high maintenance temperatures, either.

We were already pretty sure that the source could only be found in the natural habitat of these loricariids, given that the fishes were already displaying the disease in an advanced stage as they arrived at the importers. A report by HUSMAN, quoting LUCANUS as noting that such diseased *Parotocinclus jumbo* only reach the trade during the dry season in their natural habitat, seamed to give a clear indication that the affliction appears in connection with poor environmental conditions at the fish's natural habitat. And indeed, this suspicion could be confirmed. During a trip to eastern Brazil, one of the coauthors (EVERS) was able to visit during the dry season a common capture site of the species in the vicinity of the city of Recife. This allowed him to analyze the living conditions of the fish firsthand. He determined the waters in the vicinity of Recife to be quite warm (temperature during the dry season usually in excess of 30°C). The streams, which during the rainy season are probably a few degrees cooler and flow faster, and in all likelihood serve as spawning grounds, had shriveled into slow-flowing remnants. At the gates of Recife, the *Parotocinclus jumbo* congregated in unbelievable quantities in the extremely polluted, oxygen-poor waters. During a single afternoon, a fisherman from the local exporter D´AGUA was able to capture approximately 10,000 specimens. It is easy to imagine that the fishes at the time of capture—and under such polluted conditions—were severely weakened and easy prey for any disease that came along. The source of the red-sore-disease is probably to be found among these conditions.

It is likely that most of the *Parotocinclus jumbo* that live in the sewers of the City of Recife during the dry season are sentenced to death anyway, and that the export as aquarium fish is possibly the only real chance of survival for at least a few hundred of these fish. It is therefore not surprising that when the fish arrive at their export destination during this period—even if they are not overtly displaying the symptoms of the disease—they do so in a deplorable state. The aquarist may only be advised to carefully inspect the fish prior to purchase. Fish in trouble are easily spotted due to their abnormal posture. With optimal care, it is probable that even some of these "preinjured" fish can be brought "back onto their feet." HUSMAN reports that an importer placed sick LDA 25 into an algae-covered aquarium, and these fish recovered on their own. Maintenance indications for this loricariid can be found in the species section of this volume.

Metacercaria

Most diseases we observe on suckermouth catfishes are a direct or indirect result of the shipping (import) process. Due to the extended transport times, the constantly changing environmental conditions, and surely in-

Photo top right:
Encapsulated trematode larvae (metacercaria) on the ventral side of a *Peckoltia* sp. (L 134).

Photo bottom right:
This *Hypostomus* is infested with black encapsulations.

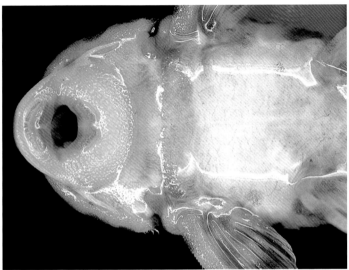

I. Seidel

I. Seidel

adequate handling of the fishes on occasion, the immune system is weakened. Additionally, the very high holding densities the fishes are exposed to periodically facilitate a spreading of disease of epidemic proportions. Furthermore, there is a great number of parasites which may commonly be already encountered on the fishes in their natural habitat. Usually they are co-imported as stowaways ("by-catch") and due to their cryptic habits may even pass unnoticed through the quarantine period. Consequently, it may happen that an infestation with such parasites will be diagnosed in the aquarium of a hobbyist after he or she has purchased a loricariid at a reputable dealer, even after the fish had previously passed through an appropriate quarantine period.

The parasites which may find their way into the aquaria of hobbyists due to their cryptic lifestyle and low pathogenicity may be isopods, the better-known carp lice, and, especially, metacercaria. The latter are encapsulated trematode larvae which, in suckermouth catfishes, usually appear on the ventral side as black, yellowish, or pink inclusions beneath the skin. These bumps may be several millimeters in size and often something moving may be distinguished in their midst. It is also quite common for fishes to harbor several of this worm larvae at once. Nevertheless, there is no reason to panic. As long as it is not a very heavy infestation, there is hardly any danger for the condition to turn fatal.

According to BAUER (1991), these parasitic worm larvae belong to the Digenea (Trematoda), a group of worms consisting of more than 7,000 species.

Metacercaria represent the larval stage of similarly endoparasitic trematodes which are hermaphrodites and sport two suction cups (one anteriorly, the other ventrally at the center of the body). Fishes are only the second intermediate host of these advanced worms. They have an unusual lifecycle. The larvae (cercaria) live initially in gastropods (snails) and later leave this first host by the hundreds. They have an often forked flagellum which they can use to swim towards their next host. Usually the cercaria remain motionless in the water column, and only move towards the source of a change in condition, as in the case of a sudden variation in brightness or difference in water flow (current). In this manner it is highly likely that the animals will reach their next intermediate host. As they penetrate into the fish, the cercaria abscise their flagellum; it is no longer needed. In the fish they metamorphose into their next developmental stage, the metacercaria. During this stage they remain confined in the fish and cannot leave. There they wait for the intermediate host to be predated by a bird. That bird becomes the final host once the infected fish is digested.

Naturally, as a consequence of entering the fish, the cercaria cause damage in the dermis, the muscular tissue, and possibly also in internal organs. Newly infested specimens therefore frequently exhibit bloody areas, swim restlessly, breath heavily, and on occasion scrape against the aquarium decor. Once the metacercaria have reached their final resting position, the fishes usually resume their normal behavior. Most metacercaria are encapsulated; but some species of parasites improve the probability that the host will fall prey to a bird. These species migrate to the brain or the eyes of the fish, causing abnormal (and more noticeable) behavior. It is in the bird where the worm reaches maturity. The eggs of the adult worms fall back into the water with the feces of an infected bird. Small ciliated miracidia larvae hatch. These, in turn, infect aquatic snails, hereby starting the cycle for another round.

Given that dead larvae cannot be excreted by an infected fish, no medication against the metacercaria should be used, lest the host might die of protein poisoning. A slight infestation should therefore remain untreated, especially since the larval worms, once encapsulated, cause no more harm. However, for severe cases we recommend that the fish be euthanized. Since trematode larvae may also be introduced into our aquaria with snails we bring from ponds, lakes, and streams, we advise against introducing these snails into an aquarium with fishes. Transferring snails from one aquarium to another, of course, is a different matter. The lifecycle of the trematode is interrupted (no bird phase) and consequently the worms cannot multiply in an aquarium.

Carp Lice

Although very few species are in actuality parasites on cyprinids, the crustacea of the family Branchuria are commonly referred to as carp lice. These are shield-shaped crustacea, 4–12 mm in diameter, whose strongly flattened body consists of two parts: a large, round anterior section (the cephalothorax) and a small, elongated posterior body (the pleon). According to BAUER (1991) there are three genera, *Argulus*, *Dolops,* and *Chonopeltis*. *Argulus* is represented by over 50 species, and with them has the broadest distribution worldwide. Members of this genus are characterized by having two suctorial discs on the first pair of maxillae and a moveable stinger on the anterior body half. These parasites adhere to their host by means of the suctorial discs and introduce the stinger into the tissue of the host. A toxic anticoagulating agent is injected, which can already be lethal for smaller fishes. Then they proceed to suck blood and tissue fluids from the host through the same stinger. Representatives of the genera *Dolops* and *Chonopeltis* lack this stinger and the first maxillae are modified into fastening hooks instead. Only the South American genus *Dolops*, with approximately 10 species, is of interest to the suckermouth catfish hobbyist. The monotypic genus *Chonopeltis* is only found in Africa and Asia.

While maintaining suckermouth catfishes, we will primarily be confronted with *Argulus* spp., if at all. We will therefore describe the lifecycle of that genus in more detail. Reproduction of *Argulus* spp. occurs in the open water. After fertilization, the females adhere the egg strings to stones and plants. The larvae pass the nauplius and metanauplius stages while still confined in the egg membrane. At 20°C, hatching requires approximately three weeks. The young immediately go in search of a host. Several molts are required for them to reach sexual maturity.

Carp lice may be introduced into an aquarium when feeding with live foods collected from infested bodies of water or with the addition of a new fish. The pictured representative of the genus *Argulus* was removed from a newly imported South American zebra suckermouth (*Hypancistrus zebra*). Infested fishes are often nervous and overall display abnormal behavior. The parasites themselves are often difficult to distinguish on the fishes, since they frequently have transparent body sections and their overall coloration is cryptic. Because suckermouth catfishes have quite an effective armor consisting of bony plates, the carp lice are usually found on the unprotected areas of the fish. It seems that the stinger has difficulty

Carp lice prefer to affix themselves onto naked body sections, like here, the lower lip of a *Sturisoma*.

in penetrating the armor. Consequently, the parasites tend to choose the naked, unprotected regions along the dorsal fin base, the ventrum, and the borders of the eyes as a point of penetration. The vicinity of the sting frequently becomes infected and the membranes swell. There is especially a danger of secondary bacterial or fungal infections which the weakened host cannot control very effectively. After having taken sufficient blood, the carp lice abandon their host and swim freely in the water until they later search for another host. The mechanisms by which carp lice acquire their new host are not dealt with in detail in the literature. They are probably too slow for an active pursuit, therefore it is likely to involve an element of surprise and ambush of a passing fish. We were able to observe a carp louse, imported from South America on an armored catfish, how it laid itself motionless on its back in waiting for an approaching host. As such approached to determine if this was an edible morsel and to grab it with its mouth, the parasite

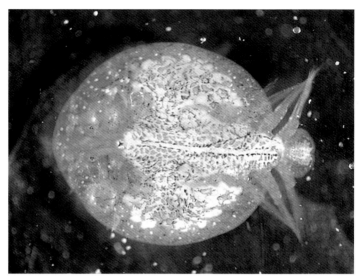

Argulus sp. found on a newly imported *Hypancistrus zebra.* I. Seidel

quickly flipped over and fastened itself onto the mouth of the fish. The usual control method of carp lice recommended in the literature involves the use of Masoten (0.4 mg/l) in a quarantine aquarium. Those of us who are familiar with the sensitivity of the Loricariidae in front of this active ingredient will surely be in shock when reading such recommendations. Since usually we are dealing with individual "stowaways" on the fishes, such treatment would surely be a case of overkill. Such individual parasites are best removed manually from their host with pinchers. Still, we have been able to observe repeatedly that in import shipments from South America there might be a box full of suckermouth catfishes infested with numerous tiny carp lice.

In such cases, it has been virtually impossible to remove the parasites manually, and the use of the "chemical club" becomes unavoidable. However, in such cases, too, Masoten should *not* be used. Suitable alternatives constitute short baths in water with sodium chloride (table salt) or potassium permanganate in a separate receptacle. In salt water (dosage: 10–15 g/l for 20 minutes) the parasites will soon separate. The fishes are then transferred into a parasite-free quarantine tank. A short potassium permanganate bath (10 mg/l for 10–30 minutes or 2–4 mg/l for 1 hour) is said to be even more effective, i.e., lethal for the parasites. With this treatment it is important that the fishes remain under constant observation and that the maximum bath times are not exceeded, lest the fishes are also poisoned.

Whereas UNTERGASSER (1989) considers a reproduction of carp lice in an aquarium as unlikely, BAUER does accept this as a possibility and suggests that the aquarium be disinfected (after transferring all the fishes, of course!). This is also indicated simply because, according to BAUER, carp lice may survive without food for three weeks if need be.

Aquatic Isopods

For many years, parasitic isopods have been among the rarest of observed pathogens in our aquaria. They are therefore only superficially presented in the literature on fish diseases. However, since in recent times we had to confirm the presence of parasitic isopods on several newly imported suckermouth catfishes, it seems fair to assume that in reality the problem is not all that rare. An infestation with these parasites often remains undetected and, more often than not, the weakened hosts are unable to complete their import journey alive. Whereas other diseases are often the consequence of improper handling of the fishes (excessive holding densities, polluted water, stress, etc.) which makes the explosive multiplication of pathogens possible in the first place, an infestation with piscine isopods is something completely natural. The suckermouth catfishes have to deal with them in their natural habitat just the same, i.e., the condition is not exasperated by the import/transport activities.

According to BAUER (1991), there are approximately 450 species of parasitic isopods, most of which are marine inhabitants. Some species live on the skin of fishes, others parasitize the branchial arches and cause great harm to their hosts in the process. Whereas some isopods feed on carrion, others may not even be considered para-

An infestation with endoparasitic isopods—this *Ancistrus* sp. (L 159) has a parasite laterally in its abdomen—is often difficult to diagnose.

sites, but outright predators which pursue weakened fishes and over-power them. Isopods are easily distinguished from carp lice based on their elongated body shape and the typical segmentation of their body (seven thoracic and six abdominal segments). There are spe-cies which grow to six centimeters in length, but the few freshwater species remain significantly smaller. In the case of suckermouth cat-fishes, the representatives of the family Cymothoidae are likely to cause the most trouble. These species are primarily endoparasitic (espe-cially the females). As they attack the fish in the most varied places, they can be found in the branchial, oral, and abdominal cavities. Some, however, may sit on the surface of the fish, in a manner reminiscent of carp lice, and are easier to spot in that case. The host may be severely injured by the isopods' sharp and powerful oral structures. According to Thatcher (1991), isopods feed primarily on blood, mu-cosa, and the epithelium. The resulting injuries are fertile ground for secondary infections.

A closer look reveals the legs of the isopod. I. Seidel

Artystone sp., an inadvertent "by-catch" of an imported *Ancistrus* sp. "Rio Araguia."

I. Seidel

263

According to Bauer, the isopods of the family Cymothoidae are protandric hermaphrodites, i.e., one and the same specimen is initially male and later turns into an equally functional female. The lifecycle includes two larval stages, when they only have six pairs of legs. The adult male (something that happens after several molts) has seven pairs of legs and, after several further molts, displays the typical sexual characteristics. Males are smaller and slimmer than females and have natatory bristles, which turn them into nimble swimmers. As ectoparasites, they frequently change hosts and in the end search for a female. The inner sexual organs consist of three pairs of testes and primodial ovaries which develop with subsequent molts, something that occurs concurrently with a regression of the male characteristics. Associated with the change of gender, occurs a change of parasitic behavior. The endoparasitic females lose the ability to swim, increase significantly in size, and develop ovaries and an incubation chamber where the eggs develop.

The nine genera with a total of 23 species listed by Schaefer (1992) for the family Cymothoidae in South America have meanwhile been augmented by several new descriptions. According to Bauer, these South American isopods can be classified into two different groups. The first group—mostly marine species with a cosmopolitan distribution—includes the genera *Nerocila* and *Livoneca*. The second group is made up of the genera *Artystone* and *Riggia,* which deviate clearly from the marine forms, both in morphology as well as in regard to their biology and ecology. These have apparently undergone a distinct adaptation to life in freshwater. These isopods live in pouches of the ventral skin of their hosts, deep in the abdominal cavity. Due to their cryptic location, they commonly remain undetected.

There are various genera which cannot be classified into either of the two groups. They represent intermediate, transitional forms. *Braga* is one such genus which may on occasion be found on suckermouth catfishes. Szidat (1955) reports that *Braga fluviatilis*, a species inhabiting the basins of the Río de la Plata, the Río Paraguay, and of the Río Uruguay, is especially common and parasitizes loricariids in particular. The female of this species specifically grabs hold of the tongue of the catfishes and sucks blood, something that—understandably—may cause a great deal of irritation

Otocinclus vittatus, a victim of isopod parasitism. I. Seidel

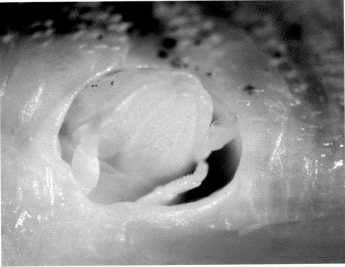

Detail of the breathing orifice and the posterior corporal segments of an isopod. I. Seidel

Artystone cf. *bolivianensis*; dissection reveals the parasitic isopod.   I. Seidel

in the host. Often the much smaller male can also be seen as it sits on the brooding pouch of the female.

The various species of Cymothoidae are often specialized to a particular host species. On suckermouth catfishes, the species of the second group are the most commonly encountered, as they live in the abdominal cavity. According to THATCHER & SCHINDLER (1999), the isopod genera *Artystone* and *Riggia* are still small, only grouping six species in total among them. However, some of these descriptions are very recent, which indicates that the process of species discovery is in full process and in the future additional species will surely follow. Especially from regions rich in endemic fish species we must expect to find also different, specialized parasites.

The genus *Artystone* is being especially "productive," and therefore it must be expected that newly acquired, wild-caught catfishes might be infested with it. Coauthor SEIDEL could determine the independent infestation with *Artystone* spp. on ancistrine catfishes acquired from three different pet shops, as well as on three specimens of the dwarf suckermouth catfish *Otocinclus huaorani* from a single delivery. Especially hypoptopomatinids seem to be prone to an *Artystone* infestation. However, it usually remains undetected because the fish simply die sometime down the road. How frequent these parasites can really be, was demonstrated through an investigation by SCHAEFER (1992), who, after detecting a specimen in a type series of *Hisonotus maculipinnis,* studied in detail all 213 specimens hailing from four different localities in Paraguay: he found 79 compromised fishes. From these 79 preserved fish, he was able to isolate 113 isopods, mostly of the species *Artystone minima.* In 20 fish, SCHAEFER detected two parasites each, in seven it was even three. SCHINDLER (oral comm.), too, determined in several Bolivian biotopes a massive presence of such isopods. Host to the parasites was in this case the dwarf suckermouth catfish *Otocinclus vestitus.* THATCHER & SCHINDLER later identified the isopods as a new species, which they described in 1999 as *Artystone bolivianensis.* SCHINDLER found up to four parasites on a single *Otocinclus,* usually one female and several males. The endoparasitic creatures are connected to the outside world by a breathing hole only a few millimeters in size. It is located somewhere on the flank of the fish. In the dermal pouch, the isopods achieve a comparatively enormous size, which makes it impossible for them to ever leave their host. They die with their host, but not before leaving a numerous progeny. The hole on the side of the fish is so small that only the posterior body segment of adult isopods may protrude. Commonly, however, only the ends of the appendages appear at the opening and the site is so inconspicuous that a positive diagnosis usually requires a good second look. The trigger is usually that the host is noticed to be markedly deteriorated and one is searching for possible causes.

Cymothoidae of the first group are also encountered on occasion on suckermouth catfishes. SCHAEFER (1992) described the discovery of two *Nerocila armata* specimens on the outside of *Hisonotus maculipinnis,* close to the ventral fins. SCHAEFER indicated at the time that the first pair of hooks of the 4–5 mm isopods penetrated deeply into the skin between the bony plates, which caused a swelling of the surrounding tissue. Interestingly, both specimens on

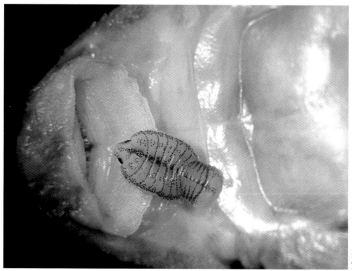

I. Seidel

Nerocila spp. are ectoparasites. Here the female is adhered to the lower lip of a *Pseudancistrus* sp. (L 17/L 67) which died during import.

which Schaefer had detected the *Nerocila*, were additionally infested with a further isopod, this time a member of the genus *Artystone*. Likewise, the pictured isopods, which had fastened themselves onto the head of a *Pseudancistrus* sp. (L 17/L 67) that died during import, are probably representatives of the genus *Nerocila*. It is likely that the parasitic infestation had weakened the fish to the point where it was unable to withstand the rigors of long distance travel. Here, too, it is probably a pair, the smaller specimen being the male.

In the standard fish disease literature (e.g., Bauer) it is repeatedly expressed that parasitic isopods cannot multiply in an aquarium. However, we have our doubts about that, given that frequently two parasites of both sexes are found on or in the same host. It is certainly not a bad idea to immediately quarantine a diseased fish as a precautionary measure. According to Bauer, the parasites are easily controlled with masoten (0.4 mg/l). However, as mentioned earlier, since loricariids do not tolerate this medication, a warning is in order. Still, a simple removal of the isopod is usually also impossible. Isopods fastened to the skin or within the oral cavity are so strongly adhered that their removal would imply a severe injury to the host. This is why the parasite has to be killed first, something achieved by squashing it with tweezers or injecting it directly with a needle (the isopods are usually large enough). Subsequently, it is much less injurious to remove the isopod. The situation turns much more difficult with those isopods that lodge themselves in a dermal pouch in the abdomen. These may reach a length of 15 mm and a width of 10 mm, and can therefore not be removed through the small breathing orifice without injuring the host. BAUER recommends in such cases to leave the parasite in the fish. Unfortunately, we have commonly observed that in the long run there comes a point when the condition of the host has deteriorated to such a degree that the need to kill the parasite becomes of paramount importance. On one occasion, the coauthor SEIDEL was able to successfully remove surgically a single isopod female—which apparently had been discovered just in time—from the abdominal cavity of an adult *Ancistrus* sp. (L 159). During the operation, the parasite, with an approximate size of 15 mm, was initially killed and then immobilized with tweezers introduced through the lateral opening. With a second, pointed pair of tweezers the body of the isopod was cut up and pulled through the opening in pieces, until the pouch was empty. The injury healed well and the cured fish developed splendidly and was still alive years later.

"Infusoria"

A frequently occurring phenomenon—especially in newly established aquaria—is an explosive reproduction of microorganisms which can form literal clouds when the filtration is turned off. One speaks of "infusoria turbidity" or "bacterial bloom" without really being aware of what microorganisms specifically are involved. Visible under the naked eye only as a tiny speck, the microscope reveals very nimble, almost circular organisms. The catfishes display clear signs of distress when they are subject to a massive bloom of these "infusoria." It is probable that the bloom interferes with their breathing. If no control measures are implemented opportunely, the consequence can even be lethal. Although extensive water exchanges will temporarily lower the density of the microorganism population, their reproductive rate is such that within a couple of days the problem reappears. Not much is known about the effectiveness of the various fish medications to control these organisms, but other effective methods of control do exist. For example, they can be filtered out using diatomaceous earth as the filtration medium. Another effective method is the use of UV radiation in the filtration circuit, which in a matter of a few hours will have reduced the population density to a harmless level.

Breeding Setup

Aquarists with a community aquarium in their living room sooner or later will be keeping a suckermouth catfish. If it is one of the common *Ancistrus* species, and if suitable caves form part of the aquarium decor, it is likely that in due time some fry will appear adhering to one of the aquarium panes. In reality it is not necessary to make a special effort to get some of the species to breed. If maintenance is appropriate, the consequence will soon be the spawning of the suckermouth catfish in the aquarium. Substrate spawners—like the popular *Sturisoma,* for example—soon surprise the caretaker with a spawn which is adhered to a glass pane, usually in the filter current. It will be guarded by the male. By introducing appropriate breeding caves, the conditions will be given for other genera to breed, too. PVC or bamboo tubes with a diameter of approximately 2 cm (there must be enough space in the tube to allow male and female to lie tightly next to each other) and a length of 15–25 cm are excellent spawning substrates for whiptail catfishes of the genera *Hemiloricaria, Rineloricaria* and related genera. Often a simple trick is enough to provide suitable conditions for successful reproduction.

However, if the breeding of more demanding species—which cannot fully feel at ease in a com-

Photo top right:
The correct type of spawning cave is often decisive for the breeding success when working with cave-spawning species. Several homemade models of slate and clay are presented.

Photo bottom right:
Breeding tank for ancistrine suckermouth catfishes. The caves are arranged in such a manner as to allow a visual control of their inside with a flashlight from outside the aquarium.

I. Seidel

I. Seidel

munity aquarium—is attempted, the aquarist may furnish a dedicated species tank in complete accordance to the need of a particular charge.

The beautiful species in the genus *Hypancistrus*, for example, require just a bit more effort to be reproduced in captivity. Breeding is contingent upon providing elevated water temperatures of at least 27°C, better higher, a very strong current, and appropriately dimensioned brood caves. By means of dedicated nutrition and frequent water exchanges, the ripening of the females is promoted. These, in turn, will then seek the males in their caves to spawn. The caves are best built by the hobbyist him- or herself. Even small clay tubes with one opening or caves built of slate plates glued together with silicone in a size in accordance to the size of the fish have proven themselves effective over time. If the cave is then placed in the current in such a manner as to allow a peek inside with a flashlight, a good control of the activities within will be greatly facilitated.

The reproduction of suckermouth catfishes is not as easily managed as is the case when breeding characins or barbs, for example. Loricariids are not "just set up to breed." The first step with difficult species is always the maintenance in a dedicated tank. Only in such a setting is it possible to arrange and provide everything in a manner as suggested by the information garnered on the species' natural habitat. Even if all the right environmental conditions are provided, the aquarist may still face a drawn-out confrontation with patience. We, too, who have been continuously dealing for several years with the reproduction of these fishes, have been unable to entice some "tough nuts" to breed. With some species it has taken up to five years until the first batch of eggs could be sighted. In conclusion, all that remains to be said is that the aquarist who is well-informed about the habits and requirements of the species to be bred will have a better chance to be successful then a hobbyist who just puts male and female together, waiting for what might well be a miracle.

This is not necessarily a new nugget of wisdom, but it is still surprising how little some aquarists bother to get to know the detailed requirements of his or her charges, only to later complain all the louder on how the "useless beasts" are reluctant to spawn.

Reproductive Biology

Considering the plethora of shapes found among suckermouth cat-fishes, it comes as no surprise that there is a great variety in re-productive strategies represented in this family as well. It can be presumed that most Loricariidae practice some type of broodcare, and in virtually all species known to care, it is the male who does so. A distinction, however, may be made between open spawn-ers, cave spawners, and mouthbrooders. It is only in relation to several members of the genera *Otocinclus, Parotocinclus,* and their allies that there is no active broodcare, but that the eggs are ad-hered to the substrate in a manner reminiscent of the Corydora-dinae (family Callichthyidae), i.e., to be subsequently ignored. As a rule, open and cave spawners are substrate spawners. The open spawners adhere their eggs onto plants, branches, or rocks, whereas cave spawners in nature use cavities or crevices in rocks and wood as a spawning cave. Most loricariids practice this kind of broodcare. The most advanced broodcare behavior can be found among sand-dwelling whiptail catfishes, where the males retain the egg mass with their mouth and carry it around every-where they go. Some species even take this a step further and burrow in the sand together with their spawn. Suckermouth catfish spawns virtually always consist of relatively few eggs, but, com-pared to other piscine families, they are very large. A greater num-ber of eggs would also be unnecessary, given that after the fry have consumed their yolk sac, they are already independent and have very good odds at survival because of their cryptic lifestyle. The success of this concept is demonstrated by the great species diversity and population densities that are encountered in South American rivers.

Broodcare of suckermouth catfishes is not limited to the cleaning and defense of the spawn (usually an egg cluster). The caring individuals do much more than what would be expected. The male specimen—after fertilization—cares for the further development of the spawn also by periodically mouthing the eggs in order to free them of settling organisms and sedimentary particles in general. This controls the colonization by bacteria, which, if left unchecked, would plug up the vital pores of the egg and bring metabolism to

I. Seidel

Pseudohemiodon spp. are mouthbrooders and often will even burrow themselves in the sand, spawn and all.

a halt. According to BREMER (1999) the broodcaring fishes additionally cover the eggs—and later also the larvae—with mucus secreted by specialized cells found in the oral cavity. This mucus is identical to the mucus found all over the body and which is said to help in the prevention of negative environmental influences and injury. It is a bactericidal and fungicidal secretion and it contains so-called phagocytes which help defend against ectoparasites. The parent animal, therefore, passes some of its immunity to its progeny with the mucus—something necessary because the eggs have not yet developed any comparable defense mechanisms.

Artificial Incubation of Eggs

The importance of parental care is demonstrated time and again by the results typically obtained when various fishes, also of other families, are artificially incubated and raised (as one of the most blatant examples let us mention that of the angelfish, *Pterophyllum scalare*). Artificially incubated fry as a rule grow much slower and less uniformly.

Unfortunately, in loricariids, too, one is repeatedly confronted with a situation where oviposition and fertilization of the spawn proceed normally, only for the male later at some point to abruptly abandon broodcare. This may be due to various factors. Often the broodcaring males are very sensitive in front of disturbances and react by abandoning the nest, but they may even devour it all. Especially the cave-spawning whiptail catfishes of the genus *Hemiloricaria* tend to cannibalize their own spawn, even without apparent external motivation. Their mouthbrooding relatives (*Loricaria* and others) may also easily abandon their spawn if under stress. Ancistrine suckermouth catfishes are more reliable parents, although broodcare is not a sure and uneventful thing with these loricariids either.

If an abandoned spawn is found in the aquarium or if the spawn was removed from the male in order to avoid it being devoured, one has the problem that now the responsibility of the eggs' welfare is dependent on the hobbyist. Those of us who have already tried to artificially incubate a suckermouth catfish spawn, which—depending on species—may take over 10–12 days, are aware of the hard work demanded of the parent fish during that time. If the spawn is left to its own fortunes, it will soon die and be covered by fungus.

What must be done? Because the caretaker will not have the luxury of providing the spawn with the immunological mucus to prime the fries' defenses, the eggs must be brooded in an environment as sterile as possible. According to BREMER (1999), the main danger does not come from fungal spores but rather from waterborne bacteria which seek to colonize the outer shell of the egg. A fungal infestation usually only appears once the metabolism in the egg has collapsed and it is dead. Consequently, preventive measures should be directed primarily towards preventing a bacterial buildup in the water and less towards the control of fungal organisms. To artificially incubate the eggs, it is best to use a small container (e.g., an acrylic tank) filled with tempered water. Obviously, the temperature and chemical characteristics of the water should

When artificially incubating eggs, optimal and virtually sterile conditions should be strived for.

approximate as much as possible the requirements demanded by the fish species in question. Aquarium water is usually unsuitable, because its bacterial load is very high in relation to fresh ("new") water. With the help of a diffuser, the water is aerated to the extent that there is a good current in the receptacle, but not so much as to whirl the eggs around excessively. This way we can avoid contaminants settling on the eggs.

There is a great variety of chemicals which may be added to the water as a prophylactic against excessive multiplication of egg-pathogenic organisms. One of the best-known is methylene blue (from the pharmacy), a blue powder which must be handled with care due to its strong pigmentary characteristics. A tiny speck is sufficient—in conjunction with moisture—to leave a spot in clothing, furniture, carpeting, etc. that is hard to remove. The dose in the incubation water should tend to moderate, as an overdose may cause malformation of the larvae. A good, and not quite as complicated, alternative is the yellow dye, acriflavine, which is also the active ingredient in several aquarium fish medications available in the pet trade. Additionally, however, there is a whole range of natural water additives which should always be preferred over the "chemical club," since no secondary effects must be feared. Bacteriostatic in this relation are especially humic acids and tannins, leached from fallen leaves, tree bark, etc. Particularly easy to collect in late fall are alder cones, which should be dried and later added individually to the water. Already the addition of a single alder cone per liter turns the water intensely brown in a very short time.

Nevertheless, even if these fundamental conditions for successful breeding are given, the caretaker still has further responsibilities. Now is the time for daily maintenance of the brood tank. With a pipette or a section of air tubing a small water stream can be directed at the eggs in such a manner as to clean off the debris that has settled on them despite the appropriate level of aeration and general presence of currents. Subsequently the spawn is carefully lifted out of the container, which is cleaned and refilled with new water and the appropriate additives. Then the eggs are reintroduced. If an egg dies, something easily and quickly detected due to its unique white coloration, quick action is also called for. Since the eggs of loricariids usually are strongly adherent, it is virtually impossible to remove a single egg without injuring the surrounding eggs. However, using a small stick-mounted needle, the egg may be punctured and then it may be either suctioned off with a pipette or washed out. Besides the egg membrane, nothing should remain behind because these are excellent substrates for pathogens. The water should be exchanged every time a dead egg is removed.

Besides the greatest of efforts, artificially rearing of the fry is not successful in all species. Especially the whiptail catfish relatives are very difficult to incubate. Under such conditions, there are several species which suffer premature hatch, others are possibly unable to hatch unassisted, and under certain circumstances the exact time for hatching help may have to be respected. This requires some practice and a very lucky hand. One thing is painfully clear, to be a father is no easy job in fishes either. However, there is also a trick to facilitate hatching of the larvae. Once it has been determined—based on the coloration of the eggs—that hatching is imminent, the spawn is removed from the water for a few minutes to slightly dry the shells, i.e., until the eggs turn slightly wrinkly. As a consequence, the egg membrane contracts slightly and the fry can rupture the shell shortly after the egg has been reintroduced into the water. If need be (e.g., if the correct maturity level has not yet been achieved) this process may be repeated after some time. Even with the hatching of the larvae, which initially have a relatively large yolk sac, the critical phase is not quite over. The larvae still are—immunologically speaking—very weak and should therefore be protected with the addition of bacteriostatic or bacteriocidal compounds in low concentrations. Naturally, the hatched fry must be managed with the same care as the eggs. Dead larvae must be removed immediately and a periodic cleaning of the receptacle remains important. Only once the yolk sac has been assimilated and the fully developed juvenile accepts the first independent food, comes an opportunity when the caretaker can momentarily relax.

The various breeders all have little personal tricks to induce an artificial hatch. Often the spawn is hung into the aquarium in a sieve, whereby the current is to protect the eggs from sedimentation. However, the addition of a bactericide is contraindicated due to the piscine "house population" present. This method may only work if the water is not overly loaded with microorganisms (on the other hand, it might be very advantageous to exchange the water just before introducing the sieve). Success, however, is especially uncertain with this approach. Still, if this is the chosen path, the stocking of some trumpet snails may be very advantageous (do not introduce any other, possibly egg-eating snails). These can very effectively graze the aufwuchs off the spawn. The use of a UV sterilizer is also positive.

Recently, specially built incubators have shown to be very effective. The basic principle considered is the fact that the brood-caring male mouths the eggs to

Photo top right:
Often the spawn is simply placed in a suspended sieve in the aquarium. However, this method is moderately successful at best.

Photo bottom right:
Trumpet snails can be used successfully in the cleaning of a loricariid spawn, because these snails only feed on dead eggs.

I. Seidel

I. Seidel

clean them of foreign matter. In the incubators of the most varied homegrown types, the spawn is placed on a sponge substrate and the eggs are moved around by a constant air stream. As a consequence, the eggs brush the sponge and are "automatically" wiped clean. It is amazing how successfully this method is being used even with difficult genera such as *Pseudohemiodon* or *Loricaria*. Instructions on building such an incubator can be found in BURKARD (2000).

Rearing the Fry

Once the biggest hurdle has been conquered and the first fry have appeared, the aquarist is confronted with the next set of problems. Rearing most suckermouth catfish fry is not an easy task. In most cases it requires a lot of experience in handling juveniles in order to rear the young without incurring into too many losses. One particular characteristic is of great use. The fry of most suckermouth catfishes are quite large after the yolk sac has been absorbed in its entirety (an exception are only the fry of the subfamily Hypoptomatinae, which often are quite small) and, consequently, the mouth is quite able to handle comparatively large food items. The breeders of characins or other fishes with tiny young have the problem during the first days to provide food items that are small enough. That is not a problem the suckermouth catfish hobbyist has to solve. The main problems facing the aquarist are the sensitivity of the fry in front of a deterioration in water quality and the choice of suitable foods.

In order to facilitate the proper care, the young should be transferred post-hatching into a separate rearing container. This is usually a smaller aquarium with its own filtration. However, this is not necessarily needed. For example, small, so-called breeding boxes that are available in the trade may be installed in the regular community aquarium. It is important that the circulation holes are located on the sides and not on the bottom of such a box. Creative types prefer self-made creations of glass or acrylic with glued-in gauze, which allows for a uniform water current within the rearing container. A simple lifting and reflooding by putting the box back in place is the fastest

Ancistrus sp. larva. Only once the large yolk sac has been assimilated, do such fry begin seeking food.

H.-G. Evers

Spawning boxes for livebearers are readily suited to raise loricariids. Those with holes are better suited than those with slits.

method of water exchange. Additionally, the environment is more stable in a large aquarium than in a small one—the lethal infusoria bloom rarely appears. The transfer of the fry is best accomplished using a pipette or they are aspired using air tubing. The spawn of broodcaring *Sturisoma* or *Farlowella* may advantageously be pilfered by rubbing the eggs with a siphon hose just prior to hatching, in such a manner as to break the egg membranes, allowing for the larvae to be carried away by the water suction through the hose. Hatching is imminent in these genera when the male displays a heightened level of activity and the eggs are virtually entirely black. Once a couple of larvae have hatched, that is a sure sign that the correct moment for intervention has arrived.

The tubes of whiptail catfishes, complete with broodcaring male inside, can be comfortably lifted out of the aquarium and transferred into a separate rearing tank, where the larvae may hatch without the constant threat of being predated. For this procedure, however, it is a good idea to introduce the tube, still under water,

Self-made rearing container made of gauze. The water exchange is greatly facilitated and food organisms are still effectively contained.

into a small glass jar to preclude the male from fleeing or damaging the eggs. Similar procedure also applies to the males of the genera *Hemiodontichthys*, *Loricariichthys*, and *Pseudohemiodon*. In this case, the broodcaring males are gently induced to enter a small acrylic jar with the spawn still on their mouth. Then they are transferred into a rearing tank. With a little practice the procedure becomes very straightforward and the spawn is easily put to safety. Young suckermouth catfishes are constantly in contact with a substrate, be it an aquarium pane, the various decorations, or the bottom. On one hand these substrates are scoured for food, on the other, unfortunately, these areas are also the places where the highest bacterial concentrations are found and they are consequently in constant contact with the young. The density of germs in an aquarium, especially in a denser populated rearing tank, is enormous. In nature, even in tap water, the density of germs is lower by several orders of magnitude. If, as a breeder, one wants to keep the number of germs low, the water must be constantly

Breeding tubes of whiptail catfishes are easily transferred into a dedicated rearing tank.

exchanged. Some breeders also use UV sterilizers in the filtration circuit to reduce the pathogenic load. In bare rearing tanks it helps to brush the glass, especially the bottom pane. Frequent water exchanges also help maintain the nitrate concentration low. The brushing clean of the aquarium panes is unnecessary in the case of many ancistrine species which constantly "graze" what the aquarist perceives as a slimy layer. It is therefore a well-proven trick that when other species are reared, a few small *Ancistrus* are also added to the tank to keep the panes relatively clean.

Another very important aspect in successfully rearing suckermouth fry is the provision of appropriate food. Not all loricariids are correctly nourished if fed with vegetable fare. Quite to the contrary, some whiptail catfishes also need food in the form of nauplii of aquatic crustacea (*Artemia*, *Cyclops*, *Diaptomus*) or rotifers. These are best fed dead; the food soon settles on the bottom, where it is quickly found and consumed by the suckermouth catfishes. A catchall recommendation for the optimal menu of young loricariids

I. Seidel

Juvenile suckermouth catfishes (*Hypancistrus zebra*, in this case) are sensitive to contaminants in their rearing container. Success is conditional upon the implementation of a regular and thorough cleaning schedule.

is impossible to give. However, the caretaker himself should be aware of what food items are preferred by the parent animals, which less so, and which are flat out refused. That is a good starting point to choose the menu items that should be given to their offspring. The young of ancistrine and hypostomine species have well-developed oral discs and constantly rasp on all smooth surfaces within the aquarium. This is also the case for some loricariid fry related to the genera *Sturisoma* and *Farlowella*. The aquarist can take advantage of this circumstance and brush a food mash onto flat stones. These are air-dried and subsequently introduced in the aquarium for the catfishes to graze. This mash is easily made out of flake foods and water, but also any other appropriate foods we can think of can be fed in this manner. Suitable fare includes all types of quality flake food, various pureed vegetables (peas, spinach, cauliflower, etc.), and livefoods (*Daphnia, Cyclops*, etc.). All ingredients are placed together in a blender, then smeared

I. Seidel

Rearing containers for *Artemia salina*. Artemia are an important fry food for many species.

onto stones, placed on a heater to slightly dry, and are ready. Whatever is not going to be fed right away can be stored for later use in the freezer. Adding a binding agent, such as agar agar or gelatine (without flavor), is also a very viable possibility. In that case, the frozen food mash can be cut into cubes and fed as is. The suckermouth catfish fry will sit directly on the cubes and graze them. Tablet foods—by now readily available in several appropriate formulations—are eaten in the same manner.

For pronounced algivores there is an additional feeding option. An aquarium is situated in the sunniest place out in the open. With an appropriate holding structure, a great number of small glass panes can be suspended within the aquarium. After a short period of time, these inserts will be covered by green algae. These glass pieces, placed in the rearing tank, are covered virtually immediately by grazing young.

When rearing members of the genera *Otocinclus* and *Hypoptopoma,* the use of *Artemia* nauplii should be avoided at all costs. The same applies to such difficult juveniles as those of the genera *Sturisoma*, *Farlowella*, and *Sturisomatichthys*. The artemia, in fish culture a true blessing, obstruct the intestines of *Otocinclus* and *Hypoptopoma,* and are much to proteinaceous for herbivorous fry. Only with advancing age may *Artemia* nauplii be supplementally fed. On the other hand, *Artemia* nauplii may be readily fed to the fry of the genera *Hemiloricaria* and *Ancistrus*, to mention only two examples. But caution, dead *Artemia* very quickly foul the water! Unhatched *Artemia* cysts may also become a problem and not rarely lead to "unexplained" deaths among a batch of fry.

A common mistake made by the aquarist is that he or she assumes that the fast-growing young do not need such constant attention after one or two months. Not a few hobbyists thought to have been successful with their *Sturisoma* offspring when, all of the sudden, within a few days the 5 cm long young died "like flies." An initially inappropriate diet may have fatal consequences even after months. Furthermore, a fail-safe solution has not yet been found, especially for the genera *Sturisoma*, *Sturisomatichthys,* and *Farlowella*. Success still depends on the very particular characteristics of each case. No reading of a however detailed report will assure success, every aquarist must first acquire his or her own experiences with rearing fry before speaking of a "new solution."

287

Ancistrus spp. require a mixed animal and vegetable diet.

H.-G. Evers

Fry of whiptail catfishes must be "swimming in food."

I. Seidel

Pseudohemiodon lamina; deformed specimens, such as this one, should necessarily be killed by the breeder.

A Final Word of Advice

Last but not least, we wish to appeal to all aquarists who want to become suckermouth catfish breeders (or of any other type of fish, for that matter) to adhere to strict selection criteria. Especially very prolific species often present deformed offspring which in the aquarium environment might be able to survive—much to the contrary to what would happen in nature. There is therefore a failure of natural selection in the captive environment. In order to be able to maintain our breeding strains in a stature and condition similar to nature, selection is unavoidable. Even if it might sound heartless, this selection in an aquarium setting is mostly up to us. It is recommended to euthanase malformed specimens as soon as possible.

Habitat of two *Parotocinclus* sp.: the Issano Creek in Guyana.

I. Seidel

Subfamily Hypoptopomatinae
EIGENMANN & EIGENMANN, 1890

The subfamily Hypoptopomatinae comprises a relatively homogenous group of small suckermouth catfishes which share many characteristics. These fishes are elongated loricariids, often with an extremely dorsoventrally flattened body.

The eyes are usually far apart outward on the head—in the genera *Hypoptopoma*, *Oxyropsis* and others almost on the edge—so that specimens adhering to the front pane of the aquarium can see the hobbyist. In members of larger-growing genera this characteristic is particularly notorious, but the small *Otocinclus* and other genera, too, share this outer placement of the eyes. In nature, these fishes frequent the flooded grasses and adhere to the stalks. Their eyes allow them a very effective view of their surroundings.

The particular skeletal structure of the pectoral fins distinguishes this subfamily from all other suckermouth catfishes. Ventrally, the odontode-covered skeleton of the pectorals has no tissue other than a surrounding thin skin (see GARAVELLO et al., 1998).

All members of this subfamily have a ossified bridge ventrally which connects the base of both pectoral fins. According to newest studies (REIS & SCHAEFER, 1998), all genera—with the exception of *Pseudotocinclus*, *Otothyris*, and *Schizolecis*—share an additional characteristic: a small slit, 0.2–0.5 mm in length, just above the base of the pectoral fins. The function of this pectoral slit is unknown.

The area of distribution of the Hypoptopomatinae extends throughout the entire South American continent, with the exception of Chile and southern Argentina. The center of distribution with the largest number of genera present is in the eastern Brazilian states along the Atlantic coast. In the waters of the so-called Atlantic coastal rain forest many species can be found in sometimes astoundingly large numbers.

Brazilians call these fishes "cascudinhos," a diminutive of "cascudo," the common Brazilian denomination for larger suckermouth catfishes. This is mentioned here, because this common name of the Hypoptopomatinae has also been adopted by science (SCHAEFER, 1997, 1998). In any case, we find this name quite fitting and certainly much friendlier than constantly having to pronounce the official subfamily designation!

The most varied bodies of water are inhabited by the Hypoptopomatinae, i.e., they are not restricted to fast-flowing bodies, as one might be tempted to assume based on the shape of their body. Quite to the contrary, in most instances they inhabit the areas close to shore. There they hang—often at high densities—on plant leaves and stalks in a strong current. It is interesting to note that apparently there are several species that can breathe atmospheric oxygen (see the section on morphological characteristics of the Loricariidae). This may be observed in the aquarium when the oxygen concentration drops quickly (filtration failure). The fishes scoote upward along the plant stalks or the aquarium pane and stick their snout above the water's surface in order to pump air into the gastrointestinal tract. *Otocinclus* and similar small-growing genera either quickly swim to the surface and take air, in a manner similar to *Corydoras*, or sit as described just beneath the surface, stick their head out somewhat above the water surface and let the water circulate over their gills and mouth (see photograph on the following page).

Fam.: Loricariidae
Subfam.: Hypoptopomatinae

LÜLING (1978, p. 76) mentions this behavior for the first time in the aquaristic literature. We have also been witness to such a behavior in nature. We observed a massive presence of *Otocinclus vittatus*, in the Venezuelan Llanos. These

Hypoptopomatinae sp. LG 2 breathing atmospheric oxygen, as described in the text.

fish were adhering to reed stalks. In our efforts to capture some, we whorled up a lot of sediment. It is likely that as a consequence the level of dissolved oxygen dropped rapidly. The *Otocinclus* reacted by coming to the water surface along the stalks.

A phenomenon, which to our knowledge has not yet been reported, was observed by coauthor EVERS in the central Brazilian State of Goiás June 1999. The following is an excerpt from his travel journal [transl. from German]:

"Wednesday, June 30th 1999:

After a cloudy morning, the clouds break around noon and the ambience becomes oppressingly hot. We reach the Rio Isabel Paz, a white-water river with a slow current. Now, during the dry season, its water level is very low and the temperature, with 30°C, quite hot. The sun is warming the water further and my travel companions point out to me the presence of dark, cloudlike formations in the middle of the river, close to the surface. "Cardume, Hans, olhe!" It is a school (Port.: = cardume) of *Otocinclus* sp. which swim in dense formation through the water and

every once in a while break the water surface, which I can discern by the tiny circular waves. 'This is a typical behavior during the dry season, when oxygen concentrations are low,' explains my friend Paulo. 'When we capture such a school, we sometimes manage to capture over 10,000 specimens in our net!' Like a dark shadow, the school slowly advances through the water and I am deeply impressed."

SCHAEFER (1997) discovered that *Otocinclus* have a richly vascularized blind branch of the esophagus, the esophageal diverticulum, where in all likelihood the gas exchange with the swallowed atmospheric oxygen occurs.

While investigating various clear-water and white-water rivers in southeastern Brazil, within a few minutes and along a short distance, many hundred individuals could be collected from among the shore vegetation with a dip net. It was interesting to note that usually members of two, and sometimes three, genera and species were found sympatric.

Stomach contents analyses (DITTMAR & EVERS, 2000) revealed that although these fishes were captured on the same plant, they were feeding on a different diet, although it was always consisting of mostly vegetable components and small organisms of animal origin, i.e., the so-called aufwuchs being grazed by all.

At present, the subfamily Hypoptopomatinae is considered to be comprised of approximately 70 species distributed in 18 genera (three additional, as yet undescribed taxons from southeastern and central Brazil are mentioned by SCHÄFER [1998]). According to SCHAEFER (1998) and REIS & SCHAEFER (1998), 16 genera are considered valid, and they are subdivided into two tribes: A new tribe was added with the description of the new genus *Lampiella* by ISBRÜCKER, 2001. The contested description of the genus *Macrotocinclus* ISBRÜCKER & SEIDEL, 2001 raised the number of genera to 18.

Rio Isabel Paz in central Brazil's Goias state. H.-G. Evers

H.-G. Evers

The presence of several thousand *Otocinclus hasemani* is revealed by a dark shadow.

Fam.: Loricariidae
Subfam.: Hypoptopomatinae

Tribe Hypoptopomatini SCHAEFER, 1991
Hypoptopoma GÜNTHER, 1868
Otocinclus COPE, 1872
Oxyropsis EIGENMANN & EIGENMANN, 1889
Acestridium HASEMAN, 1911
Nannoptopoma SCHAEFER, 1996
Niobichthys SCHAEFER & PROVENZANO, 1998
"*Macrotocinclus*" ISBRÜCKER & SEIDEL, 2001

Tribe Otothyrini   SCHAEFER, 1991
Microlepidogaster EIGENMANN &
                                EIGENMANN, 1889
Hisonotus EIGENMANN & EIGENMANN, 1889
Parotocinclus   EIGENMANN &
                                EIGENMANN, 1889
Pseudotocinclus NICHOLS, 1919
Otothyris MYERS, 1927
Pseudotothyris BRITSKI & GARAVELLO, 1984
Schizolecis BRITSKI & GARAVELLO, 1984
Eurycheilichthys   REIS & SCHAEFER, 1992
Corumbataia BRITSKI, 1997
Epactionotus REIS & SCHAEFER, 1998

New Tribe Lampiellini ISBRÜCKER, 2001
Lampiella ISBRÜCKER, 2001

In recent years, several new and—aquaristically speaking—interesting species of this subfamily have been imported. In several cases, detailed maintenance and, in some cases, also breeding reports have already been published. The following pages describe in greater detail some of the mentioned genera. Unfortunately, only a counted few have appeared in the hobby.
The genus *Oxyropsis* is very similar to *Hypoptopoma*. However, its members are much more dorsoventrally compressed than *Hypoptopoma*, particularly the posterior section of the body is flattened. We (BOHNET, EVERS, SCHLÜTER & SEIDEL) were only able to capture a single specimen in the Igarapé Piraruaia, a tributary of the Brazilian Rio Tefé. The individual survived the transport to Germany unharmed and is not any more demanding in its maintenance requirements than its close relatives of the genus *Hypoptopoma*. Nevertheless, captive breeding of imported

Oxyropsis cf. *wrightiana* has been successful (see general description of the genus).
According to recent investigations (SCHAEFER, 1998), both *Microlepidogaster* and *Hisonotus* are considered valid. SCHAEFER studied once again various osteological characteristics of these fishes and discovered that these genera belonged into another tribe than the one suggested by himself (SCHAEFER, 1991). This illustrates just how difficult it is even for a scientist to classify correctly some of the Hypoptopomatinae even to genus level. The average aquarist—if he or she is interested at all—will simply despair on such efforts. The genus *Eurycheilichthys* was described from the south Brazilian State of Rio Grande do Sul. Initially, there was some confusion as to the correct genus designation, since the original choice, *Eurycheilus,* had already been assigned to a fossil (REIS & SCHAEFER, 1993). Consequently, the name was changed to *Eurycheilichthys.*
Nannoptopoma, a close ally of the genus *Hypoptopoma,* has just been recently described (SCHÄFER, 1996a) .
SCHAEFER (1991) already mentioned a new genus from southern Venezuela (Neblina region) which was recently described by SCHAEFER & PROVENZANO (1998) as *Niobichthys*. The Brazilian ichthyologist Haraldo A. BRITSKI described the genus *Corumbataia* in 1997. The most recently described genus is *Epactionotus* REIS & SCHAEFER, 1998.
In addition to these cascudinhos which have been classified into one of the existing genera, in recent years, every once in a while, there appeared specimens which could not be classified down to the genus level. We have decided to present these fishes with the designation Hypoptopomatinae sp. at the end of the listing of genera and species. Several of these genera are presently being revised, so that there is a high probability that these species will soon be classified more precisely.

Tribe Hypoptopomatini

Genus *Acestridium* HASEMAN, 1911

Acestridium colombiensis RETZER, 2005	Colombia, Río Inirida
Acestridium dichromum RETZER, NICO & PROVENZANO, 1999	Southern Venezuela
Acestridium discus HASEMAN, 1911	Brazil, Rio Negro
Acestridium martini RETZER, NICO & PROVENZANO, 1999	Southern Venezuela

At the beginning, this genus was placed within the subfamily Loricariinae (tribe Acestridiini). ISBRÜCKER & NIJSSEN (1974a) initially placed the genus into its own subfamily, Acestridiinae, without further explanation. Subsequently, however, NIJSSEN & ISBRÜCKER (1987) placed the genus *Acestridium* into the subfamily Hypoptopomatinae, based on the fused bony bridge connecting the bases of the pectoral fins. It is arguable if this characteristic alone justifies this classification, but the genus *Acestridium* is currently considered a member of the Hypoptopomatinae (SCHAEFER, 1991, 1997; RETZER, NICO & PROVENZANO, 1999).

For a long time this was a monotypic genus, represented by the lone species *Acestridium discus* HASEMAN, 1911. Only recently have RETZER et al. (1999, 2005) described three additional species. However, it is to be expected that additional species will soon follow (ISBRÜCKER, pers. comm.). Finds of various specimens at often very distant locals from each other have made it clear that there are very pronounced differences in the length of the rostrum, the development of the rostral disc, body coloration, etc.

This genus is characterized by a long rostrum, terminating in a species-specific disc, and a graceful, elongated body. Furthermore—under close observation—small bumps become apparent on the bony plates. At first sight, full-grown specimens are similar to juvenile *Farlowella*.

HASEMAN described 1911 the type locality of *Acestridium discus* as a "grassy, cool, shady, swampy creek..."), which at the time (November 30th, 1909) was called Igarapé de Cachoeira Grande and was located in the vicinity of Manaus. Has this creek survived the extreme expansion of the metropolis of Manaus? This question seems to have been bothering R.L. HASSUR (1970), who reported on the rediscovery of *Acestridium discus*. According to his publication, additional specimens were found approximately two hours by boat up the Rio Negro to a small tributary of the Igarapé Castanha. HASSUR studied these specimens in addition to others—captured by Carl TERNETZ in 1924 also in the general vicinity of Manaus—and found rows of 3–4 small hooklets on the rounded tip of the snout. He broadened the genus definition of *Acestridium* and included the rounded caudal fin bereft of any filamentous elongations, the relatively rounded dorsal, anal and ventral fins, and the arrangement of the ventral bony plates as further genus-defining characteristics. SCHAEFER (1997) indicated the Rio Pamoni in Venezuela as the habitat of *Acestridium discus*, which expanded the known area of distribution. Our own collecting efforts have meanwhile confirmed the presence of the species in the entire central and lower Rio Negro. EVERS was able to confirm repeatedly the presence of the species around Manaus (Praia Grande) and in the Anavilhanas.

Fam.: Loricariidae
Subfam.: Hypoptopomatinae

In recent years it has been repeatedly possible to capture *Acestridium* spp. in nature. Consequently, there is extensive ecological information available in regard to their habitat, some of which we will address further below. Perhaps there are tropical travelers who will look closer at what they have captured and will not throw the "insignificant *Farlowella*" carelessly back into the water.

H.-G. Evers and Michael Schlüter (Hamburg) captured an *Ancestridium* sp. in November 1997 at the upper Rio Negro, close to the city of São Gabriel da Cachoeira. A few specimens could be netted from the overhanging branches in the waters of a black-water carrying igarapé, close to its confluence into the Rio Negro. The water of the igarapé was dark tea-colored, very acidic (pH significantly below 5), and had a conductivity of less than 10 µS/cm. The water temperature was 26°C.
Colorwise, this species has little to offer. The plain beige-brown flanks are crossed by a darker longitudinal band. It is likely that this species is *Acestridium martini*, described recently (1999) by Retzer, Nico & Provenzano. Apparently, that species not only inhabits the upper Orinoco and the Casiquiare, but also parts of the upper Rio Negro basin. Retzer, Nico & Provenzano (1999) confirm the water values mentioned above for the biotopes of *Acestridium martini* and *Acestridium dichromum*.
The Hamburg aquarist Bernd Schmitt (pers. comm.) captured another *Acestridium* sp. in a fast-flowing clear-water river in southern Venezuela. The fish became entangled in the fine mesh of the dip nets used to comb the shore vegetation and had to be freed with care. Unfortunately, the captured specimens proved very sensitive and could only be maintained alive for a few weeks in the aquarium. Full-grown specimens were only 5 cm long and Schmitt was initially re-

minded of juvenile *Farlowella*. Under closer observation, however, a reddish longitudinal band and the hemidisc on the tip of the rostrum—typical for *Acestridium*—became apparent.
A particularly attractive species was captured by Kai Arendt January 1997 in the Caño El Toro, a clear-water creek in the Venezuelan Llanos. Newly-captured specimens of *Acestridium dichromum* are quince-green and just as small and delicate as the other congeners. The Caño El Toro is a typical clear-water river with a low conductivity and undetectable hardness. The pH of such waters is around 5 and the water temperature is usually quite high at approximately 30°C. According to Retzer, Nico & Provenzano (1999), it is known of *Acestridium dichromum* to change its color in adaptation to its substrate. In nature, the species colonizes overhanging shore vegetation, whereas the syntopic *A. martini* is found among roots, on small branches, and on leaves. *A. martini* does not change color according to substrate and remains brown, whereas as *A. dichromum*—placed on a brown leaf—will change within one or two days from light green to brown. A unique capacity in the world of suckermouth catfishes!

The momentary last encounters that H.-G. Evers had with *Acestridium* were in March 1998 and June 1999 in the Rio das Mortes basin of central Brazil. He also collected a few specimens of a similarly plain brown species from among the roots of trees reaching into the strong currents of the Rio Cristalino. There, these fish live together with juvenile *Farlowella henriquei* and *Hemiloricaria lanceolata*. The pH was 5, the water temperature 29°C both years, and the conductivity of the crystal-clear water was 8 µS/cm.

These relatively common finds, all made by knowledgeable people in the area of suckermouth catfishes, indicate that this

Close-up of the rostrum of *Acestridium* sp. from Venezuela.   H.-G. Evers

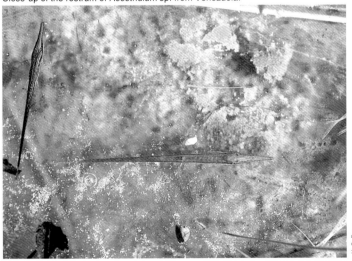

H.-G. Evers

Birds-eye view of a just captured *Acestridium* sp. "Rio Cristalino." Top left a syntopic juvenile *Farlowella henriquei* for comparison.

297

genus has a relatively broad area of distribution and it should be "normal" to find it in suitable biotopes. It is likely that these fishes have been regularly overlooked by other captors, or indeed were thought to be juvenile *Farlowella*.

For enthusiasts of offbeat suckermouth catfishes, this species is surely a treat. However, its suitability for aquarium maintenance is questionable at best, being that capture and transport alone may already cause irreparable damage. The few specimens successfully imported to Germany have only survived a short period of time in the aquarium. To improve the chances of a successful transport and long-term survival, a dedicated capture and import trial is needed. Sensible maintenance and feeding (vegetable fare, *Artemia* nauplii, tablet foods) on site and an adjustment of the aquarium's water to the natural water values are surely necessary. Many questions remain unanswered in regard to this genus, such as its reproductive biology. How many eggs and of what size might be laid by

a loricariid so small? Does their breeding biology follow *Farlowella* or is it more in line with *Hypoptopoma*? Initial answers to these questions might be given based on the observations of M. SCHLÜTER, Hamburg, (pers. comm.). SCHLÜTER kept in an aquarium with strong current several *Acestridium discus* captured at the central Rio Negro. After about 6 months, some females matured. He found 3 eggs (elliptical, diameter ca. 1 mm and a length of 3 mm) lying on the bottom of the maintenance aquarium, probably unfertilized. Water values were: pH 5.5, conductivity 50 µS/cm and temperature 26°C. The diet of these fish consisted of *Artemia* nauplii, frozen *Cyclops* and water fleas, tablet foods, and many algae rasped from the rocks and aquarium panes.

Acestridium sp. "Rio Cristalino"

H.-G. Evers

Acestridium sp. "Rio Cristalino," ventral view.

H.-G. Evers

Acestridium dichromum
RETZER, NICO & PROVENZANO, 1999

F.: Retzer, M. E., L. G. Nico & F. Provenzano R. (1999): Two new species of *Acestridium* (Siluriformes: Loricariidae) from Southern Venezuela, with observations on camouflage and color change. – Ichthyol. Explor. Freshwaters, 10 (4): 313–326.

Syn.: None.

Hab.: Venezuela: upper Rio Orinoco and tributaries of the Rio Casiquiare. Northern Brazil: upper Rio Negro basin. Apparently also in the Llanos, Caño El Toro (Apure basin).

M. & B.: Sensitive and difficult to maintain. Provide a species tank with strong current and supplement algae by introducing covered rocks and leaving the algae on the aquarium glass. Reproductive biology is unknown.

S: Three unpaired central bony plates are located anterior to the base of the dorsal fin. *A. dichromum* has a much broader body than the other two congeners described. The light green coloration is maintained in the aquarium as long as there are long-leaved aquatic plants (*Vallisneria* sp.) present. Otherwise, the fish will change its color (see genus introduction).

T: 24°–28°C, L: 7 cm, A: 60 cm, R: b

Acestridium dichromum, dorsal view.

H.-G. Evers

300

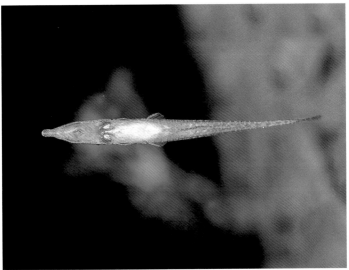

Acestridium dichromum, ventral view.

H.-G. Evers

Acestridium dichromum from Caño El Toro, Venezuela.

H.-G. Evers

Acestridium discus HASEMAN, 1911

F.: Haseman, J.D. (1911): Descriptions of some new species of fishes and miscellaneous notes on others obtained during the expedition of the Carnegie Museum to Central South America.– Ann. Carnegie Mus., 7(3–4): 315–328.

Syn.: None.

Hab.: Brazil: Rio Negro from Manaus to the upper course. Venezuela: Río Pamoni.

C. & R.: Difficult charge. The delicate fish graze on algae and aufwuchs and readily accept *Artemia* nauplii as substitute fare. Still, after a few months, the specimens become progressively thinner, apparently due to a deficient diet. This species must be handled with great care, even as adults, in a manner similar to that of juveniles of species difficult to reproduce,

such as *Sturisoma*. It is possible that with time there will be a chance at breeding this species successfully.

S: *A. discus* is the type species of the genus. It only has two unpaired, median bone plates anterior to the base of the dorsal fin. The pictured specimen was captured at the lower Rio Negro in the Arquipelago dos Anavilhanas. The site is located within the accepted area of distribution of the species. An additional specimen was part of an import shipment coming directly from Manaus. The characteristics of *A. discus* apply, especially the disclike ending of the rostrum. In the other species presented, the disc is by far not as pronounced.
Care of *A.* sp. "Río Cristalino" (only photo, no text) follows that of *A. discus*.

T: 26°-30°C, L: 6 cm, A: 60 cm, R: b

Acestridium discus from the Arquipelago Anavilhanas.

H.-G. Evers

Acestridium discus, ventral view.

H.-G. Evers

Portrait of *Acestridium discus*.

H.-G. Evers

Fam.: Loricariidae
Subfam.: Hypoptopomatinae

Acestridium martini
Retzer, Nico & Provenzano, 1999

F.: Retzer, M. E., L. G. Nico & F. Provenzano R. (1999): Two new species of *Acestridium* (Siluriformes: Loricariidae) from Southern Venezuela, with observations on camouflage and color change.– Ichthyol. Explor. Freshwaters, 10 (4): 313–326.

Syn.: None.

Hab.: Venezuela: upper Rio Orinoco and tributaries of the Rio Casiquiare, northern Brazil, upper Rio Negro drainage. We were able to find this species in the Igarapés of the upper Rio Negro at São Gabriel da Cachoeria (see genus introduction). Type locality is the Caño Pozo Azul at Puerto Ayacucho, where its presence could be confirmed by Seidel in April 2001.

M. & B.: Similar to its congeners.

S: Three unpaired median bony plates can be seen anterior to the dorsal fin. A very delicate, plain brown species. Locally it is found syntopically with *Acestridium dichromum* (see Retzer, Nico & Provenzano, 1999).

T: 24°–28°C, L: 7 cm, A: 60 cm, R: b

Photo below:
Biotope of *Acestridium martini*: the Igarapé São Miguel, close to its confluence with the Rio Negro at São Gabriel da Cachoeira. The fish adhere to branches hanging into the water.

H.-G. Evers

A. martini, vicinity of São Gabriel da Cachoeira, upper Rio Negro.

H.-G. Evers

Acestridium martini, ventral view.

H.-G. Evers

Genus *Hypoptopoma* Günther, 1868

It is amazing that precisely the oldest genus—and type genus of this subfamily at that—is still awaiting its scientific review. Boeseman described in 1974 a new species from Suriname (*H. guianense*) and listed a total of 12 valid species for this genus. Unfortunately, Boeseman did not perform the necessary analyses of the types, which makes the list appear questionable. It is therefore presently virtually impossible for the aquarist to correctly identify a fish if the exact origin of the specimen is ignored. It is hoped that a future revision of the genus will bring clarity to the situation. Just how complex the present situation is, becomes clear in a publication by Schaefer (1996b), who with great difficulty uncovered the old types (in this case, *Hypoptopoma steindachneri* Boulenger, 1895) among old museum material and "rediscovered" the holotype. *Hypoptopoma* spp. are characterized by eyes located far apart on the head and especially by their heavy body armor. The species are also armored ventrally—in many cases the pattern of these bony plates is species-specific. The aquarist quickly notices just how strong this armor is as he or she tries to capture the nimble fishes from the aquarium. The animals hit the aquarium panes with readily audible cracking sounds as they flee in haste. However, *Hypoptopoma* are normally particularly calm charges. They may stay for hours apparently motionless in a given place. This "unbridled activity" and their usually gray, monotone coloration often turn the initial enthusiasm of the hobbyist for these fishes into bored indifference. Nevertheless, these species have an extremely interesting reproductive biology. The males guard the spawn and larvae, the latter until the yolk sac has been absorbed and the fry become independent. The first witness to this interesting behavior was the Hamburg aquarist Michael

Schlüter (see Evers, 1992c). As far as presently studied, the other genera in the subfamily have a significantly more primitive reproductive behavior and care neither for spawn nor fry.

Hypoptopoma colonize similar biotopes as the smaller *Otocinclus* spp. We have captured them in the most varied South American countries. It is noteworthy that most of these biotopes were white-water systems. The fish adhere in the current either to wood or inundated terrestrial shore vegetation or can be found in lentic (static) environments adhering close to shore to plant stalks and similar substrates. The very laterally located eyes allow the fish a complete line of sight when it is adhering to a thin stalk. Those hobbyists who use, for example, thin bamboo in their aquarium as decoration, will have noticed that *Hypoptopoma* preferably stay on such a substrate. If the caretaker approaches with a dip net, the fish "slides" around the stalk, well aware of the approach. It has also been observed that the fish prefer to spawn on such sites or on the long leaf stalk of lotus leaves that reach to the surface in order to take advantage of the overview such a site provides. Rearing the tiny fry is not easy. The most success has been achieved with tiny vegetable fare. *Artemia* nauplii are contraindicated, since this protein-rich food is detrimental to the young. The *Artemia* may quickly plug up the intestine of the young.

With the exception of one unequivocal identification, we have waved identification to the species level in the following species descriptions and numbered them consecutively instead. Five species include ventral views to indicate that these fishes can also be readily distinguished based on their ventral coloration. Additionally, we do not list the species in this

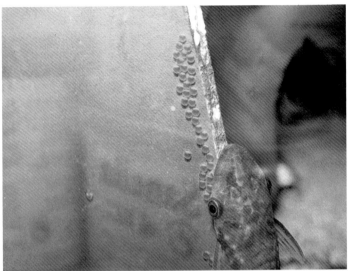

Hypoptopoma sp. "Yarina Cocha" ♂ "brooding" the spawn. H. Wendenburg

Newly hatched fry are still being guarded. H. Wendenburg

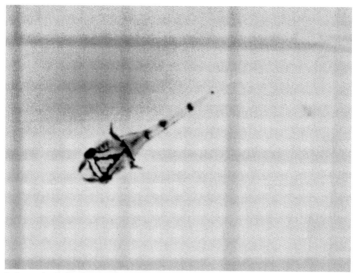

Independently feeding fry. Broodcare by the father is now over.

H. Wendenburg

genus and their habitat, as we do for
other genera. We simply do not have
enough information about these facts.
Until the genus is revised, we should accept this way of dealing with the subject,
since it is difficult to "unlearn" erroneous
names given in haste at this stage.
A star example for such misidentified
fishes is, among others, *Ancistrus dolichopterus* or *Otocinclus* "*negros*" (here
identified as Hypoptopomatinae sp. LG 2
from Paraguay).

Hypoptopoma gulare

Hypoptopoma gulare Cope, 1878
Flatnose dwarf suckermouth catfish

F.: Cope, E.D. (1878): Synopsis of the fishes of the Peruvian Amazon, obtained by Professor Orton during his expeditions of 1873 and 1877. Proc. Amer. phil. Soc., 17(101): 673–701.

Syn.: *Hypoptopoma joberti, Aristommata inexpectata, Hypoptopoma inexpectata.*

Hab.: Peru, Colombia: Río Meta Basin; Venezuela: Río Apure Basin. Schäfer (in Lundberg et al., 1996, Internet communication) mentions this area for Venezuela. Evers and Seidel were able to confirm the widespread presence of this species in 1992 in white-water carrying rivers of the Venezuelan Llanos. All these waters are part of the Apure Basin. Notable were the high temperatures (usually over 30°C at the end of the rainy season) of these lotic

environments. The *Hypoptopoma* adhere to plant stalks and overhanging shore vegetation, often in respectable currents. The species is so common, in virtually every pass with the dip net along the shore there were several specimens being captured.

M. & B.: It cannot be ascertained with certainty which of the *Hypoptopoma* spp. present in the hobby have been bred, since accurate identification is presently next to impossible (see genus introduction). Males claim small spawning territories, usually exposed to a moderately strong current. Thick stalks of aquatic plants (e.g., *Nymphea*) or bamboo stalks are readily accepted as spawning substrates. Ripe females seek the male territory to spawn. External sexual differ-

Fam.: Loricariidae
Subfam.: Hypoptopomatinae

H.-G. Evers

The Sabanas de Rascamula, the habitat of *H. gulare* in the Venezuelan Llanos.

ences cannot be determined, since even a distended body cannot be discerned due to the strong body armor. Initially, rearing is successful with tiny fry foods (pureed microworms, pulverized dry foods). *Artemia* nauplii should not be offered due to poor digestibility in this case. Additionally, *Artemia* cysts may obstruct the intestinal passage, leading to a quick death of the fry. Growth of the fry is slow, and it may take up to a year until the offspring have reached a length of 3–5 cm and can then be offered to fellow hobbyists. Breeding these fish is a challenging endeavour for the serious catfish hobbyist.

S: This is the type species for the subgenus *Diapeltoplites* FOWLER, 1915. The status of this subgenus is presently in question, ISBRÜCKER (1980) lists it as synonymous to *Hypoptopoma*.

T: 24°–30°C, L: 9 cm, A: 80 cm, R: b

Hypoptopoma inexpectata from northern Argentina.

H.-G. Evers

Hypoptopoma inexpectata (HOLMBERG, 1893)

F.: Holmberg, E.L. (1893): El nuevo género Aristommata, Holmb. Rev. Jardin Zool. Buenos Ayres, 1(3): 96.

Syn.: *Aristommata inexpectata.*

Hab.: Northern Argentina, provinces of Formosa and Corrientes, Drainage of the Río Paraguay, Paraguay.

M.&B.: Maintenance requirements do not differ from its congeners. However, it has to be maintained cooler at times, commensurate to its natural habitat, where during the winter water temperatures frequently fall below 20°C.

S: The initiative of S. KÖRBER (Mülheim a.d.R.) made it possible to picture the species in this book. Although the systematics of this genus are insufficiently revised, we base ourselves on AQUINO (1997), who considers *Hypoptopoma inexpectata* as a valid species, listing it as one of four hypoptopomatine species in Argentina. It is interesting to note that *H. inexpectata* lacks an adipose fin—in contrast to most of its congeners.

T: 18°–26°C, **L:** 10 cm, **A:** 80 cm, **R:** b

Hypoptopoma sp. I

With a full-grown length of approximately 10 cm, this species is quite large. In recent years it has been regularly imported from Peru. It was this species which was bred by SCHLÜTER (see genus introduction; EVERS, 1992c). The fish is relatively deep–bodied and mostly uniform gray. Only the fins show black pigmentation.

Hypoptopoma sp. I   H.-G. Evers

Hypoptopoma sp. I, ventral view.

Hypoptopoma sp. II

This species, with its conspicuous design and red eyes, is occasionally found among Brazilian imports. The red ocular ring and the marble coloration of this relatively small species are not unattractive. Unfortunately, its exact origin is unknown. Maintenance of the few specimens imported heretofore has proven complicated. It seems, this is one of the smaller members. There are no breeding reports.

Hypoptopoma sp. II   H.-G. Evers

Hypoptopoma sp. II, ventral view.

312

Hypoptopoma sp. III

Based solely on the vague description of origin as "Brazil," this species cannot be identified. The spotted ventral design is very attractive.

Hypoptopoma sp. III   H.-G. Evers

Hypoptopoma sp. III, ventral view.

Hypoptopoma sp. IV

This is another species with an attractive design. Unfortunately, it was impossible to ascertain its origin, even in general terms. The requirements of this attractive catfish in regard to maintenance mirror those of its congeners.

Hypoptopoma sp. IV   I. Seidel

Hypoptopoma sp. IV, ventral view.   I. Seidel

313

Hypoptopoma sp. V "Yarina Cocha"

The pictured specimen was captured by SEIDEL in Yarina Cocha, Ucayali drainage, Peru. The relatively long and slender caudal peduncle is the most conspicuous characteristic of this species, and even though its origins are known with precision, no species identification is possible. Several species have been described from Peru, but their status is unknown based on a lack of a review of the genus.

The species has been bred repeatedly by Helmut WENDENBURG (Fulda, Germany). Rearing the fry proved problematic. Algae fare is the optimal rearing food, but a combination of powdered flake food, frozen rotifers, and even a few, carefully dosed *Artemia* nauplii allowed for rearing success. Still, the young grow very slow.

Hypoptopoma sp. V "Yarina Cocha"   I. Seidel

Hypoptopoma sp. V, ventral view.   I. Seidel

Hypoptopoma sp. VI "Ucayali"

This robust species from the Ucayali drainage (Peru) is another one brought by SEIDEL to Germany. This species is characterized by a pronounced longitudinal band. After the genus has been revised, such characteristics should help in a reasonably accurate identification of the species. Unfortunately, this has not happened yet.

Hypoptopoma sp. VI "Ucayali"   I. Seidel

Hypoptopoma sp. VII "Río Paraguay"

Wolfgang Staeck (Berlin) captured this somewhat elongated species in the Bolivian drainage of the Río Paraguay, close to the city of Puerto Quicharo (across from Corumba). There is an obvious similarity to *Hypoptopoma* sp. V "Yarina Cocha." However, based on their divergent origins we list them separately as two species (?).

Hypoptopoma sp. VII "Río Paraguay"

W. Staeck

Hypoptopoma sp. VIII "Rio Tapajós"

The aquarist Christoph Seidel (Bonn, Germany) captured this fish in the Brazilian Rio Tapajós. This stout species has a notorious black coloration on the upper and lower caudal fin lobes.

Hypoptopoma sp. VIII "Rio Tapajós"

C. Seidel

Hypoptopoma sp. IX "Rio Araguaia"

This species calls the white-water tributaries of the central Rio Araguaia (central Brazil) its home. It appears to be full-grown at 8 cm total length. H.-G. Evers encountered this fish quite numerously in remnant lagoons of the Rio Vermelho during the extreme dry season. Fishing in the floating meadows along the shore, virtually every pass with the dip net will yield one or several specimens. The species is not demanding in regard to aquarium care.

Hypoptopoma sp. IX "Rio Araguaia"

H.-G. Evers

Hypoptopoma sp. X "Rio Xingu"

I. Seidel

Hypoptopoma sp. X "Rio Xingu"

The pictured specimen was imported by the company AQUATARIUM (Garbsen) from the central Xingu at Altamira. There were no *Hypoptopoma* species known from this central Brazilian river. The design of the species is unusual, the black bands on the dorsal and anal fin in particular. Similar to *H. inexpectata,* there is no adi-pose fin, although most congeners do have one. Maintain the species along the guidelines given for its congeners. Breeding has not been successful.

T: 25°–29°C, **L:** 10 cm, **A:** 80 cm, **R:** b

"*Macrotocinclus*" sp. "São Paulo" is an independent species, and not synonymous with *O. affinis*.

Genus "*Macrotocinclus*" ISBRÜCKER & SEIDEL, 2001

"*M.*" *flexilis* (Cope, 1894)	Argentina, Brazil, Paraguay, Uruguay
"*M.*" sp. "São Paulo" (= *O. affinis* sensu SCHAEFER, 1997)	São Paulo, Brazil

Two species within the genus *Otocinclus* had already been marked aside from its congeners by SCHAEFER (1997) under the designation of "*Otocinclus affinis* complex." ISBRÜCKER & SEIDEL (in ISBRÜCKER et al., 2001) completed the classification by placing both species—*Otocinclus affinis* and *Otocinclus flexilis*—into a genus of their own. "*Macrotocinclus*" *affinis* was designated type species by the authors. Both species differ from their previous congeners of the genus *Otocinclus* by the "series of pairwise-arranged central scutes of the body." The edge of the pupil has a triangular or raglike indentation (diverticulum of the iris).

Both species of the genus "*Macrotocinclus*" are 50 mm long on average, i.e., much larger than the average of their former congeners (36 mm SL).

The description of the genus is particularly short in comparison to modern common practice, which has already produced criticism. Additionally, it has to be noted that SCHAEFER (1997) already suffered of a confusion of *Otocinclus affinis*, from the state of Rio de Janeiro, with that species from São Paulo, which was presented in the 1st ed. [German] as *Otocinclus* sp. "São Paulo" (p. 326). The characteristics of this species are highly divergent of other *Otocinclus* spp. and does present the qualities listed for "*Macrotocinclus*." On the other hand, the true *Otocinclus affinis* (pp. 334 and 335) is a typical small *Otocinclus* and in no way a candidate for classification into "*Macrotocinclus*!" This is highly unfortunate, since precisely *Otocinclus affinis* was designated the type species of the new genus "*Macrotocinclus*." Hopefully there will soon be a defining argument from a scientific point of view. EVERS tried repeatedly in the years 2000 and 2001 to rediscover *Otocinclus affinis* in the state of Rio de Janeiro, but has been unsuccessful. The rivers in the area are highly polluted and it is difficult to find undisturbed biotopes.

Normal morph of "*Macrotocinclus*" *flexilis* from Rio Grande do Sul (Brazil).   H.-G. Evers

"*Macrotocinclus*" *flexilis* (COPE, 1894)

F.: Cope, E.D. (1894): On the fishes obtained by the Naturalist Expedition in Rio Grande do Sul. Proc.Amer.phil.Soc., 33: 84–108.

Syn.: *Otocinclus flexilis, Otocinclus arnoldi, Otocinclus fimbriatus.*

Hab.: Argentina: Paraguay Basin, Buenos Aires; Brazil: States of Rio Grande do Sul and Santa Catarina; Paraguay: Depto. Caaguazu, Parana Basin; Uruguay: Depto. Cerro Largo, Uruguay Basin, Río Negro.

Inhabitant of clear-waters, but may be found occasionally in black-waters. This otocinclus lives syntopically with *Corydoras paleatus*, a similarly colored species. It could not be ascertained if there is a cleaner relationship between the two.

M. & B.: "*M.*" *flexilis* requires cool maintenance temperatures. Its area of distribution is even subject to occasional nocturnal frost, and water temperatures below 10°C are not rare. Although the species is readily maintained in an aquarium, its life expectancy is shortened by constant high temperatures. There are no breeding reports; however, for this purpose, simulation of summer/winter in maintenance expressed through changes in temperature and currents should be provided.

S: A morph (?) from Uruguay was imported in significant quantities to Germany in 1999 for the first time. This species is significantly darker in its overall coloration than "*Macrotocinclus*" *flexilis* from further north, but their maintenance requirements are the same.

T: 15°–24°C (periodic changes), L: 8 cm, A: 80 cm, R: b

318

Dark morph of "*Macrotocinclus*" *flexilis* from Uruguay.

H.-G. Evers

A beautifully planted aquarium. In such aquaria, the Amazonian *Otocinclus* spp. control the algae population on decoration and the aquarium panes.

H.-G. Evers

Fam.: Loricariidae
Subfam.: Hypoptopomatinae

"*Macrotocinclus*" sp. "São Paulo"

Hab.: Brazil, State of São Paulo. The presence of the species in both clear- and white-water has been confirmed by EVERS, LACERDA, and BEYER.

In the clear-waters of the Rio das Pedras the following environmental values were determined as of April 14th, 1995 (7:00 a.m.): air temperature 25°C, water temperature 23°C, pH 7.15, conductivity 140 µS/cm.
The current was swift over a bed of gravel and rubble ("cachoeiras"). This "*Macrotocinclus*" sp. could be captured individually and required high concentrations of dissolved oxygen during transport. In the clay-laden, slow-flowing waters of the Rio Juquiá at the town of Juquiá, on the next day (April 15th, 1995, 7:00 a.m.) the following measurements were obtained: air temperature 25°C, water temperature 28°C, pH 6.3, conductivity 42 µS/cm. This "*Macrotocinclus*" sp. was present in large quantities and syntopically a few *Hisonotus leucofrenatus* were also found. Capture was easy along the submersed branches of the shore vegetation. The captured specimens displayed distended stomachs and several females were ripe.

M. & B.: This species is highly suited for aquarium maintenance, but with a caveat. They have the unpleasant custom to adhere to the flanks of tankmates to graze on their mucus layer, consequently, a species tank will have to be given serious thought. To interpret this behavior as cleaning is questionable, since the "beneficiaries" clearly display great unease while being grazed. In one particular instance, a large *Corydoras gossei* female was molested to such an extent that the entire dermis became white, peeled off, and soon showed a fungal infection. This female could not be saved. The suckermouth catfish is completely peaceful among its own kind.

S: In all likelihood this species is undescribed and possibly was constantly being confused with *Otocinclus affinis*, a fish from the vicinity of Rio de Janeiro with the same design but smaller. Based on size and behavior, "*Macrotocinclus*" *flexilis* seems to be its closest relative. LACERDA (pers. comm.) confirms the common presence of this species in the Rio Grande do Sul and Santa Catarina. The area of distribution expressed by SCHAEFER (1997) for *O. affinis* coincides with the distribution of this species. The collection of new material is needed to clarify the current situation.

T: 23°–27°C, **L:** 8 cm, **A:** 80 cm, **R:** b

"*Macrotocinclus*" sp. "São Paulo"

H.-G. Evers

H.-G. Evers

"*Macrotocinclus*" sp. "São Paulo" in a photo tank, shortly after being captured. The flanks have a metallic green sheen.

Genus *Nannoptopoma* Schaefer, 1996

Nannoptopoma spectabilis (Eigenmann, 1914)	Venezuela, Colombia
Nannoptopoma sternoptychum Schaefer, 1996	Peru: Tambopata

The genus *Nannoptopoma* is closely allied with *Hypoptopoma,* but its two representatives are much smaller, reaching only a length of 3 cm and they seem "compressed." These should be interesting aquarium residents. Lacerda (pers. comm.) captured a likely congener in the Rio Abuná, at the Brazilian-Bolivian border. Unfortunately, only the preserved specimens were available to be photographed. The fish did not even survive the transport to Rio de Janeiro.

In October 2000 H.-G. Evers visited the Rio Abuná in search of this species; unfortunately, all efforts were in vain. The Rio Abuná is a white-water stream with various clear-water tributaries, where the *Nannoptopoma* are said to live. Some other, more fortunate aquarist will hopefully one day be able to bring this interesting suckermouth catfish alive to Germany.

Shortly before printing a new species *Nannoptopoma* sp. "Peru" has been imported. This is a beautiful zebra-striped species.

We were able to pick out a single *Nannoptopoma* sp. specimen—probably the genotype *N. spectabilis* (see species descriptions)—from among an import of thousands of *Otocinclus vestitus.*

Nannoptopoma sp. "Rio Abuná," just captured.

M.T.C. Lacerda

A preserved specimen of *Nannoptopoma* sp. "Rio Abuná."

H.-G. Evers

Nannoptopoma sp. "Peru", a new species

H.-G. Evers

Nannoptopoma cf. *spectabilis*

H.-G. Evers

Nannoptopoma spectabilis (Eigenmann, 1914)

F.: Eigenmann, C.H. (1914): On new species of fishes from Colombia, Ecuador, and Brazil.– Indiana Univ. Studies 2: 231–234.

Syn.: *Otocinclus spectabilis*.

Hab.: Colombia: Dpto. Meta, Quebrada Cramalote; Venezuela: Apure-Basin; Ecuador: Río Napo, Río Pastaza; Peru: Dpto. Amazonas.

M.&B.: Highly noteworthy are the first successful breeding reports involving this species. The aquarists Petra Dotzer and Thomas Weidner (Penzberg) successfully bred *Nannoptopoma* cf. *spectabilis* in an aquarium. According to their observations, this species practices broodcare. In a manner reminiscent of the genus *Hypoptopoma*, male *Nannoptopoma*

guard their eggs. The following is an extract [transl. from German] of the annotations by Thomas Weidner:

H.-G. Evers

Nannoptopoma cf. *spectabilis*, ventral view.

324

Nannoptopoma spectabilis, male with spawn.

T. Weidner

- Aquarium 60 ∞ 50 ∞ 35 cm—decoration consisting of wood, rocks, fine sand, and several cryptocorynes, *Anubias,* and Java fern.
- Tankmates: 8 *Characidium steindachneri* and 3 *Pseudolithoxus tigris.*
- "Breeding group:" 12 specimens—proportion of sexes unknown. Apparently, males are smaller than females.
- Filtration: sponge plates and hydropneumatic pumping connected to a central blower (a total of 40 m≈/h for 9000 l water).
- Water characteristics: 25°C; 3°dGH; 0–1°dKH; pH 6.0; conductivity 150 μS/cm; nitrite and ammonia undetectable; nitrate 10–25 mg/l. Weekly water exchange of approximately 40%–50% (rainwater 80%, remainder tap water).
- Feeding: ample dry foods: algae wafers; spirulina tablets and "normal" tablet foods; frozen *Artemia*, mosquito larvae, glass worms, lobster eggs, and daphnia. Sporadically live microeels and artemia. Feeding frequency: twice during the day plus at night. Every now and then a day of fasting.
- Spawning occurred on the inferior side of the central brace, because the water level was always very high.
- The first spawn consisted of 60 eggs, the second of only 11. Apparently the male guards the spawn. He always remains nearby and sporadically sits on top of the spawn.
- The eggs are greenish.
- The larvae hatch after approximately 60–80 hours and have a huge yolk sac.
- Unfortunately, the first time only 22 eggs could be separated after 48 hours, the other eggs were either removed by the male or disappeared in some other way.
- Subsequent rearing occurred in a 10-l-tank. Filtration was also powered by air.
- First feeding occurred after 100 hours with dust-size flake food, since the first larvae had metabolized virtually their entire yolk sac.

Fam.: Loricariidae
Subfam.: Hypoptopomatinae

Nannoptopoma cf. *spectabilis,* newly hatched fry.

- Sporadically, live micro eels and newly-hatched *Artemia* were fed.
- One week after the larvae swam free, they started to die. Apparently they had starved to death, having received too little food or the wrong kind.
- The second spawn received a diet supplemented with lettuce, and the rearing tank was placed on the window sill. The sunlight allowed for the development of an edible aufwuchs. Perhaps the fry will find appropriate edibles in grazing this mucus layer. Perhaps that works!?

These first successes surely entice other aquarists, too, to try their hand at catfish species which have not yet been bred in captivity. The biggest hurdle, unfortunately, is finding the species offered in the first place, since genera such as *Nannoptopoma* are particularly rare in the trade. The firm TRANSFISH (Planegg by

Munich) has in the past been repeatedly successful in importing this rare species from Venezuela.

S: The pictured specimen was a by-catch of *Otocinclus vestitus* and is thought to be *Nannoptopoma* cf. *spectabilis*. It is surprising that given the species' expansive area of distribution, by-catches seem to be rare. This is the type species of the genus. The only other congener is *N. sternoptychum* SCHAEFER, 1996.

T: 25°–28°C, L: 3 cm, A: 60 cm, R: b

Nannoptopoma sternoptychum

H.-G. Evers

Nannoptopoma sternoptychum (Schaefer, 1996)

F.: Schaefer, S. A. (1996): Nannoptopoma, a New Genus of Loricariid Catfishes (Siluriformes: Loricariidae) from the Amazon and Orinoco River Basins.- Copeia, 1996 (4): 913-926.

Syn.: None.

Hab.: Peru, Río Tambopata; Ecuador, Río Napo; Bolivia, Río Beni drainage; Colombia, Amazon Basin at Leticia; Brazil, Río Urubu. The pictured specimen was captured at the type locality, Puerto Maldonado, Peru. Since 2003, the firm Mimbon Aquarium regularly obtains specimens from the drainages of the Madre de Dios and Tambopata rivers.

M.&B.: Only a few specimens have been imported to date, and these have not yet been bred in captivity. However, its reproductive strategy is expected to follow the general guidelines given for *Nannoptopoma spectabilis*.

S: Although this small loricariid enjoys a broad distribution, for a long time it was impossible to import for the aquarium hobby. An interesting, albeit complicated, charge for advanced catfish hobbyists.

T: 25°–28°C, **L:** 4 cm, **A:** 60 cm, **R:** b

Genus *Niobichthys*
SCHAEFER & PROVENZANO, 1998

Niobichthys is a monotypic genus. Similar to the genera *Acestridium* and *Oxyropsis*, it has a much flattened posterior body and caudal peduncle.

Niobichthys ferrarisi lives in the border area between Venezuela and Brazil, in the area of the famous Table Mountains. These waters house, among others, the captivating ancistrine suckermouth catfishes of the genus *Neblinichthys*. Unfortunately, no import of these interesting loricariids is to be expected from the protected Neblina region, which harbors many suspected endemics.

Fortunately, it was possible to include a few photographs of the holotype and another preserved specimen of *Niobichthys ferrarisi*. This way, the reader has a better idea as to what these catfish look like.

Niobichthys ferrarisi, ZMA 121.791, dorsal view.   I. Seidel

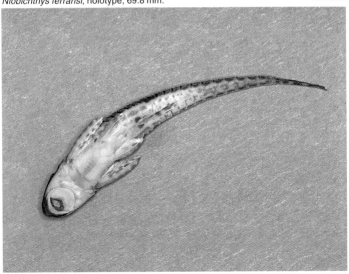

Niobichthys ferrarisi, holotype, 69.8 mm.

S.A. Schaefer

Niobichthys ferrarisi, ZMA 121.791, ventral view.

I. Seidel

Genus *Otocinclus* Cope, 1872
Otocinclus

The species in the genus *Otocinclus* according to Schaefer (1997):	
Otocinclus affinis Steindachner, 1877	Brazil: Rio de Janeiro, São Paulo
Otocinclus bororo Schaefer, 1997	Brazil: Mato Grosso, Rio Paraguay Basin
Otocinclus caxarari Schaefer, 1997	Brazil: Madeira Basin, Guaporé; Bolivia: Rio Mamoré
Otocinclus hasemani Steindachner, 1915	Brazil: Tocantins and Parnaiba
Otocinclus hoppei Ribeiro, 1939	Brazil: Peru
Otocinclus huaorani Schaefer, 1997	Colombia; Ecuador; Peru
Otocinclus macrospilus Eigenmann & Allen, 1942	Colombia; Ecuador; Peru
Otocinclus mariae Fowler, 1940	Bolivia; Brazil: Mato Grosso
Otocinclus mimulus Axenrot & Kullander 2003	Paraguay, Río Monday
Otocinclus mura Schaefer, 1997	Brazil: Amazon
Otocinclus tapirape Britto & Moreira, 2002	Brazil: Goiás, Rio Pintado
Otocinclus vestitus Cope, 1872	Bolivia; Paraguay; Peru
Otocinclus vittatus Regan, 1904	Argentina; Bolivia; Brazil; Colombia; Paraguay; Peru
Otocinclus xakriaba Schaefer, 1997	Brazil: Bahia, Minas Gerais

The small urchins of this genus [in German called "Ohrgitterwelse" = ear-grid-catfishes (Gr. ous= ear, possessive: otos, Gr. kinklis = grid, an allusion to a perforated post-temporal bone, reminiscent of an eardrum)] are probably known to every aquarist. The trade usually offers the light gray to beige species with a black longitudinal stripe. Especially hobbyists with lushly vegetated aquaria appreciate these goblins, since they effectively control algal growth while not harming higher plants.

The positive identification of the various species is usually difficult, especially when the precise origin of the specimen in question is ignored. The most common names under which the *Otocinclus* are traded are *Otocinclus vittatus* and *O. affinis*. The latter hardly has played a role in our [German] aquaria and does deviate significantly in color from the "standard" species (see species descriptions). Trade lists now and then also include the invalid taxon *O. arnoldi*. This is a synonym of *"Macrotocinclus" flexilis*! At least two species are known to be from southeastern Brazil (*"M." flexilis* and "M." sp. "São Paulo"). Full-grown, these two are about 8 cm in total length and therefore significantly larger than the other species, which generally are full-grown at a total length of 3–5 cm. Some of these smaller species can be readily bred in dedicated aquaria if a group is maintained. The majority in such a group should be males. The males pursue the ripe females throughout the aquarium and try to place themselves in front. Once a male is successful, a T-shaped position results from the combination and the female expels one or two eggs which are simultaneously fertilized by the male. The eggs, which can be found on the aquarium panes and plants throughout, are not cared for by the parents. Sometimes, oviposition can be observed in the aquarium, but the rearing of the fry cannot be assured. For those interested further in the care and breeding of the small *Otocinclus* and similar small species specifically, a se-

Rio Macabu in the State of Rio de Janeiro. *Otocinclus affinis* can be found syntopically with *Corydoras nattereri* and *Scleromystax prionotos*.

Fam.: Loricariidae
Subfam.: Hypoptopomatinae

ries of articles by SCHRAMM (1991 a, b; 1992) or the indications by WENDENBURG (1993, 1996, 1997) [in German] offer highly recommended reading.

A new scientific revision of the genus *Otocinclus* had been urgently awaited. SCHAEFER (1991) already indicated such a need, but limited himself initially to mentioning so-called species-groups (without taxonomic status). In 1997, SCHAEFER finally closed the long-gaping hole. The genus *Otocinclus* is monophyletic—i.e., it comes from a single branch—as SCHAEFER could confirm after studying the most varied morphological characteristics. As a result of the revision, various species were reclassified into other genera or declared synonymous to preexisting ones. On the other hand, five new species were described, bringing the present total to 14 valid species. Type species is *Otocinclus vestitus* COPE.

There are several, apparently very similar, species within this genus. However, ichthyologists will find clear distinguishing features based on skeletal differences, the trajectory and distinctiveness of the longitudinal band on the flanks, as well as the pigmentation of the caudal fin. The two morphologically similar species from southeastern Brazil, "*Macrotocinclus*" sp. São Paulo and "*Macrotocinclus*" *flexilis,* constitute one unit and were seperated here (see part of "*Macrotocinclus*", page 317).

A big obstacle for the scientific revision of the genus was the paucity of preserved specimens in scientific collections. That is surely the foremost reason for the extended abandonment of these catfishes from a systematic point of view.

Otocinclus spp. inhabit the entire tropical and subtropical sections of South America. The northern limit of their distribution is in Colombia. No finds have been reported from the Rio Magdalena basin. It is in the Rio Meta basin (Orinoco drainage) where the northernmost finds are confirmed. The genus is cis-Andean, no trans-Andean captures have been performed. The southern limit of the genus' distribution is in northern Argentina (Paraguay-Paraná drainage). Additionally, SCHAEFER (1997) presents his conclusions in regard to the biogeography of the *Otocinclus* spp. in relation to their phylogenesis, stating that species formation must have happened prior to the appearance of the Brazilian highlands; according to this theory, the species must be very old.

Of the species presented here, those which could not be classified into any of the known taxons with certainty are presented as *Otocinclus* sp. in addition to their area of origin. This seems more sensible than to adopt personal creations or trade names. Still, the trade names of common usage—if available—are mentioned for each species. The same approach was taken with the presently undeterminable *Parotocinclus*.

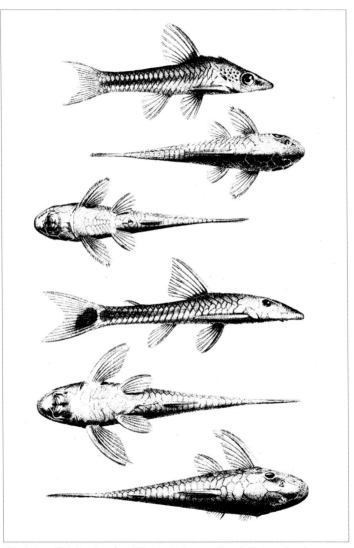

Otocinclus affinis (top three) and *Parotocinclus maculicauda* (bottom three).

Drawings from STEINDACHNER: Die Süßwasserfische des südöstlichen Brazil, 1876.

Otocinclus affinis Steindachner, 1877
Dwarf otocinclus, golden otocinclus

F.: Steindachner, F. (1877): Die Süßwasserfische des südöstlichen Brasilien IV. Sber.Akad.Wiss.Wien, mathem.–naturwiss. Cl. 76(1): 217–230.

Syn.: None.

Hab.: Brazil: states of Rio de Janeiro and Espirito Santo, all other recognitions might be a mix up with "*Macrotocinclus*" sp. "São Paulo". Usually found in whitewater rivers, but sometimes also in clearwater biotopes.

In white-waters, *Corydoras nattereri* and *Scleromystax prionotos* are syntopic species. These corycats have the same coloration as the *Otocinclus* and it is not unusual to find, under close scrutiny, the otocinclus as a by-catch in shipments of these two corydoras. The *O. affinis* have been repeatedly observed sucked unto the skin of the corydoras, grazing on them. Sometimes such a small suckermouth catfish sits on a cory and the impression is that the latter enjoys it. Is it possible that the otocinclus fulfill some kind of cleaner function? "*Macrotocinclus*" sp. "Sao Paulo," a much larger species, but with a similar design, behaves similarly, but the "victim" is visibly bothered.

M. & B.: Maintain as described in the genus introduction. The cool temperatures required complicate matters somewhat.

S: Most *Otocinclus*, imported from every which way, are erroneously being offered as *Otocinclus affinis*. The true *O. affinis* is more gray and has a small hook-shaped growth on the bony plate behind the head. The species is rarely imported commercially and even rare in nature due to heavy pollution.

T: 18°–22°C, L: 4 cm, A: 60 cm, R: b

Otocinclus affinis

H.-G. Evers

H.-G. Evers

White-water river in the State of Espirito Santo, southern Brazil. The habitat of *Otocinclus affinis* and the syntopic *Corydoras nattereri* and *Scleromystax prionotos*.

Otocinclus hasemani STEINDACHNER, 1915

F.: Steindachner, F. (1915): Ichthyologische Beiträge (XVIII). Sitzungsber. K.K. Akad. Wiss. Wien, mathem.–naturwiss. Cl., 124 (8–10): 567–591.

Syn.: None.

Hab.: Brazil: States of Goias and Pará in the Tocantins Basin, Maranhão, Parnaiba Basin.

M. & B.: In line with its congeners, *O. hasemani* is an unproblematic charge.

S: The species is sporadically imported from Brazil. A relatively narrow longitudinal band that extends distinctly into the caudal fin is characteristic of this species.

In nature, *O. hasemani* could be observed in dense schools of several thousand specimens swimming through the open water (see introduction to the subfamily).

T: 25°–28°C, L: 3–4 cm, A: 60 cm, R: b

Otocinclus hoppei RIBEIRO, 1939

F.: Ribeiro, A. de Miranda (1939): Alguns novos dados ictiológicos da nossa fauna.– Bol. biol. São Paulo (n.s.), 4(3): 358–363.

Syn.: None.

Hab.: Brazil: State of Pará, Belém, State of Rondônia, Madeira Basin; Peru: Ucayali drainage.

M. & B.: *O. hoppei* is imported in huge numbers and is the poster child for peaceful and delicate algae control in the domestic underwater jungle.

S: According to SCHAEFER (1997), this species has a greater area of distribution than initially suspected.

O. macrospilus is its closest relative, but both species are readily told apart by the pigmentation of the caudal fin. The caudal spot of *O. hoppei* is smaller and does not run into the caudal fin. Whereas *O. hoppei* only has one crossbar, *O. macrospilus* has two.

T: 24°–28°C, L: 3.5 cm, A: 50 cm, R: b

Otocinclus hasemani

H.-G. Evers

Otocinclus hoppei

I. Seidel

Otocinclus huaorani SCHAEFER, 1997

F.: The Neotropical cascudinhos: Systematics and biogeography of the *Otocinclus* catfishes (Siluriformes: Loricariidae).– Proc. Acad. Nat. Sci. Philadelphia, 148: 1–120.

Syn.: None.

Hab.: Colombia and Peru: western Amazonia: drainages of the rivers Meta and Ucayali.

M. & B.: Like all the other similarly colored species that are sporadically imported from the Amazon Basin, *O. huaorani* is straightforward in its care. Every once in a while, the fish can be discovered in regular import shipments, even though it is subsequently offered to the hobby under the "standard" taxons of *Otocinclus affinis* and *Otocinclus vittatus*.

S: Based on its typical caudal fin design, *O. huaorani* is readily distinguished from other species. The upper and lower fin lobes are covered by two rows of vertical hemicircles. The corporal longitudinal band is very broad and in many specimens includes the spot on the caudal peduncle. In some specimens, a small gap between caudal spot and longitudinal band can be discerned, as is the case with the pictured specimen.

T: 26°–30°C, L: 3.5 cm, A: 50 cm, R: b

Otocinclus macrospilus EIGENMANN & ALLEN, 1942

F.: Eigenmann, C.H. & W.R. Allen (1942): Fishes of western South America (Univ. Kentucky, Lexington): 1–494 (S. 201).

Syn.: None.

Hab.: Colombia: Amazon, Japurá, and Caquetá basins; Ecuador: Napo Basin; Peru: ample distribution in the Amazon Basin and the rivers Nanay, Marañon, and Morona; Brazil: Rio Juruá.

M. & B.: Following the oft-described methods, breeding is straightforward. A species tank is preferable to allow better control. See also the introduction to the genus.

S: *O. macrospilus* was described based on Peruvian specimens. NUMRICH (pers. comm.) captured a very similar form at the Brazilian side of the border region to Peru, in the upper Juruá River. These fish evidence only slight differences to the Peruvian imports and are probably also *O. macrospilus*.

T: 24°–28°C, L: 4 cm, A: 50 cm, R: b

Otocinclus huaorani

I. Seidel

Morph of *Otocinclus macrospilus*, see also the photos on the following page.

I. Seidel

339

Morph of *Otocinclus macrospilus*, see previous page for text.

H.-G. Evers

Otocinclus cf. *macrospilus* from the Rio Juruá, Brazil.

H.-G. Evers

Otocinclus sp. "Amapá"   F. Bitter

Otocinclus sp. "Amapá"

Hab.: The pictured specimen was captured by F. Bɪᴛᴛᴇʀ (Hesepe) in the northern State of Amapá in Brazil.

M. & B.: Unfortunately, there are no reports on breeding. Maintain in a manner suitable for similar species. Maintenance temperature should consider its natural biotope, i.e., not be lower than 25°C.

S: The species could not yet be identified. It might be an undescribed species.

It seems that the dorsal design, where three faint crossbands cover the dorsum—varying in intensity according to the state of the individual—is a characteristic of this species.

T: 25°–28°C, **L:** 4 cm, **A:** 50 cm, **R:** b

Otocinclus sp. "Guapó"

This species was captured June 1998 by Paulo VALERIO DA SILVA and Hans-Georg EVERS close to the city of Guapó in a white-water river, part of the Rio Meia do Ponte drainage basin, Sate of Goias, Brazil. The species was found syntopically with *Corumbataia tocantinensis* and *Aspidoras* cf. *taurus*.

T: 25°–30°C, L: 4 cm, A: 60 cm, R: b

Otocinclus sp. "Guapó"   H.-G. Evers

Otocinclus sp. "Rio do Peixe"

This small species—somewhat reminiscent of *Parotocinclus longirostris*—lives in the clear-water carrying Rio do Peixe, Brazilian State of Goias. However, it lacks an adipose fin and is therefore presented as *Otocinclus* sp. "Rio do Peixe." This fish is sensitive and H.-G. EVERS only brought back a few specimens to Germany in June 1998. There are no experiences in regard to its reproduction.

T: 25°–30°C, L: 2,5 cm, A: 60 cm, R: b

Otocinclus sp. "Rio do Peixe"   H.-G. Evers

Otocinclus sp. "Río Ucayali"

This small cascudinho was captured by SEIDEL and cotravelers in the Peruvian Río Ucayali Basin. The caudal peduncle is completely black, a characteristic unique within this genus. The care of this species mirrors that of others from Amazonia with a similar design.

T: 25°–30°C, **L:** 4 cm, **A:** 60 cm, **R:** b

Otocinclus sp. "Rio Ucayali" H.-G. Evers

Otocinclus sp. "Rondônia"

This species is a sporadic import from the Brazilian State of Rondônia. It is common around Porto Velho, in the Rio Madeira drainage. H.-G. EVERS captured it in the Rio Jaciparaná, a direct tributary of the Madeira, for example. *O.* sp. "Rondônia" inhabits white-waters. Its design is somewhat reminiscent of *Otocinclus hasemani*. The narrow longitudinal band extends straight into the caudal peduncle, without ending as a dot.

The presence of an iris lobe is particularly interesting, as it is a rare feature within this genus. It is highly probable that this species is as of yet undescribed.

T: 25°–28°C, **L:** 3,5 cm, **A:** 50 cm, **R:** b

Otocinclus sp. "Rondônia" I. Seidel

Otocinclus sp. "Xingú"

Jens GOTTWALD, Hannover (Germany), received a shipment from Brazil which included this apparently undescribed cascudinho. It came from the basin of the Rio Xingú, central Brazil. Although well-suited for aquarium maintenance, it is rarely imported.

Otocinclus cocama REIS, 2004
Zebra-Otocinclus

E.: Reis, R. (2004): Otocinclus cocama, a new uniquely colored loricariid catfish from Peru (Teleostei: Siluriformes), with comments on the impact of taxonomic revisions to the discovery of new taxa.- Neotropical Ichthyology, 2(3): 109-115.

Syn.: -

Hab.: Peru, Provinz Loreto, Quebrada Yanayacu bei Jenaro Herrara.

M. &. B.: Regularly available in the trade since 2001. Maintainance is not different from the other *Otocinclus*. Because of the attractive colour pattern several aquarists already succeeded in breeding this species. Without any other species but *O. cocama* in the tank, the fry will grow up without any problems. An imitation of a dry season followed by drastic water changes ("rainy season") triggers the spawning.

S: *Otocinclus cocama* was described shortly before printing of this book. We could only correct the name but had to leave it at its current place in the book.

T: 24°–28°C, L: 4 cm, A: 60 cm, R: b

Otocinclus cocama   I. Seidel

Otocinclus cocama

H.-G. Evers

Otocinclus cocama

F. Schäfer

Otocinclus vestitus

I. Seidel

Otocinclus vestitus COPE, 1872

F.: Cope, E. D. (1872): On the fishes of the Ambyiacu River. Proc. Acad. Nat. Sci. Philadelphia, 23 (3): 250–294.

Syn.: None.

Hab.: Peru: tributaries of the Ambiyacu; Bolivia: Province of Beni, Madeira Basin; Paraguay: Paraná Basin. WENDENBURG (1997) captured the fish in the tributaries of the Peruvian Rio Utiquinea (Ucayali drainage). They were collected in the vegetative zone at the edge.

M. & B.: Simple, follows the indications given in the genus description. See WENDENBURG (1997) for additional information.

S: *O. vestitus* is the genotype. It can be readily identified based on the design of the caudal fin. At its base there is only a narrow spot, the black longitudinal band continues into the anterior third of the caudal fin, where it is framed by a light zone. The caudal fin has also two cross-bands.

T: 25°–30°C, L: 3.5 cm, A: 60 cm, R: b

Ripe *Otocinclus vestitus* ♀

H.-G. Evers

Habitat of *Otocinclus vestitus* in the Llanos of Venezuela

H.-G. Evers

Fam.: Loricariidae
Subfam.: Hypoptopomatinae

Otocinclus vittatus REGAN, 1904
Striped otocinclus

F.: Regan, C.T. (1904): A monograph of the fishes of the family Loricariidae.– Trans. zool. Soc. London, 17(3): 191–350.

Syn.: None.

Hab.: Bolivia: Dept. Beni, Mamoré Basin; Brazil: State of Mato Grosso, Rio Paraguay system; Peru; Colombian and Venezuelan llanos.
Hans-Georg EVERS & Ingo SEIDEL captured this species in August 1992 (rainy season) in flooded shores of larger lagoons at Calabozo (Venezuela). The fish was observed sitting on the plant stalks. WENDENBURG (pers. comm.) visited these llanos during the dry season and found the species both in lotic environments (Rio Orituco) and in lentic areas (Caño Caicara at Mantecal). In all cases, these were white-water biotopes with temperatures of 26°–28°C, pH 7.0 to 7.8 (Orituco) or 5.9 to 6.5 (Caicara), and conductivities of 10–28 µS/cm (Caicara) or 80–270 µS/cm (Orituco).

M. & B.: Breeding is straight forward in a species tank. WENDENBURG (DATZ 3/96: 148–150) reports extensively on the matter.

S: This well-known species apparently has a very expansive area of distribution and is regularly imported in large quantities. The typical design of the caudal fin is readily apparent on the photographs, facilitating in great measure an unequivocal identification by the aquarist.

T: 25°–28°C, L: 4 cm, A: 50 cm, R: b

Pair of *Otocinclus vittatus*, ventral view

H.-G. Evers

Otocinclus vittatus ♂, Venezuela

H.-G. Evers

Otocinclus vittatus ♀

H.-G. Evers

Otocinclus xakriaba

I. Schindler

Otocinclus xakriaba SCHAEFER, 1997

F.: Schaefer, S.A. (1997): The Neotropical cascudinhos: Systematics and biogeography of the *Otocinclus* catfishes (Siluriformes: Loricariidae).– Proc. Acad. Nat. Sci. Philadelphia, 148: 1–120.

Syn.: None.

Hab.: Brazil: Bahia, Minas Gerais, Rio São Francisco drainage. Ingo SCHINDLER (Berlin) found the species in the State of Pernambuco, also in the São Francisco drainage.

M. & B.: No details are known and breeding has not yet been successful.

S: The unusual design of this species distinguishes it from all other congeners.

T: 22°–26°C, L: 4 cm, A: 50 cm, R: b

Oxyropsis cf. *wrightiana*, trio. See following page for additional photos.   T. Weidner

Genus *Oxyropsis* Eigenmann & Eigenmann, 1889

O. acutirostris Miranda Ribeiro, 1951	Upper Orinoco Basin, upper and lower Rio Negro
O. carinatus (Steindachner, 1879)	Upper and central Amazon Basin
O. wrightiana Eigenmann & Eigenmann, 1889	Central and upper Amazon Basin

The genus was revised by Aquino & Schaefer (2002), and nowadays three species are considered valid. The genus *Oxyropsis* is very similar to the genus *Hypoptopoma*, but may be told apart, nevertheless, by the following characteristics:

A single line of enlarged odontodes runs along the body, just above the lateral line. The posterior body and the caudal peduncle of *Oxyropsis* are flat, whereas *Hypoptopoma* has a circular section. Typical for the genus is also that the eyes are located protruding on the head; however, this characteristic is shared by *Hypoptopoma*.

All of the currently valid species we are able to present with a photograph. The first [German] edition (pp. 334, 335) presented *Oxyropsis* sp. "Tefé," a species which in all likelihood is identical to *Oxyropsis carinatus* (Steindachner, 1879). In April 2001, coauthor I. Seidel was able to capture an additional *Oxyropsis* species in the drainage of the upper Río Orinoco in Venezuela, *O. acutirostris*, the beautiful species with the red spots on every bony plate!

The aquarists Petra Dotzer and Thomas Weidner were able to acquire import specimens of an *Oxyropsis* species from Peru, which is likely to be *Oxyropsis wrightiana*. It was possible to aquarium breed this species after a relatively short time, the details of which hardly differ from the customs observed in *Hypoptopoma* or *Nannoptopoma* species. Here, too, the male is the broodcaring gender until the larvae hatch. Rearing has to be considered difficult. Apparently, it is difficult to get the small fry to feed.

Oxyropsis cf. *wrightiana*, ♂ at the spawn.

T. Weidner

Oxyropsis cf. *wrightiana*, fry right after hatching.

T. Weidner

Oxyropsis acutirostris from the upper Río Orinoco at Menicia.   I. Seidel

Oxyropsis acutirostris Miranda Ribeiro, 1951

F.: Mirando Ribeiro, P. de (1951): Sobre Oxyropsis Eigenmann & Eigenmann, 1889 (Pisces, Nematognathi—Loricariidae). Bol. Mus. Nac. Rio de Janeiro, 104: 1–3.

Syn.: *Hypoptopoma acutirostris, Hypoptopoma acutirostre.*

Hab.: The distribution includes both the upper Orinoco drainage in the border region between Colombia and Venezuela, and the basin of the central and lower Rio Negro of Brazil. Both river systems are connected through the Río Casiquiare. In March 2001, I. Seidel found the species in the Orinoco, still above the confluence of the Rio Atabapo, close to the town of Menicia. There it could be captured in the currents among the branches of a tree that had fallen into the water. The water was very warm, relatively soft, and showed an acid pH.

M.&B.: A sensitive species requiring particular care. The delicate fish feed primarily on vegetable matter, but also appreciate dry foods and tablets, as well as live and frozen daphnia and cyclops. A water pump should provide optimal oxygen saturation. Given that only few representatives of *O. acutirostris* have been maintained in aquaria, breeding could not yet be considered. Perhaps this beautiful species will eventually be imported on a commercial basis?

S: Particularly notorious of this comparatively small species is the long, narrow head—the characteristic that served as basis for its scientific name. Especially interesting are the red dots that decorate every bony plate, with the exception of the lighter ventral region. However, these are only apparent under a certain angle of the illumination and general well-being of the specimens.

T: 25°–29°C, L: 5–6 cm, A: 60 cm, R: b

Oxyropsis carinatus (STEINDACHNER, 1879)

F.: Steindachner, F. (1879): Über einige neue und seltene Fisch-Arten aus dem k.k. zoologischen Museum zu Wien, Stuttgart und Warschau. Denkschr. Akad. Wiss. Wien 41:1–52.

Syn.: *Hypoptopoma carinatum, Hypoptopoma carinatus, Oyropsis carinatum.*

Hab.: A broadly distributed species in the central and lower Amazon Basin of Peru, and especially Brazil. It apparently inhabits all water types. According to AQUINO & SCHAEFER (2002), it can be found both in the white-water of the Rio Solimões and the black-water of the Rio Negro. The authors captured the fish in the clearwater of the Igarapé Piraruaia (a tributary of the Rio Tefé, state of Amazonas), where they were found on branches laying in the water.

M.&B.: This is arguably the species that is the easiest to maintain of this genus. *O. carinatus* appreciates warmth, but also requires optimal oxygen concentrations. Fortunately, no particular demands are placed on the chemical makeup of the water. Aquaria for this fish should be decorated with long-stalked plants, thin bamboo stalks, or with finely branched roots, since in nature, the specimens are preferentially found adhered to thin stalks in current-swept stream sections. To adhere, they do not use their suctorial mouth, but, as can be seen on the photograph, use their ventral fins as clasping organ.
Feeding algae, vegetable fare, tablet foods, and small live and frozen foods is possible.

S: Ignoring the characteristic coloration of *O. carinatus,* the species can still be readily identified based on anatomical peculiarities. The caudal peduncle is less flattened in this species than in the other two congeners described, and the scutes of the caudal peduncle are less degenerate. Above and below the central lateral, keellike row of odontodes of the caudal peduncle, *O. wrightiana* and *O. acutirostris* only have 1–2 rows of smallish odontodes. In contrast, *O. carinatus* has 5–6.

T: 26°–29°C, L: 8–9 cm, A: 80 cm, R: b

Igarapé Piraruaia, habitat of *Oxyropsis.*

Oxyropsis carinatus

H.-G. Evers

Oxyropsis carinatus, ventral view.

H.-G. Evers

Oxyropsis sp. "Potaro River", lateral view

I. Seidel

Oxyropsis sp. "Potaro River"

The first German edition (p. 402) presents this fish under the heading of "Unidentified Hypoptopomatinae, new genus LG 5." Meanwhile, we are convinced that this species from Guyana is likely to be an undescribed member of the genus *Oxyropsis*. We therefore present it with the identifier of "Potaro River." In the year 2003, a similar species was captured by Evers and Schlüter in the Rio Tapajos.

On a fish collection trip during August 2000, Ingo Seidel and cotravelers captured this small, very interesting Hypoptopomatine species. Unfortunately, it could not be classified to genus. The fish live in the Potaro River and were captured close to Tumatomari. At first glance its shape is reminiscent of the genus *Hypoptopoma*, but the caudal peduncle appears much more delicate. If it were flattened, a classification into the genus *Oxyropsis* could be considered. However, at present we do not classify this fish in any of the existing genera.

The species grows to a length of about 4 cm and is somewhat problematic in the aquarium. However, its care seems relatively straightforward in a small species tank with copious vegetable fare.

No breeding experiences could be gathered in the short time between its first import and the conclusion of the manuscript for this edition of the book.

T: 24°–28°C, L: 5–6 cm, A: 60 cm, R: b

Oxyrospis sp. "Potaro River", ventral view

Oxyropsis sp. "Rio Tapajos"

H.-G. Evers

Oxyropsis sp. "Rio Tapajos"

On an ichthyological trip into the area of the central and lower Rio Tapajos, Brazil, EVERS and SCHLÜTER captured an apparently still undescribed *Oxyropsis* sp. in a clear-water-carrying stream at the road from Ruropolis to Santarém (approximately 140 km south of Santarém). The water was crystalline and, with a temperature of 25.6°C, relatively cool. The pH was 5.0 and the electrical conductivity at 16 μs/cm. The *Oxyrospis* were adhered in large numbers to submersed leaves of a type of grass, which gently swayed back and forth in the middle of the stream.

It was with great effort that EVERS and SCHLÜTER stood in the chest-deep waters lifting the heavy leaves with their dip nets. However, the reward was apparent: up to 20 specimens per haul! The high density came as a complete surprise. By the way, a syntopic species was, besides various characins, a particularly unusual dwarf catfish of the family Heptapteridae, which might also be awaiting its scientific description.

O. sp. "Rio Tapajos" is quite sensitive in the aquarium and, despite the greatest efforts, some of the eight specimens brought back to Germany died within eight months—without even being able to say what should have been done differently.

T: 24°–27°C, L: 4 cm, A: 60 cm, R: b

Oxyropsis sp. "Rio Tapajos", ventral view

H.-G. Evers

Heptapteridae sp.   H.-G. Evers

Biotope of *Oxyropsis* sp. "Rio Tapajos"   H.-G. Evers

Fam.: Loricariidae
Subfam.: Hypoptopomatinae

Tribe Otothyrini SCHAEFER, 1991

Genus *Corumbataia* BRITSKI, 1997

Corumbataia cuestae BRITSKI, 1997	Brazil: São Paulo, upper Paraná.
Corumbataia tocantinensis BRITSKI, 1997	Brazil: Araguaia, Tocantins.

This small genus only comprises two species and constitutes a kind of intermediate between the broad-headed *Parotocinclus* and *Otocinclus*. *Corumbataia* lack an adipose fin and the body appears stouter than in *Otocinclus*. Both species in the genus have a dark band along their body. The distribution of the genus is discontinuous—no additional forms have been described from the areas in between. However, one of the co-authors (EVERS) was able to capture *Corumbataia tocantinensis* in the State of Goiás, but in a white-water tributary of the Rio Meia Ponte. This is a river of the Paranaiba Basin and is therefore located between the areas of distribution mentioned for this genus.

Corumbataia cuestae BRITSKI, 1997

F.: Britski, H.A. (1997): Descrição de um novo gênero de Hypoptopomatinae, com duas espécies novas (Siluriformes, Loricariidae). Papeis Avulsos de Zool., S. Paulo, 40(15) : 231–255.

Hab.: Brazil, federal state of São Paulo, upper Paraná, Serra Piracicaba, vicinity of the city of Analândia at the Rio Corumbatai.
During November 2001, Maik BEYER (Maricá at Rio de Janeiro) and H.-G. EVERS drove through the state of São Paulo in the search of fishes. On road SP310 from Araraquara towards Campinas, EVERS suddenly saw the sign to Corumbataí and remembered a publication by BRITSKI (1997), where the species is described from the Rio Corumbatai at Analândia. The genus name is derived from that city, said to be the birthplace of BRITSKI. After some searching, several small streams were found where the owners of the local ranches allowed to fish. Since it had rained for several days, the creeks were flooded, the waters turbid. Water temperature was 24°C, pH ca. 6.0, and the conductivity was 22 µS/cm. Besides hundreds of *Corumbataia cuestae* which adhered to the flooded grasses in the current, several "white" characins of the subfamily Tetragonopterinae were also captured, together with the omnipresent trahiras, *Hoplias* sp., several knifefish (*Gymnotus carapo*), and *Corydoras aeneus*.
Given that it was at the beginning of summer, it is likely for the temperature to be significantly lower during the winter. Maik BEYER reports (pers. comm to EVERS) that he has previously captured the species at another site during the winter at temperatures below 20°C.

360

Corumbataia cuestae

H.-G. Evers

M.&B.: Cool, current-rich aquaria are required for maintenance. Apparently, *C. cuestae* is an aufwuchs feeder which has no problems with flake or tablet foods. The only challenge facing the hobbyist is the cool quarters that must be provided.

S: Type species of the genus. It will probably remain a rare import. The few specimens that EVERS attempted to bring to Germany perished due to the heat experienced in transport during the following days. The photos were taken in Rio de Janeiro in a photo tank in order to preserve a pictorial record of the species.

T: 18°–24°C, **L:** 3–4 cm, **A:** 60 cm, **R:** b

Biotope of *Corumbataia cuestae* at Corumbatai in the state of São Paulo.   H.-G. Evers

Habitat of *Corumbataia tocantinensis* at Guapó, State of Goias, Brazil.   H.-G. Evers

362

Corumbataia tocantinensis

H.-G. Evers

Corumbataia tocantinensis Britski, 1997

F.: Britski, H. A. (1997): Descrição de um novo gênero de Hypoptopomatinae, com duas espécies novas (Siluriformes, Loricariidae).– Papéis Avulsos de Zool., S. Paulo, 40(15): 231–255.

Syn.: None.

Hab.: Central Brazil: State of Goias, Rio Vermelho, Rio Maranhão, Rio Tocantins. H.-G. Evers and P. Valerio captured this species together in Goiás. The habitat was a fast-flowing white-water creek. The species was rare and an *Aspidoras* sp. was found to be syntopic. The small suckermouth catfish could be captured among the submersed, overhanging shore vegetation.

M. & B.: As long as hygiene is respected, maintenance is straightforward. Successful reproduction has not been reported.

S: The company Trop Rio (Rio de Janeiro) has sporadically exported this species all over the world. *C. tocantinensis* is surely better suited for aquarium maintenance than its brother, *Corumbataia cuestae,* the type species of the genus, from the cooler regions of the State of São Paulo. Gender can be readily determined in both species based on the differing morphology of the genital papilla. Additionally, males have longer pectoral fins. Evers (1998c) initially introduced the species to the hobby under the erroneous name of *Otocinclus* sp.

T: 24°–28°C, **L:** 3–4 cm, **A:** 60 cm, **R:** b

Genera
Epactionotus REIS & SCHAEFER, 1998
Eurycheilichtys REIS & SCHAEFER, 1992

Epactionotus aky AZPELICUETA et. al, 2004	Argentina: Río Uruguay
Epactionotus bilineatus REIS & SCHAEFER, 1998	Brazil: Rio Grande do Sul, Rio Maquiné, Rio Três Forquilhas
Epactionotus gracilis REIS & SCHAEFER, 1998	Brazil: Santa Catarina, Rio Ararangua
Epactionotus itaimbezinhos REIS & SCHAEFER, 1998	Brazil: Santa Catarina, Rio Grande do Sul
Epactionotus yasi ALMIRÓN, AZPELICUETA & CASCIOTTA, 2004	Argentina: Rio Iguazú
Eurycheilichtys limulus REIS & SCHAEFER, 1998	Brazil: Rio Grande do Sul, Rio Jacui
Eurycheilichthys pantherinus REIS & SCHAEFER, 1992	Brazil: Rio Grande do Sul, Rio Uruguay

These Brazilian catfishes hail from the southern Brazilian states of Santa Catarina and Rio Grande do Sul. These are endemics, where each is only found in a restricted area. The genus *Eurycheilichtys* (two species) and the genus *Epac-tionotus* (five species) have not yet appeared on the aquarium stage. These are elongated, small species with a characteristic longitudinal band design. *Eurycheilichthys* has seven branched pectoral fin rays.

Genera
Hisonotus EIGENMANN & EIGENMANN, 1889
Microlepidogaster EIGENMANN & EIGENMANN, 1889

H. bourguyi (MIRANDA RIBEIRO, 1911)	Brazil
H. depressicauda (MIRANDA RIBEIRO, 1918)	Brazil, São Paulo, Sorocaba
H. depressinotus (MIRANDA RIBEIRO, 1918)	Brazil, São Paulo, Piracicaba
H. francirochai (IHERING 1928)	Brazil, Rio Grande do Sul
H. insperatus BRITSKI & GARAVELLO, 2003	Brazil, São Paulo, Rio Tieté
H. laevior COPE 1894	Brazil, Rio Grande do Sul
H. leptochilus COPE, 1894	Brazil, Rio Grande do Sul
H. leucofrenatus (MIRANDA RIBEIRO, 1908)	Brazil, São Paulo, Rio Juquiá
H. maculipinnis (REGAN, 1912)	Argentina, La Plata
H. nigricauda (BOULENGER, 1891)	Brazil, Rio Grande do Sul
H. notatus EIGENMANN & EIGENMANN, 1889	Brazil, Rio de Janeiro
H. paulinus (REGAN, 1908)	Brazil, São Paulo, Piracicaba
H. ringueleti AQUINO, SCHAEFER & MIQUELARENA, 2001	Argentina, Rio Uruguay
H. taimensis (BUCKUP, 1981)	Brazil, Rio Grande do Sul

Capture of *Hisonotus leucofrenatus* in the Rio Juquiá, State of São Paulo. _{H.-G. Evers}

For a long time, both genera were considered invalid. NIJSSEN & ISBRÜCKER (1987) revalidated the genus *Microlepidogaster* and SCHAEFER (1998) confirmed it. A more recent revision of the genera *Microlepidogaster* and *Hisonotus* is still outstanding.

Recently, AQUINO et al. (2001) described *Hisonotus ringueleti* and BRITSKI & GARAVELLO added the 14th nominal species in the form of *Hisonotus insperatus*. The scientific analysis of the genus *Hisonotus* has not concluded, and is being continued by the American ichthyologist Scott A. SCHAEFER.

According to REIS & SCHAEFER (1998), the genus *Microlepidogaster* is monotypic, i.e., *M. perforatus* is its only member. All other species would therefore belong to the genus *Hisonotus*. According to SCHAEFER (written comm.), a revision of *Microlepidogaster* by BRITSKI, GARAVELLO & SCHAEFER is currently in the works. The members of these genera are typical "central and south Brazilians," i.e., inhabitants of clear- and white-water biotopes of the Planalto region and the Atlantic coastal rain forest. The species are strongly reminiscent of the genus *Otocinclus*, but clearly more elongated. No further differences will be mentioned, as a definitive scientific genus definition is still outstanding. The species of this group that have appeared in aquaristic circles are presented together on the following pages. The exact scientific classification is something that will happen in the future.

According to experience, these species are quite sensitive under aquarium conditions, but still readily maintained. As is the case for all Hypoptopomatinae, the aquarist must pay close attention in providing clear water, frequent water exchanges (50% per week), a strong filtration with adequate current, and a balanced diet which needs to include vegetable fare.

Experience in regard to breeding of these genera is scant, but it has been determined that their behavior by and large follows that of the genus *Otocinclus*, i.e., eggs and larvae are not guarded or otherwise cared for.

Hisonotus laevior COPE, 1894

F.: Cope, E. D. (1894): On the fishes obtained by the Naturalist Expedition in Rio Grande do Sul.– Proc. Americ. Phil. Soc., 33: 84–108.

Syn.: *Otocinclus laevior*.

Hab.: Brazil: Rio Grande do Sul, Rio Jacui, Rio Cubatão; Uruguay: Río Santa Lucia, Arroyo Colha. According to J. REICHERT, Montevideo (pers. comm.), this species is relatively common in southern Uruguay. The pictured specimen was captured at the Isla de Colha, District of Canelones-Floridae. *H. laevior* is likely to inhabit lotic biotopes, both in clear- as well as whitewater. The aquarist R. NORMANN brought this species to Germany in 1999 from Paraguay.

M. & B.: A fish for cool aquaria, which promptly turns sickly when the temperature is excessive. The water temperatures obtained in Argentina are exceptionally high, normally the species requires cooler conditions. For several weeks to months the water temperature may reach 23°–25°C. It is also important to know the origin of the fish. Wild-caught specimens from Uruguay surely require cooler conditions than individuals from Paraguay.

The specimens brought home from Paraguay by NORMANN spawned during the month of October 2000 at Stefan HETZ (Berlin). The few eggs—a maximum of 20 very large eggs—per female, require 4–5 days at 24°C to develop. The young grow relatively slow in comparison to other Hypoptopomatinae species.

S: *Hisonotus leptochilus*—described by COPE from brazilian Rio Grande do Sul—is another species with presently uncertain classification.

T: 15°–22°C, L: 7 cm, A: 60 cm, R: b

Hisonotus leucofrenatus (RIBEIRO, 1908)

F.: Ribeiro, A. de Miranda (1908): Peixes da Ribeira. Resultados de excursão do Sr. Ricardo Krone, Membro Correspondente do Museum Nacional do Rio de Janeiro.– Kosmos, Rio de Jan., 5: 1–5.

Syn.: *Otocinclus leucofrenatus, Microlepidogaster leucofrenatus*.

Hab.: Brazil: State of São Paulo, Rio das Pedras, Rio Juquiá, State of Rio de Janeiro. Both clear- and white-waters are inhabited. Specimens inhabiting clear-water display a richer contrast and appear more attractive.

The following values were measured in the clear-water Rio das Pedras (April 14th, 1995, 7:00 a.m.): aerial temperature 25°C, water 23°C, pH 7.15, conductivity 140 µS/cm. The species was only rarely found and it lived sympatrically with *Parotocinclus maculicauda* and "*Macrotocinclus*" sp. "São Paulo" (the latter of which is also a partner in the white-waters of the Rio Juquiá. Water values see there).

M. & B.: *H. leucofrenatus* is somewhat more exacting in its care than *H. notatus*. A deterioration in water quality not rarely ends with immediate death. This sucker-

Hisonotus laevior from Uruguay.   H.-G. Evers

Hisonotus leucofrenatus from Rio Juquiá, State of São Paulo.   H.-G. Evers

mouth catfish in not a species for the beginner and requires constant attention by its caretaker.

S: The attractive cephalic design of these fish readily distinguishes them from the otherwise similarly built and colored *H. notatus*. SCHAEFER (1998) classified *H. leucofrenatus* and *H. notatus* under the genus *Hisonotus*. A more exacting differentiation between the genera *Hisonotus* and *Microlepidogaster* is anticipated and in all likelihood will depend on a revision of the genus that will be performed as part of the genus *Microlepidogaster* (SCHAEFER, written comm.).

T: 20°–24°C, L: 6 cm, A: 60 cm, R: b

Capture of *Hisonotus leucofrenatus* and "*Macrotocinclus*" sp. "São Paulo" during the morning twilight at the Rio Juquiá.

M. Beyer

Hisonotus cf. *ringueleti* from Argentina.

H.-G. Evers

Hisonotus notatus, full-grown.

H.-G. Evers

Hisonotus notatus EIGENMANN & EIGENMANN, 1889
Marked otocinclus

F.: Eigenmann, C.H.& R.S. Eigenmann (1889): Preliminary notes on South American Nematognathi II.– Proc.California Acad.Sci., (2) 2: 28–56.

Syn.: *Otocinclus notatus, Microlepidogaster notatus.*

Hab.: Brazil: states of Rio de Janeiro and São Paulo.
Mostly white-water rivers are populated. The fish can be found in large quantities attached to the submersed overhanging shore vegetation.

M. & B.: An easy aquarium resident, although the initial acclimation period is critical. No breeding success has been reported.

S: Sporadically, xanthic specimens are captured in nature. But true albinos have not been discovered. *H. notatus* is often confused with Hypoptopomatinae sp. LG 2 from Paraguay, but its body is more elongated and adult size is at least 1 cm longer.

T: 20°–24°C, L: 5 cm, A: 60 cm, R: b

Hisonotus notatus, juvenile pair from the State of Rio de Janeiro, Brazil.   H.-G. Evers

Hisonotus notatus, xanthic specimen.   H.-G. Evers

Hisonotus cf. *ringueleti* from the Arroyo Tirica, Paraná drainage, Argentina. I. Seidel

Hisonotus ringueleti
Aquino, Schaefer & Miquelarena, 2001

F.: Aquino, A. E., S. A. Schaefer & A. M. Miquelarena (2001): A New Species of Hisonotus (Siluriformes, Loricariidae) of the Upper Rio Uruguay Basin. Americ. Mus. Novitates, 3333: 1–12.

Hab.: Uruguay, at the border to Brazil, federal state of Rivera, Rio Quaraí, a tributary of the Rio Uruguay. The pictured specimen was captured by S. Körber in northern Argentina in the Arroyo Tirica, Paraná drainage. At the time, we felt it was a morph of *Hisonotus laevior* (see 1st ed. [German], p. 340).
S. Körber captured this *H. laevior*, but in northern Argentina, in the Tirica Creek (Paraná Basin). The physical characteristics of the habitat on January 5th, 2001 at around 12:30 p.m. were: temperature of the slightly turbid water: 27°C, pH 7.4, and conductivity: 40μs/cm. *Hisonotus* were found among the shore vegetation (grass).

M.&B.: According to its origin, *H. ringueleti* maintenance temperatures should be rather cool. Breeding is unknown.

S: Typical for *Hisonotus ringueleti* is a light spot design on the upper and lower caudal fin lobes. The specimen brought back by Körber displayed exactly this design. However, it is not certain to be *H. ringueleti*, because *H. ringueleti* has to date only been confirmed from the type locality. A distribution—even within Argentina—has not been scientifically corroborated. Therefore, we prefer to present the species as *Hisonotus* cf. *ringueleti*.

T: 20°–26°C, **L:** 4 cm, **A:** 60 cm, **R:** b

Epactionotus aky
AZPELICUETA, CASCIOTTA, ALMIRÓN & KÖRBER, 2004

F: Azpelicueta, M. de las Mercedes, J. Casciotta, A. Almirón & S. Körber (2004): A new species of Otothyrini (Siluriformes: Loricariidae: Hypoptopomatinae) from the Río Uruguay basin, Argentina.- Verh. Ges. Ichthyol., Bd.4: 81-90

Syn.: -

Hab.: Argentina, Prov. Misiones, Río Uruguay, Arroyo Garibaldi, Arroyo Fortaleza. S. KÖRBER (Mühlheim, Germany) and travel companions captured these beautiful fish in the Argentinian province of Misiones in the Rio Uruguay drainage. *Epactionotus aky* is confined to a small area in the Fortaleza Creek, close to the city of Paraiso. The fish rest on the submerged leaves of an unspecified *Echinodorus* (Amazon sword plant). This was the only place where this fish could be captured. The following environmental data were collected close to 10:00 am on January 7th, 2001: water temperature 23.4°C, pH 7.5, total hardness <3°DH, and a conductivity of 40 μS/cm. The water was clear and had a moderate current.

M. & B.: *Epactionotus aky* must necessarily be provided with subtropical temperatures in the aquarium, since the temperature measurement was taken during the local summer, and it will definitively be much lower during the Argentinian winter. In the aquarium, this suckermouth catfish, too, rests preferably on aquatic

H.-G. Evers

The ventrum of *Epactionotus aky* is unpigmented.

Photo right:
During the summer of 2003, TROP RIO discovered this very species, or a very closely related one, in the state of Rio Grande do Sul, near the city of Porto Alegre, southern Brazil. These specimens also have a green body and require cool waters with a swift current.

H.-G. Evers

vegetation. At that time they adopt a beautiful green coloration. If maintenance conditions are deficient in illumination, the catfish become darker overall. Unfortunately, it is highly unlikely that there will ever be an import of this species from the limited area in which it was found.

S: *Epactionotus aky* was described shortly before printing of this book. We could only correct the name but had to leave it at its current place in the book.

T: 16°–24°C, L: 3.5 cm, A: 50 cm, R: b

Epactionotus aky, lateral view.

I. Seidel

Epactionotus aky, dorsal view. Plant leaves are the substrate of choice in the aquarium.

I. Seidel

Hisonotus sp. "Itapemirim"

This possibly still undescribed species was captured July 1999 by Maik BEYER and Hans-Georg EVERS in the Brazilian State of Espirito Santo. It inhabits the clear-water-carrying Rio Itapemirim, near the city of Cachoeiro de Itapemirim. Many specimens could be captured among the submersed overhanging grasses, always at sites with strong current.
This species grows to a length of approximately 6 cm.

The design is somewhat reminiscent of *Hisonotus leucofrenatus*, a species from further south, but it has a beautiful yellow cephalic design which is hardly visible in *Hisonotus* sp. "Itapemirim." Such a characteristic would be unexpected for a clear-water morph of *H. leucofrenatus*.

T: 20°–24°C, L: 4 cm, **A**: 60 cm, **R**: b

Microlepidogaster perforatus
EIGENMANN & EIGENMANN, 1889

F.: Eigenmann, C.H.& R.S. Eigenmann (1889): Preliminary notes on South American Nematognathi II.– Proc.California Acad.Sci., (2) 2: 28–56.

Syn.: *Otocinclus perforatus*.

Hab.: Brazil: Minas Gerais, Rio das Velhas Basin, Rio Carandahi.

M. & B.: See introduction to the genus. This problematic charge is something for the experienced aquarist only.

S: The positive identification of this specimen as *Microlepidogaster perforatus* requires further study. Marco T.C. LACERDA and Paulo VALERIO DA SILVA captured this fish May 1998 for the company TROP RIO in the basin of the Rio São Bartolomeu

(Rio das Velhas Basin), close to the Brazilian capital, Brasilia. That locality is part of the Paraná drainage. Although the distance to the type locality of *M. perforatus* is not great (for Brazilian conditions), the Rio das Velhas flows into the São Francisco, which introduces an element of uncertainty in the identification of the fish presented here as *Microlepidogaster* cf. *perforatus*. The long caudal peduncle catches one's eye, as it gives the fish an unusual appearance. EVERS received a few specimens to photograph. Unfortunately, they did not survive long in the aquarium, which might possibly be in connection with transport stress. This unusual species would surely be an interesting aquarium charge.

T: 23°–26°C, L: 8 cm, **A**: 60 cm, **R**: b

374

Hisonotus sp. "Itapemirim"

H.-G. Evers

Microlepidogaster cf. *perforatus* from the Rio São Bartolomeu.

H.-G. Evers

Genus *Otothyris* MYERS, 1927

Otothyris lophophanes (EIGENMANN & EIGENMANN, 1889)	Rio de Janeiro
Otothyris juquiae GARAVELLO, BRITSKI & SCHAEFER, 1998	São Paulo, Rio Ribeira
Otothyris rostrata GARAVELLO, BRITSKI & SCHAEFER, 1998	Santa Catarina,
	Rio Grande do Sul
Otothyris travassosi GARAVELLO, BRITSKI & SCHAEFER, 1998	Espirito Santo, Bahia

The previously monotypic genus was revised by GARAVELLO et al. in 1998. During the course of this work, it was discovered that the aquaristically known species *Otothyris canaliferus* has to be considered a synonym of *O. lophophanes*. Three additional species were described as members of this genus; all of them found in the rivers of the coastal plain in southeastern Brazil.

A notable attribute of this genus—shared only with the genus *Pseudotothyris*—is an ossified extension of the postcranial plate. Viewed from the side, these fishes seem to have an indention posteriorly on the head. Maintenance is difficult, and should follow the guidelines given for the genera *Pseudotothyris*, *Pseudotocinclus*, and *Schizolecis*.

Otothyris juquiae
GARAVELLO, BRITSKI & SCHAEFER, 1998

F.: Garavello, J.C., H.A. Britski & S.A. Schaefer (1998): Systematics of the Genus *Otothyris* Myers, 1927, with Comments on Geographic Distribution (Siluriformes: Loricariidae: Hypoptopomatinae).– Amer. Mus. Novitates, 3222: 1–19.

Syn.: None.

Hab.: Southeastern Brazil: State of São Paulo, basin of the Rio Ribeira de Iguapé. The species inhabits the clear- and white-water tributaries. Water temperatures in this habitat are often significantly below 20 °C. The current is locally swift.

M. & B.: EVERS has trial-imported several specimens, and had to determine that

this *Otothyris* species is probably the most difficult species to maintain of all. Based on the location and the characteristics of their natural habitat, the water temperature in our aquaria is bound to be much too high. Additionally, the need for algae fare is difficult to satisfy over the long run with substitutes.

S: *Otothyris juquiae* is rarely imported and should not be acquired by anyone but specialists with cool aquaria.

T: 16°–20°C, L: 3 cm, A: 50 cm, R: b

Otothyris juquiae

H.-G. Evers

H.-G. Evers

Capture of *Otothyris juquiae, Hisonotus leucofrenatus,* and "*Macrotocinclus*" sp. "São Paulo" in the Rio Juquiá, State of São Paulo, Brazil.

Otothyris lophophanes
(EIGENMANN & EIGENMANN, 1889)

F.: Eigenmann, C. H. & R. S. Eigenmann (1889): Preliminary notes on South American Nematognathi, II.– Proc. California Acad. Sci. 2d ser., 2: 18–56.

Syn.: *Rhinelepis lophophanes, Otocinclus lophophanes, Microlepidogaster lophophanes, Otocinclus cephalacanthus, Otothyris cephalacanthus, Otothyris canaliferus.*

Hab.: Brazil: states of Rio de Janeiro and southern Espirito Santo. The species inhabits both white- and clear-water biotopes.

M. & B.: Breeding this sensitive species has not been successful. It is difficult enough to acclimate the imported specimens to their new home. Additionally, most imports come from the cooler State of Rio de Janeiro, where the species inhabits fast-flowing biotopes of the coastal plain. This must necessarily be considered when choosing a correct maintenance temperature. Carefully provide *Artemia*-nauplii and sufficient vegetable fare. Impeccable water management is a must. Even experienced aquarists will have trouble with this species!

S.: For decades, this species was known in the aquarium hobby under the synonym *Otothyris canaliferus*. Only the revision of the genus by GARAVELLO et al. (1998) determined that the species name given by MYERS in 1927 was a synonym to the old name given by EIGENMANN & EIGENMANN. The latter described these dwarfs as belonging to the genus *Rhinelepis*, for us today a strange decision!

T: 18°–22°C, at times 2°–4°C higher, L: 3 cm, A: 50 cm, R: b

Otothyris travassosi
GARAVELLO, BRITSKI & SCHAEFER, 1998

F.: Garavello, J. C., H. A. Britski & S. A. Schaefer (1998): Systematics of the Genus *Otothyris* Myers, 1927, with Comments on Geographic Distribution (Siluriformes: Loricariidae: Hypoptopomatinae).– Amer. Mus. Novitates, 3222: 1–19.

Syn.: None.

Hab.: Brazil: states of Espirito Santo and southern Bahia. An inhabitant of the coastal plains. A white-water tributary of the Rio Junchai in the State of Espirito Santo (BR 101, km 3 at Posto Chapadão, a gas station) had the following values as of April 21st, 1995 (1:15 p.m.): Air temperature 29°C, water temperature 27°C, pH 6.7, conductivity 112 µS/cm. The *Otothyris* were hanging on the submersed overhanging shore vegetation in water with moderate current and a depth of up to 80 cm. In the same state, the species can also be found in the Ribeirão do Engano, a clear-water stream. On April 21st, 1995 (11:00 a.m.) the air temperature was 29°C, water temperature 26°C, pH 6.96, and the conductivity 140 µS/cm. This is a shallow clear-water river. The river bed consisted of sand and rocks, where small rapids ("cachoeiras") formed. The *Otothyris* were found on the rocks and escaped with the swift current as our shadows approached. The clear-water specimens were much harder to transport than those from white-water.

Otothyris lophophanes

H.-G. Evers

Otothyris travassoi

H.-G. Evers

M. & B.: As indicated for *O. lophophanes*.

S: Only a few specimens have been imported. Commercial fishing is very incipient in Espirito Santo. Usually it is the similar *O. lophophanes* from Rio de Janeiro which is exported.

T: 19°–25°C, **L:** 3 cm, **A:** 50 cm, **R:** b

Fam.: Loricariidae
Subfam.: Hypoptopomatinae

Genus *Parotocinclus*
EIGENMANN & EIGENMANN, 1889

P. amazonensis GARAVELLO, 1977	Brazil: Rio Solimões
P. aripuanensis GARAVELLO, 1988	Brazil, Mato Grosso
P. bahiensis (RIBEIRO, 1918)	Brazil: Bahia
P. britskii BOESEMAN, 1974	Suriname
P. cearensis GARVELLO, 1977	Brazil: Ceara
P. cesarpintoi RIBEIRO, 1939	Brazil: Alagoas
P. collinsae SCHMIDT & FERRARIS, 1985	Guyana
P. cristatus GARAVELLO, 1977	Brazil: Bahia
P. eppleyi SCHAEFER & PROVENZANO, 1993	Venezuela: Orinoco
P. doceanus (RIBEIRO, 1918)	Brazil: Espirito Santo
P. haroldoi GARAVELLO, 1988	Brazil: Piau
P. jimi GARAVELLO, 1977	Brazil: Bahia
"*P.*" *jumbo* BRITSKI & GARAVELLO, 2002	Brazil: Paraiba and Pernambuco
P. longirostris GARAVELLO, 1988	Brazil: Amazonas
P. maculicauda (STEINDACHNER, 1877)	Brazil: Rio de Janeiro, São Paulo
P. minutus GARAVELLO, 1977	Brazil: Bahia
P. planicauda GARAVELLO & BRITSKI, 2003	Brazil: Minas Gerais, Rio Doce
P. polyochrus SCHAEFER, 1988	Venezuela: Río Baria Basin
P. prata RIBEIRO, MELO & PAREIRA	Brazil: Rio São Francisco
P. spilosoma (FOWLER, 1941)	Brazil: Paraiba, Campina Grande
P. spilurus (FOWLER, 1941)	Brazil: Ceara

Recent scientific publications (GARAVELLO, 1977 and 1988, SCHÄFER, 1991, and SCHÄFER & PROVENZANO, 1993) have contributed to an increased awareness of this genus in aquarist circles. In the aquarium literature, too, various species of the genus were presented (LACERDA & EVERS, 1996). Nowadays, 21 species are known to belong to the genus *Parotocinclus*, which is distributed among four main areas:

1) Species of the Guyana Highlands, southern limit are the main branches of the Amazon, western limit the main branches of the rivers Orinoco and Negro.

2) Amazonian species.

3) Species from northeastern Brazil; Atlantic coastal rivers.

4) Species from the eastern and southeastern coastal rivers of Brazil (Atlantic coastal rain forest).

Well known to aquarists are several species (?) of small suckermouth catfishes which caused quite a stir in Europe under the denominations of "pitbull pleco" and LDA 25. Recently, BRITSKI & GARAVELLO (2002) described precisely said LDA 25 from the east Brazilian states of Paraiba and Pernambuco as "*Parotocinclus*" *jumbo*, something we consider somewhat surprising. Even under cursory observation, "*P.*" *jumbo* differs from all its congeners, given that it reaches a total length of up to eight centimeters, has a stout head shape, and is deep-bodied. Unique is also the anterior edge of the snout, densely covered with papillalike odontodes and which in juveniles even resemble small spines. A typical characteristic of the Hypoptopomatinae, a bony bridge between the pectoral fins, is shared by "*P.*" *jumbo*—although difficult to discern. However, even though the species is very unusual, it does in fact share most typical characteristics listed for *Parotocinclus* by SCHAEFER (1998). This is the reason why BRITSKI & GARAVELLO classified the fish into *Parotocinclus*, but with a caveat in regard to a possible reclassification in the future.

Aquaristically the best-known species is *Parotocinclus maculicauda*, the type-species of the genus. This catfish is regularly imported from the vicinity of Rio de Janeiro and has occasionally been bred in captivity (ELSHOLZ & ELSHOLZ, 1992). All other species mostly inhabit areas not subject to commercial fishing activities. It is only because of the private initiative of individual aquarists that they appear every once in a while on the aquaristic scene (LACERDA, 1994 a, b). No species is easy to keep. They all need clear, unpolluted and oxygen-rich water and they appreciate vegetable fare, although not exclusively. The feeding of *Artemia* nauplii has given good results during the acclimation period of wild-caught specimens. A readily visible characteristic of *Parotocinclus* spp. is the presence of an adipose fin, a trait that distinguishes them from all other genera in this subfamily. It is notorious how this genus includes not only species in excess of 5 cm length with a rather robust appearance, but also true dwarfs (e.g., *P. britskii*, *P.* cf. *longirostris* "Rio Cristalino") with a distinctly elongated cephalic profile.

Parotocinclus cf. *longirostris* in its natural habitat, the Rio Agua Preta, central Brazil.

Fam.: Loricariidae
Subfam.: Hypoptopomatinae

Parotocinclus aripuanensis GARAVELLO, 1988

F.: Garavello, J. C. (1988): Three new species of *Parotocinclus* Eigenmann & Eigenmann, 1889 with comments on their geographical distribution (Pisces, Loricariidae).– Naturalia, São Paulo, 13: 117–128.

Syn.: None.

Hab.: Brazil: Mato Grosso, Rio Canumã.
The Canumã River is a tributary of the Ju-
ruena River (Tapajós Basin). EVERS captured the pictured specimen in the Rio
Suia-Missú and Rio Sete de Setembro
(Xingú Basin). It coincides with the photograph in GARAVELLO, 1988. The species
colonizes clear-water, even in strong currents. The submersed overhanging shore

vegetation did not yield many specimens,
the species was not commonly found in
general.

M. & B.: Suitable dwarf species, but requires attention in maintenance. Due to the
lack of available specimens, no breeding
has been attempted.

S: *P. aripuanensis* is readily distinguished
from the similar morphs (?) of *Parotocinclus
longirostris*. The long snout is similar, but
the body seems stouter. An interesting
species for specialized hobbyists.

T: 26°–29°C, L: 2.5 cm, A: 50 cm, R: b

Parotocinclus britskii BOESEMAN, 1974
Alligator otocinclus

F.: Boeseman, M. (1974): On two Surinam species of Hypoptopomatinae, both
new to science (Loricariidae, Siluwhen-for-
mes, Ostariophysi).– Proc. Kon. Nederl.
Acad. Wetensch., 77(3): 257–271.

Syn.: None.

Hab.: Suriname: Coppename, Nickerie.
The pictured specimen was imported
from Suriname. Ingo SEIDEL captured August 2000 a *Parotocinclus* in the Mazaruni drainage in Guyana which probably
was *Parotocinclus britskii*. We present
that specimen here, too—but as *Parotocinclus* cf. *britskii*—because, for example, the brown design deviates somewhat from the species description.

M. & B.: A sensitive dwarf which requires
much attention. Maintain only in a dedicated species tank. If it is to be associated, then only with peaceful dwarf species which do not represent immediate
food competitors. The species is readily

fed with *Artemia* nauplii and copious
amounts of vegetable matter.

S: This dwarf is the only species from the
Guyana Highlands that has reached Germany, at least in the form of individual
specimens. The characteristic design—
pictured in GARAVELLO (1977)—allowed for
a positive identification.

T: 26°–29°C, L: 3 cm, A: 60 cm, R: b

P. cf. *britskii* from Guyana   I. Seidel

382

Parotocinclus aripuanensis

H.-G. Evers

Parotocinclus britskii

H.-G. Evers

Fam.: Loricariidae
Subfam.: Hypoptopomatinae

Parotocinclus cesarpintoi RIBEIRO, 1939
Cesar Pinto's otocinclus

F.: Ribeiro, P. de Miranda (1939): Um novo *Parotocinclus* de nordeste brasileiro.– Bol. Biol. S. Paulo, 4: 364–366.

Syn.: None.

Hab.: Brazil: Alagoas, Rio Paraiba do Norte, Quebrângulo.

M. & B.: Although somewhat similar to *Parotocinclus* sp. "Recife," the areas of distribution do not overlap. LACERDA & EVERS (1996, DATZ 2/96: 88–95) presented the species for the first time in detail to the aquarist. It is only thanks to the initiative of M.T.C. LACERDA that this species can be presented in a photograph. Due to the small number of specimens that have reached Germany, there are no breeding reports.

S: *P. cesarpintoi* lives in its habitat together with much more numerous *Parotocinclus* cf. *jumbo*. Interestingly, the same occurs with *P*. sp. "Recife," which shares its habitat with the real "*Parotocinclus*" *jumbo*.

T: 24°–28°C, L: 5 cm, A: 60 cm, R: b

P. cesarpintoi, subadult.   H.-G. Evers

Parotocinclus cesarpintoi, adult. The coloration can be lighter or darker, depending on its surroundings, as is the case with many suckermouth catfishes.

Parotocinclus cesarpintoi, pair, ventral view.

H.-G. Evers

Parotocinclus collinsae SCHMIDT & FERRARIS, 1985

F.: Schmidt, R.E. & C. J. Ferraris Jr., (1985): A new species of *Parotocinclus* (Pisces: Loricariidae).– Proc. Biol. Soc. Wash., 98(2): 341–346.

Syn.: None.

Hab.: Guyana: Essequibo Basin. Ingo SCHINDLER (Berlin) successfully captured this aquaristically unknown species in the Mazaruni River.

M. & B.: Due to the paucity of specimens, there are no reports.

S: The species has characteristic spots on the caudal peduncle. This trait facilitates the differentiation from other species hailing from the Guyana Highlands.

T: 25°–28°C, L: 3 cm, A: 50 cm, R: b

Parotocinclus cristatus GARAVELLO, 1977
Yellow-spot otocinclus

F.: Garavello, J.C. (1977): Systematics and geographical distribution of the genus *Parotocinclus* Eigenmann & Eigenmann, 1889 (Ostariophysi, Loricariidae). Arq. Zool. S. Paulo, 28(4): 1–37.

Syn.: None.

Hab.: Brazil: State of Bahia: Ilhéus, Fazenda Almada.

M. & B.: Readily maintained in the aquarium. This species even spawns if kept correctly. ELSHOLZ & ELSHOLZ (1994, BSSW 1/94: S. 14–19) report about breeding. About 20 eggs are laid per female.

S: The design is variable in this species and one and the same specimen can show different designs. Males usually have a design consisting of 4 crossbands covering the posterior body. Females on the other hand—sometimes, not always (!)—are covered by an arrangement of gray-brown dots.

T: 22°–25°C, L: 4 cm, A: 50 cm, R: b

P. cristatus, juvenile.

H.-G. Evers

Parotocinclus collinsae

Parotocinclus cristatus, adult.

Parotocinclus doceanus (DE MIRANDA RIBEIRO, 1918)

F.: Ribeiro, A. Miranda de (1918): Trés genéros e dessezete espécies novas de peixes brasileiros.– Rev. Mus. Paulista 10: 629–646 (717).

Syn.: *Microlepidogaster doceanus*.

Hab.: Brazil: Espirito Santo, Rio Doce. Maik BEYER (Maricá) captured the pictures specimen Spring 1999 in the Rio Doce Basin. Its habitat consists of clear-water rivers with swift current which turn very turbid during the rainy season.

M. & B.: Readily suited for the aquarium. Provide a small aquarium with wood and small foods, regular water exchanges, and powerful filtration. Breeding has not yet been successful.

S: This species is very similar to *P. maculicauda*, but remains significantly smaller. Additionally, the red coloration of the caudal fin is typical and the black longitudinal stripe is always visible, whereas in *P. maculicauda* it may make room to a rather fuzzy design. We present this species for the first time with its live colors.

T: 22°–25°C, L: 4 cm, A: 50 cm, R: b

Parotocinclus haroldoi GARAVELLO, 1988

F.: Garavello, J.C. (1988): Three new species of *Parotocinclus* Eigenmann & Eigenmann, 1889 with comments on their geographical distribution (Pisces, Loricariidae).– Naturalia, São Paulo, 13: 117–128.

Syn.: None.

Hab.: Northeastern Brazil: State of Piaui, Riacho Sanharo, Rio Parnaiba Drainage. GARAVELLO (1988) emphasizes that the area of distribution of *P. haroldoi* was heretofore unknown for the genus. Only sporadic collecting has been performed in this remote, dry northeastern (="Nordeste") section of Brazil. Therefore, it took a long time until a *Parotocinclus* sp. was described from this faraway corner.

M. & B.: There is hardly any experience to draw on due to a paucity of available specimens. This species hails from an area that is never visited by commercial fishing outfits. An import of larger numbers is therefore highly unlikely. The first specimens to reach Germany were given to W. SEUSS (Sparneck) by M.T.C. LACERDA, who himself captured the specimens close to Teresina, State of Piaui (LACERDA & EVERS, 1996). M. BEYER visited the site anew in June 1999 and was also able to capture only a few specimens. Of these we received one for photography. Breeding has not yet been successful.

S: Possibly one of the most beautiful *Parotocinclus*. The attractive spotted design is not mentioned in the original description, probably because it was lost in the preservation process. Similarly, in aquarium care, the fish adapt their coloration very much to their surroundings. Specimens maintained under excessively bright conditions lose the dark elements of their design.

T: 25°–29°C, L: 4 cm, A: 50 cm, R: b

Parotocinclus doceanus

H.-G. Evers

Parotocinclus haroldoi, see also photo on next page.

H.-G. Evers

Parotocinclus jimi Garavello, 1977

F.: Garavello, J.C. (1977): Systematics and geographical distribution of the genus *Parotocinclus* Eigenmann & Eigenmann, 1889 (Ostariophysi, Loricariidae).– Arq. Zool. S. Paulo, 28(4): 1–37.

Syn.: None.

Hab.: Brazil: State of Bahia, Rio do Peixe, a tributary of the Rio de Contas.

M. & B.: Only few specimens have been imported to date. Consequently, breeding has not yet been reported.
In regard to maintenance, the guidelines given for *P. maculicauda* also apply to this species, but with the exception of the preference for somewhat higher temperatures and the activity peak at twilight.

S: The Brazilian aquarist M. T. C. Lacerda visited the type locality and was able to capture a few specimens. A few years later (1999), M. Beyer was successful in capturing a larger number of specimens.

T: 23°–26°C, L: 5 cm, A: 60 cm, R: b

Preserved *Parotocinclus haroldoi*, ventral view. Text see previous page. H.-G. Evers

P. jimi with distinct light dorsal spots.

H.-G. Evers

Parotocinclus jimi, another possible coloration in the aquarium.

H.-G. Evers

Parotocinclus longirostris GARAVELLO, 1988

F.: Garavello, J.C. (1988): Three new species of *Parotocinclus* Eigenmann & Eigenmann, 1889 with comments on their geographical distribution (Pisces, Loricariidae).– Naturalia, São Paulo, 13: 117–128.

Syn.: None.

Hab.: Brazil: Rio Preto da Eva and other small igarapés in the Rio Negro Basin in the vicinity of Manaus.

M. & B.: Difficult to maintain. *P. longirostris* inhabits black-waters and white-waters. In nature, its main source of food is probably detritus, which is why under aquarium conditions, the usual diets are much too concentrated. Cautious feeding with algae-covered wood, possibly once in a while *Artemia* nauplii and flake foods, should ensure adequate nutrition. Tiny as the species is, a 30–40 l aquarium suffices. A species tank is recommended to facilitate dedicated care.

S: The area of distribution of this species is possibly much more extensive than the original description mentions. Besides a very large number of teeth on the upper mandible, the flattened, elongated head is particularly characteristic for *P. longirostris* (name!). Additionally, the first spine of the pectoral fins is very long. These characteristics are shared by other forms (or species?) which have been found here and there in central Amazonia. In this book, these morphs are designated as *Parotocinclus* cf. *longirostris* and their habitat is added. This way, these attractive fishes are better to tell apart. The forms are:

Parotocinclus cf. *longirostris* "Rio Agua Preta"

This fish is by far the most attractive member of the genus to date. Its green iridescent dots are unique among the suckermouth catfishes. The morph is rare in the Rio Agua Preta (central Brazil: Goias: Rio das Mortes drainage), but can also be found in the Rio Cristalino of the same basin, although in equally low numbers. At this second site it lives sympatrically with *P.* cf. *longirostris* "Rio Cristalino," which is colored differently and is even 0.5 cm smaller. The coloration strongly resembles *Parotocinclus eppleyi* from Venezuela, upper Orinoco.

Parotocinclus cf. *longirostris* "Rio Cristalino"

This morph appeared sporadically in 1995 under the trade name of *Parotocinclus* sp. "Minimus." LACERDA & EVERS (DATZ 2/96: S. 88–95) present the morph, including some data on its biotope. It is common in the Rio Cristalino, a tributary of the Rio das Mortes. It lives together with the morph from the Rio Agua Preta, but can be captured in great quantities and does not grow as large. P. VALERIO DA SILVA and H.-G. EVERS captured this morph in both rivers which are only a few kilometers apart and drain into the Rio das Mortes. It is surprising to find two such tiny species (?) in the same river system.

P. cf. *longirostris* "Rio Cristalino" is readily maintained in an aquarium. A ripe female has also been observed, although oviposition never occurred. A highly interesting charge for the suckermouth catfish specialist. Life expectancy under captive conditions is two years, whereas in nature the adults are said to disappear after the spawning season—it seems they only live one year in nature.

S: With is maximum length of only two centimeters, this is probably the smallest suckermouth catfish of all.

Parotocinclus cf. *longirostris* "Rio Agua Preta," additional photo on the following page.

Parotocinclus cf. *longirostris* "Rio Cristalino," additional photo on the following page.

Parotocinclus cf. *longirostris* "Rio Agua Preta," ventral view, see page 392 for text.

Parotocinclus cf. *longirostris* "Rio Cristalino," ventral view, see page 392 for text.

The Rio Agua Preta, in the Brazilian State of Mato Grosso, is a beautiful clear-water river.

Parotocinclus cf. *longirostris* "Tucurui"

The pictured morph (?) was captured by Paulo VALERIO DA SILVA in the vicinity of the Tucurui Reservoir, Rio Tocantins, central Brazil. This form, too, is a dwarf similar to the other morphs (?) of the *Parotocinclus longirostris* group.

A water temperature of 26°–29°C is recommended for all listed morphs. None comes even close to a length of 3 cm. What is more, *Parotocinclus* cf. *longirostris* "Rio Cristalino" only reaches 2 cm in length.

Parotocinclus maculicauda (STEINDACHNER, 1877)
Redfin otocinclus

F.: Steindachner, F. (1877): Die Süßwasserfische des südöstlichen Brasilien IV.– Sber.Akad.Wiss.Wien, 76(1): 217–230.

Syn.: *Otocinclus maculicauda, Hisonotus maculicauda, Parotocinclus steindachneri.*

Hab.: Brazil: southeastern states of Espirito Santo, Rio de Janeiro, São Paulo, and Santa Catarina. Clear-water rivers with a fast current and low to medium water depths are its habitat of choice. The fish often adhere by the hundreds to larger rocks or to submersed overhanging shore vegetation, head first into the partially raging current. Other members of the subfamily are frequent companions. Therefore, the water values given for *Schizolecis guntheri* and *Pseudotothyris janeirensis* also apply to this species.

M. & B.: As this species is a common presence in the aquarium trade, there is an extensive body of knowledge in regard to maintenance requirements. Cool temperatures, good water hygiene, and copious supplies of vegetable fare induce this species to ripen, and even a sporadic oviposition has been observed. ELSHOLZ & ELSHOLZ (1992) report in great detail about its reproductive biology. However, it is said not to be easy to induce.

S: This is the type-species of the genus *Parotocinclus*. Intraspecific variability is unknown. It is not certain that the *Parotocinclus* sp. "São Paulo," from the State of São Paulo, pictured here are also part of *P. maculicauda*, since with a length of only 3.0–3.5 cm they do not grow as large, and they have a somewhat differing coloration.

T: 18°–23°C, **L:** 5.,5 cm, **A:** 60 cm, **R:** b

Parotocinclus cf. *longirostris* "Tucurui"

H.-G. Evers

Parotocinclus maculicauda

H.-G. Evers

Fam.: Loricariidae
Subfam.: Hypoptopomatinae

Parotocinclus minutus GARAVELLO, 1976

F.: Garavello, J. C. (1976): Systematics and geographical distribution of the genus *Parotocinclus* Eigenmann & Eigenmann, 1889 (ostariophysi, Loricariidae).– Arq. Zool., S. Paulo, 28(4): 1–37.

Syn.: None.

Hab.: Brazil: State of Bahia, Rio Vasa-Barris. The pictured specimen is tentatively identified as *Parotocinclus* cf. *minutus* and was captured by commercial fishermen for the company TROP RIO close to the Chapada Diamantina, a well-known nature reserve in the heart of Bahia. The type locality of *P. minutus* is further north, at Canudos.

M. & B.: Not an easy charge, requiring special attention. Breeding has not been successful due to a paucity of individuals.

S: The type locality of *Parotocinclus bahiensis* (Senhor do Bonfim in Bahia) is much closer to the Chapada Diamantina. But unfortunately, not even GARAVELLO (1977) gives a detailed account in regard to the presence of the species. The design of the pictured specimen coincides with the portrayal given in the original description of *P. minutus*, especially in regard to the number and arrangement of the corporal crossbands. It must be noted, however, that only a comparative analyses of the type material of both species can bring a definitive answer. GARAVELLO (1997) does not compare *P. minutus* to *P. bahiensis* (RIBEIRO, 1918).

T: 24°–26°C, L: 3.5 cm, A: 60 cm, R: b

Parotocinclus maculicauda in their natural habitat. The fish face the current.   H.-G. Evers

Parotocinclus cf. *minutus* from the Chapada Diamantina.

H.-G. Evers

Rio Açude at Delmiro Gouveia, heavily polluted habitat of *Parotocinclus* sp. Delmiro Gouveia"

Parotocinclus sp. "Delmiro Gouveia"

Hab.: January 2000, coauthor EVERS discovered this somewhat unusual *Parotocinclus* species together with Marcos WANDERLEY (D'AGUA, Recife) in the drainage basin of the Rio São Francisco in the east Brazilian state of Alagoas. The site was located at the town of Delmiro Gouveia, about 20 km from the Rio São Francisco. The river Açude, slowly flowing through town, did not correspond at all to what a typical suckermouth catfish biotope is supposed to look like. The river was extremely polluted by the sewer discharges of town and presented itself in an unhealthy turbid gray color. At the same time, the temperature was extremely high; EVERS measured 34°C close to shore. Nobody would imagine suckermouth catfishes in such a biotope, let alone in such numbers. On a single afternoon, a collector for D'AGUA, equipped only with a cast net, "harvested" approximately 15,000 specimens at this very site!

M.&B.: Based on the habitat description, above, it is readily apparent that during the dry season this species can be present in an unbelievable population density and under extremely unfavorable conditions. Such environments are only survived by very robust and tolerant fishes. Correspondingly, *Parotocinclus* sp. "Delmiro Gouveia" forgives the occasional lapse in aquarium maintenance. In its requirements, no significant differences could be determined in relation to the similar "*Parotocinclus*" *jumbo*.
Breeding has probably not yet been successful, for this species has been in the trade for too short a time and is seen too rarely.

S: *Parotocinclus* sp. "Delmiro Gouveia" is easily distinguished from its similar species based on a divergent coloration. It has a light design on a dark-gray body.

T: 25°–30°C, **L**: 4.5–6.0 cm, **A**: 60 cm, **R**: b

Parotocinclus sp. "Essequibo"

Ingo SCHINDLER (Berlin) captured this new dwarf species in the Essequibo River Basin, Guyana. At the time this book was being written, the original description had been turned in for publication.
No information is available in regard to aquarium maintenance, much less captive breeding,

Parotocinclus sp. "Delmiro Gouveia"

H.-G. Evers

Parotocinclus sp. "Essequibo"

I. Schindler

Parotocinclus sp. "Mazaruni"

The pictured specimen was captured in a small tributary of the Mazaruni River of Guyana, the Issano Creek. This, too, is a dwarf species which hardly is expected to exceed 3 cm in total length as a adult. In appearance, this fish is somewhat reminiscent of the species surrounding *Parotocinclus longirostris*, especially in regard to the long snout. Ingo SEIDEL captured the species in August 2000 in Guyana, and was able to return to Germany with several specimens. Unfortunately—in line with the experience gathered with many of these dwarf hypoptopomatinids—the species was very sensitive and soon all specimens had died.

Parotocinclus sp. "Minas Gerais"

H.-G. EVERS, M.T.C. LACERDA, M. BEYER, and P. VALERIO DA SILVA captured this specimen October 1996 in the drainage of the Rio das Velhas, Rio São Francisco Basin, State of Minas Gerais, Brazil.
At the time, only 5 individuals of this beautiful species were captured over a period of 6 days in various clear-water rivers. Unfortunately, it turned out that all the fish that had reached Germany on that occasion were females. These all matured in the tap water of Hamburg, and after several months they all died, apparently from egg binding. Autopsy revealed 60–80 whitish eggs per female. The species is readily suited for aquarium maintenance. However, it is highly questionable that this species will ever reappear in the hobby, since there is no commercial fish collecting in the area.

T: 22°–25°C, L: 4 cm, A: 60 cm, R: b

H.-G. Evers

Parotocinclus sp. "Minas Gerais," very egg-laden.

Parotocinclus sp. "Mazaruni"

I. Seidel

Parotocinclus sp. "Minas Gerais"

H.-G. Evers

Parotocinclus sp. "Pernambuco"

We present this species (?) prior to the aquaristically broadly distributed *Parotocinclus* sp. "Recife" to facilitate a comparison. These fish are similar to the species which has been imported in large quantities for the last 10 years for the aquarium hobby from the vicinity of Recife (State of Pernambuco, Brazil). However, the new morph (?) is stouter and the yellow design elements on the body tend to be more linear and more disperse, including the dorsum. We do not want to decide here if it is indeed another species or a sport of *Parotocinclus* sp. "Recife." It is important to note that *Parotocinclus* sp. "Pernambuco" is also captured together with "*Parotocinclus*" *jumbo*. This *Parotocinclus*, too, is much rarer than the pitbulls. The habitat is located in the southern part of the State of Pernambuco.

T: 24°–28°C, **L:** 6 cm, **A:** 60 cm, **R:** b

H.-G. Evers

Biotope of *Parotocinclus* sp. "Pernambuco" and "*P.*" *jumbo* in the basin of Rio Ipojuca, State of Pernambuco.

Parotocinclus sp. "Pernambuco"

H.-G. Evers

Parotocinclus sp. "Pernambuco" ♂, dorsal view.

H.-G. Evers

Parotocinclus sp. "Peru"

The first import of this species by the company AQUARIUM DIETZENBACH in the year 2000 caused quite a stir (see EVERS, 2000b). The fish came from Iquitos as part of a shipment by the company AQUARIUM RIO MOMON. The exact habitat is unknown. This is the first *Parotocinclus* sp. reported from Amazonian Peru, all others come either from the Guyana Highlands or from extensive areas in Brazil. This species is a dwarf with a total length of 2.5 cm and has an attractive design. Especially conspicuous are the rust-red spots on the nape and the base of the caudal fin, as well as the crossbands which include the ventral region. The species is reminiscent in habitus to *Parotocinclus longirostris* from the central Amazon Basin, but is probably still undescribed. After *Parotocinclus* cf. *longirostris* "Rio Cristalino," *Parotocinclus* sp. "Peru" is the smallest species in the genus.

T: 25°–28°C, L: 2.5 cm, A: 50 cm, R: b

P. sp. "Peru," ventral view. The bands are readily distinguished.

Parotocinclus sp. "Peru," dorsal view. Note the rust-red spot on the nape!

Parotocinclus sp. "Rio Parnaiba"

Ingo SCHINDLER (Berlin) captured this interestingly patterned *Parotocinclus* in the Rio Parnaiba Basin in the State of Maranhão, Brazil. Its unusual design—especially of the caudal fin—clearly distinguishes this species from its congeners.

Parotocinclus sp. "Peru," lateral view.

H.-G. Evers

Parotocinclus sp. "Rio Parnaiba"

I. Schindler

Parotocinclus sp. "Recife"

Hab.: Brazil: State of Pernambuco, vicinity of port city of Recife.

M. & B.: Maintenance follows the guidelines given for P*arotocinclus maculicauda*, only somewhat warmer. Various aquarists have witnessed oviposition and it is common for well-fed females to ripen. Following extensive water exchanges with cooler water, the males become active. The eggs have a diameter of 2 mm. R. MELZER (Berlin) was repeatedly successful in rearing the fry, and the American aquarist Derek HEATH reported very extensively on the internet about reproduction (www.planetcatfish.com). This species is being imported on a regular basis for several years now and it would be desirable for this catfish to be also regularly captive-bred. An unfortunate characteristic of this catfish is that it occasionally nibbles on the aquatic vegetation. However, with adequate vegetable fare, the expression of this negative trait is minimized.

S: The identification of a catfish as *P. spilosoma* (Aquarium Atlas Vol. 5, p. 393) is questionable, despite the habitats are not far apart. It seems that the name *P. spilosoma* was adopted by the aquarium hobby without even glancing at the original description. In FOWLER (1941) is the description of a fish which has 6 large dark spots on a light brown body, beginning approximately at the dorsal fin. Additionally, the head of the true *Parotocinclus spilosoma* is dark. There is no mention of small white or yellow dots or stripes in the original description of *P. spilosoma*! These can be seen in correctly preserved *P.* sp. "Recife." However, since FOWLER described the species in 1941, after the types had already been collected by R. VON IHERING in 1936, it could be conceivable that the guanine pigmentation, which is responsible for the dot and line design, was destroyed over the interim by light and/or formaldehyde. As a consequence, FOWLER did not see the design when he drew the fish (see FOWLER, 1941 and 1954). Only a direct comparison between the type material and preserved *Parotocinclus* sp. "Recife" specimens could clarify the situation. Even more confusion was added with the import of another similar species from the same state, *Parotocinclus* sp. "Pernambuco" (see there).

Parotocinclus sp. "Recife" lives syntopically with "*Parotocinclus*" *jumbo*. The latter is always captured in larger numbers. At the most, only 10% of the captured loricariids are *Parotocinclus* sp. "Recife". A confusion with *P. haroldoi* is possible until the distribution of the dots on the body is studied more attentively, making the differences obvious.

T: 24°–27°C , **L**: 5 cm, **A**: 60 cm, **R**: b

Subadult *Parotocinclus* sp. "Recife" sometimes have a design on the caudal peduncle that is very similar to that shown in the drawing by FOWLER (1941, 1954) for *P. spilosoma*.

Parotocinclus sp. "Recife," ripe ♀.   H.-G. Evers

Parotocinclus sp. "Recife," ventral view of the same ♀.   H.-G. Evers

409

Parotocinclus sp. "São Paulo"

H.-G. Evers

Parotocinclus sp. "São Paulo"

This small species was captured by H.-G. EVERS, M. T. C. LACERDA, and M. BEYER in 1995 in a small clear-water stream in the vicinity of the city of Parati, State of São Paulo, Brazil. Initially it was taken to be a young specimen of the common *Parotocinclus maculicauda*, but they did not continue to grow in the aquarium and displayed a jet-black longitudinal band, which was always visible. It seems this species is rare, hardly any more specimens could be captured since then.

T: 18°–22°C, L: 3 cm, A: 60 cm, R: b

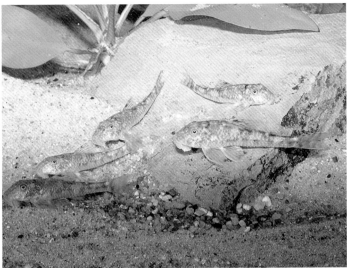

"*Parotocinclus*" *jumbo*; group in an aquarium.

I. Seidel

Goby plecos

The representatives of this group are small loricariids of only 4.5–6.0 cm total length, as is typical for members of the subfamily Hypoptopomatinae. For a long time, it did not even occur to us that these unusual fishes would be members of this subfamily. Rather we speculated them to be members of an undescribed genus of the subfamily Hypostominae. However, according to Britski & Garavello (2002) they do have the hypoptopomatinid-typical naked pectoral girdle, although it is difficult to detect in live specimens. LDA25, a well-known loricariid, has recently been described as "*Parotocinclus*" *jumbo* by Britski & Garavello (2002). But in the description it is already allowed for it to be an unusual species and clearly different from all other *Parotocinclus* species. For example, the specimens have

on the anterior edge of their mouth a row of small odontodes. Their function is unknown. Furthermore, the number of anal scutes is much reduced, which produces a large naked anal region. Those and other details make these catfish unique among the Hypoptopomatinae. The description of a new genus would have been justified, but Britski and Garavello do not go that far, in its stead indicating that phylogenetic analyses of the heteromorphic genus *Parotocinclus* are still pending. We place the two species at the end of the description of the genus *Parotocinclus*, because we consider the differences to their congeners as significant enough as to warrant a separation. This is also why in this book we write their genus name in quotes.

Fam.: Loricariidae
Subfam.: Hypoptopomatinae

The loricariids discussed below have a social beahvior similar to that of *Otocinclus* spp. or *Corydoras*, for example. SCHRAML (1996) was reminded by these fishes of a particular breed of dog, which is why the common name of "pitbull-loricariids" was coined. Later, however, he had to admit that he did not have the pitbull in mind, but rather the bullterrier. However, that's all water under the bridge, because once published, such mistakes are virtually impossible to correct.

In BAENSCH & RIEHL (1997) the common name of goby catfish [=Gründlingswels] is used, something that in our opinion is a far more fitting nomen for these delightful small aquarium charges.

The systematic classification of them within the subfamily Hypoptopomatinae does not come easy to us. Although the goby pleocs are remotely reminiscent of several representatives of the genus *Parotocinclus* given the presence of an adipose fin, but further close relatives within the subfamily cannot be named offhand.

Viewed from above, these fishes are quite strongly reminiscent of the east Brazilian *Parotocinclus* species, syntope in some of their habitats. However, the goby plecos are quite a bit deeper-bodied. The metallic sheen of the specimens is notorious, and it varies significantly according to the state of mind and substrate. It is probably the result of the degree of expression of the epidermal pigments. Since the metallic sheen is produced beneath the transparent scutes, the pigmentation of the surface modulates its expression.

The entire surface of these fishes appears only slightly rough. Although delicate odontodes can be seen on the scutes under a microscope, even in sexually active males the naked eye will virtually not discern such growth. Therefore, at present we can describe the sexual differences only on the basis of the greater length and smaller girth displayed by males. Still, such characteristics are sufficient to allow for an unequivocal identification among adult specimens. Ventrally, the fishes are naked with the exception of several rows of tiny scutes in the area between the pectorals. Finnage is similar in both sexes. There is an adipose fin as well as an anal fin, and no fin has a particularly high or low ray count. The fin formulas are: dorsal fin I/7, pectoral fins I/6, ventral fins I/5, anal fin I/5, caudal fin I/14/I. The hard rays (spines) of the fins (pectoral and ventral fins in particular) are usually shorter than the soft rays that directly follow. In regard to their dentition, goby plecos remind us of numerous representatives of the genus *Hypostomus*. They have an "all-around-dentition," which should do an adequate job rasping algae aufwuchs from rocks or wood as well as ingesting other types of food (detritus, plant fragments, insect larvae). Approximately 30 thin and long teeth are in each half of their upper and lower mandible. They are bicuspid, with a longer and a shorter tip.

It appears that the distribution of the goby plecos is limited to the eastern states especially of Pernambuco and Alagoas in Brazil. At present, there is only one representative in this new genus which is regularly imported in appreciable numbers. "*Parotocinclus*" *jumbo* is captured for export in large quantities in the vicinity of the city of Recife, the capital of the federal state of Pernambuco. A second species, which is found approximately 220 km further south at Quebrangulo, has already been presented by LACERDA & EVERS (1996) (unfortunately without illustration.). However, since its area of distribution lies far removed from traditional commercial fishing areas, only few specimens have been imported into Germany. The two goby plecos from Recife and

"*Parotocinclus*" sp. "Quebrangulo" in its natural habitat.

M.T.C. Lacerda

Quebrangulo are difficult to tell apart based on color alone. Although there are subtle differences in their design, these are difficult to pinpoint given the large chromatic variability of these fishes. The table below—based on data by LACERDA & EVERS (1996)—demonstrates quite clearly the differences in corporal proportions between them. Standard length is given in millimeters, whereas all other data are presented as a percentage thereof.

The table makes clear that especially the interorbital distance is a valid differentiating criterium between these two species. In comparison to "*Parotocinclus*" jumbo, "*Parotocinclus*" sp. "Quebrangulo" has, in addition to a distinctly greater distance between the eyes, a larger ocular diameter, a somewhat deeper and broader body, as well as a longer head.

After an initial complete ignorance as to the origin of these new suckermouth catfishes, there appeared the rumor in the hobby that these fishes needed cool water with a high oxygen saturation. This supposition got started because newly imported specimens frequently were sick and displayed a very notorious symptomatology, i.e., large rust-red spots (rust-spot disease, see chapter "Diseases"). It was inferred that these fishes had become ill because of erroneous holding conditions, that they had been maintained too warm. Observations in the natural habitat of these fishes, however, showed that this supposition is unfounded. Goby plecos occur in nature also at very high water temperatures. During the dry season, no biotope where the fishes were found in large numbers was determined to have a temperature below 30°C. Furthermore, the normal

Fam.: Loricariidae
Subfam.: Hypoptopomatinae

n = 5	"*Parotocinclus*" jumbo (LDA 25)	"*Parotocinclus*" sp. "Quebrangulo"
Standard length (SL) (mm)	28.5 – 32.4	24.1 – 33.4
Head length (% SL)	22.8 – 26.2	24.3 – 28.1
Depth of body (% SL)	15.2 – 17.5	19.0 – 20.6
Width of body (% SL)	22.8 – 24.1	25.0 – 26.7
Ocular diameter (% SL)	5.2 – 6.5	5.8 – 7.5
Interorbital distance (% SL)	7.4 – 8.4	9.7 – 10.0

temperature during that time of the year, especially in stagnant waters, was even as high as 34°–35°C. Of course, the waters close to mountain ranges in the Brazilian highlands are subject to large variations. They are surely somewhat cooler, have a higher oxygen concentration, and a swift current during the rainy season—the spawning season of the goby plecos. In October 2003, EVERS was able to capture "*Parotocinclus*" *jumbo* in significant quantities in the Rio Ipojuca, state of Pernambuco. There, the species inhabits shallow, clear waters (26.1°C, pH 6.0, 41μS/cm) over gravel substrates. Syntopic species include the corycat *Aspidoras depinnai*, an *Parotocinclus* sp. "Pernambuco", and all species are difficult to tell apart when seen lying in the shallow current.

The two loricariids "*Parotocinclus*" *jumbo* and *Parotocinclus* sp. "Delmiro Gouveia," meanwhile imported in larger numbers, are naturally captured at places where it is easiest, i.e., in the vicinity of cities, where they are found in astonishing numbers. However, these sites close to civilization turn into regular sewers during the dry season (the main fishing season) and carry extremely polluted waters. The fact that goby plecos tolerate such water contamination is a tribute to their hardiness, showing how robust and adaptable these fishes really are. However, that fishes captured under such conditions will suffer from some form of disease is only logical. An observation by LUCANUS (found at

HUSMANN, Internet) in the sense that the rust-spot disease only appears during the dry season—the time of least favorable living conditions—seems to corroborate this theory. This disease—microsporidia are probably the causative agent—is dealt with in greater detail in the chapter on diseases..

The previously mentioned social lifestyle of goby plecos shows parallels to the popular corydoras. The maintenance requirements of these plecos, too, follows many aspects of cory maintenance. At times they burrow in fine sand, only the head remaining visible above. It follows that maintenance benefits greatly from the presence of a sand substrate. In a such decorated aquarium, the fishes frequently stay in depressions exposed to the current.

Goby plecos are typical aufwuchs feeders which in the aquarium are busy scraping the algae from smooth surfaces. It is even said (RAITH, Internet) that they feed on blue algae. On the other hand, goby suckers can easily be kept on a diet consisting of the standard commercially available fare such as tablet and flake foods, pellets, vegetable fare (e.g., potatoes, cucumbers, and spinach), as well as small live and frozen foods (*Artemia*, *Cyclops*, *Daphnia* etc.).

In regard to the reproductive biology of goby plecos, it was to be expected that

414

The rust-spot disease commonly observed in "*Parotocinclus*" *jumbo* is probably the result of unfavorable environmental conditions in its natural habitat.

species which are found at such densities in nature would deviate in behavior from most other suckermouth catfishes. We suspected, therefore, that there would be no broodcare, especially since the equally schooling *Otocinclus* species and *Corydoras* do not practice such. It remained open, however, if these sand-dwellers would adhere their eggs to a substrate as *Otocinclus* and *Corydoras* species do, or if they would even bury their eggs in the sand, along the lines of some African *Chiloglanis* species. A description of a successful reproduction of LDA25 in an aquarium by Römer (in Baensch & Riehl, 1997) seems to confirm that the first alternative is the correct one. According to Römer, a successful stimulation of the breeders with the addition of cooler and desalinated water, was followed with unrest and group formation among the breeder goby plecos. The next morning he found eggs at various places in the aquarium. These must have been relatively small, because the larvae did not eat any *Artemia* nauplii until several days later. It seems that similar stimulation as in *Corydoras* is effective with goby plecos. The same recipe employed for *Corydoras* should therefore also lead to success in goby plecos (simulation of the dry season, i.e., higher temperatures, avoidance of water exchanges, followed by a simulation of the onset of rains, i.e., copious water exchanges with cooler water).

In the Internet (www.l-welse.com), there is a discussion forum where it is also reported that "*Parotocinclus*" *jumbo* breeds without broodcare. Photographs of eggs and young can be found there, too.

The social goby plecos appreciate aquarium sections that are subject to swift currents.

Habitat of "*Parotocinclus*" *jumbo*: Rio São Francisco, dry season

H.-G. Evers

Habitat of "*Parotocinclus*" *jumbo,* drainage of the Rio Ipojuca, state of Pernambuco.

Habitat of "*Parotocinclus*" sp. "Quebrangulo," a water remnant of a direct tributary of the Rio São Francisco.

"*Parotocinclus*" *jumbo* Britzki & Garavello, 2002

F.: Britski, H. A. & J. C. Garavello (2002): "*Parotocinclus*" *jumbo*, a new species of the subfamily Hypoptopomatinae from northeastern Brazil (Ostariophysi: Loricariidae).- Ichthyol. Explor. Freshwaters, 13(3): 279–288.

Syn.: LDA 25 (Das Aquarium 3/96).

Hab.: The oft-cited supposition that these fish hail from cool, swiftly flowing, oxygen-rich waters in the vicinity of Recife is erroneous. It seems the opposite is true. In fact, one will search in vain for cool waters in the vicinity of Recife, one of the warmest areas of Brazil. According to the testimony of an employee of the ornamental fish exporter D'AGUA (Recife), the species hails from similarly warm and extremely polluted habitats in the vicinity of the city as those described for *Parotocinclus* sp. "Delmiro Gouveia." The biotopes (as far as they can still be called such around Recife) are subject to strong seasonal changes. During the rainy season, they surely change into faster flowing and more oxygen-rich streams with somewhat lower temperatures than they are during the dry season. In Pernambuco, however, the species can also be found in undisturbed clear-water biotopes (see goby pleco introduction) and basically virtually everywhere. "*Parotocinclus*" jumbo is arguably the most common loricariid species in Pernambuco and can be found in coastal streams as well as further inland in stable streams, including the area of influence of the Rio São Francisco.

M.&B.: These droll small plecos probably have requirements most similar to *Corydoras*. Although they have to deal with completely different conditions during the dry season, they seem to be rheophilic. In the aquarium, they preferably stay in depressions made in the sand by the currents. Although every once in a while they bump into each other, they can be considered very peaceful and social. "*P.*" jumbo feeds on everything that can be tackled by its small suctorial mouth. Preferred are, besides algae aufwuchs, all kinds of flake and tablet foods, pellets, and small live and frozen foods, such as *Cyclops*, *Daphnia*, *Artemia*, and grindal worms. RÖMER (in BAENSCH & RIEHL, 1997) reports on a breeding success following an abrupt water exchange using deionized water at only 20°C. As a result of the stimulus, RÖMER reports that individual animals began swimming restlessly. After the illumination had been turned off, small groups formed. Spawning itself could not be observed. The next morning, eggs were discovered at various locations throughout the aquarium. These were whitish transparent, and slightly oval. After ca. 10 days, several tiny young could be discerned on the sand substrate of the aquarium, which, according to RÖMER, had to content themselves during the first days with whatever food was available in the aquarium. It was only after 14 days that the few surviving fry accepted *Artemia* nauplii. Further breeding did not occur, since a short time thereafter the breeders had also died.

S: This species seems to have a distinctly larger mouth than its fellow goby pleco. The trade frequently offers the species together with a still undescribed *Parotocinclus* species, which here is called *P.* sp "Recife." However, the proportion of this *Parotocinclus* is usually very small. Very frequently, the newly imported "*Parotocinclus*" jumbo suffer from the rust-spot disease described in more detail in the chapter on diseases. Apparently the disease is contagious.
Based on the living conditions described above for its natural habitat, it is highly unlikely, that the fish acquire the disease

"*Parotocinclus*" *jumbo* from the vicinity of Recife.

H.-G. Evers

"*Parotocinclus*" *jumbo,* pair; male left, female right.

I. Seidel

because of detrimental holding conditions. The disease probably surfaces because of the stress caused by water pollution and a high concentration of pathogens. After all, the fish is captured for export during the dry season from sewerlike waters.

"*P.*" jumbo is a highly atypical *Parotocinclus* species; the describers already indicated the possibility of requiring its own genus. This is the reason why we present the two goby plecos in quotes and after the *Parotocinclus* species proper.

T: 25°–30°C, **L:** 4.5–6.0 cm, **A:** 60 cm, **R:** b

"*Parotocinclus*" sp. "Quebrangulo"

S: Lacerda, M.T.C. & H.-G. Evers (1996): *Parotocinclus*-Arten aus Brazil. DATZ 49(2): 88–95.

Hab.: In December 1992, the Brazilian ornamental fish exporter M. Lacerda (Trop Rio, Rio de Janeiro) discovered a second goby pleco during an excursion to the Rio Paraiba (Rio Paraiba do Norte, to be exact) in the state of Alagoas. Since close to the city of Quebrangulo the river was extremely polluted, the collection team drove several kilometers upriver. There the waters presented themselves as swiftly flowing and clean. Since it was the dry season, the water level was very low and the temperature extremely high. Daytime temperatures reached 35°C and above. Syntopically to the Quebrangulo goby pleco—as we propose to call the species—there was also a *Parotocinclus* species. However, in this case it was *Parotocinclus cesarpintoi*. In shallower water, primarily younger specimens were

found over sand. Older specimens concentrated in deeper waters (at least one meter in depth) around larger rocks. As Lacerda went several kilometers upriver, he saw thousands of goby plecos. Apparently, the distribution of this species extends significantly further west, almost the locality where "*Parotocinclus*" jumbo was discovered. January 2000, coauthor Evers was able to capture light-colored goby plecos about 30 km east of Delmiro Gouveia in a water remnant of a Rio São Francisco tributary close to the city of Piranhas—probably members of the same species. The stream, which had a steep slope, and therefore is likely to have a very swift current during the rainy season, had a temperature of 35°C, a pH of around 7, and a conductivity of 80 µS/cm.

M.&B.: See "*Parotocinclus*" jumbo.

S: Lacerda & Evers (1996) describe quite extensively this species and "*Paroto-*

"*Parotocinclus*" sp. "Quebrangulo;" ♂   H.-G. Evers

The Rio Paraiba close to the locality of Quebrangulo.   M.T.C. Lacerda

cinclus" jumbo in their publication about Brazilian *Parotocinclus* species, and also mention the differences between the two goby plecos. However, there is no representation of the Quebrangulo goby pleco—due to a mistake, there is an *Hypostomus* species depicted in its stead. It might be then that the photo shown here is the first time a graphic representation appeared in the German aquarium literature [German ed.].

There are unequivocal differences to "*Parotocinclus*" jumbo. Especially anatomical differences can be named. Although there are also differences in coloration, these are difficult to specify, because the coloration of both species is extremely variable and is influenced by the mood of the animal and the substrate it is on. Whereas the two species are virtually identical in relation to the length they achieve, there are significant divergences in their body proportions. Foremost difference is the interorbital distance, i.e., the shortest distance between the eyes. It is significantly larger in animals from Quebrangulo compared to "*Parotocinclus*" jumbo. Additionally, it seems the eyes of this species are somewhat larger, the body somewhat broader and deeper, and the head somewhat longer.

Whereas "*Parotocinclus*" jumbo has been imported for the hobby in significant quantities for years, the Quebrangulo goby pleco is unlikely to be so even in the foreseeable future. The habitat of this species is far off the areas commercially fished for the trade. Only coauthor EVERS received a small group of animals from M. LACERDA (TROP RIO) from Brazil, but was unable to breed them.

T: 25°–30°C, L: 4.5–6.0 cm, A: 60 cm, R: b

Genera
Pseudotocinclus NICHOLS, 1919
Pseudotothyris BRITSKI & GARAVELLO, 1984
Schizolecis BRITSKI & GARAVELLO, 1984

All members of these small genera live in the area of the southeastern Atlantic coastal rain forest. The genus *Pseudotothyris* comprises 2 species, whereas *Pseudotocinclus* and *Schizolecis* are both monotypic. *Pseudotothyris janeirensis* and *Schizolecis guntheri* are occasionally imported. *Pseudotocinclus tietensis* was captured for the first time alive at the end of 1998 by M.T.C. LACERDA and M. BEYER in the upper Rio Tieté (State of São Paulo), and was exported in small quantities by the company TROP RIO to the United States and Japan. All these species are very sensitive in regard to suboptimal water conditions. Additionally, a species tank is recommended for the maintenance of these sensitive algae-eaters, because of their dietary requirements. Given their reduced size, even small aquaria of 20 l volume suffice for a group of 6–10 specimens. Only the *Pseudotocinclus* require 50 l as a minimum aquarium volume. Weekly partial water exchanges of at least 50%, a diet rich in vegetable and animal fare, and especially a constant, somewhat subtropical temperature of below 23°C, with momentary drops to 18°C, should be sufficient to acclimate these loricariids. Under such conditions they will even ripen. The successful maintenance and even the eventual reproduction of one of these species should be a goal of the advanced aquarium hobby.

Pseudotocinclus tietensis ♀, see next page for text.

H.-G. Evers

Pseudotocinclus tietensis ♂

H.-G. Evers

Pseudotocinclus tietensis (VON IHERING, 1907)

F.: Ihering, R. v. (1907): Diversas espécies novas de peixes nematognathas do Brasil.– Notas Prel. Mus. Paulista, 1: 13–39.

Syn.: Otocinclus tietensis, Pseudotocinclus intermedius, Microlepidogaster tietensis.

Hab.: Brazil: State of São Paulo: Rio Tieté, Campo Grande.
The headwaters of the Tieté River are the habitat of this unusual species. The area is characterized by smallish clear-water tributaries with partially raging currents flowing over a gravel and stone bed.

M. & B.: A very exacting charge, *P. tietensis* only has a chance when maintenance conditions are kept cool. An unheated aquarium, best in the basement, or in its defect with a chiller, is a necessity for the summer months. Once the acclimation hurdle is overcome, the catfish prefers vegetable fare, but has omnivorous habits. Frequent water exchanges and a strong current are additional maintenance requirements for successful care and possible breeding.

S: A rare species for the suckermouth catfish specialist. The initiative of M. T. C. LACERDA and M. BEYER (both Rio de Janeiro) has been key to introduce this species at least once to Germany.

T: 16°–22°C, L: 8 cm, A: 80 cm, R: b

Pseudotothyris janeirensis BRITSKI & GARAVELLO, 1984

F.: Britski, H.A.& J.C. Garavello (1984): Two new southeastern Brazilian genera of Hypoptopomatinae and a redescription of *Pseudotocinclus* Nichols, 1919 (Ostariophysi, Loricariidae): – Papéis Avulsos Zool., S. Paulo, 35(21): 225–241.

Syn.: None.

Hab.: Brazil: State of Rio de Janeiro: Rio das Macacos, Rio da Taquara. H.-G. EVERS and M. T. C. LACERDA found this species in the Rio Lilico (State of Rio de Janeiro, at Barro Branco). The clear-water had the following characteristics (October 14th, 1996, 14:00 hrs.): Temperature 23.5°C, pH 6.5, and a conductivity of 38 μS/cm. As is the case for so many bodies of water in the region, the increase in population with its consequential pollution is the main threat of the piscine community. Commercial fishermen confirm a marked decrease in population densities, especially of sensitive species in newly colonized areas.

M. & B.: In mid 1995 this species reached Germany for the first time in appreciable numbers. The characteristics outlined for *Otothyris lophophanes* also apply to this species. It is sensitive and difficult to care for.

T: 18°–24°C; L: 4 cm, A: 50 cm, R: b

Pseudotocinclus tietensis ♀, ventral view. For additional photos see page 423.

H.-G. Evers

Pseudotothyris janeirensis

H.-G. Evers

Pseudotothyris obtusa, adult.

H.-G. Evers

Pseudotothyris obtusa (RIBEIRO, 1911)

F.: Ribeiro, A. de Miranda (1911): Fauna Brasiliense. Peixes. Eleuterobranchios Aspirophoros.– Arq. Mus. Nac. Rio de Janeiro, 16: 1–504.

Syn.: *Otocinclus obtusus.*

Hab.: Brazil: southeastern states of São Paulo, Santa Catarina, and Paranagua. H.-G. EVERS, M.T.C. LACERDA, and M. BEYER captured this species on April 15th, 1995 (16:00 hrs.) in small, black-water channels of the Rio Preto system at Itanhaém (State of São Paulo). The aerial temperature was 27°C, water temperature 24.5°C, pH 5.65, and the conductivity 62 μS/cm. The bottom consisted of snow-white quartz sand and the water was one meter deep at the most. There was no aquatic vegetation *per se*, but the *Pseu-dotothyris* adhered to the submersed branches of the shore vegetation hanging into the water.

M. & B.: A complicated charge, compare with *Otothyris lophophanes*. This species is said to also occur in clear-water biotopes. The specimens brought back to Germany hailed from black-water, were difficult to feed, and only survived for a short period of time in the aquarium.

T: 21°–25°C, **L:** 3.5 cm, **A:** 50 cm, **R:** b

Pseudotothyris obtusa, juvenile from black-water at Itanhaém.   H.-G. Evers

Schizolecis guntheri, ventral view. See following page for text and additional photos.

Schizolecis guntheri (Ribeiro, 1918)

F.: Ribeiro, A. de Miranda (1918): Trés géneros e dessezete espécies novas de peixes brasileiros. Rev.Mus.Paulista, 10: 629–646.

Syn.: *Microlepidogaster guntheri, Microlepidogaster güntheri, Pseudotocinclus ribeiroi.*

Hab.: Brazil: coastal clear-water streams and rivers with swift current of the Atlantic rain forest in the states of Rio de Janeiro and São Paulo. The characteristics of interest of two selected biotopes are described below:
Rio da Mata (tributary of the Rio Capivari, State of Rio de Janeiro), April 18th, 1995 (15:00 hrs.), air temperature 25.5°C, water temperature 23°C, pH 7.4, conductivity 25 µS/cm; and Rio Barra Grande near Parati (State of Rio de Janeiro), April 16th, 1995 (10:00 hrs.), air temperature 25°C, water temperature 23°C, pH 6.8, conductivity 18 µS/cm. Ripe *Schizolecis* females were captured here. It is unknown if there is a particular spawning season, because the water level of these waters is fairly constant throughout the year. However, there are two rainy periods (January/February and June–August).

M. & B.: This species is not quite as exacting as the members of the genus *Otothyris*, but should be maintained under similar conditions. With a good diet, some females will ripen, but apparently no successful captive reproduction has occurred. Every once in a while the species is imported, sometimes even under the correct name.

S: The species must be called "*guntheri.*" It is only several pages later that the original describer calls the same species "*güntheri,*" in honor of the British ichthyologist Albert Günther. The genus is monotypic.

T: 18°–24°C (change periodically), **L:** 5 cm, **A:** 60 cm, **R:** b

H.-G. Evers

An additional variation of *Schizolecis guntheri* appearing in the trade, see also the photo on the previous page.

Schizolecis guntheri from the Rio Barra Grande at Parati.

H.-G. Evers

Schizolecis guntheri has a variable design.

H.-G. Evers

Lampiella cf. *gibbosa* from Rio do Azeite

H.-G. Evers

New Tribus Lampiellini ISBRÜCKER, 2001

Genus *Lampiella* ISBRÜCKER, 2001

Lampiella gibbosa (MIRANDA RIBEIRO, 1908)	Rio Betari, São Paulo, Brazil

During the revision of the genus *Oto-cinclus* (SCHAEFER, 1997), already one species was clearly set aside based on morphological differences and its classification as to genus remained open. In the 1st ed. [German] the species was presented under the heading of Unidentified Hypoptopomatinae, new genus LG 1. The only species, "*Otocinclus*" *gibbosus*, has now received its classification as *Lampiella gibbosa* (MIRANDA RIBEIRO, 1908) due to a description of the genus *Lampiella* by ISBRÜCKER (in ISBRÜCKER et al., 2001). The specimen of *Lampiella gibbosa* pictured here hails from the type locality of Iporanga, Rio Betari, in the state of São Paulo. Co-author EVERS was able, in 1995 and 2001, together with Maik BEYER (Maricá), to capture in the nearby Rio do Azeite a morph (?) of *Lampiella*.

However, there are distinct differences in coloration in comparison to the true *Lampiella gibbosa*. The variant is presented here under the designation of *Lampiella* cf. *gibbosa*. This is also the variant which has sporadically been imported to Germany.

Simultaneously with the description of the genus, *Lampiella* was placed into the new tribe Lampiellini ISBRÜCKER (in ISBRÜCKER et al., 2001). Therefore, the subfamily Hypoptopomatinae has now three tribes (Hypoptopomatini, Otothyrini, and Lampiellini). The tribe Lampiellini is the sister group of all other Hypoptopomatinae and appears to be the most ancient (most plesiomorph) representative of the subfamily.

430

Lampiella gibbosa (Ribeiro, 1908)

F.: Ribeiro, A. de Miranda (1908): Peixes da Ribeira. Resultados de excursão do Sr. Ricardo Krone, Membro Correspondente do Museu Nacional de Rio de Janeiro. Kosmos, Rio d.J., 5:1–5.

Syn.: *Otocinclus gibbosus.*

Hab.: Brazil: State of São Paulo: Rio Betari at Iporanga.
Evers, Lacerda & Beyer captured the species in the vicinity of the town of Iporanga on April 14th, 1995 (13:00 hrs.) with the following biotope characteristics: clearwater, swift current, shallow water over gravel. Water temperature 21°C, pH 7.67, conductivity 96 µS/cm. The catfish sit on top of round stones in the swift current. When threatened, they dart into the crevices of the rubble zone.
An additional, less attractive variant (?) was captured in greater numbers in a small tributary of the Rio do Azeite, the Rio do Passagem at Itariri (State of São Paulo). On April 15th, 1995 (10:30 hrs) the characteristics were: water temperature 22°C, pH 6.5, and conductivity 16 µS/cm.

M. & B.: With high concentrations of dissolved oxygen, the species is readily maintained. A fast descent in oxygen levels and/or a temperature increase above 25°C has fatal consequences for the entire population. Ripe females could be observed while the fish were maintained for over a year. However, no spawning was detected.

Lampiella gibbosa, ventral view.

S: *Lampiella gibbosa* occupies a special place due to its body shape and gorgeous coloration. Schaefer (1997) removed the species from the genus *Otocinclus* without describing a new genus for the species. Following Isbrücker (2001) this species has been changed into the new genus *Lampiella*.

T: 18°–22°C, **L:** 5 cm, **A:** 60 cm, **R:** b

431

Lampiella gibbosa, variant I.

H.-G. Evers

Lampiella gibbosa, variant II.

H.-G. Evers

Lampiella gibbosa, variant III.

H.-G. Evers

Capture of *Lampiella gibbosa* in the shallow waters of the highlands of São Paulo, Rio Betari

Unidentifiable Hypoptopomatinae

While researching for this book, repeatedly appeared species we could not classify into any of the described genera, despite a thorough analysis. Therefore, we decided to present these species at the end of the corresponding subfamilies and assign them a code. Since we begin with the Hypoptopomatinae, we start here with LG 1. "L" stands for the family—here Loricariidae—and the G for genus. The Hypoptopomatinae and Loricariinae contain a manageable quantity of such species, but in the Ancistrinae and Hypostominae—in Volume 2—there will be significantly more codes, since, for example, the many L-catfishes will be assigned such a LG-code in case a corresponding genus cannot be assigned unequivocally. We hope to contribute this way to a better overview of the hard to classify species.

Undetermined Genus LG 1

The pictured dwarf suckermouth catfish was captured by M. BEYER, M. T. C. LACERDA, and H.-G. EVERS April 1995 in the Rio Barra Grande at Parati, in the State of São Paulo, southeastern Brazil. *Schizolecis guntheri* is a syntopic species on the submersed overhanging shore vegetation.
Genus and species classification are unknown. Initially we suspected them to be juveniles of *Kronichthys*, a hypostomine genus living in the same general area. However, the specimens brought to Germany basically did not grow over a period of eight months until, on a hot summer day, they succumbed to a water temperature in excess of 30°C. Maintain the species at moderate temperatures.

T: 16°–20°C, L: 5 cm, A: 60 cm, R: b

Undetermined Genus LG 2

Trade name: *Otocinclus* sp. "Negros," sometimes also *Otocinclus* "paulinus," but that is a different species, hailing from the Brazilian State of São Paulo, and placed by SCHAEFER (1997) into the genus *Hisonotus*. BILKE (1992) calls the species erroneously *Otocinclus notatus* (see *Hisonotus notatus*). In the VDA-Work-Group "Barbs, Characins, Loaches, Catfishes" the species is also called "KBO" ("Kleiner Brauner Oto" [= small brown oto]). The eyes are situated higher in this species than in *Otocinclus*, and an adipose fin is lacking. The cephalic profile is less elongated than in *Hisonotus* or *Microlepidogaster*. At present, there is no way to express an opinion as to the scientific classification of these fish, which is a pity, since this species is constantly being offered in the aquarium trade.

Hab.: Imported in large quantities from Paraguay, and also occurs in northern Argentina (B. SCHMITT, Hamburg, pers. comm. to EVERS). At those latitudes, the temperatures are lower during the winter (= summer in northern latitudes), a fact that should be taken into account for aquarium care.

LG 1 from the Rio Barra Grande.

H.-G. Evers

LG 2, adhered to the aquarium pane.

H.-G. Evers

This Hypoptopomatinae sp. is very similar to LG 2, but lays larger eggs.   I. Seidel

M. & B.: Undemanding. Cool temperatures to 24°C are appreciated and, even with a normal diet, ripe females can be observed. Brief periods of temperatures in excess of even 30°C are tolerated. Females grow to almost twice the size of males, and when egg-laden, have considerable girth. Daily exchanges with cool water and an increased current stimulate oviposition and often lead to group spawning.

One or several males will court a ripe female in a manner reminiscent of *Corydoras*. The males constantly attempt to cross the female in front. Once successful, the male bends around the head of the female until it encloses the flanks in a semicircle. The females to not adhere to the ventral fins of the male. There are both "lefties" and "righties." This is the moment of oviposition and fertilization.

The eggs adhere to the spawning substrate, may it be wood, plants, or the panes of the aquarium. Spawn and fry are not molested by the fish. Rearing the tiny fry is simple with a diet based on frozen rotifers, and even finely-ground flake foods are an option. *Artemia* nauplii are also taken and the occasionally ingested cyst is excreted without detriment (see photographs). Fry of other members in this subfamily are much more sensitive in this regard. With good care and an appropriate diet, the fish are already mature at an age of 3–4 months and spawn for the first time a few weeks later. Another detailed breeding report is given by BILKE (1992).

T: 18°–24°C, **L:** 3–4 cm, **A:** 50 cm, **R:** b

LG 2

H.-G. Evers

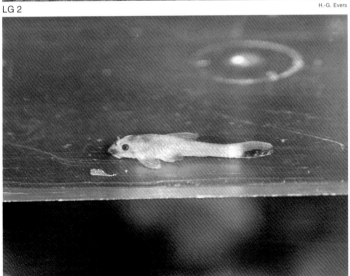

LG 2, a xanthochromic sport.

R. Melzer

Fam.: Loricariidae
Subfam.: Hypoptopomatinae

Spawning sequence LG 2: Two ♂♂ court an egg-laden ♀.

S.Hetz

Spawning sequence LG 2: the ♀ during oviposition.

S. Hetz

S. Hetz

LG 2: Spawning sequence. Spawn on a leaf.

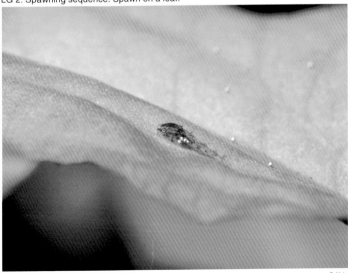

S. Hetz

LG 2: fry with *Artemia* cysts in its gastrointestinal tract.

LG 3 (small photo: LG 3 from the central Xingú River at Altamira)

I. Seidel

H.-G. Evers

Undetermined Genus LG 3

This small species is somewhat reminiscent of the genera *Hisonotus* or *Microlepidogaster* or the small *Parotocinclus*, but lacks the adipose fin. The elongated head and greenish hue of newly-captured specimens are characteristic for this miniature. H.-G. Evers, M.T.C. Lacerda, and P. Valerio da Silva captured this species at several sites in the Serra do Roncador (Brazil, State of Mato Grosso) in the basin of the Rio Suia-Missú, one of the headwaters of the Xingú. All sites carry clear-water, have a swift current, a low conductivity, a pH around 5, and a temperature of 27°–29°C. Scott Schaefer (written comm.) received preserved specimens for analysis. Schaefer (1998)

mentions several taxons which still require definition. One ("new taxon 1") is probably this species. Only a few live specimens were brought to Germany for photography, so there are no data on breeding. However, it seems this dwarf is another one of the interesting species for aquarists. Some specimens collected during a second trip (June 1999) to the mentioned area, spawned in the transport bag! Several green, relatively large (ca. 1.2 mm diameter) eggs were found on the wall of the bag. The females of this species are easily twice as large as the males.

T: 26°–29°C, L: 3 cm, A: 60 cm, R: b

Sturisoma festivum ♂, see page 520 for text.

H.-G. Evers

Subfamily Loricariinae BONAPARTE, 1831

Previously, the whiptail catfishes and their associates were the best-known suckermouth catfishes to aquarists. Today—although still popular with many hobbyists—it is the members of the subfamily Ancistrinae with their superior coloration that are undoubtedly the most popular of the loricariids. Due to their lifestyle, the loricariin suckermouth catfishes are colored rather plain, with a distinct predominance of gray and brown hues. This disadvantage (in the hobbyists eyes), however, is compensated by the sometimes outrageous shape of several of its members. Additionally, these species are by and large suited for aquarium maintenance and—with some effort—may even breed in captivity.

All Loricariinae have a dorsoventrally very flattened caudal peduncle and a row of bony plates runs along each of their flanks. These fishes, too, as is the case with virtually all suckermouth catfishes, have a gastrointestinal tract of at least body length—in most species the length is even triple and more that of their body. The intestines are often wound up in a spiral inside the abdomen. Since many species either have only small bony plates (scutes) ventrally or lack them completely, the observer can readily distinguish the filled intestinal loops inside the abdomen of specimens adhering to the front pane of the aquarium. In completely armored species this is impossible to distinguish. The intestinal anatomy is a good indication of the animal's diet. Many Loricariinae are appropriately fed with a diet based exclusively on vegetable matter (*Farlowella*, *Sturisoma*, and many others), but readily accept supplemental fare of animal origin. Along these lines, most *Rineloricaria* and related genera should more appropriately be classified as omnivores. The main diet in nature often consists of detritus. In benthic (bottom-oriented) species this should not come as a surprise. Nevertheless, it would be a mistake to generalize. In much of the older literature, general statements such as [transl.] "typical algivore, best maintained on a diet of blanched lettuce and peas" and so on can be found everywhere. If this advice would be applied to the voracious and large species of the genus *Spatuloricaria*, a group of four specimens would already demand a daily ration of at least a whole head of lettuce! Naturally, such a solution would only spell major trouble. Therefore, prior to the acquisition of such large species, the sensible thing is to inform oneself exactly as to the requirements of the prospective charge. Practically every species uses alternate sources of food in nature, i.e., occupies a different ecological niche. This point is particularly evident in the heterogenous genus *Rineloricaria*. *Rineloricaria* sp. aff. *latirostris* from the vicinity of Rio de Janeiro has a relatively long intestinal tract and in its natural habitat consumes enormous quantities of detritus, i.e., sediments, to a greater or lesser extent. In the aquarium, on the other hand, this species reveals being an omnivore, feeding on large quantities of vegetable, but also animal fare.

To raise the fry of many of the whiptail catfishes—i.e., those of the genus *Hemiloricaria*—only vegetable fare used to be provided. As a result, the young grew poorly or even starved on occasion. Only the feeding with rotifers and *Artemia* nauplii brought consistently positive results. *Hemiloricaria lanceolata* fry, for example, depend on animal fare, whereas other species are raised more successfully with a combination of animal and vegetable feeds.

The publications by POWER (1984a and b) made clear that a main influencing fac-

H.-G. Evers

Rineloricaria latirostris in its natural biotope. The cryptic design camouflages the fish perfectly.

tor of diet in nature is the size of the specimen. Large fishes are particularly vulnerable to piscivorous birds when entering shallow waters. Therefore, the daylight hours are spent in deeper areas of their habitat. Fry and juveniles are smaller and therefore their presence in the shallows is less obvious. Additionally, most Loricariinae have a cryptic coloration. They adapt their corporal design and coloration to their surroundings and are very difficult to discern from above, looking into the water. This allows these smaller specimens to venture into the shallows even during the day and use the thick algae stands present in these areas as their energy source. The central Panamanian Río Frijoles studied by POWER is the habitat of a total of four suckermouth catfish species belonging to three subfamilies ("*Hemiancistrus*" *panamensis*, Anci-

strus spinosus, *Chaetostoma fischeri*, and *Fonchiiichtys uracanthus*). All these species feed on algae and their associated aufwuchs, but prefer differing depths at various times of the day and night. These spatial-temporal niches are what makes the coexistence of these species possible to begin with.

In the aquarium, most Loricariinae are readily provided for by the standard foods supplied. There are various prepared diets on the market that are readily accepted. Besides flakes, there are also tablet foods with algae (*Spirulina*) supplementation or even the pellets from commercial table-fish aquaculture. Besides these, the catfishes will also feed on all other common feeds in live or frozen form. However, some feeding specialists, e.g., some members of the genera *Aposturisoma*, *Harttia*, *Lamontichthys*, or

443

Fam.: Loricariidae
Subfam.: Loricariinae

Pseudohemiodon lamina, feeding on tablet foods. Immediately after the tablets have been introduced into the aquarium, the fish emerge from the sand.

Pterosturisoma are hard to adapt to substitute fare when introduced in our aquaria as wild-caught specimens. Their care is also uncharacteristically exacting. Possible specialties in this regard are mentioned in the corresponding genus or species descriptions that follow.

The mouths of loricariin catfishes are by far not as uniformly discoid as in the other subfamilies. Some genera (*Farlowella*, *Sturisoma*, *Harttia*, etc.) have discs suitable to adhere on the aquarium panes. In nature, these fish indeed live in habitats with strong currents and must be capable of attaching themselves to rocks, wood, or plants. The genera with more bottom-oriented lifestyles (*Loricariichthys*, *Loricaria*, etc.,) have modified lips which play a predominant role during reproduction.

The pinnacle of lip-specialization can be found, for example, in the genera *Pseu-*dohemiodon and *Crossoloricaria*. During the day, these fishes live buried in fine sand. The lips are hardly comparable to a disc, but are finely branched into delicate "threads." In the cover of darkness, these catfishes dig themselves up and scurry the substrate for edibles with the aid of these fine barbels. During the reproductive season, the males fasten the egg mass onto their lips and bury themselves in the sand, eggs and all.

These few examples already show the obvious: the systematics of this subfamily are complex and hard to summarize. At present, approximately 200 species in 35 genera are recognized. Some of these genera are in dire need of a modern revision, something that is not very easy. In many cases, the fishes have already been known scientifically for a long time, and the descriptions published in years past were on occasion not as detailed in

444

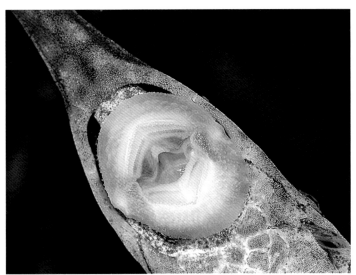

Farlowella sp., oral disc suitable of adhering to a substrate.

H.-G. Evers

Comparison of the oral anatomy between two genera: *Loricaria lata*, left; *Loricariichthys* sp. "Goias," right.

Fam.: Loricariidae
Subfam.: Loricariinae

Hemiloricaria fallax, oral disc.

I. Seidel

Pseudohemiodon sp. "Peru II," view of the pinnate structure of the lips.

H.-G. Evers

regard to type locality, distinguishing characteristics in reference to related species etc., as is demanded in this day and age. Additionally, some type specimens have been lost, have dried up, or were destroyed during war. Thanks to the efforts of the Amsterdam ichthyologist I.J.H. ISBRÜCKER, many genera and species have been brought to the attention of interested aquarists. This has been shedding some light on the confusion

reigning in many groups. It is therefore not surprising if the reader frequently encounters the name ISBRÜCKER, particularly in this section.

Systematically, the Loricariinae are divided at present into three tribes: Harttiini, Farlowellini, and Loricariini. We adopt this sensible arrangement and follow the description of the individual tribes with the corresponding descriptions of member genera and species.

Overview of the Subfamily Loricariinae BONAPARTE, 1831*

Tribe Harttiini		Subtribe Loricariina	
Subtribe Harttiina		Loricaria	(11)
Harttiella	(1)	Paraloricaria	(3)
Harttia	(20)	Brochiloricaria	(2)
Lamontichthys	(4)	Proloricaria	(2)
Pterosturisoma	(1)	Subtribe Planiloricariina	
Sturisomatichthys	(4)	Planiloricaria	(1)
Sturisoma	(15)	Rhadinoloricaria	(1)
Quiritxys	(1)	Dentectus	(1)
Subtribe Metaloricariina		Pseudohemiodon	(7)
Metaloricaria	(2)	Crossoloricaria	(5)
Tribe Farlowellini		Pyxiloricaria	(1)
Farlowella	(25)	Apistoloricaria	(4)
Aposturisoma	(1)	Subtribe Rineloricariina	
Tribe Loricariini		Rineloricaria	(20)
Subtribe Ricolina		Dasyloricaria	(5)
Ricola	(1)	Ixinandria	(2)
Subtribe Reganellina		Spatuloricaria	(10)
Reganella	(1)	Fonchiiichthys	(2)
Subtribe Hemiodonthyina		Hemiloricaria	(24)
Hemiodontichthys	(1)	Leliella	(1)
Subtribe Loricariichthyina			
Loricariichthys	(18)		
Subtribe Pseudoloricariina		Furcodontichthys	(1)
Pseudoloricaria	(1)		
Limatulichthys	(1)		

---

* The tribes and subtribes have been listed here to aid in the overview. The corresponding member genera are also listed, followed by the number of species in each genus in parenthesis. The genus *Furcodontichthys* has not yet been classified scientifically into any tribe and is listed here as part of the tribe Loricariini, without being classified into any of its 8 subtribes specifically.

Tribe Farlowellini Fowler, 1958

This smallest of the tribes only contains two genera. The twig-shaped members of the genus *Farlowella* are known to all aquarists. They have been called twig catfishes for decades and every once in a while the hobbyists deal in the reproduction of these fragile fishes. Unfortunately, the other genus, *Aposturisoma*, a relative newcomer described in 1983, is basically unknown.

Genus *Aposturisoma*
Isbrücker, Britski, Nijssen & Ortega, 1983

This unusual genus is monotypic. Its sole member is *Aposturisoma myriodon* Is-BRÜCKER, BRITSKI, NIJSSEN & ORTEGA, 1983 from the Peruvian Ucayali Basin. The species inhabits the clear-water tributaries of the Río Aguaytia. The shape of the snout is somewhat reminiscent of *Sturisoma*, the remainder of the body, however, is closer to *Farlowella*, which is why this genus was placed in the same tribe.

The elongated, flat body in conjunction with the typically rounded head with broadened edges completely void of bristles and the short rostrum are unique among the Loricariinae. It could be said that *Aposturisoma* is a link between *Sturisoma* and *Farlowella*.

Biotope of *Aposturisoma myriodon*, the Peruvian Río Huacamayo.   I. Seidel

Aposturisoma myriodon from the Río Huacamayo, Peru. Head detail of the holotype (SL 159 mm).

L. A. van der Laan

Aposturisoma myriodon
Isbrücker, Britski, Nijssen & Ortega, 1983

F.: Isbrücker, I.J.H., H.A. Britski, H. Nijssen & H. Ortega (1983): *Aposturisoma myriodon*, une espéce et un genre nouveaux de Poisson-Chat cuirassé, tribu Farlowellini Fowler, 1958 du Bassin du Rio Ucayali, Pérou (Pisces, Siluriformes, Loricariidae).– Rev.fr.Aquariol., 9(4): 39–48.

Syn.: None.

Hab.: Peru: Ucayali Basin: clear-water rivers in the Aguaytia drainage. Ingo Seidel successfully imported live specimens captured in the Rio Huacamayo. The water there is clear, has a swift current, and is relatively shallow. *Aposturisoma* are inhabitants of the shallow, current-exposed areas with a rubble substrate.

M. & B.: The specimens brought back to Germany proved extremely difficult in their care and only survived the initial weeks. No food intake could be con-firmed for that period. Still, at least the provided *Artemia* nauplii must have been eaten during the night, since the presence of fecal strands could be observed sporadically. Despite additional pumps and optimal oxygen concentrations, acclimation was unsuccessful. The fish died one by one despite the most intense of efforts. One clear problem was a severe infestation with oodinium.

According to this experience, it is questionable if this species is suitable for aquarium maintenance at all.

S: *A. myriodon* as such is already something special. The exotic body shape makes it interesting for the hobbyist. Too bad it is so difficult to keep!

T: 23°–26°C, **L:** 20 cm, **A:** 100 cm, **R:** b

Aposturisoma myriodon, pair.

I. Seidel

Aposturisoma myriodon, ventral view.

H.-G. Evers

Fam.: Loricariidae
Subfam.: Loricariinae

Genus *Farlowella* Eigenmann & Eigenmann, 1889
Twig or stick catfishes

Isbrücker (1980) assigns 37 species to this genus. However, for the aquarist that meant over thirty question marks in regard to the correct identification of his or her charges. That, fortunately, has changed with the recent revision of this genus by Retzer & Page (1997), two American ichthyologists. Now only 25 species are considered valid and an identification key is also included for all of these. However, the amateur aquarist still has a hard time to identifying the species in the aquarium. Furthermore, even the authors confess that some species can hardly be distinguished from one another (e.g., *F. hahni, F. oxyrhyncha,* and *F. reticulata*) without the use of meristic data to compare corporal proportions; something very complicated for an aquarist to do. Who can actually say with precision which species he or she cares for? Hardly anybody is current on the primary literature, not to mention anything about the specific origin of the fish. Given this situation, there have been, and continue to be, misidentifications in the hobby literature. And it is very laborious to find the correct taxon for a specimen even knowing its origin. An example: type species of the genus is *Farlowella acus* (Kner, 1854), and the type locality given in the original description is expectedly short: Caracas. One should not infer that it is easy to find twig catfishes in the vicinity of the Venezuelan capital. The rivers of the Caribbean Andes around Caracas are totally polluted, and if one drives southward from Caracas into the plains (llanos), the fish to be found is *Farlowella vittata*, a species with a very extensive distribution in Venezuela. Retzer & Page (1997) do not restate the type locality of the species, but declare that *Farlowella acus* cannot be found in the vicinity of Caracas, but only at Lake Va-

lencia and in the Río Torito, completely north, at the Caribbean coast! Most *Farlowella* in the aquaristic literature are simply and carelessly called *Farlowella acus*. Where does the confidence of these people come from, or is one copying from the other? We are especially careful in this regard here with *Farlowella*.

The genus is broadly distributed over extensive areas of the South American continent. It has been confirmed to live in the Amazon, Orinoco, Paraguay and Paraná basins, as well as in several rivers of the Guyana Highlands and the Maracaibo Basin, which flow into the Atlantic. There are no reports from the southeastern Brazilian coastal area.

The fish usually live in areas of swifter currents and adhere there on wood, grasses, and similar substrates. They completely rely on their camouflage and are therefore collected with relative ease. So far, we have found *Farlowella* in Bolivia, Brazil, Peru, and Venezuela, always in similar biotopes and in white-, clear-, and black-waters. At the end of the Venezuelan rainy season, particularly many juveniles were captured with our nets, but we also captured them—albeit in lesser numbers—in various Brazilian river systems at the end of the dry season. According to what we could determine, *Farlowella* prefer current-swept zones. We found them on the shore vegetation hanging into the fast current, as well as on dead wood piled up in current-swept sections. With a sturdy dipnet thrust beneath this wood and pulled upward out of the water, these fishes are an easy catch.

Retzer & Page (1997) studied all the type material of the described species and any additional material they could get their hands on, making it possible for

452

them to obtain the meristic data for 1100 specimens. Based on these numbers, phylogenetic analyses were performed and the authors established a total of six monophyletic groups for 19 species. Six additional species were not assigned to any group. Furthermore, six new species were described and many old taxa were listed as synonyms in this publication. Here, we follow this classification in groups, but maintain the alphabetic order of the various species descriptions.

At first sight, these species may appear very similar. This is the case especially in regard to coloration, although here, too, differences do exist (reticulated head vs. black longitudinal band, presence of ocelli on the caudal fin, etc.). However, under closer scrutiny, there are distinct differences also in cephalic shape. Initially, there are differing degrees of development of the rostrum. Some species have very short, blunt rostra (*F. curtirostra*

group), others have thin, more pointed ones (*Farlowella nattereri* group), and particularly broad, long rostra (e.g., *F. amazona, F. henriquei*) with varying degrees of bristling on the sides of sexually active males. Another, readily visible characteristic is the development of a so-called preorbital ridge, a bulge on the head directly in front of the eyes. In this regard we can distinguish between hardly developed, short bulges (*F. mariaelenae*) and very elongated, well-defined types (*F. amazona*).

We recommend wholeheartedly, to any interested aquarist, to consult the quoted publication by RETZER & PAGE (1997).

Farlowella sp., ♂, albinotic morph.

H.-G. Evers

Fam.: Loricariidae
Subfam.: Loricariinae

The following species are presently considered members of the genus *Farlowella*
(RETZER & PAGE, 1997):

Farlowella curtirostra Group

Farlowella curtirostra MYERS, 1942	Venezuela: Maracaibo Basin
Farlowella taphorni RETZER & PAGE, 1997	Venezuela: Maracaibo Basin

Farlowella mariaelenae Group

Farlowella mariaelenae MARTIN SALAZAR, 1964	Venezuela, Colombia

Farlowella nattereri Group

Farlowella hasemani EIGENMANN & VANCE, 1917	Brazil (?)
Farlowella isbruckeri RETZER & PAGE, 1997	Brazil: Paraguay Basin
Farlowella jauruensis EIGENMANN & VANCE, 1917	Brazil: Paraguay Basin
Farlowella nattereri STEINDACHNER, 1910	Guyana, Brazil, Colombia, Peru, Ecuador
Farlowella odontotumulus RETZER & PAGE, 1997	Venezuela, Ecuador

Farlowella acus Group

Farlowella acus (KNER, 1853)	Venezuela: Lake Valencia
Farlowella colombiensis RETZER & PAGE, 1997	Colombia: Rio Meta Basin
Farlowella martini FERNANDEZ-YÉPEZ, 1972	Northern Venezuela: Río Yaracuy
Farlowella venezuelensis MARTIN SALAZAR, 1964	Northern Venezuela: Guaripiche
Farlowella vittata MYERS, 1942	Colombia, Venezuela: Orinoco

Farlowella amazona Group

Farlowella amazona (GÜNTHER, 1864)	Amazon, Paraná, Gurupi
Farlowella henriquei RIBEIRO, 1918	Brazil: Araguaia
Farlowella platorynchus RETZER & PAGE, 1997	Brazil, Peru: Amazon
Farlowella rugosa BOESEMAN, 1971	Guyana, Suriname

Farlowella knerii Group

Farlowella knerii (STEINDACHNER, 1883)	Ecuador: Napo, Pastaza
Farlowella schreitmuelleri AHL, 1937	Brazil: lower Amazon

Species with uncertain relationships

Farlowella gracilis REGAN, 1904	Colombia: Caqueta
Farlowella hahni MEINKEN, 1937	Paraguay, Argentina
Farlowella oxyrrhyncha (KNER, 1953)	Amazon, Caura, Gurupi
Farlowella paraguayensis RETZER & PAGE, 1997	Paraguay, Brazil
Farlowella reticulata BOESEMAN, 1971	Guyana Highlands
Farlowella smithi FOWLER, 1913	Brazil: Madeira Basin

Suckermouth Catfishes

When a few ground rules are respected, care of *Farlowella* species is not particularly difficult. In nature, the fishes feed primarily on algae and their associated aufwuchs. This type of food is present in such amounts that the ventrum of the fishes is always fully distended when they are captured. During the initial few hours, they defecate black-green strands. In captivity, all kinds of dry foods, including the usual vegetable feeds, are accepted. Additionally, *Cyclops*, *Daphnia*, and mosquito larvae (frozen), if accessible, are also consumed. Important aspects of their care include frequent partial water exchanges and the absence of food competitors. Other suckermouth catfishes usually dominate and may keep the *Farlowella* from accessing the food appropriately. When feeding is adequately managed, *Hemiloricaria* or *Sturisomatichthys* sp. can be recommended as tankmates. On the other hand, suckermouth catfishes from the subfamilies Ancistrinae and Hypostominae are usually too agile and dominate over the delicate twig catfishes. It is advised to associate *Farlowella* spp. only with peaceful characins, dwarf cichlids, and similar groups of fishes, lest the whiptails will suffer in the short term. Several articles have been published in regard to *Farlowella* reproduction (EVERS, 1991; HARTL, 1996). The fry are similarly delicate to those of *Sturisoma* and look astonishingly similar. The commonly available twig catfishes are appropriate charges for the aquarist that has had his or her first successful experiences maintaining and breeding suckermouth catfishes. Even an albino morph has appeared for a brief period of time on the aquarium scene. It is particularly delicate in its care and problematic in its reproduction. Consequently, the albinos could not be preserved for the hobby for an extended period of time.

With appropriate care, ♀ *Farlowella* albinos also readily ripen.

I. Seidel

Photograph left:
Farlowella sp. ♂, guarding the spawn.

H.-G. Evers

Ten-hour old eggs of *Farlowella* sp.

H.-G. Evers

Farlowella amazona from the Rio Tefé, Brazil. See also following page.   H.-G. Evers

Farlowella amazona (GÜNTHER, 1864)
Amazon twig catfish

F.: Günther, A. (1864): Catalogue of the Physostomi containing the families Siluridae, Characidae, Haplochitonidae, Sternoptichidae, Scopelidae, Stomiatidae, in the collection of the British Museum.– Trustees British Museum Natural History, 5: 1–455.

Syn.: *Acestra amazonum, Acestra gladiolus, Farlowella carinata, Farlowella oliveirae, Farlowella paranaensis, Farlowella pleurotaenia, Farlowella pseudogladiolus.*

Hab.: Brazil: upper and central Amazon tributaries, usually close to the main stream; Rio Paraná Basin. The area of distribution of this species is vast and probably the reason for the multiple descriptions. H.-G. Evers, I. Seidel, M. Schlüter, and V. Bohnet captured the species repeatedly in the igarapés of the Rio Tefé, approximately 100 km and more from the Solimões (the Amazon down to the confluence with the Río Negro). These are black-water igarapés exclusively, with very low conductivity, pH 5 and below, and water temperatures of 28°–32°C (extreme low water season, October 1997). Additional individual *Farlowella* were found in sections with swift current and high oxygen concentrations on submersed overhanging shore vegetation. The species was not numerous.

Continued on the following page.

Farlowella amazona (2), ventral view. Note the very long rostrum.

H.-G. Evers

Continued from previous page (*Farlowella amazona*):

M. & B.: See genus description. Breeding has not been reported with certainty, since species identification has always been tentative.

S: A close relative of *Farlowella henriquei*, a species with a similarly distinct reticulated rostrum and pronounced preorbital ridge. However, *F. henriquei* is only known from the Rio Araguaia Basin in the central Brazilian state of Goias.

T: 26°–30°C, **L:** 23 cm, **A:** 80 cm, **R:** b

Farlowella curtirostra MYERS, 1942
Short-snouted twig catfish

F.: Myers, G.S. (1942): Studies on South American fresh-water fishes I.–Stanford ichth.Bull., 2(4): 89–114.

Syn.: None.

Hab.: Venezuela: Maracaibo Basin: Río Motatan.

M. & B.: Maintain along the guidelines given in the genus description. A somewhat sensitive *Farlowella* species. Breeding has not been successful.

S: A few specimens were imported in the early '90s, but have since then disappeared. Notable characteristics are the very short nostrum with the strong lateral bristles displayed by the males.

T: 24°–27°C, L: 12 cm, A: 80 cm, R: b

F. curtirostra, ventral view.   H.-G. Evers

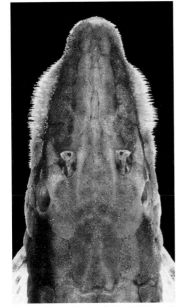

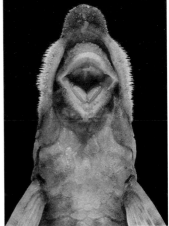

L. A. van der Laan (2)

Farlowella curtirostra ♂ (SL 108,6 mm), head study. No information on origin. See following page for additional photos.

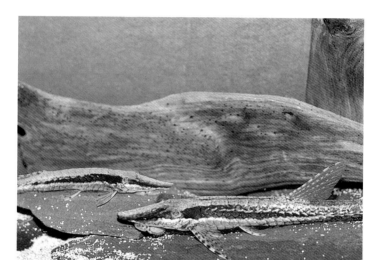

Farlowella curtirostra, pair. See previous page for text.

H.-G. Evers

Farlowella curtirostra, ventral view.

H.-G. Evers

Farlowella henriquei, Rio Vermelho.

H.-G. Evers

Farlowella henriquei RIBEIRO, 1918
Araguaia twig catfish

F.: Miranda Ribeiro, A. de (1918): Três gêneros e dezessete espécies novas de peixes brasileiros, determinados nas coleções do Museu Paulista.– Revta Mus. Paul., 10: 629–646.

Syn.: None.

Hab.: Brazil: Goias: upper Araguaia, Rio Vermelho. H.-G. EVERS was able to fish March 1998 in the Rio Vermelho. This is a white-water river, carrying reddish clay-laden water (from there its name, Port.: "vermelho" = vermillion). March is high water season, so it was very difficult to capture any fishes at all. However, the *Farlowella* are widely distributed on the upper and central Araguaia River and are regularly exported to all over the world.

M. & B.: Breeding has surely been successful, since this species is commonly in the trade. However, with the difficulties surrounding the correct identification of *Farlowella* spp., a specific breeding report cannot be quoted.

S: One of the species with a particularly long rostrum, similar to *F. amazona*. It is unknown whether or not males develop cephalic bristles during the spawning season. The caudal fin lobes are of equal length and have black striations. Additionally, each has a small ocellus. The rostrum is very long, but shorter and narrower on the base when compared to *F. amazona*.

T: 26°–29°C, **L:** 16 cm, **A:** 80 cm, **R:** b

Farlowella odontotumulus RETZER & PAGE, 1997

F.: Retzer, M. E. & L. M. Page (1997): Systematics of the Stick Catfishes, *Farlowella* Eigenmann & Eigenmann (Pisces, Loricariidae).– Proc. Acad. Nat. Sci. Philadelphia, 147: 33–88.

Syn.: None.

Hab.: Ecuador: Río Aguarico. Venezuela: upper Orinoco. H.-G. EVERS and I. SEIDEL captured, August 1992, the pictured species in the southern Venezuelan state of Bolivar, in the vicinity of Puerto Ayacucho. The habitat was a clear-water river in the Orinoco drainage. The species was rare in the Pozo Azul, as the creek was called, and distinguished itself by its uncommon size. Water temperature 28°C, pH 5.6, and conductivity 1 µS/cm. The current was very swift (rainy sea-

son!). The *Farlowella* were adhering to wood at particularly current-swept sites and were easy to overlook. HEMMANN (Gera) could bring this species back from there a few years later.

M. & B.: No live specimens were taken to Germany. There are no reports available.

S: The species lacks all black pigmentation in its monochrome fins. During the breeding season, the males grow distinct odontodes along the flanks (fourth row of the lateral body plates). A characteristic which it shares only with *Farlowella isbruckeri* from the Río Paraguay-Basin, Brazil.

T: 26°–29°C, L: 20 cm, A: 100 cm, R: b

Farlowella paraguayensis RETZER & PAGE, 1997

F.: Retzer, M. E. & L. M. Page (1997): Systematics of the Stick Catfishes, *Farlowella* Eigenmann & Eigenmann (Pisces, Loricariidae).– Proc. Acad. Nat. Sci., Philadelphia, 147: 33–88.

Syn.: None.

Hab.: Paraguay, Brazil: Río Paraguay Basin.
This fish was brought to Germany by the NORMANN (Satow) couple in 1999 from a fishing trip to Paraguay. The species is relatively common in the Río Paraguay drainage.

M. & B.: There are still no mayor experiences with this species. It is quite possible that it has been maintained "incognito" and that it has even bred successfully. The few "official" specimens that

have reached Germany from Paraguay were content with straightforward aquarium maintenance and have not been more sensitive than their congeners.

S: *Farlowella hahni* is another twig catfish described from the same area, but it has a much longer rostrum than this species.

T: 22°–26°C, L: 15 cm, A: 80 cm, R: b

Farlowella odontotumulus from Pozo Azul.

M. Hemmann

Farlowella paraguayensis in the aquarium.

I. Seidel

Fam.: Loricariidae
Subfam.: Loricariinae

Farlowella platorynchus

Farlowella platorynchus RETZER & PAGE, 1997
Crosshair twig catfish

F.: Retzer, M. E. & L. M. Page (1997): Systematics of the Stick Catfishes, *Farlowella* Eigenmann & Eigenmann (Pisces, Loricariidae).– Proc. Acad. Nat. Sci. Philadelphia, 147: 33–88

Syn.: None.

Hab.: Peru: Ucayali Basin: vicinity of Pucallpa: Yarina Cocha; Ecuador: Río Bobonaza; Brazil. According to RETZER & PAGE (1997), the species enjoys a wide distribution in the upper Amazon drainage and includes the lower Amazon tributaries. *F. platorynchus* is exported from Peru with regularity. SEIDEL captured this species in appreciable numbers in white-water tributaries of the Río Ucayali close to Pucallpa.

M. & B.: Besides *F. vittata*, this is the most commonly maintained and bred species. Raise as described in the genus description. Maintenance is not hard, but rearing the fry is complicated. Rainer MELZER (Berlin) has been repeatedly successful in its breeding. He placed particular emphasis on intensive quality nutrition.

S: This species is part of the group of *F. amazona* and *F. henriquei*, both of which have a distinctly longer rostrum. The rostrum of *F. platorynchus* appears as if cut, with a broad base, and displays very faint reticulation above. On the ventral side of the base, there is often a circular design, reminiscent of crosshairs.

T: 26°–29°C, L: 16 cm, A: 80 cm, R: b

Farlowella platorynchus from the vicinity of the city of Pucallpa.

Farlowella platorynchus, ventral view of the rostrum.

Farlowella smithi in the aquarium.

H.-G. Evers

Farlowella smithi Fowler, 1913

F.: Fowler, H. W. (1913): Fishes from the Madeira River, Brazil.– Proc. Acad. Nat. Sci., Philadelphia, 65: 517–579.

Syn.: None.

Hab.: Brazil: states of Amazonas and Rondônia: central Madeira Basin. H.-G. Evers captured the species repeatedly October 2000 in the vicinity of Porto Velho (Rondônia). The species is relatively rare and can usually be found in sections of strong current of small Madeira River tributaries. Both clear-water and white-water biotopes are inhabited. According to commercial fishermen, nowhere does *F. smithi* appear in great numbers. That is possibly the reason why this *Farlowella* has not been imported in large numbers.

M. & B.: According to the scant information available, the requirements of this species do not differ significantly from those of its more readily available congeners.

S: According to Retzer & Page (1997), *F. smithi* cannot be classified within any of the species groups of the genus. The holotype is only 10 cm long and apparently sexually mature. Nevertheless, final size is definitely larger. The largest specimen captured by Evers had a total length of 15 cm. The design on the caudal fin of *F. smithi* is characteristic. While the upper half is darkly pigmented, the lower lobe is transparent. The rostrum of medium length is a good further characteristic to distinguish this species from its congeners.

T: 26°–29°C, L: 15 cm, A: 80 cm, R: b

466

Farlowella smithi, portrait.

H.-G. Evers

Farlowella smithi; the species-typical design of the caudal fin.

H.-G. Evers

Farlowella sp. "Caño El Sapo"

S. Ploeger

Farlowella sp. "Caño El Sapo"

The aquarist S. PLOEGER captured this fish in the Venezuelan Caño [creek] El Sapo, eastern Maracaibo Basin. There are certain similarities to *Farlowella martini* from the northern states of Carabobo, Aroa, and Yaracuy, but a positive identification cannot be performed based on a slide alone. Unfortunately, there has not yet been a live import.

T: 26°–29°C, L: 15 cm, A: 80 cm, R: b

Farlowella sp. "Río Guamá"

The company AQUATARIUM (Hannover) imported this *Farlowella* sp. from the north Brazilian Rio Guamá. The long, pointed rostrum is very notorious and is strongly reminiscent of *Farlowella amazona*. Aquarium breeding of this sensitive species is unknown.

T: 26°–29°C, L: 15 cm, A: 80 cm, R: b

Farlowella sp. "Río Urucuta"

SEIDEL captured this species in the Bolivian Río Urucuta. We have not yet been able to unequivocally identify it. Its care does not differ from the better-known species.

T: 23°–26°C, L: 12 cm, A: 80 cm, R: b

Farlowella sp. "Rio Guamá"
I. Seidel

Farlowella sp. "Río Urucuta"
I. Seidel

Farlowella vittata MYERS, 1942

F.: Myers, G.S. (1942): Studies on South American fresh-water fishes I.– Stanford ichth.Bull., 2(4): 89–114.

Syn.: *Farlowella angosturae, Farlowella guaricensis, Farlowella agustini, Farlowella roncalli.*

Hab.: Venezuela and Colombia: extensive areas of the Orinoco Basin, in part also rivers that flow into the Caribbean. The authors found this species, among other places, in the white-water-carrying rivers of the Apure Basin in the Venezuelan Llanos. At pHs of 6–7, conductivities of up to 80 µS/cm, and high water temperatures around 30°C, the numerous specimens were always found among the submersed overhanging shore vegetation. However, it can also be found in clear-water biotopes with much lower pH and conductivity.

M. & B.: Respecting the basic conditions, oviposition is not difficult to achieve. Often two or more females want to participate. Additional males disrupt the spawning process; therefore, pairwise maintenance is recommended in small aquaria. *F. vittata* is regularly imported, and most breeding reports are likely to be dealing with this species.

S: Most twig catfishes in the hobby are likely to be this species, which inhabits an extensive and commercially active area. The catfish belongs to the *F. acus* group, where all males have pronounced odontodes on the sides of their rostrum. The length of the rostrum may vary somewhat in this species, depending on the geographic location.

T: 24°–28°C, **L:** 15 cm, **A:** 80 cm, **R:** b

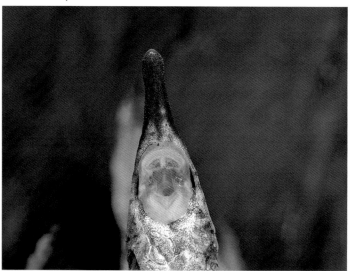

Farlowella vittata, ventral view of the rostrum.

H.-G. Evers

Farlowella vittata, pair.

H.-G. Evers

Farlowella vittata, a distinctly ripe ♀.

H.-G. Evers

Farlowella spp. from the Trade

Farlowella sp. "trade I"   H.-G. Evers

In the process of dealing with the genus *Farlowella* for this book, we repeatedly received *Farlowella* without an exact designation of origin. In those cases it was practically impossible to identify the specimen. We preliminarily present these fishes here without further comment under the designation of *Farlowella* sp. "trade," in order to at least give a glimpse at the variability of the twig suckermouth catfishes.

Farlowella sp. "trade II"   H.-G. Evers

Farlowella sp. "trade I," ventral view of the rostrum.

H.-G. Evers

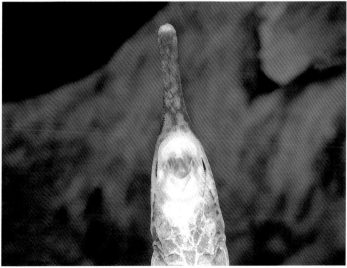

Farlowella sp. "trade II," ventral view of the rostrum.

H.-G. Evers

Tribe Harttiini BOESEMAN, 1971

The seven genera of the tribe Harttiini are subdivided into two subtribes. Whereas the subtribe Metaloricariina only comprises the single genus *Metaloricaria*—an aquaristically unknown genus from French Guyana—the subtribe Harttiina includes seven genera with several well-known members. The genus *Sturisoma* has been maintained and bred in our aquaria for many years, and in the past 10 years representatives of the genera *Sturisomatichthys*, *Pterosturisoma*, and *Lamontichthys* have also found their way into the aquaria of interested hobbyists. Most species in this tribe grow to over 20 cm total length (except for most *Sturisomatichthys*, *Harttiella*, and the clear-water *Harttia*) and are therefore a little too big for normal aquaria. A minimum volume of 200 l is required for such specimens.

Subtribe Harttiina BOESEMAN, 1971

Genus *Harttia* STEINDACHNER, 1876

This one-hundred-and-twenty-year-old genus was revised in detail during the last twenty years, and at least scientifically it is well known. OYAKAWA (1993) described five new species, ISBRÜCKER (1980) had already accepted five species, and only recently (LANGEANI et. al. 2001) an additional species was described, for a total of 11 species in this genus. RAPP PY-DANIEL & OLIVEIRA (2001) described seven new species from the Guyana Highlands and the Amazon lowlands. Several species listed in the 1st [German] edition under the generic "sp." section have now an appropriate taxon. Furthermore, the authors determined that the characteristics previously described to distinguish the species from the genus *Cteniloricaria* are insufficient in order to speak of two independent genera. For example, the degree of development of the ventral scutes is variable to such an extent that the distinction for *Cteniloricaria* (ventrum covered with scutes) in front of *Harttia* (ventrum naked) is unsustainable. *Cteniloricaria* must today be considered synonymous of *Harttia*, and the three species of the former genus *Cteniloricaria* are now also part of *Harttia*. As a result, we have now 20 species, since the previous *Harttia leiopleura* has been reclassified into the newly created genus *Quiritixys* ISBRÜCKER, 2001. The center of distribution of the genus is located in eastern and southeastern Brazil but, as indicated by RAPP PY-DANIEL & OLIVEIRA (2001), there are also several species in the Guyana Highlands and the Amazonian lowlands.

Type species of the genus is *Harttia loricariformis* STEINDACHNER, 1876. Notorious for all members—besides the rounded cephalic profile—is the very broad, flattened cau-

Harttia carvalhoi Ribeiro, 1939	Brazil: Rio Paquequer
Harttia depressa Rapp Py-Daniel, 2001	Brazil: Rio Ritinga, Amazon
Harttia dissidens Rapp Py-Daniel & Oliveira, 2001	
	Brazil: Rio Tapajos
Harttia duriventris Rapp Py-Daniel & Oliveira, 2001	
	Brazil: Rio Tocantins
Harttia fowleri (Pellegrin, 1908)	French Guyana: Camopi-System
Harttia garavelloi Oyakawa, 1993	Brazil: Rio Jequitinhonha
Harttia gracilis Oyakawa, 1993	Brazil: Upper Paraná
Harttia guianensis Rapp Py-Daniel & Oliveira, 2001	
	French Guyana, Approuague River
Harttia kronei Ribeiro, 1908	Brazil: Rio Betari
Harttia longipinna Langeani, Oyakawa & Montoya-Burgos, 2001	
	Brazil: Rio São Francisco
Harttia loricariformis Steindachner, 1876	Brazil: Upper Paraiba
Harttia maculata (Boeseman, 1971)	Suriname: Corantijn-System
Harttia novalimensis Oyakawa, 1993	Brazil: Rio São Francisco
Harttia platysoma (Günther, 1868)	Suriname
Harttia punctata Rapp Py-Daniel & Oliveira, 2001	
	Brazil: Rio Tocantins
Harttia rhombocephala Ribeiro, 1939	Brazil: Rio Farias
Harttia surinamensis Boeseman, 1971	Suriname, French Guyana
Harttia torrenticola Oyakawa, 1993	Brazil: Rio São Francisco
Harttia trombensis Rapp Py-Daniel & Oliveira, 2001	
	Brazil: Rio Trombetas
Harttia uatumensis Rapp Py-Daniel & Oliveira, 2001	
	Brazil: Rio Uatumã, Amazon

dal peduncle. *Harttia* appear, therefore, very plump. This fact, together with its rather modest coloration, surely conspires against the popularity of these fishes. Only a few specialized aquarists are likely to find interest in these catfishes.

Evers, one of the coauthors, was able to capture several *Harttia* spp. on his various trips to southeastern Brazil. Therefore, there are reports on the genus' natural biotopes. These are mentioned in the individual species descriptions. The genus has been encountered both in clear-water as well as white-water. The species inhabiting clear-water biotopes with swift currents are without exception small (up to ca. 10 cm total length) and have exacting requirements in regards to water quality. Using a cast net in larger white-water rivers, only adults of 15–20 cm length of other species could be cap-

tured. At present, it seems that there are two "groups" within the genus, which differ significantly in regards to origin and maximum size. However, without additional analyses of the population, further statements would be pure speculation. Southeastern Brazil—and particularly the mountainous areas—have seasonally low air and water temperatures, a situation that necessarily needs to be taken into account during the design of the maintenance conditions.

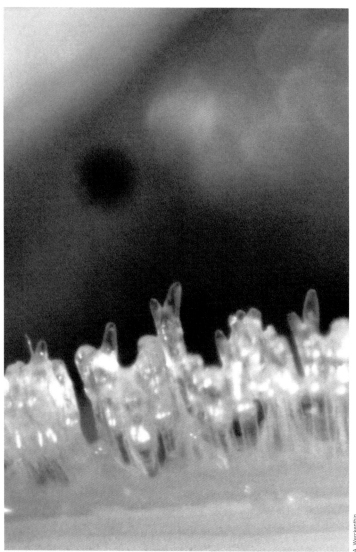

Dentition of *Harttia* (right, lower mandible, 66 x). The teeth are bicuspid.

A. Werckenthin

Harttia carvalhoi, Rio Preto, Rio de Janeiro. Recently captured. See also photo on the following page.

Harttia carvalhoi RIBEIRO, 1939

F.: Ribeiro, P. de Miranda (1939): Sóbre o genero *Harttia*, Steind. (Peixes: Loricariidae).– Bol.biol.São Paulo (n.s.), 4(1): 11–13, pl. 2.

Syn.: None.

Hab.: Brazil: state of Rio de Janeiro: Rio Paquequer. The pictured specimen was captured in the Rio Preto. This river serves as the drainage of various small streams from the Petropolis Mountains and, despite its name (preto = black), carries turbid white-water. H.-G. EVERS and M.T.C. LACERDA obtained on the 12th of October 1996 at 17:00 hours, in the Vale do Rio Preto at São José on the Boa Vista road towards Teresopolis, the following measurements: water temperature 22°C, conductivity 54 μS/cm, and a pH of 7.0. The river was about 50 m wide at the site, had a depth of several meters and flowed with a moderate current. We were able only to capture very few *Harttia carvalhoi* with a cast net.

M. & B.: Despite their natural habitat (white-water), the few imported specimens showed to be demanding charges with a need for oxygen and cool temperatures. Feeding is no problem, as long as adequate quantities are provided for these large suckermouth catfishes. Breeding has not yet been successful.

S: *Harttia loricariformis* from the Rio Itabapoana, also state of Rio de Janeiro, is a similar species. Both species hail from white-water and differ distinctly in size and coloration from the clear-water members of the genus. Is it possible that their taxonomy may suffer a change in the future?

T: 20°–23°C, **L:** 15 cm, **A:** 120 cm, **R:** b

Harttia carvalhoi, the same specimen (prev. page) shortly thereafter in the aquarium.

View of the Rio Preto in the state of Rio de Janeiro, habitat of *Harttia carvalhoi*.

Harttia dissidens; just-captured specimen from the Rio Tapajos at Pimental.

Harttia dissidens RAPP PY-DANIEL & OLIVEIRA, 2001

F.: Rapp Py-Daniel, L. H. & E. C. Oliveira (2001): Seven new species of Harttia from the Amazonian-Guyana region (Siluriformes: Loricariidae).- Ichtyol. Explor. Freshwaters, 12(1): 79–96.

Syn.: None.

Hab.: Brazil, Pará, Rio Tapajos at Pimental. In September 2003, coauthor EVERS was able to capture *H. dissidens* himself at Pimental. The species lives directly in the rapids, in the swiftest currents. Water values were as follows: temperature: 29°C; pH 5.5, and conductivity 22 µS/cm. The species grazes rocks in knee- to hip-deep waters.

M. & B.: This inhabitant of extreme biotopes can only be maintained in aquaria with great difficulty. The complete oxygen saturation of the water and the virtually infinite supply of algae (intestinal length in this species is 9–10x body length!) and associated microfauna needed are requirements not easily met. However, it is not impossible, as demonstrated by the breeding successes reported for *H. guianensis* (see there).

S.: A plain species, but it seduces with its unusual body shape. Juveniles up to a length of 4–5 cm could be collected in the smaller tributaries of the Rio Tapajós. They were dark green in color and were hardly noticeable in the shallow water. As adults, their ventrum is completely covered by small, densely placed scutes. Previously, this was considered a characteristic of the genus *Cteniloricaria*, but was rated as useless by RAPP PY-DANIEL & OLIVEIRA, which is why *Cteniloricaria* is nowadays considered a synonym of *Harttia*.

T: 26°–30°C, L: 20 cm, A: 120 cm, R: b

Fam.: Loricariidae
Subfam.: Loricariinae

Harttia fowleri (Pellegrin, 1908)

F.: Pellegrin, J. (1908): Description de
deux poissons nouveaux de l 'Amerique
du Sud, de la famille des Loricariidés. –
Bull.Soc.zool.Fr., 31: 124–127.

Syn.: *Oxyloricaria fowleri, Cteniloricaria
fowleri.*

C: L 40.

Hab.: French Guyana: Camopi System.
Von Drachenfels (1989) captured adult
specimens over rocks without any cover.
Juveniles also stayed above rocks, but
among dense vegetation in shallow water. The pictured specimen was captured
by Jens Gottwald (Aquatarium, Hannover)
in the Crique Voltaire (Maroni drainage),
French Guyana.

M. & B.: Experience is scant due to a lack
of imported specimens. These catfish
grow to a respectable size and should be
maintained in aquaria with a minimum
volume of 200 l. Strong filtration and a

H. fowleri, ventral view. I. Seidel

good oxygen saturation of the water are
primary conditions for successful care.
New imports are difficult to adapt to the
usual substitute fare. Breeding biology is
unknown.

S: Difficult species; beginners should
preferably look elsewhere.

T: 25°–28°C, L: 18 cm, A: 100 cm, R: b

Harttia guianensis Rapp Py-Daniel & Oliveira, 2001

F.: Rapp Py-Daniel, L. H. & E. C. Oliveira
(2001): Seven new species of Harttia from
the Amazonian-Guyana region (Siluriformes: Loricariidae). Ichthyol. Explor.
Freshwaters, 12(1): 79–96.

Hab.: French Guyana, Approuague River.

M.&B.: Thomas Weidner (Penzberg) introduced some specimens from French
Guyana. Various sizes of the fish were
captured in 1999 and 2001 in the Approuague in the rapids at Saut Mapao.
One pair spawned on May 12, 2002. The
male practices broodcare. On May 19,
the first young hatched. These were
cared for by Weidner's girlfriend Petra

Dotzer. It follows an excerpt from the diary about the breeding of *Harttia guianensis* [transl. from German]:

- Aquarium: 120 x 60 x 30 cm decorated with wood and black slate, fine
  sand, some *Anubias* and Java fern.
- Tankmates: 3 *Dicrossus filamentosa*
  and 2 *Luciocephalus* sp. "spotted."
- Breeders: 5 specimens; 1 male and 2
  females, others gender uncertain.
- Filtration: sponge plates and hydropneumatic lifter connected to a blower
  (for a total of 40 m≈/h in 9000 l water).
- Water values: 28°C; 3°dGH; 0–1 °dKH;
  pH 6.0; conductivity 150 µS/cm; nitrite

Harttia fowleri

I. Seidel

Harttia guianensis, breeder.

T. Weidner

Fam.: Loricariidae
Subfam.: Loricariinae

Harttia guianensis, newly hatched larvae on the lateral pane.   T. Weidner

and ammonia not measurable; nitrate 10–25 mg/l. Water is exchanged weekly at a rate of 40–50% (rainwater 80% remainder tap water).

- Feeding: many dry foods: "algae wafers," *Spirulina* tablets, and "normal" tablets; frozen *Artemia*, mosquito larvae, glass worms, lobster eggs, and *Daphnia*. On occasion live microeels and *Artemia*. Feeding twice daily and nocturnal supplementation. Every once in a while a day of fasting.

- Oviposition occurred on a slate plate leaning against the back pane.

- The spawn was difficult to see, the number of eggs only estimated: somewhere around 30, 40 at the most.

- Apparently, after five days the spawn became smaller. Therefore, the slate with the eggs was transferred to a 25-l-tank. Only 22 could be counted.

- After only seven days, the first 12 fry hatched from the 2–3 mm eggs.

- After an additional 24 hours, six additional fry hatched, whereas the last four had to be freed from their egg membranes after no hatching occurred during an additional 24 hours.

- During the subsequent seven days, at total of six fry died, whereas the remaining 16 stayed in good health.

- The fry were ca. 12 mm long upon hatching, after 14 days they measured ca. 15 mm, and after four weeks they had reached two centimeters in length. After three months the fry were a good three centimeters long.

- Their diet consisted primarily of newly hatched *Artemia* nauplii, microeels, and fine dry foods or *Spirulina* tablets (s. above). Feed was given up to five times daily.

Fourteen-day-old fry.

T. Weidner

- The movement of the fry is initially very limited. Only once they feel safe in the aquarium (or if transferred into a larger one), do they start moving around. From the start, feed is taken from the bottom (initially only at night).

- An additional circulation pump was installed in the juvenile rearing tank, since in the Riviere Approuage juveniles had been found in the sections with the strongest current.

Further details can be read in an article [in German] by Petra DOTZER and Thomas WEIDNER (Das Aquarium, 407, May 2003: 20–26).

Harttia guianensis, 14-day-old fry on the aquarium pane.

T. Weidner

S: WEIDNER reported that sexually active males have pectoral fin spines covered by odontodes. Soon after broodcare (within five days, at the most), these odontodes have been "discarded."

T: 24°–27°C, **L:** 15 cm, **A:** 120 cm, **R:** b

Harttia kronei from the Rio do Passagem.

H.-G. Evers

Harttia kronei RIBEIRO, 1908

F.: Ribeiro, A. de Miranda (1908): Peixes da Ribeira. Resultados de excursão do Sr. Ricardo Krone, Membro Correspondente do Museu Nacional do Rio de Janeiro.– A Lavoura, Soc.nac.Agric., 11: 185–190.

Syn.: None.

Hab.: Brazil: state of São Paulo: clear-water tributaries of the Rio Ribeira. On April 15th, 1995 the following water values were determined in the Rio do Passagem, a small tributary of the Rio do Azeite: temperature 20°C, pH 6.5, and conductivity 16 μS/cm. The water depth was quite shallow at some places (20 cm) and the current was swift over fist-sized pebbles. The *Harttia* grazed the aufwuchs on the larger, current-swept rocks. When threatened, they hid in the interstices. Coloration is cryptic, camouflaging them effectively among the substrate. They are virtually in-visible from outside the water, providing effective protection in front of piscivorous birds—and apparently fishing aquarists, too, because we only captured a few specimens.

M. & B.: A difficult charge with a high oxygen requirement. Maintain the temperature cool.

S: Along the lines of most loricariids from the clear-waters in the state of São Paulo, this species is difficult to care for. Only experienced aquarists should attempt maintenance of *H. kronei*. A commercial import is out of the question anyway, since this species does not survive the rigors of traveling in commercial shipping channels. This is without a doubt the most sensitive of all imported *Harttia* species.

T: 18°–22°C, **L:** 12 cm, **A:** 100 cm, **R:** b

484

Rio do Azeite, São Paulo, Habitat of *Harttia kronei*.

H.-G. Evers

Harttia loricariformis STEINDACHNER, 1876

F.: Steindachner, F. (1876): Die Süß-wasserfische des südöstlichen Brasilien III.– Sber.Akad.Wiss.Wien, mathem.–naturwiss. Cl., 74: 1–136.

Syn.: None.

Hab.: Brazil: state of Rio de Janeiro: upper Paraiba do Sul: Rio Itabapoana. The species has been captured by EVERS, LACERDA & BEYER in the Rio Itabapoana. Water values (April 22nd, 1995, 14:00 hours): temperature 27°C, pH 7.3, conductivity 44 µS/cm. At this place the river was about 100 m wide and its current made swimming across impossible. The cast net was thrown from intermediate rock islands reached per boat. The *Harttia* were usually seen in pairs adhered to rock faces.

M. & B.: With adequate filtration, this becomes a species that can be readily maintained. Males have thicker and longer pectoral fins; their first rays are densely covered by odontodes. Unfortunately, breeding has not yet been successful.

S: This is the type species of the genus. Its heavy constitution and the usual inactivity make this an unattractive species for all but the most serious specialist.

T: 24°–28°C, L: 20 cm, A: 120 cm, R: b

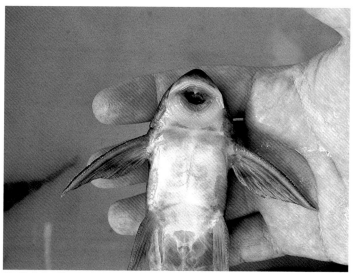

Harttia loricariformis ♂, note the longer and broader first pectoral fin rays.

H.-G. Evers

Harttia loricariformis in the aquarium.

H.-G. Evers

Harttia loricariformis ♀, for comparison. Ventral view.

H.-G. Evers

Harttia punctata Rapp Py-Daniel & Oliveira, 2001
Dotted whiptail

F.: Rapp Py-Daniel, L. H. & E. C. Oliveira (2001): Seven new species of Harttia from the Amazonian-Guyana region (Siluriformes: Loricariidae).- Ichtyol. Explor. Freshwaters, 12(1): 79–96

Syn.: None.

Hab.: Brazil, Pará, Rio Tocantins, below the Tucurui Dam, lower and central Rio Araguaia.

M.&B.: As with all Amazonian *Harttia* species, care should be reserved for experienced aquarists, even though it is easier than that for species hailing from cooler regions. Oxygen-rich, swiftly flowing water and a diet consisting primarily of vegetable fare are conditions for successful maintenance of these specialists.

S: *H. punctata* is imported [to Germany] every now and then from the Tocantins and Araguaia rivers. The irregular design of dots covering body and fins facilitates species identification.
The head is relatively short and stout in comparison to other species. The ventrum is virtually naked, only at the anal region and at the base of the pectoral fins are there some small bony plates. In the 1st [German] edition, the fish was presented as *Harttia* sp. "Rio Tocantins."

T: 26°–29°C, L: 15 cm, A: 120 cm, R: b

Dry saison at the Rio Araguaia (Ilha do Bananal)

H.-G. Evers

Harttia punctata

I. Seidel

Harttia punctata, ventral view

H.-G. Evers

Harttia surinamensis

I. Seidel

Harttia surinamensis BOESEMAN, 1971

F.: Boeseman, M. (1971): The comb–toothed Loricariinae of Surinam, with reflections on the phylogenetic tendencies with the family Loricariidae (Siluriformes, Siluroidei).– Zool. Verh. Leiden, 116: 1–56.

Syn.: None.

Hab.: Suriname: Surinam River; French Guyana: Mana Basin, Oiapoque Basin. The species was introduced to Germany by Jens GOTTWALD (Hannover). It can be found both in the Mana Basin (Saut Continent) as well as in the Oiapoque drainage (Saut Maripa). At first sight, it is easy to confuse this species with *Harttia fowleri*. However, the ventrum is naked and the caudal fin is not notched.

M. & B.: Although *H. surinamensis* tolerates higher temperatures in the aquarium than its congeners, maintenance is still difficult. At the slightest lapse in water quality management, there will be trouble and if oxygen concentrations fall, immediate death will be the consequence.

S: Beautiful species which unfornunately is not seen very offen in the trade.

T: 25°–28°C, **L:** 20 cm, **A:** 150 cm, **R:** b

Harttia surinamensis, portrait.

Harttia surinamensis, ventral view.

Harttia torrenticola Oyakawa, 1993

F.: Oyakawa, O.T. (1993): Cinco espécies novas de *Harttia* Steindachner, 1876 da região sudeste do Brasil, e comentários sobre el género (Teleostei, Siluriformes, Loricariidae).– Comun.Mus. Cienc. PUCRS, ser. zool., Porto Alegre, 6: 3–27.

Syn.: None.

Hab.: Brazil: state of Minas Gerais: Rio São Francisco Basin. H.-G. Evers, M. T. C. Lacerda, P. Valerio da Silva, and M. Beyer found the pictured species in the Rio Vermelho, a clear-water tributary of the Rio das Velhas. On October 5th, 1996, the following water values were determined: temperature 22°C, pH 7.0, and conductivity 40 μS/cm. The shallow water had a very swift current. The *Harttia* inhabited, at low densities, the areas with coarse gravel substrates at a maximum water depth of 30 cm. The piscine syntopic fauna included—besides various characins—especially catfishes (*Rineloricaria* sp., *Trichomycterus reinhardti*, *Hepapterus* sp., Pimelodidae sp.). It was always a small species or juvenile specimens. The *Harttia*, on the other hand, were full-grown. Captured juvenile specimens were released, since survival was going to be improbable given the long transport distances required.

M. & B.: With good filtration, the species is readily maintained, but continues to be a demanding charge. The remote location of its area of distribution makes commercial imports unlikely.

S: Of the three clear-water species that have reached the German hobby, *H. torrenticola* is clearly the best suited.

T: 21°–24°C, L: 10 cm, A: 80 cm, R: b

Harttia trombetensis Rapp Py-Daniel & Oliveira, 2001

F.: Rapp Py-Daniel, L. H. & E. C. Oliveira (2001): Seven new species of Harttia from the Amazonian-Guyana region (Siluriformes: Loricariidae).- Ichtyol. Explor. Freshwaters, 12(1): 79–96.

Syn.: None.

M.&B.: Follow the indications given for *H. guianensis*. The few specimens imported to date have not survived long. The import of a significant number of individuals is still pending. However, interest in this species is likely to be limited to specialists and catfish connoisseurs.

S: In the 1st [German] edition (p. 440) this species was presented as *Cteniloricaria* sp. "Rio Trombetas." Shortly after its publication, Rapp Py-Daniel & Oliveira (2001) published its original description. *H. trombetensis* can be told apart from all its congeners based on the unorthodox arrangement of the small ventral scutes. The ventrum is virtually naked with the exception of the anal region, a narrow belt between the bases of the ventral fins, and an irregular row of tiny scutes which runs from one side to the other on the posterior third of the ventrum.

T: 26°–29°C, L: 20 cm, A: 120 cm, R: b

Harttia torrenticola

H.-G. Evers

Harttia trombetensis

C. Seidel

Harttia trombetensis, photographed in its natural biotope.

B. Kilian

Harttia sp. "Essequibo"

Apparently the genus *Harttia* has more members than suspected just a few years ago. Ingo SEIDEL was able to capture this possibly still undescribed species in Guyana in August 2000 in the basin of the Essequibo River. Based on the ventral bony platelets, this specimen could be unequivocally classified into the ge-

nus *Harttia*. The pictured specimen was very weakened by the extended transport (apparently it was a juvenile) and did not survive very long. In consequence, no indications for aquarium care can be given.

Harttia sp. "French Guyana"

The pictured specimen was captured and photographed by Helmut WENDEN-BURG in French Guyana. Unfortunately, it could not be identified to species. Nevertheless, for completeness sake, the

specimen is at least being presented in a photograph.

T.: 25°–28°C, **L**: 15 cm, **A**: 80 cm, **R**: b

Harttia sp. "Essequibo"

I. Seidel

Harttia sp. from French Guyana.

H. Wendenburg

Harttiella crassicauda, preserved specimen (RMNH19418).

I. Seidel

Genus *Harttiella* BOESEMAN, 1971

A monotypic genus, with its only member *Harttiella crassicauda* (BOESEMAN, 1953) from Suriname. The specimens known to date are relatively small (not more than 5 cm standard length). According to BOESEMAN (1971), this species represents an intermediate form between the genera *Harttia* and *Neoplecostomus* (subfamily Neoplecostominae).

No aquarist has seen this species alive. According to I. ISBRÜCKER (pers. comm.) a description of an even smaller species from French Guyana is in preparation.

I. Seidel

Ventral view of the specimen pictured to the right.

Genus *Lamontichthys* RIBEIRO, 1939

Lamontichthys filamentosus (LA MONTE, 1935)	Amazonia, widely distributed
Lamontichthys llanero TAPHORN & LILYESTROM, 1984	Venezuela: Llanos
Lamontichthys maracaibero TAPHORN & LILYESTROM, 1984	
	Venezuela: Maracaibo Basin
Lamontichthys stibaros ISBRÜCKER & NIJSSEN, 1978	Ecuador

The genus is comprised of four relatively large and attractive species. ISBRÜCKER & NIJSSEN (1978b) recognized the genus created by P. DE MIRANDA RIBEIRO with the type species *Lamontichthys filamentosus* (LA MONTE, 1935) and described *L. stibaros* from Ecuador as an additional member. *L. filamentosus* is distributed in Brazil, Bolivia, Ecuador, and Peru; i.e., it can be found in extensive areas of Amazonia. TAPHORN & LILYESTROM (1984) described two additional species—*L. maracaibero* and *L. llanero*—from Venezuela. Typical for *Lamontichthys*—besides the round head, the relatively deep body, and the flattened caudal peduncle, all characteristics found either in *Sturisoma* or *Harttia*, but never together—are the seven divided (soft) pectoral fin rays. This last characteristic is exclusive to *Lamontichthys* within the subfamily.

At least three species are aquaristically known and all have proven to be difficult charges with exacting demands in regard to water quality and their vegetarian diet. It is notable how these fishes prefer to adhere to the aquarium panes. Even during feeding it is a rare occurrence to see these shy catfishes briefly swim onto the bottom to feed. Usually it is a matter of just a few seconds, when a few bites are grabbed, before resuming the vertical, adhered posture. Aquariums with naked bottom, without any sand or gravel, make these loricariids move to the ground, where they can be fed easier.

Lamontichthys filamentosus (LA MONTE, 1935)
Filamentous whiptail

F.: La Monte (1935): Fishes from Rio Jurua and Rio Purus, Brazilian Amazonas.– Am.Mus.Novitates, 784: 1–8.

Syn.: *Harttia filamentosa*, *Harttia filamentissima*, *Parasturisoma filamentosa*.

Hab.: Brazil: state of Amazonas: Rio Juruá drainage; Bolivia: Río Chapare drainage; Peru: Province of Loreto: Río Huallaga; Ecuador: Province of Pastaza: Río Bobonaza. SEIDEL and companions captured the species in the Peruvian Rio San Alejandro, a clear-water river of the Ucayali drainage. A detailed description of the biotope can be found in the chapter on habitats. BARZANTI & OLDANI (1976) report the existence of *Lamontichthys filamentosus* in Argentina. However, that is based on a confusion with the more recently described genus *Brochiloricaria*.

M. & B.: Sensitive species. Despite optimal water conditions, the fish only reluctantly accept captive diets. Do not maintain with related tankmates, such as members of the genus *Sturisoma*, since these will be unbeatable food competitors for the shy *Lamontichthys*. These beautiful fish are complicated in their maintenance, since even the slightest lapse in their care might have fatal consequences. It seems the *Lamontichthys* require large aquaria for their well-being. Gender can be determined with relative ease in full-grown specimens. Mature males have distinct spines on the first pectoral fin ray, the females do not. The Swiss aquarist Dani MADÖRIN was successful in breeding the species in an aquarium of the well-known ZOLLI in Basel. Here are the highlights of the success:

Breeding aquarium: 280 l volume.
Total installed pumping capacity: 4000 l/hr.
One of the pumps was directed with its effluent in such a way as to produce a current along the back pane of the aquarium. Spawning occurred in that zone, at a hidden place behind rock piles and roots.
Breeders: The breeding group consisted of 5 animals, 4 full-grown specimens of ca. 20 cm length and one smaller one of ca. 12 cm length, which later turned out to be the male involved in the spawn. Two weeks prior to oviposition the water was changed every other day, hereby lowering its conductivity.
Water values at time of oviposition: temperature 27°C, pH 7.3, and conductivity 50 µS/cm.
Chronology of events: February 20th, 1999: Discovered first spawn on a barely visible site. Only consisted of nine eggs. Many eggs had sunk to the substrate and it was attempted to raise these separately.
Feb. 28th: male still cares for the spawn. However, at this point, D. MADÖRIN had to leave for several days and had to cut his observations short.
March 6th: Newly laid second spawn. This time it could be observed how two large specimens and the small one stayed at the spawning site. It could not be deter-

mined if the two large fish were females or not. Only one specimen had a distended abdomen. Surprisingly, only the 12 cm fish—a male— guarded the 45–50 eggs.
March 14th: The fry hatch. Thirty-eight young could be siphoned out.
Measurements: The eggs had a size of 3.7–3.9 mm. After hatching, the fry were 12 mm long and had a 1 mm filament. Eggs and larvae are distinctly larger than in *Sturisoma*. The fry have a very rounded head.

Unfortunately, the young died a few weeks later due to carelessness on part of another caretaker. However, these first partial successes give reason to be optimistic about the future breeding of this species, which should be pursued in earnest. The Berlin aquarist R. MELZER observed several spawns and had also no success in raising the fry. Obviously this remains still a miracle (?).

S: *L. filamentosus* is the type species of the genus and at the same time the only one with long filamentous fins. Not a fish for the beginner!

T: 26°–28°C, **L:** 20 cm, **A:** 120 cm, **R:** b

Lamontichthys filamentosus

I. Seidel

Lamontichthys filamentosus, eggs and a recently hatched fry.

J. Leuenberger

Fry of *Lamontichthys filamentosus*, 3 weeks old

I. Seidel

Lamontichthys stibaros, see page 505 for text.

H.-G. Evers

L. llanero, subadult from the Río Orituco, Venezuela

H.-G. Evers

Lamontichthys llanero TAPHORN & LILYESTROM, 1984

F.: Taphorn, D.A. &. S. Lilyestrom (1984): *Lamontichthys maracaibero* y *L. llanero,* dos especies nuevas para Venezuela (Pisces, Loricariidae). Rev. Unellez de Cien. y Tecnol., 2(2): 93–99.

Syn.: None.

Hab.: Venezuela: Llanos in the Apure Basin. The type localities are all white-water rivers with seasonally swift currents (rainy season) and puddles with hardly any flow at all (extreme dry season). The repeated capture of juvenile and occasional adult specimens was successful at the Río Orituco near Calabozo. The water temperatures at the site were quite high (28°–32°C), but are seasonal. The pH fluctuated from slightly acidic to slightly alkaline. Water hardness was hardly measurable. It is amazing how the species tolerates such fluctuating aquatic parameters in nature, and in the aquarium it is so sensitive. The source of the problem can surely be found in the inadequate diet provided in captivity.

M. & B.: Similar to *L. filamentosus.* The reasons for *L. llanero* being so sensitive are surely due to the extended transport, the deficient diet, and a constant state of stress.

M. HEMMANN, aquarist from Gera, Germany, has had preliminary success in breeding *Lamontichthys llanero.* Here an excerpt from his diary [transl.]:

Breeding aquarium: 50 x 50 x 30 (ca. 75 liters).
Filtration: Maximal air-driven filter and Aquabee pump, 500 l/h.

Fam.: Loricariidae
Subfam.: Loricariinae

Lamontichthys llanero, ventral view.

H.-G. Evers

Water values: tap water (city of Gera) 27°C, 11°dGH, 620 µS/cm, pH ca. 7. Weekly water exchange of ⅓ of aquarium volume.

Breeders: wild-caught 2/2 from Venezuela in care since 1998—total length of only ca. 12 cm—have not reached their final size achieved in nature.

First Spawn
<u>May 11, 2003</u>
First spawn: 16 eggs.
Most eggs were scattered on the bottom pane—three were adhered on a vertical plate of slate placed in the back of the aquarium.
Out of fear of losing the eggs to cannibalism, I transferred the strongly adhesive eggs into an *Artemia* net which I left in the aquarium.

<u>May 12, 2003</u>
6 eggs fungused—the remaining 10 l transferred into a self-built incubator. During the following days, two more eggs died.

<u>May 16, 2003</u>
Two larvae hatch prematurely—they do not survive.

<u>May 18, 2003</u>
The remaining larvae hatch throughout the day. They are transferred into a 12 l rearing tank. Filtration with a Minimaximal filter. Small roots are introduced as shelter.

<u>May 22, 2003</u>
The yolk sac appears used-up to me—I begin with supplemental feeding (*Artemia, Chlorella vulgaris,* algae powder, *Spirulina* powder, and ground Dulplarin G, and a parboiled lettuce leaf is constantly in the tank).

The food is not all introduced at once, but distributed into small doses given throughout the day, to see what the fish truly eat. Old foods are always siphoned out and the water is replaced with aged water. Unfortunately, the fish are not voracious—no ingestion can be confirmed.

May 23/24, 2003

Same song and dance as described for 5/22. The fish do not appear starved! On the evening of 5/24 several specimens show whitish eruptions directly behind the head?! (Secondary fungal infection?!) Despite meticulous hygiene! The death of four fry follows.

May 26, .2003

All fry dead—end of first spawn.

Second Spawn
July 7, 2003

10 eggs, scattered throughout the aquarium—this time the eggs remain in the breeding tank.

July 14, 2003

5 eggs remain, the rest died or were not fertilized. Hatching commences (3 of 5). The eggs can be left in the breeding tank, the parents do not bother them. No broodcare to observe in either spawn?

July 15, 2003

The other two eggs hatch.

July 17, 2003

Yolk sac metabolized—feeding commences! This time only *Chlorella* and *Spirulina,* as well as Duplarin G—no live foods!

July 22, 2203

Two fry dead (starvation).

July 31, 2003

Two additional fish die without overt symptoms of any disease—no concave ventrum either.

August 3, 2003

Death of last young of the second spawn?!

Conclusion: I theorize that the mortality is the result of an inadequate food offering—unfortunately I did not have any other alternatives at my disposal at the time. There will be further spawns and I will continue to search for the optimal methodology.

Additional note: Meanwhile HEMMANN succeeded in raising several spawns under almost sterile circumstances with a big wordload. They feed on flake food best.

T: 26°–28°C, **L:** 16 cm, **A:** 120 cm, **R:** b

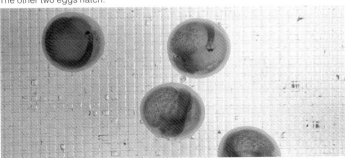

Lamontichthys llanero - eggs 3 days old

M. Hemmann

Fam.: Loricariidae
Subfam.: Loricariinae

L. llanero - ventral view, shortly after hatching   M. Hemmann

L. llanero - lateral view - 5th day   M. Hemmann

L. llanero dorsal view - 5th day   M. Hemmann

Lamontichthys stibaros, see the following page for an additional photo.

H.-G. Evers

Lamontichthys stibaros ISBRÜCKER & NIJSSEN, 1978

F.: Isbrücker, I. J. H. & H. Nijssen (1978): The neotropical mailed catfishes of the genera *Lamontichthys* P. de Miranda-Ribeiro, 1939 and *Pterosturisoma* n. gen., including the description of *Lamontichthys stibaros* n. sp. from Ecuador (Pisces, Siluriformes, Loricaridae).– Bijdr. Dierk., 48(19: 57–80.

Syn.: None.

Hab.: Ecuador: Río Bobonaza. The species is sporadically imported from Peru.

M. & B.: Breeding is still unknown. The species is less attractive than the very active, diurnal *L. filamentosus*. But these fish, too, are all day long in search of food. Besides flake and tablet foods, frozen *Daphnia* and *Cyclops* are also readily accepted. Vegetable fares such as spinach and cooked cauliflower are also appreciated. At M. SCHLÜTER (Hamburg), who cared for a female for a long time, there was oviposition of approximately 20 large eggs. These rested directly beneath the female on the substrate. The large aquarium (800 l) housed several *Planiloricaria cryptodon* and *Hemiloricaria teffeana* as tankmates, a community where each species held its own and had adequate access to food.

S: *L. stibaros* is difficult to distinguish from *L. llanero*. The ocular distance is less than that of *L. filamentosus* or *L. llanero*. The wedge-shaped spot of *L. llanero* is rarely as distinct in *L. stibaros*. The pectoral fins of adult *L. stibaros* are yellowish. *L. stibaros* is readily distinguished from *L. filamentosus* because the former lacks the name-giving filaments on the fins of the latter. That is important to know, because the species, on occasion, come mixed from Peru and this way they can be accurately differentiated.

T: 26°–28°C, **L:** 22 cm (SL), **A:** 120 cm, **R:** b

Genus *Pterosturisoma* ISBRÜCKER & NIJSSEN, 1978

The monotypic genus is notoriously similar to *Lamontichthys*, and indeed, there are mayor concordances. However, *Pterosturisoma* only has six divided pectoral fin rays (vs. seven for *Lamontichthys*) and was therefore placed in its own genus. The dentition consists of only one row, in *Lamontichthys* there are two. *Pterosturisoma* lacks the dermal appendage that covers the pupil proportionally to illumination in most suckermouth catfishes. The long fin filaments and the gray-black coloration of *Pterosturisoma* *microps* are pretty unusual and there are quite a few aquarists trying to acquire these fish. However, anybody seeking the species should be aware of the fact that this is an extremely difficult charge to take care of. Many aquarists, which failed despite concerted efforts, recommend to steer clear of this beauty. Demand begets supply and perhaps it would be sensible to replace this species with some other, more appropriate, alternatives.

Lamontichthys stibaros, ventral view of a well-fed specimen. See previous page for text.

Pterosturisoma microps, a light gray specimen.

H.-G. Evers

Pterosturisoma microps (EIGENMANN & ALLEN, 1942)

F.: Eigenmann, C.H.& W.R. Allen (1942): Fishes of Western South America. Univ. Kentucky, Lexington: 1–494.

Syn.: *Harttia microps*.

Hab.: Peru: upper Amazon at Iquitos.

M. & B.: Very sensitive in front of suboptimal oxygen concentrations and overall water conditions. New imports accept standard foods only with difficulty. Only after an acclimation period will the fish learn to take food from the bottom. Normally, these nocturnal fishes spend the day adhered to one of the aquarium panes. When feeding—a diet which should include animal fare besides peas and other vegetable matter—the fish become restless and search for food. However, it is a hesitant feeder, which never has a full belly. According to unconfirmed reports, breeding is said to have been successful, at least in principle. The catfish spawn on the aquarium panes bathed by the filter effluent current, similar to *Sturisoma* spp. Viewed ventrally, the sexes of adult specimens can be readily identified. In the genital area, a naked, trapezoidal area framed by four bony plates can be distinguished. In female specimens this area is somewhat broader, in male specimens longer and narrower. In the direct comparison of two specimens the difference becomes obvious, but taken individually it is next to impossible. Males have no bristles whatsoever, not on the sides of the head and not on the pectoral fin spines either.

S: The long fin filaments have usually broken off during import, but with appropri-

Pterosturisoma microps, a virtually black specimen.

I. Seidel

ate care, they regenerate over time. In this species, only the pectoral fins and the caudal fin are adorned with such a filament. In *Lamontichthys filamentosus* the dorsal fin has an additional filament. A difficult species which is only suitable for the experienced catfish hobbyist.

T: 26°–28°C, L: 20 cm, A: 120 cm, R: b

Pterosturisoma microps, ventral view.

I. Seidel

The Amazon River at Iquitos.

H.-G. Evers

Quiritixys sp. "Sao Paulo," in the 1st ed. presented as *Harttia*.   H.-G. Evers

Genus *Quiritixys* ISBRÜCKER, 2001

Q. leiopleura (OYAKAWA, 1993)	Rio São Francisco, Brazil

Initially described as a member of the genus *Harttia*, ISBRÜCKER (in ISBRÜCKER et al., 2001) placed the species *Harttia leiopleura* into the new genus *Quiritixys*. Based on its unique sexual dimorphism, the genus is readily distinguished from all other suckermouth catfishes. Sexually active males develop widely scattered odontodes along their flanks. Therefore also the genus name (quiris, -itis, Lat. = spear of the Sabin and ixys, gr. = size). The genus is monotypic.

It must still be determined, if indeed this genus is monotypic or if perhaps there are further member species. As can be seen on the photograph, the *Quiritixys* sp. "São Paulo" pictured here are sexually active males with a strong covering of odontodes over their entire posterior body. Based on the observations by WEIDNER (written comm.), according to which male *Harttia guianensis* loose all of their hypertrophied odontodes from the pectoral fins within days, as well as on observations of other loricariids with very "spiny" bodies (e.g., *Rineloricaria* sp. aff.

latirostris), which similarly develop such bristles only at specific times of the year, the question arises as to the possible existence of numerous unrecognized *Quiritixys* species. This might especially be the case, since there are hardly any fully developed males among the specimens preserved in museums. Even further, the question could be asked if not all of the smaller southern *Harttia* species—which do differ morphologically to some extent from their Amazonian relatives—are indeed *Quiritixys*. In that case, however, the genus would only be a younger synonym to *Harttia*, and a new genus would have to be established for the Amazonian species. At present, this is all purely speculative, although it does illustrate that within the Harttiini tribe there are still some significant unresolved issues awaiting clarification.

510

Genus *Sturisoma* Swainson, 1838
Sturgeon Catfishes

Sturisoma aureum (Steindachner, 1900)	Colombia: Magdalena Basin
Sturisoma barbatum (Kner, 1854)	Brazil: Mato Grosso
Sturisoma brevirostre (Eigenmann & Eigenmann, 1889)	Amazon
Sturisoma festivum Myers, 1942	Venezuela: Maracaibo
Sturisoma frenatum (Boulenger, 1902)	Ecuador
Sturisoma guentheri (Regan, 1904)	Peru: upper Amazon
Sturisoma kneri (de Filippi, 1940)	Venezuela: Maracaibo
Sturisoma lyra (Regan, 1904)	Brazil: Rio Juruá
Sturisoma monopelte Fowler, 1914	Guyana: Rupununi River
Sturisoma nigrirostrum Fowler, 1940	Peru: Ucayali Basin
Sturisoma panamense (Eigenmann & Eigenmann, 1889)	Panama
Sturisoma robustum (Regan, 1904)	Brazil: Rio Paraguay
Sturisoma rostratum (von Spix, 1829)	Brazil
Sturisoma tenuirostre (Steindachner, 1910)	Venezuela: Río Meta Basin

Who doesn't know the beautiful suckermouth catfish with the large caudal, dorsal, and pectoral fins? Hardly any other member of the subfamily has stirred the souls of breeders more, or caused more discussion about the appropriate way to raise the fry. However, hardly anyone has bothered to figure out which species this long-finned whiptail catfish actually belongs to. Meanwhile it has become clear that it is not *Sturisoma panamense*, since the species in our aquaria has been imported for decades from Colombia and grows much larger than the true *Sturisoma panamense*. From Colombia, *Sturisoma aureum* (Rio Magdalena Basin), and from the Venezuelan part of the Rio Meta Basin *Sturisoma tenuirostre* have been mentioned as possible candidates. A comparison with the illustration by Steindachner of *Sturisoma aureum* lead us to the conclusion that said species is not identical with "our" golden whiptail. Rather by coincidence we ran across a photograph in Galvis et al. (1997) of *Sturisoma festivum* Myers (Galvis, Mojica & Camargo, 1997: p. 97), which shows precisely the popular sturgeon catfish.

Galvis et al. studied the ichthyofauna of the Rio Catatumbo, one of the rivers feeding into the large Lake Maracaibo in northern Venezuela. Myers (1942) described his *Sturisoma festivum* from precisely that area, and a comparison of the illustrations in Myers (1942, p. 101), showed without a doubt that the long- or sailfin whiptail catfish is indeed *Sturisoma festivum*. Apparently the species also inhabits additional territories within Colombia, because according to Isbrücker (pers. comm.) a Colombian ichthyologist has confirmed data on additional habitats. Many aquarists sustain that there are actually two species which we keep in our aquaria. One would be somewhat larger, stouter, with a lighter coloration, the other smaller, more graceful, and with a more contrasting design. However, upon closer inspection, all kinds of intermediate forms can be discovered. We are convinced that *Sturisoma festivum* enjoys a relatively broad distribution within Colombia and that it displays a pronounced variability in regard to design and coloration. Imported specimens within one and the same shipment are highly variable, may they

Fam.: Loricariidae
Subfam.: Loricariinae

H.-G. Evers

Some *Sturisoma* spp. (*S. festivum,* etc.) live with preference on dead wood close to shore, others, on the other hand, prefer sand (*S. nigrirostrum* and similar species).

originate from the same river or not. Until further confirmed information is at our disposal, we should call all long-finned whiptail catfishes *Sturisoma festivum.*
This example is typical in regard to the difficulties surrounding the nomenclature of *Sturisoma* spp. Most of these species are easy to confuse among each other, having a well-developed rostrum and only slightly elongated pectoral and dorsal fin rays. Under these circumstances, who dares to identify a species without knowing where it came from? ISBRÜCKER (1980) recognized 15 species as valid, type species being *Sturisoma rostratum* (VON SPIX, 1829). We recognize at the moment 14 species as described, because the 15th species listed by ISBRÜCKER (1980) as valid—*Sturisoma dariense* MEEK & HILDEBRANDT—was already listed as a synonym of *Sturisoma panamense* by MEEK & HILDEBRANDT (1916, p. 262) themselves.

SWAINSON (1838) took the typical elongated and flattened shape of the snout, the rostrum, of the species by SPIX as a reason to redescribe the genus. Who has access, should go through the trouble and read this old publication (pp. 335–338), because the opinions at the time sure seem somewhat strange nowadays. In any case, Mr. SWAINSON's opinion still stands and "his" genus is valid today. However, it is in urgent need of a modern revision.
The members of the genus split in two groups. The east-andean, wood-dwelling species (*S. aureum, S. festivum, S. frenatum, S. panamense*) and on the other hand, the nocturnal sand-dwelling fishes which are hardly to tell apart from each other (*S. rostratum*-group). A modern revision is in preparation and it is most likely that we will have at least two different genera than.

As far as is presently known, *Sturisoma* species primarily inhabit white-water biotopes, usually rivers with moderate to swift currents. The catfishes adhere to wood or rocks and feed on the algae and associated microfauna of their substrates. All species so far have readily accepted the usual substitute fare in aquaria.

Since these catfishes commonly reach a total length of 25 cm, the aquarium provided must not be chosen too small. A powerful filtration with its corresponding oxygen enrichment is a fundamental condition for successful maintenance. *Sturisoma* species prefer vegetable fare in the form of blanched lettuce, mashed peas, zucchini, and also cucumbers. However, any kind of frozen food is also accepted. Given the high metabolic load these fishes produce, a regular partial water exchange of at least a third per week is indicated; in situations of heightened biomass (in rearing tanks), even more water should be exchanged and more often. *Sturisoma barbatum* and *Sturisoma festivum* hybridized in an aquarium (EVERS, 1992b). Caution when choosing tankmates!

H.-G. Evers

Sturisoma nigrirostrum. The name was given in reference to the black ventral coloration of the rostrum, readily apparent here in the photograph. See page 528 for text.

Sturisoma aureum (STEINDACHNER, 1900)

F.: Steindachner, F. (1900): Das w. M. Herr Hofrath F. Steindachner erstattet im Auftrage ihrer königlichen Hoheit Frau Prinzessin Therese von Bayern einen vorläufigen Bericht über einige von ihrer königlichen Hoheit während einer Reise nach Südamerika 1898 gesammelte neue Fischarten. Anz. Akad. Wiss. Wien, mathem.-naturwiss. Cl. 37(18): 206–208.

Syn.: *Loricaria aurea.*

Hab.: *Sturisoma aureum* inhabits the Colombian Río Magdalena drainage. Further details are unknown.

Sturisoma aureum, young ♂.   I. Seidel

M.&B.: Once acclimated, this whiptail is unproblematic in its care. Nevertheless, it has a high oxygen requirement and appreciates current-swept sections in the aquarium. Those are also its preferred spawning site. A strong fall in pH is not tolerated. Therefore, *S. aureum* is best maintained in neutral water.
It is an aufwuchs feeder, which in the aquarium shows a preference for algae, vegetable fare, small live and frozen foods, as well as tablet foods.
According to our observations, the golden whiptail often spawns on the aquarium panes. The eggs are somewhat larger and less numerous than those of *S. festivum.* Likewise, the fry, which hatch after 6–7 days of sacrificial care by the father, are also quite large. Similar to its congener *S. festivum,* rearing the fry is not easy, since the young show very little interest to go in the pursuit of food. Apparently they are not used to searching for nourishment, and therefore they often starve to death if they are not "drowning" in food. Rearing them solely on crumbled tablet foods is possible.

S: It has not been long since the "true" *Sturisoma aureum* comes to us [Europe] from Colombia. Previously pictured specimens are usually *Sturisoma festivum* or aquarium populations of that species, which probably after years of breeding and possibly the crossing in of similar species, are impossible to recognize as such.
Typical for the golden whiptail are the very slim and pointed head, the shorter dorsal fin in comparison to *S. festivum* (p. 471), and the absence of an elongated first ray. Males develop a much pronounced beard and turn relatively dark.
In the 1st [German] edition, pp. 482–483, the species is still pictured as *Sturisoma* sp. "Colombia."

T: 24°–28°C, L: 20–25 cm, A: 120 cm, R: b

Sturisoma aureum, lateral view

H.-G. Evers

Sturisoma aureum, ventral view with its typical coloration.

H.-G. Evers

Sturisoma sp. "Colombia," portrait

H.-G. Evers

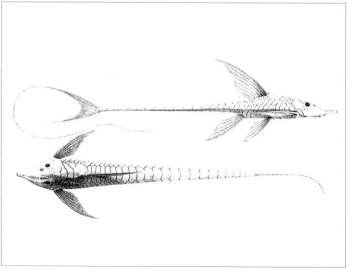

Reproduction of a drawing by STEINDACHNER, 1902: *Loricaria aurea* (today *Sturisoma aureum*).

Sturisoma barbatum x *Sturisoma festivum*, juvenile hybrid.

I. Seidel

Sturisoma barbatum x *Sturisoma festivum*, 2-year-old adult hybrid.

I. Seidel

Sturisoma barbatum

H.-G. Evers

Sturisoma barbatum (KNER, 1854)
Long-nosed whiptail catfish

F.: Kner, R. (1854): Die Panzerwelse des k.k. Hof-Naturalien-Cabinetes zu Wien. I. Abtheilung: Loricarinae.– Denkschr. Akad. Wiss.Wien, mathem.–naturwiss. Cl., 6: 65–98.

Syn.: *Loricaria barbata*.

Hab.: Brazil: Mato Grosso, Pantanal, Rio Cuiaba.

M. & B.: As indicated for *Sturisoma aureum*. Although rearing the fry is easier, getting the parents to spawn in the first place is more difficult.

S: This compact species grows quite large, and males only later develop the impressive beard on the cheeks. This differentiates *Sturisoma barbatum* from *Sturisoma nigrirostrum*. The latter is smaller, and males hardly develop a beard (odontodes) at all.

T: 25°–29°C, L: 25 cm, A: 120 cm, R: b

518

Sturisoma barbatum, head study

H.-G. Evers

Rüdiger Riehl, Düsseldorf, Germany

Scanning electron micrograph of the micropyle of an egg of *Sturisoma festivum*.

Fam.: Loricariidae
Subfam.: Loricariinae

Sturisoma festivum Myers, 1942
Long-finned sturgeon catfish

F.: Myers, G. S. (1942): Studies on south american fresh-water fishes I.– Stanford Ichthyol. Bul., 2(4): 89–114.

Syn.: None.

Hab.: Venezuela: Maracaibo Basin; Colombia: Río Catatumbo. The species enjoys a broad distribution in Colombia and is regularly imported for the aquarium hobby.

M. & B.: A popular species and, in larger aquaria, peaceful fishes are suitable tankmates. Under such conditions it may even breed. This open spawner usually lays its 100–200 eggs on smooth substrates, such as the aquarium panes, exposed to the filtration effluent current. The spawn is guarded by the male—readily recognized by his "beard"—and defended against other suckermouth catfishes by bumping into their flanks. The fry hatch after approximately seven days at 25°C and scatter throughout the tank. If rearing is to be attempted, doing so in a dedicated aquarium is the preferred method. Rearing is not easy and is only successful with optimal hygiene, frequent partial water exchanges, and a vegetable rearing diet. Algae-infested, mature aquaria provide excellent nutrition for the first days through the microorganisms they contain. Blanched lettuce, mashed peas, algae-covered rocks collected in creeks (watch out not to introduce planaria!), but also frozen rotifers, *Cyclops*, and later *Daphnia* are gladly accepted. Nevertheless, all this effort is still no guarantee for successfully rearing the fry, and entire spawns may die weeks later without apparent reason. A fish for expert breeders! For information on rearing, please refer to the following publications: Armbrust, W. (1977): *Sturisoma* sp. – Pflege und Zucht. [= maintenance and breeding] DATZ, pp. 110–112, Franke, H.-J., (1985): Handbuch der Welskunde [=Catfish Handbook], pages 55–56, K. b. J. Mack and T. Hertel (1997): Störwelszucht: Entscheidend ist das Jungfischfutter! [= Breeding whiptail catfishes: the fry food is decisive]– DATZ: 94–95.

S: For many years the question as to the correct scientific name of the aquaristically so popular sturgeon catfishes bothered the aquaristic community. Only an exhaustive study of the pertinent scientific literature has shed some light on the matter (see genus description). It has often been observed in this species that definitive females—which had already spawned before—later developed a pronounced "beard." It has even been said that these transformed males went on to guard a spawn. There is as of yet no scientific corroboration if indeed we are dealing with consecutive hermaphroditism. There is an interesting area of research waiting to be tackled by serious hobbyists!

T: 24°–28°C, **L:** 18 cm, **A:** 100 cm, **R:** b

Sturisoma festivum, ♂ with very long fins.

H.-G. Evers

Sturisoma festivum ♀

H.-G. Evers

Sturisoma festivum, ♂ guarding a new spawn.

I. Seidel

400μM   20KV   05   070   S

Rüdiger Riehl, Düsseldorf, Germany.

Sturisoma festivum egg. Scanning electron micrograph.

A few days later, the eggs are pigmented and hatching is imminent.

I. Seidel

Sturisoma festivum, fry

I. Seidel

Sturisoma festivum, a densely populated rearing tank.

I. Seidel

Rüdiger Riehl, Düsseldorf, Germany

Sturisoma festivum, preserved juvenile. Scanning electron micrograph.

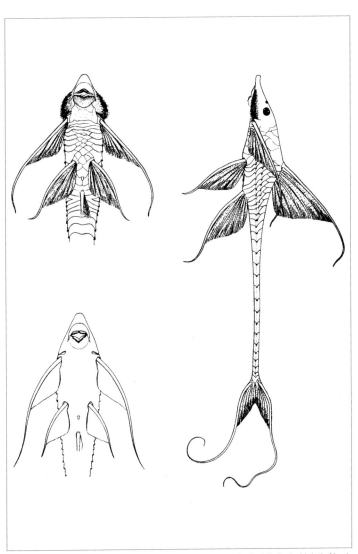

Sturisoma festivum. Illustration from the Stanford Ichthyological Bulletin Vol. 2, Nr. 4, 1942.

Fam.: Loricariidae
Subfam.: Loricariinae

Sturisoma kneri (DE FILIPI, 1940)
Kner's whiptail

F.: De Filini in Tortonese, E. (1940):
Elenco dei tipi esistenti nella collezione
ittiologica del R. Museo di Torino. Boll.
Mus. Zool. Anat. Comp. Torino (ser. 3),
48 (111): 133–144.

Syn.: *Loricaria kneri*.

Hab.: Venezuela, Maracaibo Basin. While
in search of the true *Panaque suttonorum,*
NUMRICH and LUCANUS (written comm.) visited the type locality as well as the paratype locality of this whiptail. Although both
ornamental fish wholesalers did not
achieve their original objective, at the Río
Negro, close to the mouth of the Rio
Yassa (Maracaibo-Basin) they managed
to capture *Sturisoma kneri.* NUMRICH (MIM-
BON AQUARIUM) successfully imported
Kner's whiptail for the first time to Germany. The pictured specimen is one of
that batch.

M.&B.: Maintenance follows the recommendations given for the genus in general. This is a typical representative of the
Sturisoma rostratum group, whose members are encountered on sandy or muddy
substrates and which are not quite as
oxygen-needy as, for example, *S. festivum* or *S. aureum.*

I. Seidel

S. kneri, ventral view of the head

S: The species description by de FILINI is
barely four lines long. Given that no description of color is included, it is all the
more special that, thanks to NUMRICH and
LUCANUS, we are able to include a photograph of a live specimen. A comparatively
fuzzy corporal design and the large
scutes on the base of the caudal fin are
characteristic of *S. kneri.* The lateral line
is less distinct than in *S. nigrirostrum* or
S. tenuirostre.

T: 26°–29°C, L: 25–30 cm, A: 120, R: b

Sturisoma monopelte FOWLER, 1914

F.: Fowler, H. W. (1914): Fishes from the
Rupununi River, British Guyana. Proc.
Acad. Nat. Sci. Philad. 66: 229–284.

Hab.: *S. monopelte* was described by
FOWLER from the Rupununi River in
Guyana. STAWIKOWSKI and cotravelers
found the pictured juvenile during a trip
to the Rupununi Savanna (western

Guyana) in the Takutu River, the border
stream between Guyana and Brazil. Although that river is part of the Rio Branco
drainage and therefore part of the Amazon Basin, it appears that the Takutu and
Rupununi Rivers (Essequibo Basin) are
temporarily connected during the rainy
season through the extensively flooded
savanna—something corroborated by the

Sturisoma kneri; Río Negro, Venezuela.

I. Seidel

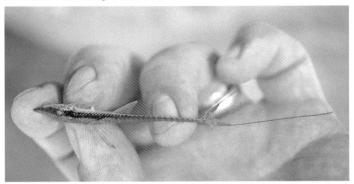

Sturisoma monopelte; juvenile from the Takutu River, Guyana.

R. Stawikowski

very similar ichthyofauna found in both streams. It follows, therefore, that *S. monopelte* inhabits the headwaters of both rivers.

M.&B.: Unknown, since the species has not been imported. However, its demands should mirror those for other members of the *S. rostratum* group, such as *S. nigrirostrum*.

S: As can be deduced from FOWLER's original description, with age, the species develops an extended filamentous elongation on the first dorsal fin spine, which at that time makes it easy to distinguish from its other congeners.

With the dorsal fin folded, the distance between the base of the dorsal fin and the caudal peduncle is said to be only about half as great as the length of the filament.

T: 26°–29°C, **L:** 25–30 cm, **A:** 120 cm, **R:** b

527

Sturisoma nigrirostrum Fowler, 1940
Black-nosed sturisoma

F.: Fowler, H.W. (1940): A collection of fishes obtained by Mr. William C. Morrow in the Ucayali River Basin, Peru.– Proc. Acad.Sci.Philadelphia, 91: 219–289.

Syn.: *Sturiosoma nigrirostrum.*

Hab.: Peru: Ucayali drainage. White-water inhabitant common in the vicinity of Yarina Cocha. Seidel and cotravelers captured the species in the Caño de Paca, an affluent of Yarina Cocha. At the end of the dry season (September), the water was very warm (28°C), clay-turbid, had a pH of 7.0, and its conductivity was 74 μS/cm. The bottom was muddy and covered with branches.

M. & B.: As indicated for *Sturisoma festivum.* The species already matures at a length of approximately 12 cm. The fry are somewhat easier to raise than those of *S. festivum.*

S: The black-nosed sturisoma is now and then imported. Ventrally, the rostrum is black. Unfortunately, all shorter-finned sturisoma are not so popular, given they are less attractive and hardly ever active. These loricariids pass the day lying on the same place, only becoming more active at twilight.

T: 24°–28°C, L: 25 cm, A: 120 cm, R: b

Sturisoma nigrirostrum ♂. See additional photo page 513.

H.-G. Evers

Sturisoma nigrirostrum, subadult from the Caño de Paca.

I. Seidel

Sturisoma nigrirostrum ♀

H.-G. Evers

Sturisoma panamense (Eigenmann & Eigenmann, 1889)
Panama sturisoma

F.: Eigenmann, C. H. & R. S. Eigenmann (1889): Preliminary notes on South American Nematognathi II.– Proc. California Acad. Sci., 2(2): 28–56.

Syn.: *Loricaria panamensis, Oxyloricaria panamensis, Oxyloricaria dariense.*

Hab.: Panama. Keijman (1999, Aquaristik Aktuell, Nr. 9–10/99: 16–18) reports about the capture of this species in the Río Parti, a river in the Río Chepo Basin of southern central Panama. It is a clear-water habitat with a temperature of 27°C, a pH of 8.0, and a conductivity of 2300 µs/cm. At least the conductivity measurement might be incorrect, because such a high value speaks for brackish water and the Panama sturisoma requires "normal" freshwater.

M. & B.: Keijman (1999) imported the species alive into Germany. Maintenance was uneventful, but there is no report in regard to its reproductive biology.

S: The holotype has a standard length of 9.5 cm and therefore must have been a juvenile specimen at the most. According to Isbrücker (pers. comm.), preserved specimens from Panama are available with a length of 30 cm. Finally, thanks to the efforts by Keijman, *Sturisoma panamense* will now not be confused any more with *Sturisoma festivum* Myers (see also the introduction to the genus). The fins are not quite as elongated as those of the Colombian species, and its back is not as tall. Nevertheless, the species has an attractive design, at least until half-grown. It is not known whether or not this design disappears with age. *Sturisoma dariense* Meek & Hildebrandt is another Panamanian species. However, the same authors (Meek & Hildebrandt, 1916, p. 262) list *Sturisoma dariense* from the drainages of the rivers Tyura and Bayano as a synonym of *Sturisoma panamense*! They go further in saying that *Sturisoma panamense* can also be found in Colombia and Ecuador. However, we do not share this opinion.

T: 26°–29°C, L: 30 cm, A: 150 cm, R: b

Sturisoma robustum (Regan, 1904)
Paraguay whiptail

F.: Regan, C. T. (1904): A monograph of the fishes of the family Loricariidae. Trans. Zool. Soc. London 17(3): 191–350, pls. 9–21.

Syn.: *Oxyloricaria robusta.*

Hab.: *Sturisoma robustum* has only been described from the Río Paraguay and Río Paraná basins. Normann & Normann captured the species during their trips to Paraguay in various rivers of the Río Paraguay drainage in the vicinity of Asunción, as well as repeatedly in the Lago Ypa-

caraí (ca. 35 km from Asunción). According to a local ornamental fish exporter, the specimens exported by him for the trade are captured in a tributary of the Lago Ypacaraí.

S. robustum inhabits sandy to muddy substrates where, close to shore, it is not difficult to capture with a cast net or dip nets. Normann & Normann determined at various times of the year water temperatures between 22° and 29°C, a pH of 6.5–7.5, and conductivities in a range between 95 and 135 µS/cm.

Sturisoma panamense

M.C.W. Keijman

Sturisoma robustum from the vicinity of Asuncion, Paraguay.

I. Seidel

Fam.: Loricariidae
Subfam.: Loricariinae

Lago Ypacaraí near Asunción, habitat of *S. robustum*.

R. Normann

Sturisoma robustum

H.-G. Evers

M.&B.: The Paraguay whiptail is comparatively undemanding in its care. In the aquarium, too, the fish lie primarily on the bottom, and are less commonly found on rocks or wood, as is frequently the case with species of the *S. panamense* group. They also appreciate calmer waters than those and are very tolerant of extremes in temperature.

Their nutritional demands are easily satisfied with tablet and flake foods, as well as small live and frozen foods.

Aquarium breeding has not been described, but has surely taken place. The reproductive biology should be comparable to that of *S. nigrirostrum*.

S: The Paraguay whiptail appears in the trade primarily as *S. barbatum*. It has not been determined if it is identical with that species which hails from the northern Rio Paraguai system (Brazilian spelling), something quite possible. Both species are very similar, and both have a short, filamentous elongation on the dorsal, pectoral, and ventral fins. In the 1st [German] edition, the species is pictured as *Sturisoma* sp. "Rio Paraguay" (pp. 482–483).

T: 22°–29°C, L: 25–30 cm, A: 120 cm, R: b

Half-grown *Sturisoma* sp. "Rio Araguaia" are relatively elongated and dark.   H.-G. Evers

Sturisoma sp. "Rio Araguaia"

This species was repeatedly captured by H.-G. Evers in the white-water tributaries of the Rio Araguaia and Rio Tocantins. The largest specimens had a total length of 20 cm. Small specimens are very dark, but as they grow, the hue lightens until adults appear yellowish. The few indi-

viduals available did not differ in their maintenance requirements from those of their congeners. Reproduction has not yet been successful.

T: 26°–29°C, L: 20 cm, A: 100 cm, R: b

Sturisoma sp. "Rio Araguaia," full-grown specimen.

H.-G. Evers

Sturisoma sp. "Rio Araguaia" from the Ilha do Bananal.

H.-G. Evers

Sturisoma tenuirostre

I. Seidel

Sturisoma tenuirostre (Steindachner, 1910)

F.: Steindachner, F. (1910): Das w. M. Hofrat F. Steindachner berichtet über eine noch unbeschriebene *Oxyloricaria*-Art aus dem Rio Meta in Venezuela und über die relativen Längenmasse bei *O. rostrata* (Sp.).– Anz. Akad. Wiss. Wien, mathem. Naturwiss. Kl., 47(25): 410–411.

Syn.: *Oxyloricaria tenuirostris*.

Hab.: Venezuela: Río Meta and Río Apure Basin. The species can be pulled onto the sandbanks of large white-water rivers with a seine. Machado-Allison & Moreno (1993) mention this species in relation to the Río Orituco (see chapter "Habitats"). Flössholzer captured a species highly reminiscent of *Sturisoma tenuirostre* in Colombia.

M. & B.: The species has certainly already been imported, albeit unrecognized, given that every once in a while fish imports reach us from the Llanos. The couple Normann captured specimens in the Rio Portugueza, also a white-water river of the Llanos.

S: Weidner (1994) includes a picture of this species, but does not recognize it as a *Sturisoma* and erroneously assigns it the code L 191. This number was subsequently withdrawn and reassigned to a different species.

T: 26°–30°C, L: 20 cm, A: 120 cm, R: b

Genus *Sturisomatichthys*
Isbrücker & Nijssen, 1979

Sturisomatichthys caquetae (Fowler, 1945)	Colombia: Río Caquetá
Sturisomatichthys citurensis (Meek & Hildebrand, 1913)	Panama: Río Tuyra
Sturisomatichthys leightoni (Regan, 1912)	Colombia: Honda
Sturisomatichthys tamanae (Regan, 1912)	Colombia: Río Tamana

A small genus which only includes four described species and at least two undescribed ones. Its members come from Panama (*S. citurensis*) and Colombia (three species from the Rio Magdalena Basin, the habitat of the undescribed species is not exactly known, but it is regularly imported from Colombia).

At first sight, the species seem members of the genus *Sturisoma*, hence the scientific name. However, they lack a well-developed rostrum. Still, males also have a pronounced beard during the reproductive season. Ventrally they are covered by three to four rows of bony plates. The area around the lips is naked. Both the upper and lower caudal fin rays are filamentous, the same for the dorsal fin. *Sturisomatichthys* is the only genus of the tribe with either 11 or 12 caudal fin rays. The other genera all have 12 (see Isbrücker, Britski, Nijssen & Ortega, 1983).

The members of this genus were by and large aquaristically unknown. In the '70s, the import of *Sturisomatichthys leightoni* was possible and Foersch was successful in its reproduction (see Franke, 1985: p. 52). Since the early '90s, an undescribed species is being imported, which since then is also being bred regularly. Initially it was thought to be *Sturisomatichthys leightoni*, but that error was soon uncovered (Evers, 1992a). It seems that in the late '90s there was an import of several Colombian species, *S. leightoni* among them, as well as another, possibly still undescribed species with pronounced odontodes on the edges of the lateral corporal plates.

Once the fishes have acclimated, the trouble is mostly over. Still, these suckermouth catfishes are more fragile than the *Sturisoma* spp. currently maintained, and especially rearing the fry is a matter best left to advanced hobbyists. These fishes are omnivores which readily accept normal substitute fare, both of animal and vegetable origin.

Sturisomatichthys leightoni ♀   W. Foersch

Sturisomatichthys leightoni (Regan, 1912)
Leighton's sturisoma

F.: Regan, C.T. (1912): Descriptions of new fishes of the family Loricariidae in the British Museum collection.– Proc.zool. Soc.London, 1912: 666–670.

Syn.: *Oxyloricaria leightoni*.

Hab.: Colombia: Honda (Río Magdalena) and further south. The once-imported specimens came from a "swiftly flowing creek 150 km to the south of Bogotá with a conductivity of 100 μS/cm, a pH of 6.5, and a temperature of 25°C" (Franke, 1985: pp. 51–52).

M. & B.: Foersch bred the species. Franke (1985, p. 52) quotes Foersch and reports about the success. The small species is somewhat more sensitive than other

whiptails, but is still a good candidate for our aquaria. The fry are about as difficult to rear as those of *Sturisoma festivum*.

S: Unfortunately, the import of this *S. leightoni* never repeated, a fact deplored by many catfish lovers. What happened to the fry and how long the species remained in the hobby is unknown to us.

T: 22°–26°C, L: 10 cm, A: 80 cm, R: b

Sturisomatichthys sp. "Colombia I"

Hab.: The undescribed species has been regularly imported from Colombia since the early '90s.

M. & B.: Small aquaria, with a minimum volume of 100 l, are suitable. Provide strong filtration and plenty of driftwood and similar items. The fish adhere to wood, plants, and the aquarium panes and accept any standard food from the (sand) substrate. Supplemental fare in the form of lettuce, peas, cucumbers, etc. brings the fish into breeding condition. Spawning is similar to that observed in *Sturisoma*, usually on the lateral panes in the current of the filter effluent. Sometimes the males have small skirmishes for the preferred spawning site, but there are never any serious injuries. The otherwise peaceful fish are constantly spawning—if in good condition—during certain seasons. A group of, for example, three males and four females can spawn weekly over a period of several months. Unfortunately, rearing the fry is not easy and should follow the guidelines given for *Sturisoma festivum.* At 25°C, the up to 80 (usually much fewer) young per female hatch after six days. SEIDEL (1993) and EVERS (1998a, Aquarium Heute 3/98: pp. 140 ff.) give very detailed reports on the matter.

S: The species appears still undescribed. A prompt scientific description would be desirable, since it has conquered a stable place in the aquarium hobby.

The design is quite variable. Besides normal specimens, there are especially marbled females. Strangely, cases have become known where individuals, which had cephalic odontodes for an extended period of time, all of a sudden laid eggs and revealed themselves as females.

Captive-bred specimens have been noted for not reaching the full size of their counterparts in nature. That is clearly the consequence of a deficient diet in captivity. Nevertheless, both *Sturisoma* and *Sturisomatichthys* can be bred over several generations in the aquarium. It's just that the bred specimens do not grow quite as large as the wild ones.

T: 24°–28°C, **L:** 10 cm (15 cm), **A:** 80 cm, **R:** b

Photo bottom right:
This wild-caught ♂ has a beautifully contrasting coloration and a pronounced beard. See the following pages for additional photos.

Sturisomatichthys sp. "Colombia I" ♂, with a rather unspectacular coloration. H.-G. Evers

H.-G. Evers

Sturisomatichthys sp. "Colombia I," ♀.

H.-G. Evers

Sturisomatichthys sp. "Colombia I," a marbled ♀.

H.-G. Evers

Spawning *Sturisomatichthys* sp. "Colombia I," ♂ below the ♀.

H.-G. Evers

Sturisomatichthys sp. "Colombia I," ♂ guarding the new spawn.

H.-G. Evers

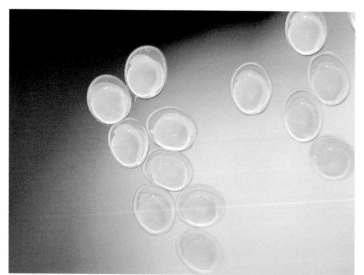

Sturisomatichthys sp. "Colombia I," spawn on the 1st day.   H.-G. Evers

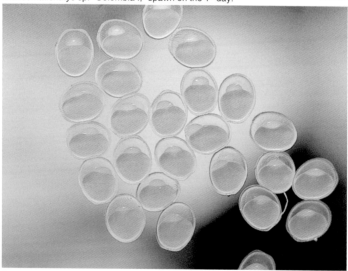

Distinct development can be discerned by the 2nd day.   H.-G. Evers

On the 3rd day, the larvae in the eggs start to have pigmentation.

H.-G. Evers

On the 4th day, development is all but complete.

H.-G. Evers

♂ covering the spawn at the end of the 4th day. Hatching is imminent.   H.-G. Evers

Newly hatched fry are virtually black, the same as fry of *Sturisoma* spp.   H.-G. Evers

Sturisomatichthys sp. "Colombia I," three-month-old juveniles.   H.-G. Evers

Lateral view of a just-hatched fry. The other fry will also be hatching soon.   I. Seidel

545

Sturisomatichthys sp. "Colombia II"

Both for its maintenance as well as for its reproduction, *Sturisomatichthys* sp. "Colombia II" should be treated along the guidelines given for *Sturisomatichthys* sp. "Colombia I." This species appeared initially in Berlin, where it was bred regularly by R. MELZER. The design is also highly variable, but it becomes apparent that on the whole it is less contrasting than that of *Sturisomatichthys* sp. "Colombia I." However, the main difference lies in the uncommonly much developed dermal odontodes on the lateral bony plates. Especially old males display this characteristic to a much greater degree than their congeners. It is nevertheless possible that we are talking about only one species.

H.-G. Evers

Detail of the odontodes on the lateral bony plates.

T: 24°–28°C, L: 10 cm, A: 80 cm, R: b

Sturisomatichthys sp. "Colombia II," front view.

H.-G. Evers

Subtribe Metaloricariina
ISBRÜCKER, 1979

Metaloricaria nijsseni (BOESEMAN, 1971)	Suriname: Sipaliwini
Metaloricaria paucidens ISBRÜCKER, 1975	French Guyana: Maroni Basin

Genus *Metaloricaria*
ISBRÜCKER, 1975

The genus *Metaloricaria* differs from the others in the tribe by its dentition, which is more reminiscent of *Rineloricaria* and *Pseudoloricaria* (both tribe Loricariini), and by having a very wide lower lip. Both species grow to a length of almost 30 cm and are therefore quite large. The area of distribution of *Metaloricaria* is limited to the Guyana Highlands (Suriname and French Guyana). It has not yet been imported to Germany. Even an intensive search for these fishes at their known habitat was unsuccessful. Therefore, we are limited to show preserved specimens from scientific collections.

Metaloricaria paucidens ♂, holotype (IRS-CNB 549), SL 270 mm, from a tributary of the Ouaqui River in French Guyana.

L.A. van der Laan

547

Metaloricaria nijsseni (ZMA 106.346), preserved specimen.   I. Seidel

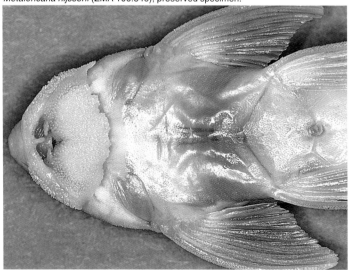

Ventral view of the specimen above. See previous page for text.   I. Seidel

Tribe Loricariini Bonaparte, 1831

A total of 24 genera in 8 subtribes are represented in the Loricariini. The monotypic genus *Furcodontichthys* Rapp Py-Daniel, 1981, must also be included, but has not been classified in any subtribe as of yet. Its only member is *Furcodontichthys novaesi* from the Amazonian Rio Tefé and the Rio Juruá Basin. The subtribe Ricolina (only genus *Ricola*, with the single species *Ricola macrops* [Regan, 1904]) and Reganellina (only genus *Reganella*) lack any presence in the aquarium trade. All other subtribes are more or less known and appreciated in the hobby. Especially in recent years, a number of interesting species could be imported, and some of them have already bred successfully.

Subtribe Hemiodontichthyina Isbrücker & Nijssen, 1979

Genus *Hemiodontichthys* Bleeker, 1862

This monotypic genus is a close relative of *Loricariichthys*. Its only member is *Hemiodontichthys acipenserinus* (Kner, 1854). The body shape with the unique rostrum is so characteristic that this genus cannot be confused with any other. Only the aquaristically unknown genus *Reganella* Eigenmann, 1905 is similar to the smaller *Hemiodontichthys*, but has a totally different head shape. The common name, knobnose whiptail catfish, for *Hemiodontichthys acipenserinus* alludes to the characteristic rostrum of this flat loricariid. Isbrücker & Nijssen (in Isbrücker, 1979) recognized the uniqueness of this genus and created its own subtribe, by the way, also for the genus *Reganella* (subtribe Reganellina). *Hemiodontichthys acipenserinus* has been aquaristically known for several years and is regularly bred.

Hemiodontichthys acipenserinus (Kner, 1854)
Knobnose whiptail catfish

F.: Kner, R. (1854): Die Panzerwelse des k.k. Hof-Naturalien-Cabinetes zu Wien. I. Abtheilung: Loricarinae.– Denkschr. Akad. Wiss.Wien, mathem.-naturwiss. Cl., 6: 65–98

Syn.: *Hemiodon acipenserinus*.

Hab.: Broadly distributed through Guyana and extensive parts of Brazil, Peru, and Bolivia. Therefore, there are color eco-morphs. In the Peruvian Caño de Paca (tributary of Yarina Cocha, white-water) the species lives together with *Farlowella platorynchus*, *Loricaria simillima*, *Hemiloricaria wolfei*, and *Sturisoma nigrirostrum* (water values see there). We were able to also capture the species numerously in the Rio Tefé and its tributaries. There it lives on sand substrates and, particularly at night, it is easy to capture with a seine over sandbanks. The white-water-carrying Rio Vermelho in the central Brazilian state of Goiás is also a habitat of this catfish. A particularly beautiful morph with contrasting design was captured by EVERS October 2000 in the Rio Abuná drainage on the Brazilian border to Bolivia. The species is quite common there and colonizes clear- and white-water tributaries of the Abuná and can also be found on sandbanks of the border river proper.

M. & B.: Breeding is easy as long as some basic conditions are met (i.e., good water management, sand bottom with sufficient open area). Detailed breeding reports are found in SEIDEL (1995) and EVERS (1996b). The males carry an egg cluster for 12–14 days in the baglike modified lips. Once the fry hatch, broodcare is finished. A male may carry a cluster up to five times during the spawning season, before taking a hiatus of several months. It is recommended that *Hemiodontichthys* be the only bottom-dweller in the aquarium, lest they fall victims to a more active food competitor. The decoration must be arranged in such a way as not to represent traps for the catfish. This species becomes stuck with its head in narrow crevices, holes, or even coarse filtration material and cannot free itself. The rostrum is covered by fine, posteriorly pointed hooklets (odontodes) which make pulling it out of such places next to impossible. The association with ancistrine suckermouth catfishes is also contraindicated. Often the knobnose swim into the provided narrow caves and are literally smashed. Death of this valuable fish is the likely consequence of such carelessness. As far as we could determine, water values are of secondary importance for breeding. In normal tap water with moderate hardness, a pH around neutral, and temperatures between 25°C and 29°C, the species spawns regularly. Young males quickly release the cluster when disturbed, but they calm down by themselves in time, and after repeated spawns, usually carry the egg cluster to term. Nevertheless, 15–20 young have to be considered a good result, we have rarely obtained a better yield. The knobnose whiptail is very sensitive to bacterial fin rot, a consequence of substandard maintenance conditions. The only hope to avoid the worst is by immediately improving the maintenance conditions and frequently changing the water. Often however, once the rot and/or hematomas have appeared on the body, any help comes too late!

S: Captive specimens do not grow to the size of their brothers in the wild. Never has a bred specimen exceeded 10 cm in length, whereas 15 cm-long wild specimens have been known to be captured. Therefore, the species is also suited for smaller aquaria. When the open sand expanse is correspondingly generous, 6–8 specimens may be readily maintained on a surface of 60 ∞ 30 cm. If the egg cluster is taken away from effectively brooding males, it can happen that they look for a substitute and "adopt" a ramshorn snail for hours, as can be seen in the photograph.

T: 24°–28°C, L: 10–15 cm, A: 60 cm, R: b

Hemiodontichthys acipenserinus ♂

H.-G. Evers

Hemiodontichthys acipenserinus ♀. See the following pages for additional photographs.

H.-G. Evers

551

Hemiodontichthys acipenserinus ♀, ventral view of the suckermouth.

I. Seidel

Note the elongated lips of this actively breeding ♂.

H.-G. Evers

♂ with an egg cluster.

H.-G. Evers

Egg cluster just prior to hatching.

H.-G. Evers

Hemiodontichthys acipenserinus, newly hatched fry.

H.-G. Evers

This ♂ has "adopted" a ramshorn snail as substitute spawn!

H.-G. Evers

Hemiodontichthys acipenserinus, captured at the Igarapé Cabure, Abunã drainage.

Hemiodontichthys acipenserinus, enlarged view of the "nose." The small hooklets that make pulling out of a "trap" such a difficult affair are readily visible.

Subtribe Loricariichthyina
ISBRÜCKER & NIJSSEN, 1979

Genus *Loricariichthys* BLEEKER, 1862
Giant Whiptail Catfishes

Loricariichthys acutus (VALENCIENNES, 1840)	Brazil
Loricariichthys anus (VALENCIENNES, 1840)	Argentina; Uruguay
Loricariichthys brunneus (HANCOCK, 1828)	Venezuela
Loricariichthys cashibo (EIGENMANN & ALLEN, 1942)	Peru
Loricariichthys castaneus (DE CASTELNAU, 1855)	Brazil, Rio de Janeiro
Loricariichthys chanjoo (FOWLER, 1940)	Peru, Ucayali
Loricariichthys derbyi FOWLER, 1915	Rio Jaguaribé
Loricariichthys edentatus REIS & PEREIRA, 2000	Argentina, Río Uruguay
Loricariichthys hauxwelli FOWLER, 1915	Ecuador, Río Ambiyacu
Loricariichthys labialis (BOULENGER, 1895)	Paraguay
Loricariichthys maculatus (BLOCH, 1794)	Suriname
Loricariichthys melanocheilus REIS & PEREIRA, 2000	Brazil, Rio Grande do Sul, Rio Uruguay
Loricariichthys microdon (EIGENMANN, 1909)	Guyana, Rupununi
Loricariichthys nudirostris (KNER, 1854)	Brazil
Loricariichthys platymetopon ISBRÜCKER & NIJSSEN, 1979	Venezuela; Paraguay
Loricariichthys rostratus REIS & PEREIRA, 2000	Brazil, Paraná, Rio Paraná
Loricariichthys stuebelii (STEINDACHNER, 1883)	Peru, Huallaga
Loricariichthys ucayalensis REGAN, 1913	Peru, Ucayali

For a long time, 16 species were considered part of the genus (ISBRÜCKER, 1980), but recently, a partial revision of the southern species was published by REIS & PEREIRA (2000). As part of their analysis, one species was invalidated (*Loricariichthys spixii* is now a synonym of *Loricariichthys castaneus*) and three new species were described. Interestingly, the names were mentioned on the Internet prior to publication. A fourth species is also mentioned on the Internet, but in the end it was not described by REIS & PEREIRA (2000).

Capturing fishes with a seine along a sandbank.

H.-G. Evers

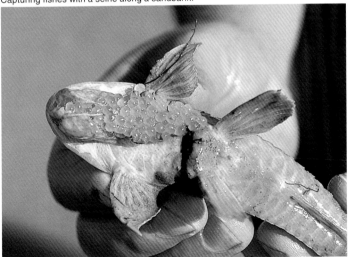

H.-G. Evers

Loricariichthys sp. "Goias", ♂ with spawn—one of the fishes captured. It can readily be appreciated how the enlarged lips frame the egg cluster.

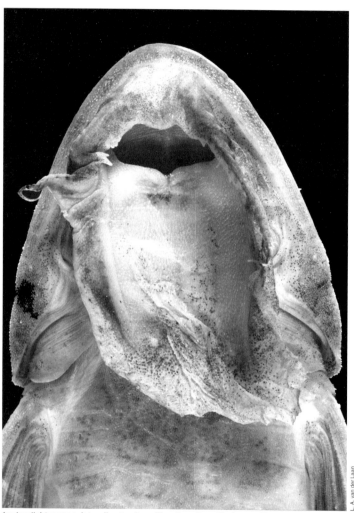

Loricariichtys maculatus, lip structure. Topotype from Suriname, Paramaribo: sexually active ♂, SL 163 mm.

L. A. van der Laan

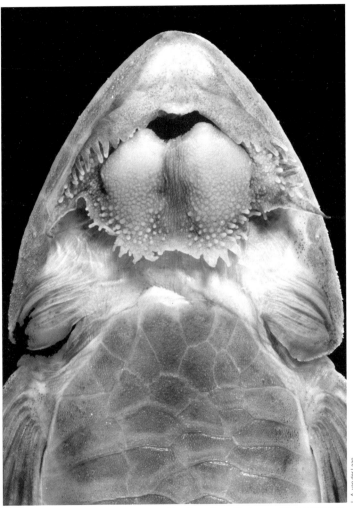

Loricariichtys maculatus lip structure. Topotype from Suriname, Paramaribo: ♀, SL 175 mm.

Fam.: Loricariidae
Subfam.: Loricariinae

The genus *Loricariichthys* is monophyletic. According to REIS & PEREIRA (2000), the genera *Reganella* and *Hemiodontichthys* are close relatives, as are the more primitive genera *Limatulichthys* and *Pseudoloricaria*.

Characteristic for the genus are the anatomy and arrangement of the lips. The upper lips are relatively small, and sometimes their edges are slightly frayed. The lower lip of juveniles, females, and sexually inactive males are much enlarged and mainly are composed of two fleshy, lighter-colored "cushions." In sexually active males, these lips transform into large dermal lobes which are used to contain the spawn.

All species grow to a respectable size, some exceeding 35 cm in total length. Of *Loricariichthys anus* it is said to even grow larger than 40 cm in total length (IS-BRÜCKER, pers. comm.). However, not all species of "Riesenhexenwelse" [~giant whiptail catfishes], as they are called in German-speaking areas, grow as large. Furthermore, aquaristic experience has meanwhile demonstrated that the *Loricariichthys* imported to date may already be maintained in aquaria of one meter in length. Under such conditions, even reproduction has been reported.

The entire slender body of the members of the genus is covered by bony plates. Usually the animals dart away, forcefully swinging their tail, and reaching a respectable speed. Sometimes they even bury within substrates of fine sand. However, this behavior is only rarely observed, especially in comparison to the true sand-dwellers from the genus *Pseudohemiodon* or, even more pronounced, those of the genus *Crossoloricaria*.

TAYLOR (1983) reports that *Loricariichthys platymetopon* and *Loricariichthys labialis* spawns comprise between 192 and 1005 eggs. The median was 508 eggs with a diameter of 2.1 millimeters! The males studied by TAYLOR had a standard length of 20–25 cm.

According to what has been observed, *Loricariichthys* live in biotopes with sandy or muddy substrates. WERNER (1992) encountered *Loricariichthys* sp. in the Brazilian Mato Grosso in dead river arms and sandy creeks with moderate current. In Colombia and Venezuela, WERNER found these fishes even in milky-murky water remnants. The water was always quite soft, had a low conductivity, and a neutral to slightly alkaline pH. Interesting is to note the high water temperatures (between 29° and 32°C) recorded by WERNER in these puddles of Colombia and Venezuela during the dry season ("Easter"). This concurs with our observations of *Loricariichthys platymetopon*, which we were able to capture during the rainy season (August 1992) in the lagoons of the Venezuelan Llanos. These biotopes were consistently muddy-turbid ponds with a muddy-clayey substrate. We did measure, however, a pH of 6–7, i.e., slightly acid to neutral, with an extremely low conductivity of up to 75 µS/cm, at the most. The temperatures there fluctuated between 28° and 35°C! We were able to observe how other catfishes, such as *Hoplosternum littorale* or *Hypostomus* sp. repeatedly came to the water surface to ingest atmospheric oxygen. The Vienna aquarist G. PALLIN (pers. comm.) observed *Loricariichthys platymetopon* in the Venezuelan Rio Parguaza during the peak of the dry season (January). The

---

Photograph top right:
Biotope photo. *Loricariichthys platymetopon* ♂ on the muddy substrate of the Río Parguaza. He carries a spawn in his labial pouch.

Photograph bottom right:
Loricariichthys spawns have been found repeatedly in nets. The eggs were adhered to leaves. This is usually typical for *Pseudoloricaria* laeviuscula.

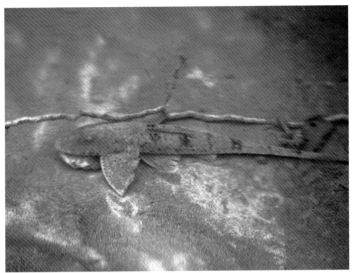

G. Pallin

C. Seidel

Fam.: Loricariidae
Subfam.: Loricariinae

male he photographed laid in the shallow water on a muddy substrate and it was readily apparent that it carried a spawn in his mouth.

There are diverging observations in regard to *Loricariichthys ucayalensis* from the Amazonian section of Peru. One of the coauthors (SEIDEL) was able to capture the species in the Rio San Alejandro, a stream that is part of the Peruvian Ucayali drainage. There, *L. ucayalensis* can be found on sandbanks in sections with swift current of this clear-water river. The captured specimens had a correspondingly high oxygen requirement.

TAYLOR (1983) reports on observations made in the natural habitat on *Loricariichthys platymetopon* and *L. labialis* in the Lago Ypacarai, close to Asunción, the capital of Paraguay. August 1979 the water there was milky turbid with a greenish/gray coloration and a visibility of less than 10 cm. In contrast to the syntopic *Loricaria simillima*, which prefer hard or rather sandy substrates, TAYLOR found both *Loricariichthys* on soft, muddy bottoms. This agrees with observations made by PALLIN in the Rio Parguaza of Venezuela. BADER (pers. comm.) also captured a *Loricariichthys* sp. in lentic waters. The fish was captured, together with many *Acarichthys heckeli,* October 1971 with a large spawn in its oral pouch in the Lago Calado, a lake in the vicinity of the city of Manacapurú, located on the Rio Solimões. The species was encountered on sandy substrates in the shallow littoral zone of the clear-water lake (sedimented white-water). Part of the habits of juvenile *Loricariichthys* became apparent to us as we fished towards the end of the rainy season in a side arm of the Río Parguaza in southern Venezuela. At a section of sandy beach virtually protected from the current, we were able to fish, in a depression filled with leaf litter and branches, several juveniles—apparently only a few days old—of a *Loricariichthys* sp. The young could grow in the

protected confines of the depression and still received sufficient food items. The oxygen concentration in the swiftly flowing clear-water was very high, however, and it was very difficult to maintain the captured fishes alive. Consequently, we were unable to avoid the demise of the captured *Loricariichthys* fry. This contrary to the experiences by WERNER (1992), who was able to bring without particular problems recently hatched fry to Germany.

The meanwhile quite extensive records on biotope characteristics beget the question about the natural diet of these fishes. It has been answered, albeit in a preliminary way, by MENEZES (1949b). MENEZES studied the stomach and intestinal lengths of "*Loricaria typus*" (according to ISBRÜCKER [1971a] and pers. comm., identical with *Loricariichthys platymetopon*) from the Parnaiba Basin in the federal Brazilian state of Piaui. Accordingly, this species has, in comparison to *Hypostomus plecostomus*—an algivore—a rather short gastrointestinal tract. That characteristic points to a rather omnivorous diet. We suspect that besides insect larvae, present in large numbers in the substrate of strongly eutrophic waters, detritus and algae also constitute a large proportion of the stomach contents. We are presently aware of only one publication dealing with stomach contents analyses of the genus *Loricariichthys*. GEISLER & BOLLE (1956) published data about a fish identified as *Loricariichthys brunneus* that had been captured in Argentina. Although *L. brunneus* is presently only known from Venezuela, that is not important in this context, because the results published by GEISLER and BOLLE can readily, although with certain restrictions, be applied to many *Loricariichthys*. The authors found in the stomach of adult specimens mostly substrate components. Besides diatoms and plant remnants, the contents of the gastrointestinal tract were made up of an appreciable quantity of benthic copepods. It seems that much sand was also ingested in the pursuit of these edibles. In stomachs of juvenile specimens, the proportion of food of animal origin was significantly greater. Notorious in this context was the large percentage of *Bosmina* found.

The available biotope observations easily lead one to assume that *Loricariichthys* species have no particular environmental requirements in regard to water quality. Compared with other, much more sensitive suckermouth catfishes from clear lotic environments, this is certainly true. However, this should not be an excuse for the aquarist to neglect his or her *Loricariichthys*. It is certainly true that the specimens will not feel any less comfortable when exposed to sensible care—resulting in good water management—than in their natural, muddy home range.

H.-G. Evers

Lagoon at Calabozo in the Venezuelan Llanos: habitat of *Loricariichthys platymetopon*.

Loricariichthys acutus from Peru, Río Utiquinea.

H.-G. Evers

Loricariichthys acutus (VALENCIENNES, 1840)

F.: Valenciennes, A. in Cuvier, G.& A. Valenciennes (1840): Histoire naturelle des poissons (Ch. Pitois, Paris & V. Levrault, Strasbourg)., 15: i–xxxi, 1–540.

Syn.: *Loricaria acuta.*

Hab.: Brazil (?), very vague in the original description: (transl. EVERS: "man glaubt, dass sie [die Art] vielleicht aus Brazil kommt") [="it is believed the species might possibly come from Brazil]. It is precisely such a "type locality" that makes research all the joy it can be! B. SCHMITT (pers. comm.) captured the pictured specimen in the Peruvian Río Utiquinea, about 20–25 km from its confluence with the Río Ucayali. The Utiquinea is also a white-water river (water temperature 28°–29°C; pH 6.6; total hardness 1° dGH;

conductivity 50 µS/cm). The animals lived on sandy, partially muddy substrates.

M.&B.: *L. acutus* spawned once at SCHMITT. Unfortunately, the abandoned spawn did not develop under artificial incubation conditions. There is still a great lack in experience with this interesting species; the animals of SCHMITT are the only specimens imported so far.

S: The pointed head profile is an unusual characteristic for this genus.

T: 25°–29°C, L: 15 cm, A: 100 cm, R: b

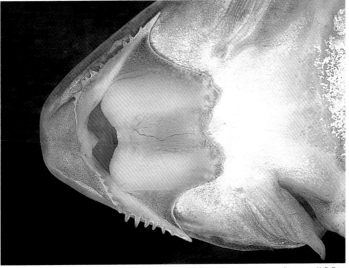

Portrait of *Loricariichthys acutus*.

Loricariichthys anus; mouth and lips in a normal state. See next page for text.

Loricariichthys anus in an aquarium

H.-G. Evers

Loricariichthys anus (VALENCIENNES, 1840)

F.: Valenciennes, A. in Cuvier, G.& A. Valenciennes (1840): Histoire naturelle des poissons (Ch. Pitois, Paris & V. Levrault, Strasbourg)., 15: i–xxxi, 1–540.

Syn.: None.

Hab.: Argentina, Province of Buenos Aires, Uruguay. The pictured specimens were fished by Danish aquarists during a trip through Uruguay. The fishes were captured at the coastal area, in a river system emptying into the Atlantic.

M.&B.: *L. anus* grows to be very large and consequently requires appropriate, generously dimensioned aquaria. It has a healthy appetite and the (sandy!) substrate is constantly rooted in search of edibles. Powerful filtration is mandatory,

as is a weekly water exchange of 30–50%. The species is robust and, as long as these precepts are heeded, simple and unproblematic in its care.
There is no information available in regard to breeding. In agreement with its southern distribution, the water temperature should be maintained relatively cool.

S: *L. anus* is readily identified based on the double row of fused bony plates ("coalescing scutes") running along its flanks.

T: 18°–22°C, L: 40 cm, A: 150 cm, R: b

Loricariichthys anus; portrait of a ca. 30 cm specimen.

H.-G. Evers

H.-G. Evers

Loricariichthys anus; characteristic are the keels running along its flanks, there where the bony plates (scutes) meet.

Loricariichthys cf. *maculatus*; Rio Trombetas.   C. Seidel

Loricariichthys maculatus (Bᴌᴏᴄʜ, 1794)

F.: Bloch, M. E. (1794): Allgemeine Naturgeschichte der ausländischen Fische, 8: 1–174.

Syn.: *Plecostomus* no. 68, *Plecostomus* no. 391, *Plecostomus cataphractus*, *Loricaria amazonica*.

Hab.: Suriname. The pictured specimen was captured by Cristoph Sᴇɪᴅᴇʟ in the Rio Trombetas. It is indeed very likely to be the actual *Loricariichthys maculatus*.

M.&B.: Unknown, since a live import [to Germany] has not yet occurred. However, no surprises are expected in relation to other, aquaristically known species. Next to the pictured *L.* cf. *maculatus*, C. Sᴇɪᴅᴇʟ found in his net a leaf with an adhered spawn. Its shape and coloration agreed

with those typical of *Loricariichthys* spp. It is quite possible that this species uses a plant leaf to protect the lower half of the spawn in addition to the protection provided by the labial pouch.

S: *L. maculatus* is a close relative of *L. platymetopon* and, especially, of *L. ucayalensis*, a species with which it is easily confused.
L. maculatus is the type species of the genus.

T: 26°–29°C, **L:** 20 cm, **A:** 120 cm, **R:** b

Loricariichthys platymetopon
ISBRÜCKER & NIJSSEN, 1979

F.: Isbrücker, I.J.H.& H. Nijssen (1979): Three new South American mailed catfishes of the genera *Rineloricaria* and *Loricariichthys* (Pisces, Siluriformes, Loricariidae).– Bijdr. Dierk., 48(2): 191–211.

Syn.: None.

Hab.: Paraguay and intriguingly also Venezuela, since there are no reports of intermediate finds (see genus introduction).

M.&B.: Simple to care for. Attains sexual maturity at a length of ca. 12 cm. Males carry a large egg cluster around with them. Although approximately 1,000 eggs could be counted in nature, in the aquarium 300 is more common. Rearing the fry is easily accomplished with *Artemia* nauplii and hygienic water conditions. They young grow quickly and may measure already 4–5 cm after 6 weeks. These large loricariids need copious amounts of food. Hungry juveniles quickly become restless and nervously swim up and down the aquarium panes. A behavior rather unusual for loricariinae, but typical for *Corydoras* and others.

S: The *L. platymetopon* captured by EVERS and SEIDEL in Venezuela cannot be distinguished anatomically from those of Paraguay. As only difference, the coloration of the Venezuelan animals remained darker through the years than that of their Paraguayan tankmates.

T: 25°–29°C, L: 20 cm, A: 120 cm, R: b

H.-G. Evers

Loricariichthys platymetopon; ♂ with spawn cluster. See next page for additional photos.

Loricariichthys platymetopon; 18-month-old subadult. H.-G. Evers

Loricariichthys platymetopon; sexually active ♂ with much enlarged lips. I. Seidel

Loricariichthys sp. "Goiás"

H.-G. Evers

Loricariichthys sp. "Goiás"

EVERS captured this species at a Sand-bank of the Rio Vermelho, close to the city of Aruanã, in the central Brazilian state of Goiás. It might possibly be *Loricariichthys derbyi* FOWLER, 1915, described from the "Rio Jaguaribé at Barro Alto, Brazil." There is a city under that name in Goiás, but the river could not be found. That may not mean much, given that in one hundred years many names in South America have suffered change. Still, we will continue calling the fish *Loricariichthys* sp. "Goiás." The particularity of this species is that a captured brooding male was carrying a green (!) spawn in its labial pouch, in the manner typical of *Loricariichthys*. However, on its congeners we could only observe yellow-orange spawns. The fish is relatively elongated and is reminiscent of the species around *Loricariichthys platymetopon* and *L. maculatus*. The captured specimens were too large; a live import [to Germany] is therefore still pending.

T: 26°–29°C, L: 25 cm, A: 120 cm, R: b

Loricariichthys sp. "Uruguay"

J. Reichert

Loricariichthys sp. "Uruguay"

The pictured species may be captured in the white-waters of the Uruguayan Paraná Basin. The species may be virtually black and is somewhat reminiscent of *Loricariichthys platymetopon*. Its full-grown size is respectable, similar to that of *Loricariichthys anus*—also an Uruguayan species—but its coloration and the morphology of the scutes distinguishes the two. It might possibly be *Loricariichthys spixii* (today a synonym of *L. castaneus*) described by STEINDACHNER. However, due to a lack of comparative material, it was not possible to substantiate this hypothesis. For aquarium maintenance, this species is expected to require cool water temperatures and ample space and feed, in a manner indicated for *Loricariichthys anus*. It has not yet been imported alive to Germany.

J. Reichert

Loricariichthys sp. "Uruguay," ventral view.

T: 15°–20°C, L: 30 cm, A: 150 cm, R: b

Subtribe Loricariina
BONAPARTE, 1831

Genus *Brochiloricaria*
ISBRÜCKER & NIJSSEN, 1979

Brochiloricaria chauliodon
ISBRÜCKER & NIJSSEN, 1979
(type species)

Brochiloricaria macrodon (KNER, 1854)

The members of the genus *Brochilori-caria* hail from Argentina (*B. chauliodon*) and southern Brazil (Rio Cuiabá). They grow to a length of 25 and 30 cm, respectively. Their main distinguishing characteristic from the genus *Loricaria* is their dentition.
Aquaristically they are of no consequence and should only be an option for very large aquaria with cool water. Both not exactly easily fulfilled recommendations for a fish aspiring to become popular!

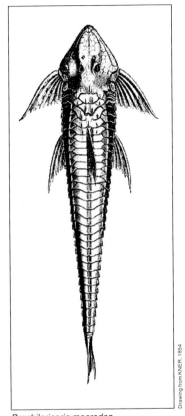

Drawing from KNER, 1854

Brochiloricaria macrodon

Brochiloricaria macrodon (KNER, 1854)

F.: Kner, R. (1854): Die Panzerwelse des k. k. Hof-Naturalien-Cabinetes zu Wien. Denkschr. Akad.Wiss. Wien, mathem.-naturwiss. Cl., 6: 65–98.

Syn.: *Loricaria macrodon*.

Hab.: Brazil, Mato Grosso, Rio Cuiabá. Distributed in the southern Pantanal. The type locality, the Rio Cuiabá, is a tributary of the Rio Paraguai, which leads one to expect its presence also in Paraguay. And indeed, since the end of 2001, the company AQUARIUM GLASER (Rodgau) imported *B. macrodon* repeatedly together with *Loricaria tucumanensis* from Paraguay.

M.&B.: Given its nervous temperament, this large species requires ample space. A sand substrate and large open expanses should be provided. Furthermore, the aquarium should not be illuminated too brightly, because the beautiful coloration will be displayed much paler. The nutritional requirements of this omnivore should be satisfied with frozen mosquito larvae or small *Mysis*, as well as with vegetable tablet foods. The diet in nature is suspected to consist mostly of detritus.
Water chemistry seems rather secondary to these white-water inhabitants, but it should be low in nitrates. Therefore, a weekly water exchange of 50% is recommended for these hearty eaters.
There has been success in breeding this mouthbrooding Loricariinae. Soon after its first import, Petra DOTZER and Thomas WEIDNER received the fish because of their large aquaria. Soon the strongest male claimed a root as his territory. There it remained all day long, until one morning a spawning disc could be observed on his mouth. It was highly reminiscent of those seen in *Loricaria* spp. The male also swam around the aquarium holding the spawn, but always returned to its slanted root territory, whereas tankmates remained on the bottom. Apparently, males prefer elevated locals, especially during the brooding period. Rearing the young has been successful following the indications given for *Loricaria* spp. A new success in breeding a whiptail, which reveals to us its reproductive strategy. *B. macrodon* is another one of the mouthbrooding suckermouth catfishes!

S: A species with a beautifully contrasting design. Especially the much elongated pectoral and ventral fins distinguish these charges.

T: 20°–26°C, L: 35 cm, A: 150 cm, R: b

Brochiloricaria macrodon from Paraguay.

I. Seidel

B. macrodon has notably elongated pectoral fins.

I. Seidel

Brochiloricaria macrodon ♂ on "its" root with a newly-laid spawn. T. Weidner

The spawn is a few days old, the fry can be discerned within the eggs. T. Weidner

Frontal view of the broodcaring ♂.   T. Weidner

Brochiloricaria macrodon, fry.   T. Weidner

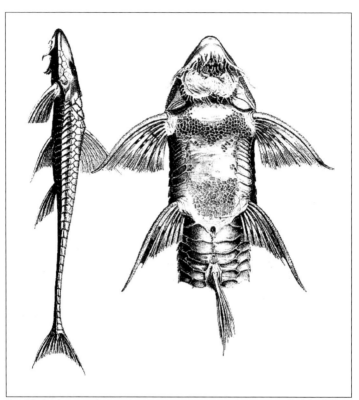

Brochiloricaria macrodon

Drawing from KNER, 1854

Genus *Loricaria* LINNAEUS, 1758
and Related Genera

At present, the following species are considered valid (according to ISBRÜCKER, 1981):	
Loricaria apeltogaster BOULENGER, 1895	Paraguay, Argentina
Loricaria cataphracta LINNAEUS, 1758	Guyana Highlands, northern Brazil
Loricaria clavipinna FOWLER, 1940	Brazil, Tapajós River
Loricaria lata EIGENMANN & EIGENMANN, 1889	Central Brazil, Araguaia River
Loricaria nickeriensis ISBRÜCKER, 1979	Suriname, Nickerie River
Loricaria parnahybae STEINDACHNER, 1907	Brazil, Parnaiba; French Guyana
Loricaria piracicabae VON IHERING, 1907	Southeastern Brazil, Piracicaba
Loricaria simillima REGAN, 1904	Ecuador, Peru, Venezuela, northern Brazil, Paraguay, Argentina
Loricaria tucumanensis ISBRÜCKER, 1979	Argentina, Tucuman
Additionally, ISBRÜCKER (1981) lists two more species(?) with an uncertain status, given that at the time there was insufficient material available for analysis.	
Loricaria sp. "Alpha"	Brazil, upper Xingú Basin
Loricaria sp. "Beta"	Ecuador, Bobonaza Basin

Since Carl von LINNAEUS described *Loricaria cataphracta* in the year 1758 as the first taxon in the family Loricariidae, 61% (ISBRÜCKER, 1981) of the extensive subfamily Loricariinae have been described as belonging to this genus. In the minds of many aquarists, this genus especially represents the whiptail catfishes of the genus *Hemiloricaria*, and the designation "*Loricaria* sp." all more or less sand-colored whiptail-like catfishes. This despite the fact that ISBRÜCKER (1981) only accepted 11 species as valid members of the genus *Loricaria*, and listed all the many misidentifications found in the scientific literature as well as the current, correct designation. Type species is *Loricaria cataphracta*. ISBRÜCKER (1981) concedes that the species *L. cataphracta*, *L. lata*, *L. simillima*, and *L. parnahybae* are very close relatives. Especially in the case of *L. lata* it is difficult to distinguish this species from *L. cataphracta* because within the known scientific material of *L. cataphracta* there are larger morphometric variations among the various populations than between it and the type material of *Loricaria lata*. Neverthe-

less, in a face to face comparison there are apparent differences which justify a separation of the two species.

The distinguishing characteristics of this genus are not necessarily easy to determine for the aquarist. For example, the dentition of the *Loricaria* species is unique in the entire family. The teeth of the upper mandible are twice as long as those of the lower mandible. The labial morphology is another classifying characteristic. The upper lip is short, its edge covered by numerous thin, simple, bifurcate or, more rarely, trifurcate barbels. The lower lip, in contrast, is fully developed and extended the most at its center. Its surface is covered by numerous small papillae with many long simple filaments along their edge.

The first pectoral fin ray is longer than the following rays; in some species, e.g., *L. clavipinna* FOWLER, 1940, they are much broadened in males. The upper, first spine of the caudal fin is much elongated in all species and may equal the length of the body. The ventrum is by and large naked, but may—depending on species,

Proloricaria lentiginosa, paratype, SL 266,5 mm, from the Rio Mogi-Guaçu, Brazil.

Loricaria nickeriensis, holotype, SL 118 mm, ♂. Suriname, Fallawatra River.

Loricaria piracicabae, SL 149 mm, from the Rio Corumbata, Brazil.

Loricaria tucumanensis, holotype, SL 122,3 mm. ♂ from Argentina, Tucumán.

Fam.: Loricariidae
Subfam.: Loricariinae

and especially on older specimens—be covered with tiny bony platelets to a greater or lesser degree.

With the exception of *L. nickeriensis* from Suriname, which seems to be smaller, the total length is quite large with 20–25 cm and that in itself makes them less than ideal charges for the "normal" aquarist.

The genus *Loricaria* has been found in virtually all South American countries, with the exception of Chile and southern Argentina. Aquaristically speaking, the best represented and most often imported and bred species is *Loricaria simillima* REGAN, 1904. But also *Loricaria cataphracta* LINNAEUS, 1758 has been bred successfully. Under close observation, the sexes of some species can be distinguished based on the thicker first pectoral fin spines of full-grown males. Initially confirmed scientifically only for *Loricaria clavipinna* and *L. tucumanensis,* differences could also be established for several other species (*Loricaria cataphracta, L. lata*).

The genus *Ricola* ISBRÜCKER & NIJSSEN, 1978 is very similar to *Loricaria* and only differs in relation to the anatomy of the labial barbels, which are much longer and more branched than those of *Loricaria* spp. *Ricola* additionally has many more teeth in the upper mandible (15) than *Loricaria* (3–5). This has led to the separation into an independent subtribe, *Ricolina*.

ISBRÜCKER (1981) published a key to differentiate among the genera of the tribe Loricariini with filamentous labial structure, which is listed here (augmented by four genera by H.-G. EVERS). Given that the key involves various subtribes, there was a problem with the placement of the key within this book. Since the genus *Loricaria* is the best-known to aquarists, it was decided to place it here. The original key has been broadened by the genera *Pyxiloricaria, Apistoloricaria, Proloricaria,* and *Dentectus,* which had not been described at the time of the creation

of the original key. It should now be possible to identify with certainty the genera within the loricariine suckermouth catfishes with filamentous labial structure. The proportional differentiations given by ISBRÜCKER under point 7 have been omitted. It is not practical for the aquarist to analyze this characteristic and the genera can also be determined without having to rely on this feature.

Loricaria species always inhabit lotic environments of all three water types, white, black, or clear. We captured *Loricaria simillima* (white-water) over sandbanks at several sites. Over rubble substrates in shallow water, about 50 cm deep, we captured *Loricaria* sp. "Alpha" (Xingú-headwaters), and over coarse sand in the middle of the river at about 1 meter depth, *Loricaria lata* was discovered in clear and turbid waters of the Araguaia drainage.

The preceding biotope information is given due to the variability expressed in the individual species descriptions. However, it still has to be noted that both in *Loricaria simillima* and *Loricaria lata,* the intraspecific coloration depends on the water makeup of their habitat. Both species, if inhabiting clear-water, were much more attractive than those specimens captured by us, the authors, in white-water. This difference is maintained even after extended aquarium care.

Loricaria spp. have similar maintenance requirements as *Loricariichthys,* but are much more exacting in regards to their requirements of water quality. Newly imported *Loricaria* are sensitive and must be slowly acclimated in order to overcome the extended transport stress that is unavoidable during import. It is not a rare occurrence for the animals to die weeks later, without the aquarist being able to say precisely where he or she went wrong or what should have been done differently. A quarantine is therefore strongly recommended for all imported specimens.

Loricaria sp. from Brazil; note the labial anatomy.

H.-G. Evers

Especially when breeding *Loricaria* species, deformations of the head region are not uncommon. This is clearly the consequence of errors committed in their rearing, since it has happened with fry brought back from South America that young reared in an aquarium became pug-nosed. Feeding enriched *Artemia* nauplii and the provision of a hearty and varied diet may help in avoiding the appearance of these deformations (see also the chapter on rearing).

Key to the Genera of the Loricariinae, Tribe Loricariini with Filamentous Labial Anatomy (from Isbrücker, 1981)

1a	Toothless upper jaw	*Planiloricaria*
1b	Teeth in upper and lower maxillaries	2
2a	Upper jaw with 6 or more teeth on each side	3
2b	Upper jaw with 5 or less teeth on each side	4
3a	Upper jaw with up to 9 teeth on each side; maxillary barbels with subbarbels, which are not subdivided into smaller branches	5
3b	Upper jaw with up to 6 teeth on each side, maxillary barbels with subbarbels, which are subdivided into smaller branches	*Apistoloricaria*
3c	Upper jaw with up to 15 teeth on each side; maxillary barbels with subbarbels, which are subdivided into smaller branches	*Ricola*
4a	Teeth of the upper jaw about twice as long as those of the lower jaw. Abdomen ventrally completely covered by scutes	*Loricaria*
4b	Teeth of the upper jaw about twice as long as those of the lower jaw. Abdomen ventrally only partially covered by scutes. Body dorsoventrally much compressed and extremely broad at the pectoral girdle.	*Proloricaria*
4c	Teeth of the upper jaw about one third longer than those of the lower jaw; teeth of the lower jaw about as long as the teeth of the upper jaw of *Loricaria*	*Brochiloricaria*
4d	Teeth of the upper jaw very small, hardly visible	*Dentectus*
5a	Abdomen naked or covered by irregularly arranged scutes, not arranged towards a median stripe	6
5b	Abdomen naked with the exception of a single median stripe consisting of rounded small scutes	*Crossoloricaria*
6a	Ventral elongations present on the rostrum	7
6b	No ventral elongations present on the rostrum	*Paraloricaria*
7a	Sides of head and rostrum more or less triangular when viewed from above	*Pseudohemiodon*
7b	Sides of the head meeting at a pointed angle, those of the snout narrow and somewhat concave when viewed from above	*Rhadinoloricaria*
7c	Sides of the head forming a distinct triangle, upper lip very frayed	*Pyxiloricaria*

L. cataphracta ♂ with spawn, see following pages for additional photos. I. Seidel

Loricaria cataphracta LINNAEUS, 1758

F.: Linnaeus, C.v. (1758): Systema naturae per regna tria naturae, secundum classes, ordines, genera, species, cum characteribus, differentiis, synonymis, locis. Tomus I. Editio decima, reformata (L. Salvii, Holmiae): 1–824.

Syn.: *Loricaria cirrhosa, Loricaria setifera, Loricaria dentata, Loricaria flagellaris, Loricaria carinata, Loricaria dura.*

Hab.: Guyana, Suriname, French Guyana, and northeastern Brazil. According to GOTTWALD (cited in SEIDEL, 1997), the species lives in French Guyana in slightly tea-colored clear-water rivers with moderate current. The water is slightly acid and soft.

M.&B.: Readily maintained and bred in an aquarium. Sexual maturity is attained at a length of approximately 10 cm. These are paternal mouthbrooders which carry the spawn around in the shape of a two-layered disc. During this phase, the males are very shy and sensitive in front of any external disturbances. SEIDEL (Aquaristik Aktuell 3/97: 22–27) is the first to publish a successful breeding report.

S: *L. cataphracta* was the first fish to be described in accordance to the presently valid taxonomic principles.
It is hoped that this interesting species will find a broad distribution through regular captive reproduction, even though it is not particularly beautiful.

T: 24°–28°C, L: 20 cm, A: 100 cm, R: b

Loricaria cataphracta

H.-G. Evers

Loricaria cataphracta, portrait, see previous page for text.

H.-G. Evers

Loricaria cataphracta ♂ with broadened first pectoral fin spine.

I. Seidel

L. cataphracta; in juveniles and ♀♀ the development of the first pectoral fin spine is "normal."

I. Seidel

Loricaria cataphracta, egg cluster.

Loricaria cataphracta, fry.

I. Seidel

Loricaria lata, ♂ with egg mass in an aquarium.

H.-G. Evers

Loricaria lata EIGENMANN & EIGENMANN, 1889

F.: Eigenmann, C. H. & R. S. Eigenmann (1889): Preliminary notes on South American nematognathi II.– Proc. California Acad. Sci., 2 (2): 28–56.

Syn.: None.

Hab.: Brazil, state of Goiás, Araguaia drainage, Rio Vermelho. The pictured specimen was captured by H.-G. EVERS and P. VALERIO in the Rio Fartura at Scanderlandia in the state of Goiás. The male carried a large egg cluster at the time it was captured. The clear-water was made turbid by hard rains and flowed over a medium-grained sand bed with a moderately swift current. The male was captured with a seine at a depth of approximately one meter. On March 21st, 1998 the following water values were determined: temperature 30.2°C, con-

ductivity 78 µs/cm, and pH 6.5. But the species can also be found in the Rio do Peixe (see chapter on "Habitats"). The half-grown specimens captured there are much more attractive (clear-water). EVERS captured the species also at the Mato Grosso side of the central Rio Araguaia, as well as in the basin of the Rio das Mortes and the tributaries of the Rio Suia Missú, a headwater of the Rio Xingú. Apparently the distribution of the species is larger than initially suspected.

M.&B.: H.-G. EVERS and P. VALERIO captured July 1999 this species anew in the Rio do Peixe. On that occasion, half-grown specimens could be captured. These withstood the rigors of transport to Germany. In the aquarium, the species is no more exacting than other—in aquaria more commonly encountered—species.

Loricaria lata in an aquarium.

H.-G. Evers

Beginning at a length of 12 cm, the females matured and after stimulation involving several water exchanges and the addition of a current-producing recirculating pump, spawning occurred at EVERS. The smaller male carried such a huge egg cluster that he had a hard time handling it. Unfortunately, after several days, most eggs were fungused and the male also abandoned the remaining healthy ones. In December 2000, a pair brought by EVERS spawned twice, and rearing was finally successful. At 26°C the fry unfortunately did not hatch on their own, but on day 14 had to be freed of their egg membranes with the aid of a needle. The rearing of 120 fry from one spawn was successful. Growth and further rearing did not differ from *Loricaria simillima*.

S: The species is very similar to *Loricaria cataphracta* from the Guyana Highlands (see genus introduction) and to *Loricaria simillima*.

T: 26°–30°C L: 20–25 cm, A: 120 cm, R: b

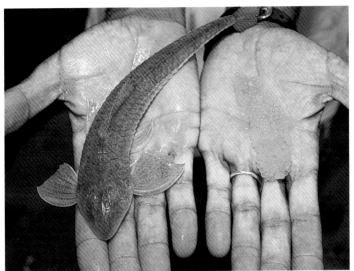

L. lata; just captured ♂. The egg cluster was released in the seine.   H.-G. Evers

L. lata; pair prior to spawning. The ♀ approaches the smaller ♂ from behind.   H.-G. Evers

Loricaria lata, full-grown specimen.

I. Seidel

Loricaria lata, 8-day-old eggs.

H.-G. Evers

Loricaria lata; ♂ with 14-day-old egg cluster, just prior to hatching.   H.-G. Evers

Loricaria lata, young in three stages: a) newly hatched, b) 3 weeks old, and c) 6 weeks old.

Fam.: Loricariidae

Subfam.: Loricariinae

Loricaria parnahybae Steindachner, 1907

F.: Steindachner, F. (1907): Dr. Steindachner berichtet ferner über zwei neue Arten von Süßwasserfischen aus dem Stromgebiet des Parnahyba, welche von ihm während der zoologischen Expedition der kaiserl. Akademie nach Brasilien aufgefunden waren sowie über eine Abart von *Loricaria lima*, Kn. aus dem Jurua, ...– Anz. Akad. Wiss. Wien, mathem.-naturw. Kl., 44 (10): 152–155.

Syn.: *Loricaria piauhiae*.

Hab.: French Guyana, Oiapoque; Brazil, States of Maranhão and Piaui, lower Parnaiba Basin. The pictured specimen hails from the Rio Guama and was imported [to Germany] from there by Jens Gottwald.

M.&B.: Breeding has not been successful. In maintenance there is no difference to *Loricaria simillima*. However, the species requires somewhat better care during the acclimation phase.

S: The longer head profile in comparison to the similar *L. simillima* is notorious. The specimens imported from Guama "fit" into the area of distribution of this species, and the head profile, too, is similar to that of *L. parnahybae*.

T: 26°–29°C, L: 20 cm, A: 100 cm, R: b

Bird-view on Rio Guama.

H.-G. Evers

Loricaria parnahybae from the Rio Guamá.

I. Seidel

Loricaria parnahybae, portrait.

I. Seidel

Loricaria simillima REGAN, 1904

F.: Regan, C.T. (1904): A monograph of the fishes of the family Loricariidae.– Trans. zool. Soc. London, 17: 191–350.

Syn.: None.

Hab.: Venezuela, Ecuador, Peru, Brazil, Paraguay, Argentina. The extensive area of distribution is proof of the species' adaptability to various environmental characteristics. *L. simillima* usually inhabits flowing waters of the white as well as clear type. SEIDEL (1997) gives some values in relation to Peruvian biotopes. It has not been possible to determine if the coloration is influenced by the type of water. There are attractive specimens in white-water and unattractive ones in clear-water as well as the other way around.
A species called *Loricaria* cf. *simillima* here was captured by the authors in the Brazilian Rio Tefé. There are no confirmed reports at this time for *L. simillima* to occur in central Amazonia. There are differences in the design covering the pectoral and ventral fins, which at the posterior edge are light in color and whose first rays are also colorless. *L.* cf. *simillima* lives in the Tefé on sandbanks and was captured at several sites with a seine (refer also to the chapter "Habitats").

M.&B.: *L. simillima* is quite undemanding and is already sexually mature when half-grown at 12 cm length. Although *Loricaria* species do not burrow into the substrate, a layer of fine sand is advantageous in accommodating their custom of rooting.
This species is bred with regularity. A spawn usually consists of approximately 100 eggs which hatch after about 12 days at 25°C. The fry need an additional 1–2 days until the yolk sac has been absorbed. Subsequently, they are readily

Loricaria similima   I. Seidel

reared with *Artemia* nauplii. A complete breeding report including a direct comparison to *L. cataphracta* can be found in SEIDEL (1997).

S: The species is imported from various sites and is quite common in the aquarium hobby. However, the prospective caretaker should consider that the fish grows to a length of 25 cm and that at that time it will require a correspondingly large aquarium.
October 2000, EVERS captured a possible variant of *Loricaria simillima* in the basin of the Rio Madeira. The species is very numerous on the Brazilian side of the border area to Bolivia (Rio Abuná drainage). Its habitat always consisted of creeks or rivers with a sandy substrate and clear- or white-water characteristics. The variant from there has a somewhat different design than the specimens hailing from Peru or the Rio Tefé (Brazil).

T: 24°–28°C, L: 25 cm, A: 120 cm, R: b

Loricaria simillima from the Rio Abuná drainage. See following page for add'l. photos.

Loricaria simillima; specimens with different designs from various sites in Peru: clear-water and white-water populations (more contrasting design).

Loricaria cf. *simillima*; Rio Tefé. See previous page for text.

I. Seidel

Loricaria simillima; ♂ with spawn.

H.-G. Evers

598

Loricaria simillima, fry, a few days old.

I. Seidel

Loricaria simillima; juveniles eight weeks old.

H.-G. Evers

599

Loricaria sp. "Alpha," from the Xingú drainage.

H.-G. Evers

Loricaria sp. "Alpha" sensu ISBRÜCKER, 1981

F.: Isbrücker, I. J. H. (1981): Revision of *Loricaria* Linnaeus, 1758 (Pisces, Siluriformes, Loricariidae):– Beaufortia, 31 (3): 51–96.

Hab.: Central Brazil, state of Mato Grosso, headwaters of the Rio Xingú. H.- G. EVERS, M. T. C. LACERDA, and P. VALERIO captured this species in a clear-water-carrying tributary of the Rio Suiazinho, part of the headwaters of the Rio Xingú. Individual specimens could be captured over gravel substrates in waters with a swift current, 26.8°C, pH 5, 4 µS/cm conductivity, high levels of dissolved oxygen.

M.&B.: The three specimens brought back to Germany placed exacting requirements on their care from the start. They refused food and became progressively thinner. Death followed too soon as to give any kind of recommendations at this time.

S: ISBRÜCKER (1981) only had juveniles available to him. He received these from Lowe MCCONNELL. There was therefore no taxonomic classification to species. The ca. 12 cm specimens brought by EVERS were sent to Amsterdam to allow a species diagnosis, but it was still pending at the time this book went to press. Since *Loricaria lata* was also found by the co-authors in the same region, it is conceivable that *Loricaria* sp. "Alpha" is only a juvenile of *Loricaria lata*. This requires further study.

T: 25°–28°C, **L:** 12 cm, maybe larger(?), **A:** 100 cm, **R:** b

600

Loricaria sp. "Alpha," head.
H.-G. Evers

Loricaria sp. "Colombia," ♂ with spawn. See following page for spawn.
H. Flößholzer

601

Loricaria sp. "Brazil"

Not much can be said about the identity of this species, given that a habitat indication of "Brazil" hardly constitutes any information that would be helpful in this endeavor. These specimens appear stouter than the more slender *L. cataphracta* or *L. simillima*.
Breeding has not yet been achieved.

T: 25°–29°C, L: 15 cm, A: 100 cm, R: b

Loricaria sp. "Colombia"
Harness Loricaria

For a long time, no *Loricaria* species were known to inhabit Colombian waters. The aquarist Hannes FLÖSSHOLZER (Austria) brought back two specimens from Colombia during March 2000, and—fortunately—these turned out to be a compatible pair.
According to FLÖSSHOLZER (written comm.), the capture site is located approximately 100 km southeast of Bogotá by car, north of Villavicencio, close to the town of Restrepo, in a clear-water river. Its water level was low during March. In the mostly dry riverbed consisting of gravel and a few sandbanks, the water-carrying section was 5–30 m wide. The *Loricaria* were always captured in the calm zones over sand, whereas three different *Chaetostoma* species were found to inhabit the rapids. Another syntopic species was *Panaqolus* cf. *maccus*. The water temperature was 26°C.

FLÖSSHOLZER successfully bred this species during September/October 2000. After initial failures where the spawn was abandoned, the male carried a spawn to term at a water temperature of 25.5°C, hardness of 6° dKH, and a pH of 7.5. The larvae hatched after 16 days. Rearing the fry with tablet foods posed no particular problems.
The cephalic design of *L.* sp. "Colombia" is of particular interest. Such a harness-like line is something never seen before among the *Loricaria* species.
Meanwhile this species was commercially exported from Colombia and been bred by several aquarists.

T: 25°–28°C, L: 20 cm, A: 100 cm, R: b

Loricaria sp. "Brazil" H.-G. Evers

Loricaria sp. "Colombia," see also the photo on page 601. H. Flößholzer

Loricaria sp. "Río Claro"

W. STAECK, Berlin, captured the pictured specimen in the drainage of the Rio Claro in Venezuela. The question is weather this is a full-grown specimen of *Loricaria* sp. "Rio Orituco," or another, independent species. The answer is not clear at this time.

Loricaria sp. "Río Madre de Dios"

Fall 2003, MIMBON AQUARIUM (Köln) imported an undescribed *Loricaria* sp. from the highly interesting Madre de Dios River of southeastern Peru. No species has been described from there, and *Loricaria simillima*, a species known from the surrounding basins, is unequivocally different. Although this new species is not overly attractive, it does sport an unusual design among the Loricaria: cloudlike dirty-gray spots on the body and pectoral and ventral fins.

Much still remains unknown about these fish, given that only a few specimens have been imported, and so we cannot report about successfully breeding the species. However, that is not expected to be overly challenging.

T: 24°–27°C, L: 20 cm, A: 100 cm, R: b

Loricaria sp. "Río Madre de Dios," portrait

H.-G. Evers

Loricaria sp. "Río Claro"

W. Staeck

Loricaria sp. "Río Madre de Dios"

H.-G. Evers

Loricaria sp. "Río Orituco"

H.-G. Evers

Loricaria sp. "Río Orituco"

Hab.: Venezuela, Guarico, Rio Orituco at Calabozo.

Although the Río Orituco (see also the chapter "Habitats") has been visited by numerous fishing aquarists, it still has a few surprises left. For example, Kai ARENDT (Helmstedt, Germany) fished, in January 1997, several specimens of the pictured species. SEIDEL was able to demonstrate, in April 2001, its presence also in the Río Portuguesa drainage. The background coloration of these specimens differs markedly from the other species known to us. Notable is also the row of odontodes along their flanks, which in other species are never so pronounced. The specimens brought to Germany proved difficult in their care, never wanting to eat and soon dying. Perhaps the transport stress was the culprit? After all, the fishes

traveled several days without food and these were juveniles approximately 7 cm in length. Perhaps a new import of this attractive species will be more successful.

Photo below right:
An additional *Loricaria* species was discovered at the company MARX AQUARISTIK of Butzbach, Germany. The origin is completely unknown and these are also only juveniles. Any indication about their identity would therefore be total speculation.

Portrait of the beautiful species.

H.-G. Evers

Loricaria sp. from the trade.

H.-G. Evers

Loricaria tucumanensis Isbrücker, 1979

F.: Isbrücker, I. J. H. (1979): Descriptions préliminaires de nouveaux taxa de la famille des Loricariidae, Poissons-Chats cuirassés néotropicaux, avec un catalogue critique de la sous-famille nominale (Pisces, Siluriformes).– Rev. fr. Aquariol. Herpét., 5 (4): 86–116.

Syn.: None.

Hab.: Argentina, Tucuman Province; Paraguay, Río Paraguay drainage. The Normanns (pers. comm.) captured, in October 1998, this species during a particularly pronounced dry season in the Río Yhaguy close to Asunción, a small stream in the Paraguay Basin. It was a slowly flowing white-water stream with a pH of 6.0 and a temperature of 23°–24°C. *L. tucumanensis* lives on sandy substrates, syntopically with *Pseudohemiodon laticeps* in shallow areas. At the time of the visit, the *Pseudohemiodon* were carrying spawns, whereas this was not the case with the *Loricaria*. Perhaps they spawn later, at the onset of the rainy season? Other suckermouth catfishes found in this river were *Hemiloricaria lanceolata* and *Otocinclus vittatus*.

M.&B.: Respecting the home range of this species, it should be maintained somewhat cooler than its Amazonian congeners. Breeding does not appear wrought with particular problems. R. Normann has already been able to achieve the first spawns.

S: Male *L. tucumanensis* display particularly thickened first spines on their pectoral fins. This characteristic clearly distinguishes them from the otherwise very similar *Loricaria simillima* and *L. lata*.

T: 21°–24°C, L: 15–20 cm, A: 100 cm, R: b

Loricaria tucumanensis in an aquarium.

I. Seidel

Loricaria tucumanensis, shortly after capture.

R. Normann

Genus *Paraloricaria* Isbrücker & Nijssen, 1979

Paraloricaria agastor Isbrücker & Nijssen, 1979	Paraguay
Paraloricaria commersonoides (Devincenzi, 1943)	Uruguay
Paraloricaria vetula (Valenciennes, 1840)	(type species) from Argentina

The latter two species reach a length of close to 40 cm, whereas *P. agastor* is known to only grow a little more than to a total length of 25 cm . Aquaristically, none of the three species plays a role in the aquarium hobby. Traveling aquarists captured in Argentina (S. Körber, pers. comm.) and Uruguay (T. Litz, pers. comm.) specimens of *Paraloricaria commersonoides*. It was always very large specimens—and very oxygen-needy to boot. Aquaristically speaking, these fishes will hardly ever be of any importance.

Genus *Proloricaria* Isbrücker, 2001

P. lentiginosa (Isbrücker, 1979)	Southeastern Brazil, upper Paraná
P. prolixa (Isbrücker & Nijssen, 1979)	Southeastern Brazil, Serra Piracicaba

A new genus was established for the giant species formerly in the genus *Loricaria* from the Brazilian state of São Paulo (Isbrücker in Isbrücker et al., 2001). Contrary to the ventral region completely covered by scutes in *Loricaria* sp., in *Proloricaria* sp. the ventral scutes are partially reduced.

The body of *Proloricaria* is much flattened and very broad at the chest. On occasion, its members remind us of the flounder whiptail species.

Type species of the new genus is *Proloricaria prolixa* (Isbrücker & Nijssen, 1979).

Coauthor Evers, together with Maik Beyer (Maricá, Brazil), was able to capture some full-grown *Proloricaria* specimens in the Serra Piracicaba. All corresponded to the *lentiginosa* type. It is not be dismissed that these reputedly two species are only one, albeit variable, species in reality; especially since both are said to occur syntopically. (see also the chapter "Habitats—River of Giants").

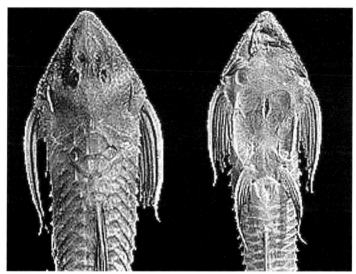

Paraloricaria commersonoides

L.A. van der Laan

Proloricaria lentiginosa, specimen from the Rio Pardo, Brazil.

M. T. C. Lacerda

Proloricaria lentiginosa in a huge aquarium.

D. Blundell

Proloricaria lentiginosa Isbrücker, 1979

F.: Isbrücker, I. J. H. (1979): Descriptions preliminaires de nouveaux taxa de la famille des Loricariidae.– Rev. Fr. Aquariol., 5 (4): 86–116.

Syn.: *Loricaria prolixa lentiginosa.*

Hab.: Brazil, state of São Paulo, upper Paraná Basin, Rio Mogi Guassu, Rio Grande. Marco T. C. Lacerda (pers. comm.) captured this species repeatedly in the Rio Pardo, a clear-water tributary of the Mogi Guaçu. The species is fairly common and is captured with a cast net. The water is soft and slightly acidic, and has temperatures which in the months from May to August lie around 16°C and rise to 22°C during the warmer part of the year. Refer also to the chapter on habitats.

M.&B.: Hardly any aquarist will be tempted to keep this giant in an aquarium with a chiller and strong current.

S: Unusual *Loricaria*. Being quite dorsoventrally flattened and having a broad head, it may easily be confused with a member of the genus *Pseudohemiodon*. *P. lentiginosa* is closely related to *Proloricaria prolixa* from the same river system and for a time was classified as a subspecies of the latter. Both species(?) differ primarily in regard to coloration. Whereas the head and dorsum of *P. prolixa* are unpigmented, *P. lentiginosa* displays a more intense mottling on the head, and the dorsum, too, is covered by distinct blotches and dots. Since both species have been described from the same river system, it is not entirely certain that indeed these are two independent species. If such would not be the case, then *P. lentiginosa* would have to be classified as a synonym of *P. prolixa*. The fact remains, however, only distinctly pigmented specimens are captured in the Rio Pardo (Rio Mogi-Guaçu Basin).

T: 16°–22°C (fluctuating with the seasons), **L:** 40 cm, **A:** 200 cm, **R:** b

Proloricaria lentiginosa, close-up showing the interesting labial morphology. D. Blundell

Proloricaria lentiginosa, shortly after capture H.-G. Evers

Subtribe Planiloricariina ISBRÜCKER, 1979

This subtribe comprises the relatively appreciated genera of the so-called flounder whiptails. All these species are quite flat and colonize sandy areas, and, by and large, burrow themselves during the day in such substrates.

Genus *Apistoloricaria* ISBRÜCKER & NIJSSEN, 1986

Apistoloricaria condei ISBRÜCKER & NIJSSEN, 1986	Ecuador, Napo basin
Apistoloricaria laani NIJSSEN & ISBRÜCKER, 1988	Colombia, Rio Metica
Apistoloricaria listrorhinos NIJSSEN & ISBRÜCKER, 1988	Colombia, Rio Metica
Apistoloricaria ommation NIJSSEN & ISBRÜCKER, 1988	Peru, Marañon

The genus is distributed in Colombia, Peru, and Ecuador. It would be an interesting addition to our aquarium fauna, for sure. Its members are probably being overlooked by the fishermen that usually do not comb the sandy regions for commercially significant species. The company GLASER imported, during the Fall of 1999, *Apistoloricaria condei* from Peru for the first time, and it turned out to be a readily suitable aquarium charge.

Their relationship with *Planiloricaria* becomes obvious considering their behavior. As "mini-editions" of their very large cousins, the members of this genus are always a little rough among themselves. At feeding time, the fish are immediately present and, during the quarrels that ensue, raise their tall dorsal fin vertically. During the Summer of 2000, a pair spawned in an aquarium of H.-G. EVERS, who was able to partially document, with photographs, their breeding behavior.

Photo below right:
Ventral view of the head of *Apistoloricaria condei*, paratype from the Río Aguarico, Ecuador. ♂ of 140.6 mm standard length. The rictal barbels are very pronounced, a fail-proof identifier of gender.

Amazonian rainforest

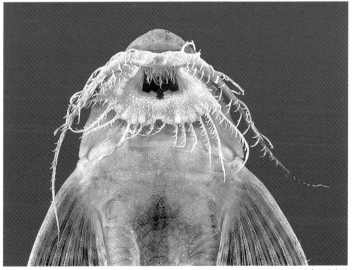

Apistoloricaria condei Isbrücker & Nijssen, 1986

F.: Isbrücker, I. J. H. & H. Nijssen (1986):
Apistoloricaria condei, nouveau genre et
nouvelle espéce de Poisson-Chat cuirassé, tribu Loricariini Bonaparte, 1831,
du bassin du Rio Napo, haute Amazone,
Equateur (Pisces, Siluriformes, Loricariidae).– Revue fr. Aquariol., 12(4): 103–
108.

Syn.: None.

Hab.: Ecuador, Río Napo drainage, Río
Aguarico, Río Tiputini. The pictured specimens were obtained from a Peruvian import.
The species description lists the habitat
as being of the white-water type, with a
visibility of 30 cm. The swiftly flowing water had a pH of 6.8 and a temperature of
25.5°–26.5°C.

M.&B.: Sand substrate, a good, current-
rich filtration of the water, and regular partial water exchanges—best 30–50% per
week—provide the most favorable conditions for eventual reproduction. The day is
spent partially buried in the sand, usually
facing the filtration current. If food is introduced to the aquarium, the fish become
restless, dig themselves out of the sand,
and sway back and forth with their body,
rictal barbels splayed far, grabbing any
food that touches them. The elongated dorsal fin filaments are impressive as they are
extended vertically and every once in a
while dip downward.
During spawning, the females are clearly
the more active gender. Ripe females are
readily identified by their fullness. Additionally, they grow 1–2 cm longer than the
males. Usually the animals lie in pairs in the
aquarium, and the female attempts every
once in a while to glide under the male from
behind. If this is successful in such a manner as to bring the genital openings close
together, the eggs are laid and the male

Apistoloricaria condei, ♂   H.-G. Evers

fertilizes them apparently in this position.
Per oviposition a few eggs are laid and
joined into a discoid egg cluster, reminiscent of *Pseudohemiodon* species. Unfortunately, the pair of Evers only spawned
once until the conclusion of the manuscript for this book in July 2000. Soon after oviposition, the male abandoned the
spawn and artificial incubation failed.
However, one fry did hatch, allowing at
least to document the development of the
egg and larva.

S: A very interesting charge, reminiscent
in habitus and behavior of its large cousin
Planiloricaria cryptodon. Since *A. condei*
is a smaller species, it is a good alternative to the large *P. cryptodon*. A fantastic new import, not only for the diehard
catfish specialist!

T: 24°–27°C, L: 15 cm, A: 100 cm, R: b

Apistoloricaria condei, ripe ♀.

H.-G. Evers

Apistoloricaria condei; view of the impressive rictal barbels of a ♂.

H.-G. Evers

A. condei pair while spawning in an aquarium. The ♀ pushes from behind under the ♂ ,...

... which soon carries a discoid egg cluster in his mouth.

H.-G. Evers

Apistoloricaria condei, 1-day-old spawn.

H.-G. Evers

A. condei, 4-day-old spawn.

H.-G. Evers

A. condei, 8-day-old spawn; unfortunately, most eggs have died.

H.-G. Evers

A preemie, hatched on day 8 and not yet viable.

H.-G. Evers

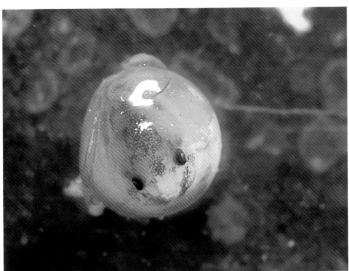

13-day-old egg, shortly before hatching.

H.-G. Evers

Newly hatched larva.

H.-G. Evers

Genus *Crossoloricaria* Isbrücker, 1979

Crossoloricaria bahuaja Chang & Castro, 1999	Peru, Tambopata
Crossoloricaria cephalaspis Isbrücker, 1979	Colombia, Magdalena
Crossoloricaria rhami Isbrücker & Nijssen, 1983	Peru, Huacamayo
Crossoloricaria variegata (Steindachner, 1879)	Panama; Colombia
Crossoloricaria venezuelae (Schultz, 1944)	Venezuela, Maracaibo

At first sight, the five species classified in the genus *Crossoloricaria* appear identical to the flounder whiptails of the genus *Pseudohemiodon* Bleeker, 1862. They are very pronouncedly dorsoventrally flattened, and their eyes are located very superiorly on a triangular head. The peculiarities of the genus *Crossoloricaria* are only discovered by the observer once the fish is turned on its back. There, where in many loricariids the ventrum is covered by small bony platelets, the *Crossoloricaria* are virtually naked. Only along the medial ventral line a row of small platelets can be discerned, and from the abdomen to the anus, two such rows can be discerned.

Members of this genus reach a maximum length of approximately 25 cm (*Crossoloricaria variegata*), but most species do not reach 20 cm in length. Therefore, *Crossoloricaria* are expected to be suitable aquarium charges. Until the Fall of 1995, the entire genus was aquaristically unknown. This changed with the introduction of *Crossoloricaria rhami* by co-author Seidel from the Peruvian Río Huacamayo and Río Chio.
The area of distribution of the genus extends from Panama (*C. variegata*) through Colombia (*C. variegata, C. cephalaspis,* and possibly sympatrically *C. venezuelae*), and northwestern Venezuela (*C. venezuelae*) to Peru (*C. rhami* and *C. bahuaja*).

During maintenance, *Crossoloricaria* showed to be extremely appreciative of hiding places. If a sand layer of 4–5 cm thickness is provided, even the trained eye has a hard time to discern where the specimens are buried. That is how deep they dig into the substrate. In contrast, the members of the genus *Pseudohemiodon* can be discerned relatively fast in the sand—no species is known to burrow that deeply. Usually, only the eyes are visible, and the contour of the head may also be distinguished. On occasion, *Crossoloricaria rhami* behaves similarly, but usually not even the eyes remain visible. The same holds at feeding time. The shy species only emerges at night, whereas all *Pseudohemiodon* known to us will quickly emerge from the sand—even in plain daylight after an acclimation phase—if there is food being offered.

Crossoloricaria cephalaspis; holotype from the Río Magdalena, Colombia (SL 108,9 mm).

L. A. van der Laan

Crossoloricaria bahuaja CHANG & CASTRO, 1999

F.: Chang, F. & E. Castro (1999) : *Crossoloricaria bahuaja*, a new loricariid fish from Madre de Dios, southeastern Peru.- Ichthyol. Explor. Freshwaters, 10 (81-88).

Syn.: None.

Hab.: Peru, Madre de Dios Province, Río Tambopata as well as upper Río Purus, Dept. Ucayali; Bolivia, Boeto Province. Fall 2003, MIMBON AQUARIUM (Köln) imported the first specimens of this relatively new species from the Río Madre de Dios. The species inhabits white-waters with sandy substrate, along the same lines as described for the other flounder whiptails.

M.&B.: *C. bahuaja* is much easier to maintain than the closely related *C. rhami*. Whereas *C. rhami* spends the entire day buried in the sand, emerging only tentatively at night to feed, *C. bahuaja* is much bolder and, at feeding time, may be seen even during the day.
Breeding has not yet been successful. The 3–4 cm long (TL) imported juveniles grew to twice the length within 2–3 months of good feeding.

The species description mentions the stomach contents of newly captured specimens. It consisted of insect larvae, sand, small seeds, and detritus.

S: At first sight, *C. bahuaja* is indistinguishable from the very similar *C. rhami*. It is interesting to note that the elongated rictal barbels of *C. bahuaja* apparently represent a sexual dimorphism. In sexually mature *C. bahuaja* males, these turn dark and appear to be thicker and longer than those of females. The holotype pictured in the description is a male. Besides this, the greater number of teeth of *C. bahuaja*, longer lower lip barbels, and a relatively longer first dorsal fin spine are additional differences to *C. rhami*.

T: 24°–28°C, L: 18 cm, A: 100 cm, R: b

Crossoloricaria bahuaja in aquarium

H.-G. Evers

The slender shape is characteristic of *C. cephalaspis*

I. Seidel

625

Crossoloricaria cephalaspis ISBRÜCKER, 1979

F.: Isbrücker, I. J. H. (1979): Descriptions préliminaires de nouveaux taxa de la famille des Loricariidae, Poissons-Chats cuirassés néotropicaux, avec un catalogue critique de la sous-famille nominale (Pisces, Siluriformes). Rev. fr. Aquariol. Herpétol. 5(4): 86–116.

Hab.: Colombia, Rio Magdalena Basin, Honda. The pictured specimen was imported from this river under the name of *Pseudohemiodon* sp. "Rio Magdalena."

M.&B.: In contrast to *Crossoloricaria rhami*—repeatedly imported from Peru—*C. cephalaspis* does not lead such a cryptic life in the aquarium. It does not burrow as deeply into the substrate and is not as shy

as *C. rhami*. Follow the maintenance guidelines given for *C. rhami*.
There is no experience in regard to breeding.

S: This, for specialists, interesting species has been repeatedly imported from Colombia by the companies AQUARIUM DIETZENBACH and TRANSFISH. It possibly lives syntopically with *Crossoloricaria venezuelae*, but there is still much too little known in regard to the distribution of these two, quite closely related species. *C. cephalaspis* differs from *C. rhami* by being darker and having a distinctly more pointed head.

T: 24°–28°C, L: 14 cm, A: 80–100 cm, R: b

Crossoloricaria rhami ISBRÜCKER & NIJSSEN, 1983

F.: Isbrücker, I.J.H.& H. Nijssen (1983): *Crossoloricaria rhami* n. sp., un nouveaux Poisson-Chat cuirassé du Rio Huacamayo.– Rev.fr.Aquariol., 10(1): 9–12.

Syn.: None.

Hab.: Peru, Río Ucayali drainage, Río Huacamayo. The species inhabits shallow clear-water biotopes exposed to a swift current at water temperatures of 24°–26°C, a pH between 6.3 and 7.8, and conductivities of up to 160 µS/cm. SEIDEL and cotravelers could confirm the presence of the species during two trips (both September) to the Río Huacamayo and Río Chio (only a few kilometers apart). The species burrows deeply into the sandy bottom. In the Chio River, a male with a spawn was captured. The spawn was similar to that of *Pseudohemiodon lamina* (see there). The species

has meanwhile been repeatedly imported to Germany by the company TRANSFISH.

M.&B.: *C. rhami* is the most cryptic aquarium resident of all the flounder whiptails being maintained. Only at night do these shy catfishes emerge to feed. There is some experience in regard to breeding this species in captivity.

S: *C. rhami* is a beautiful, but extremely rare species. Successful breeding would be desirable. CHANG & CASTRO (1999) recently described from southern Peru a very similar species, *Crossoloricaria bahuaja*. Several characteristics distinguish that species (more teeth, longer rictal barbels, and elongated dorsal filaments) from *C. rhami*, even though both have a similar design.

T: 24°–26°C, L: 15 cm, A: 80 cm, R: b

Crossoloricaria cephalaspis from the Río Magdalena, Colombia.

I. Seidel

Crossoloricaria rhami, portrait.

H.-G. Evers

Crossoloricaria rhami, juvenile.

H.-G. Evers

Crossoloricaria rhami, adult.

H.-G. Evers

Crossoloricaria sp. "Río Sipapo"   I. Seidel

Crossoloricaria sp. "Río Sipapo"

In April 2001, SEIDEL and cotravelers captured several juveniles of a pronouncedly beautiful *Crossoloricaria* sp. in the drainage of the upper Río Orinoco in Venezuela. The specimens were found in the Rio Sipapo, in a section with swift current and a sand substrate, into which the species had burrowed. Due to the youth of the specimens brought home, we are at present unable to confirm if they belong to an already described species.

T: 24°–28°C, L: 14 cm, A: 80–100 cm, R: b

Genus *Dentectus*
SALAZAR, ISBRÜCKER & NIJSSEN, 1982

When a representative of the genus *Dentectus* is seen for the first time, one is inclined to believe that it is a member of the genus *Pseudohemiodon*. As is typical for the subtribe Planiloricariina, *Dentectus* only has very small jaws with a vestigial dentition. The highly branched lips, too, are typical of this subtribe. However, viewing the oral region, several differences quickly become obvious. In comparison to the genera *Pseudohemiodon* or *Crossoloricaria*, the opening is much smaller, the outer region of the maxillary barbels and the upper lip are covered by small bony platelets. This last characteristic is unique among the family Loricariidae.

The monotypic genus *Dentectus* has only been found in Venezuela. *Dentectus barbamatus* has been captured in various northern tributaries of the central Orinoco (Río Parguaza, Río Pao Viejo, among others), but has not yet reached German aquaria alive.

The species would definitely be an asset to any specialist in flounder whiptails.

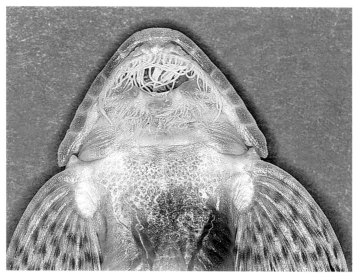

Dentectus barbamatus, ventral view of the mouth.

I. Seidel

Dentectus barbamatus (ZMA 116.648); preserved specimen.

I. Seidel

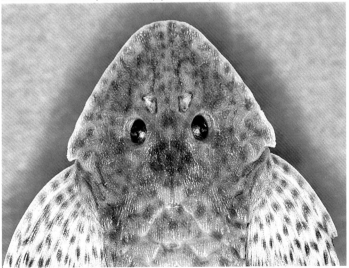

Head view of the specimen above.

I. Seidel

Fam.: Loricariidae
Subfam.: Loricariinae

Genus *Planiloricaria* ISBRÜCKER, 1971

Planiloricaria was initially described as a subgenus of *Pseudohemiodon* (ISBRÜCKER 1971b), however, later (ISBRÜCKER & NIJSSEN, 1974a) it was classified as an independent genus. This monotypic genus is not closely related to any of the others. Characteristics include the very small eyes situated very high on the head, the discoid head shape, the long filaments of the dorsal fin, and to a lesser degree, the caudal fin. In a manner shared with the other monotypic genera *Hemiodontichthys, Reganella,* and *Dentectus,* the upper mandible has no teeth. The only member of the genus is *Planiloricaria cryptodon* (ISBRÜCKER, 1971). Since the late 80's, these interesting—but in maintenance very exacting—loricariids are sporadically imported from Peru. These unusual fish can only be appropriately maintained in seriously large aquaria. Only there do they develop their peculiarities. Once they become acclimated, the hobbyists will experience much joy with them as they become active in the twilight.

Planiloricaria cryptodon (ISBRÜCKER, 1971)
Cryptic whiptail suckermouth catfish

F.: Isbrücker, I.J.H. (1971): *Pseudohemiodon* (*Planiloricaria*) *cryptodon*, a new species and subgenus from Peru (Pisces, Siluriformes, Loricariidae).– Bonn.zool. Beitr., 21: 274–283.

Syn.: *Pseudohemiodon cryptodon.*

Hab.: Peru, Río Ucayali at Pucallpa; Brazil, Rio Purus; Bolivia, Río Mamoré. These are white-water biotopes. It is likely that the species lives in the large rivers, since during many trips they have not been found in small streams, and large rivers are usually not fished by travelling aquarists. The specimens in the trade hail from the surroundings of Iquitos.

M.&B.: These large loricariids are real "feed disposal machines." Enormous quantities of food are tackled. Any large frozen foods (mosquito larvae) and tablet foods are preferentially devoured. The fish, usually halfway buried in the fine sand, immediately turn lively when, for example, a food tablet is introduced in the aquarium. The fish engulf the tablet with their mouth and rasp it into oblivion. When live water fleas are provided, the giant mouth is used as a weir-basket, and the daphnia are "filtered" out of the water. Once the presence of food is detected, the dorsal fin is excitedly erected, and the ample mouth tests the substrate with back and forth movements, until the food is located.

Breeding has not yet been successful, but it stands to reason that these are mouthbrooders. Males and females can only be distinguished with certainty when the latter is ripe or close to being so.

It remains to be confirmed after having access to more individuals, if the spots on the body are a reliable characteristic to distinguish the genders. When the anal region of full-grown specimens is observed in greater detail, sexual differences in the shape of the anal opening can be determined. In males it is elongated and small, whereas large females have a rather roundish region, with a distinctly broader papilla.

S: *P. cryptodon* can only be recommended to aquarists with sufficient space and a powerful filtration system. This is a species which can bring great joy to every catfish aficionado.

T: 24°–28°C, L: 35 cm, A: 150 cm, R: b

Planiloricaria cryptodon; view of the barbels.

H.-G. Evers

P. cryptodon; large specimen in an aquarium, additional photos on the following pages.

H.-G. Evers

Planiloricaria cryptodon: view of the genital opening of the ♂ ...

I. Seidel

... and of the ♀.

I. Seidel

Smaller conspecifics are only briefly tolerated, before being vehemently chased away.

Planiloricaria cryptodon; specimen with an uncommonly beautiful design.

H.-G. Evers

Fam.: Loricariidae
Subfam.: Loricariinae

Planiloricaria cryptodon; the caudal fin filaments are enormously elongated.

H.-G. Evers

Photographs to the right:
Two scanning electron micrographs of the caudal fin filaments: The surface is not smooth, but densely covered by small appendages. The openings become apparent under strong magnification. Are these sensory pores, perhaps? Can some kind of stimuli be perceived with the aid of these structures? These are questions that wait for answers.

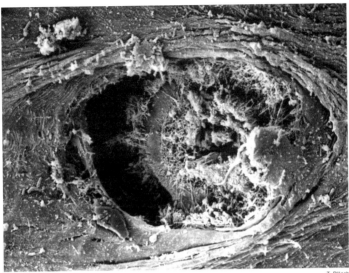

T. Plösch

T. Plösch

Genera
Pseudohemiodon BLEEKER, 1862 and
Rhadinoloricaria ISBRÜCKER & NIJSSEN, 1974
Flounder whiptails

Species in the genus *Pseudohemiodon* (ISBRÜCKER, 1980):

Pseudohemiodon amazonus (DELSMAN, 1941)	Brazil, Obidos
Pseudohemiodon apithanos ISBRÜCKER & NIJSSEN, 1978	Ecuador, Río Conejo
Pseudohemiodon devincenzii (SORIANO SENORANS, 1950)	Uruguay Basin
Pseudohemiodon lamina (GÜNTHER, 1868)	Peru; Ucayali Basin
Pseudohemiodon laticeps (REGAN, 1904)	Paraguay Basin
Pseudohemiodon platycephalus (KNER, 1854)	Brazil, Cuiabá
Pseudohemiodon thorectes Isbrücker, 1975	Bolivia, Mamoré

The genus *Pseudohemiodon* at present comprises seven species (ISBRÜCKER, 1980). Genotype is *Pseudohemiodon platycephalus* (KNER, 1854a). KNER (1854) published a beautiful drawing of the fish, back then under the name of *Hemiodon platycephalus*. The genus *Hemiodon* was established by KNER (1853a), but had to be withdrawn, because the name was already established for a genus of mollusc. What remained is the beautiful drawing, even by today's standards.

All species have extremely dorsoventrally flattened bodies with small eyes situated high on the triangular head. This anatomic feature gives a clear indication of lifestyle. *Pseudohemiodon* spend the day buried in fine sand, only emerging at nightfall to feed. If discovered, they quickly bury themselves in the substrate with lateral pendular movements. The provision of a suitably thick substrate of fine sand is therefore a condition for successful aquarium maintenance of this and similar genera.

The members of the genus *Pseudohemiodon*—as far as known—inhabit the entire tropical and subtropical South American continent, with the exception of the Guyana Highlands.

In recent years, various members of the genus have been imported [to Germany] and there has been successful reproduction in some of them. *Pseudohemiodon platycephalus* was the first species for which the unusual broodcare strategy was revealed. *Pseudohemiodon* males carry the egg cluster around with them, supported by the branched labial (rictal) barbels. The males burrow with eggs and all.

Subsequently, *Pseudohemiodon thorectes*, *P. laticeps*, the smaller *Pseudohemiodon lamina*, and some additional, possibly still undescribed, species were imported and bred. Fortunately, the first import of *Pseudohemiodon apithanos* from Ecuador—arguably the most attractive species—is not pending anymore. They are frequently being imported from Peru, Río Haya.

Pseudohemiodon, too, lacks the dentition of the upper mandible and the lips are pronounced frayed. The rictal barbels of the lower lip are particularly well developed and serve the males in holding the egg mass.

A close relative of the genus *Pseudohemiodon* is the genus *Crossoloricaria* ISBRÜCKER, 1979. However, it clearly distinguishes itself from *Pseudohemiodon* by the unique arrangement of the ventral

Pseudohemiodon apithanos; arguably the most beautiful flounder whiptail.   H.-G. Evers

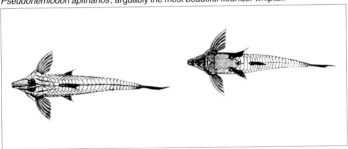

Rhadinoloricaria macromystax   Drawing from Günther (1868)

platelets (see the genus description of *Crossoloricaria*). *Apistoloricaria* Isbrücker & Nijssen, 1986, with a total of four species, is another genus with a flattened body and filamentous labial appendages, but the original describers see the closest resemblance of these rather slender fishes to the monotypic genus *Rhadinoloricaria* Isbrücker & Nijssen, 1974. *Rhadinoloricaria macromystax* (Günther, 1868), from Peru, is considered very rare. This species has a very long, pointed head, but otherwise is as flat as *Pseudohemiodon* species. *Apistoloricaria* spp. probably have the most pinnate lips, in addition to a distinct sexual dimorphism in regard to this morphology. Sexually mature male *Apistoloricaria condei* have much elongated

639

and thickened rictal barbels, which allow them to effectively hold on to the egg mass. In males, the barbels of the lower lip are reduced to short papillae, whereas females have very dense, double-branched barbels on the lower lip. The first rays of the pectoral, dorsal, and sometimes also the ventral fins are filamentously much elongated to a variable degree, depending on species.

Pseudohemiodon apithanos
ISBRÜCKER & NIJSSEN, 1978
Chameleon flounder whiptail

F.: Isbrücker, I. J. H. & H. Nijssen (1978): Two new species and a new genus of neotropical mailed catfishes of the subfamily Loricariinae Swainson, 1838 (Pisces, Siluriformes, Loricariidae).– Beaufortia, 27 (339): 177–206.

Syn.: None.

Hab.: Ecuador, Napo Province, Río Conejo, a tributary of the Río San Miguel. Peru, Río Itaya near Iquitos.

M.&B.: After acclimation, the species is not a very complicated charge. With an increase in the number of imported specimens, the first breeding successes have now been reported. Coauthor EVERS has already been able to witness the first spawns. Unfortunately, the eggs were never cared for to term, and the artificially incubated fry died shortly after hatching. The Hamburg aquarist K.-D. HARTWICH was able to observe and even photograph the spawning sequence (see page after next for photos). Males turn completely dark, almost black, prior to spawning. The female is, as usual, the more active gender and virtually forces the male to spawn. The male almost stands on his head during the release of the gametes!

HARTWICH could raise several youn *P. apithanos* by keeping absolute hygienic conditions. The fry grows quite rapidly, like *P. lamina*.

S: The imported specimen so far, can change their coloration. If previously it was almost black on the head and anterior body, turning lighter posteriorly, later it developed an attractive contrasting black-white design on the head. A day later it may appear black-brown virtually entirely.

Pseudohemiodon apithanos, portrait.

H.-G. Evers

Pseudohemiodon apithanos, virtually completely black.

I. Seidel

P. apithanos, spawning.

K.-D. Hartwich

P. apithanos, spawning.

K.-D. Hartwich

Pseudohemiodon apithanos, the same specimen a few weeks later!   H.-G. Evers

Fry of *P. apithanos*.   I. Seidel

Pseudohemiodon lamina (GÜNTHER, 1868)

F.: Günther, A. (1868): Descriptions of freshwater fishes from Surinam and Brazil.– Proc.zool.Soc.London, 1868: 229–247.

Syn.: *Loricaria lamina*.

Hab.: Sporadically imported from Peru. Habitat characteristics are unknown.

M.&B.: A fine sand substrate is a condition for maintenance, given that the animals spend the day buried in the bottom. Strong filtration with high oxygenation concentration is advantageous. The only other consideration is to check that the fish cannot wedge themselves among the decoration and become stuck. Females soon ripen when regularly fed in the evenings with tablet foods, frozen mosquito larvae, daphnia, etc. The male carries a discoid spawn with a maximum of approximately 35 large, initially yolk-yellow eggs, anchored among his barbels. He also burrows himself with them. After 12–14 days the relatively large, 1 cm larvae hatch with a huge yolk sac. It is absorbed over the course of the following two days.

The position of the larvae just prior to hatching is interesting. At that time, the spawn is taken away from the male and hatching induced (see chapter on "Artificial Incubation of Eggs"). In the process we were able to observe how the larvae in the eggs turned so as to always be with the dorsum upward. If the spawning cluster is quickly turned, one larva after the other also turn! Initial feeding is accomplished with *Artemia* nauplii, preferably in a dedicated aquarium. The fry initially are black-brown and, starting with the fourth week, slowly begin adopting the adult coloration. With frequent water exchanges and a minimum of two daily feedings, the young grow to five centimeters within three months. At that time, the worst has past. Less than optimal oxygen conditions lead to the quick demise of the entire batch. A final yield of 15–20 young is considered good, since there are always losses during egg development and after hatching.

S: The species has a particularly beautiful design and with its modest mature size, the aquarium needs not be particularly large.

T: 24°–28°C, **L:** 15 cm, **A:** 80 cm, **R:** b

Pseudohemiodon lamina

P. lamina, head shot. See following pages for additional photos.

P. lamina; sexual differences. ♀ fuller, ♂ with longer pectoral fins.

H.-G. Evers

P. lamina; ♂ with spawn. See previous page for text.

I. Seidel

P. lamina; 11-day-old spawn. Hatching is imminent.

H.-G. Evers

Pseudohemiodon lamina; newly hatched fry.

H.-G. Evers

647

P. lamina; 15-day-old fry. See page 644 for text.

H.-G. Evers

Pseudohemiodon lamina; three-month-old juvenile.

H.-G. Evers

Pseudohemiodon laticeps (REGAN, 1904)
Broadhead whiptail

F.: Regan, C.T. (1904): A monograph of the fishes of the family Loricariidae.– Trans.zool.Soc.London, 17: 191–350.

Syn.: *Loricaria laticeps.*

Hab.: Southern Brazil, Paraguay, and Argentina. Imports [to Germany] usually come from Paraguay. The specimens hailing from Brazil under the name of *P. laticeps*, and cared for and bred in the hobby for years, differ somewhat in design and head shape. They are presented here as *Pseudohemiodon platycephalus*.

M.&B.: This relatively large species requires aquaria with a correspondingly generous surface area. Other maintenance aspects as indicated for *P. lamina*. Only the water temperature for specimens coming from the southern area of its distribution range (southeastern Brazil and Paraguay) should be somewhat lower. R. NORMANN (Satow) was able to breed, on several occasions, imports from Paraguay. Raising the young was successful using the technique described for *P. lamina*. In the past, there has been repeatedly confusion with *Pseudohemiodon platycephalus*, and all breeding reports published to date under the genus *Pseudohemiodon* deal with *P. platycephalus*.

S: The photographs show very clearly the particularly broad head of the true *P. laticeps*. The coloration of the pictured catfish from the Mato Grosso, Rio Paraguay drainage, differed from animal to animal— some deer-brown, others light to dark gray. Most imports from Paraguay, however, show the beautiful deer-brown coloration.

T: 18°–24°C, **L:** 35 cm, **A:** 150 cm, **R:** b

H.-G. Evers

Pseudohemiodon laticeps; mouth and lip morphology of a full-grown specimen. See following page for additional photos.

649

Pseudohemiodon laticeps in an aquarium. See previous page for text. H.-G. Evers

Dorsal view of a specimen approximately 30 cm in length. H.-G. Evers

Pseudohemiodon platycephalus (KNER, 1854)

F.: Kner, R. (1854): Die Panzerwelse des k. k. Hof-Naturalien-Cabinetes zu Wien. I. Abteilung: Loricarinae.- Denkschr. Akad. Wiss.Wien, mathem.-naturwiss. Cl., 6: 65–98.

Syn.: *Loricaria platycephala.*

Hab.: Brazil, Mato Grosso, Rio Cuiabá. The species is a common import from Brazil.

M.& B.: SEIDEL (1994) as well as WEIDNER & ZÖLCH (1994) reported extensively about maintenance and breeding of this species. The males are, by and large, unreliable in their broodcare efforts and often abandon their spawn. They are particularly sensitive to disturbances. Artificial rearing is only successful in a limited way and labor intensive, since the water must be exchanged frequently, despite which, egg mortality is high. Hatching of the remaining viable larvae is sometimes difficult to induce. If the fry remain excessively long in the egg membrane, the vertebrate column becomes deformed. The breeder must intercede and take the large eggs gently with his fingers and very carefully tear the egg membrane apart. With some practice that procedure becomes easier than it sounds. The young have a very typical coloration. During the initial weeks, the anterior body is jet black, only later turning a lighter color. This beautiful juvenile coloration persists almost to a length of five centimeters, but then not as uniform and extensive. Small juveniles are reminiscent in coloration to the chameleon flounder whiptail *Pseudohemiodon apithanos.*

P. platycephalus   H.-G. Evers

S: This species is the aquaristically best known and surely the most commonly kept and bred *Pseudohemiodon* species. The authors considered these fish for many years as *P. laticeps* due to their common appearance in imports from Brazil, until the authentic *P. laticeps* were found in imports from Paraguay. The design is virtually identical in both species, but the Paraguayan *P. laticeps* grow even larger. However, it is mainly the head size and shape of *Pseudohemiodon platycephalus* which is significantly smaller, not appearing as obtuse triangular as that of *P. laticeps.*

T: 24°–28°C, L: 25 cm, A: 120 cm, R: b

See following pages for additional photos.

P. platycephalus; see previous page for text. H.-G. Evers

P. platycephalus; with egg disc. I. Seidel

Pseudohemiodon platycephalus; larva just after hatching.

I. Seidel

Bird's-eye view of young with their species-specific coloration of the first weeks.

I. Seidel

Pseudohemiodon sp. "marbled;" ♂ with egg cluster.   S. Schmitt

Pseudohemiodon sp. "marbled;" fry in the rearing tank.   S. Schmitt

Pseudohemiodon sp. "marbled"

Traded as a morph of *Pseudohemiodon apithanos*, early 2002 increased numbers of this undescribed Peruvian *Pseudohemiodon* reached Germany. The Hamburg aquarist B. SCHMITT was able to capture one specimen in the Río Alejandro, the imports hailed from the Río Itaya, the river where *P. apithanos* is also captured for export. P. DOTZER and T. WEIDNER have been able to breed *Pseudohemiodon* sp.

"marbled" in an aquarium. Other aquarists, too, have already had more success with this species than with the apparently more complicated *P. apithanos*. However, the young are quite sensitive during the rearing phase and losses occur repeatedly.

T: 26°–29°C, L: 15 cm, A: 100 cm, R: b

Pseudohemiodon sp. "Marbled"   I. Seidel

Pseudohemiodon sp. "Marbled"   I. Seidel

P. sp. "Marbled", eggs   I. Seidel

P. sp. "Marbled", juvenil   I. Seidel

Pseudohemiodon sp. "Peru I"   I. Seidel

Pseudohemiodon sp. "Peru I"

Neither body shape nor design of this species are similar to any other. The body is notoriously slender and the ventral fins are unusually large. When in search of edibles, these fish prop themselves on their pectoral and ventral fins and literally walk around on the aquarium substrate. The large ventral fins in particular push the body away from the bottom by back and forth movements—something that makes this species unique in the genus. The first specimens came from an import made by BERTHOLD'S WELSWELT, which was sent by AQUARIO LIMA. These specimens had a reticulate design on the head and pectoral fins, which made them quite attractive. However, it appears as if this species is quite variable, because later other specimens—definitively members of the same species—were imported by MIMBON AQUARIUM (Köln), AQUARIUM GROTTE (Hamburg), and others, and these all had a less spectacular design.

The species might be complicated during the acclimation phase. However, under good maintenance conditions, the fish quickly adapt and can be observed even during the day as they search for food.

SEIDEL achieved a first breeding success with this species. Only ca. 10 cm in size, the parent fish produced a roughly quarter-sized spawn, which was cared for by the male. Only 15, almost completely black fry, were obtained. Rearing presented no problems.

T: 25°–28°C, L: 12 cm, A: 80 cm, R: b

Pseudohemiodon sp. "Peru I," head shot.   H.-G. Evers

Pseudohemiodon sp. "Peru I"   H.-G. Evers

Pseudohemiodon sp. "Peru II," juvenile.

H.-G. Evers

Pseudohemiodon sp. "Peru II"

This flounder whiptail, with its highly contrasting design, has been repeatedly imported, although in low numbers each time. Unfortunately, breeding so far has eluded the hobbyists.

Such a coloration is unknown from any other species, and it still has to be confirmed that indeed this is a new species. Notorious is the black crossband behind the dorsal fin, which might be expressed to varying degrees. Juveniles are usually lighter in general and this band appears more pronounced, whereas older specimens turn almost dark gray and display a design consisting of small dots and lines and several faint crossbands on the body. In the author's aquaria, the species reached a size similar to that of *Pseudohemiodon lamina*.

Breeding has not yet been successful.

The species was imported to Germany by MIMBON AQUARIUM.

T: 25°–28°C, L: 15 cm, A: 80 cm, R: b

Pseudohemiodon sp. "Peru II," adult.

I. Seidel

Pseudohemiodon sp. "Venezuela." See following page for text.

H.-G. Evers

Pseudohemiodon sp. "Río Madre de Dios"   H.-G. Evers

Pseudohemiodon sp. "Río Madre de Dios"

In all likelihood, this *Pseudohemiodon* species is still undescribed. In 2003, MIMBON AQUARIUM imported for the first time to Germany various suckermouth catfishes from the Río Madre de Dios of southern Peru. The species presented here is one of them.

The small number of imported specimens does not allow for any comments in regard to breeding at this time.
Maintenance follows the general guidelines given for its congeners.

T: 24°–27°C, L: 15 cm, A: 80 cm, R: b

Pseudohemiodon sp. "Venezuela"

The Hamburg aquarist B. SCHMITT captured the pictured species in the Río Manapiare system of southern Venezuela. The clear-water tributaries had a temperature of 27°C, a pH of 6.2, a hardness of 1.5° dGH, and a conductivity of 60 μS/cm. Breeding was only successful once and was similar to that described

for *P. lamina*. This small species differs somewhat in body shape, but it is especially its coloration that sets it apart from the other species.
Still, it remains to be confirmed, if indeed this is an independent species.

T: 26°–29°C, L: 15 cm, A: 80 cm, R: b

660

Pseudohemiodon sp. "Río Madre de Dios", portrait H.-G. Evers

Pseudohemiodon sp. "Venezuela." See page before last for additional photo. H.-G. Evers

Fam.: Loricariidae
Subfam.: Loricariinae

Pseudohemiodon thorectes

H.-G. Evers

Pseudohemiodon thorectes Isbrücker, 1975

F.: Isbrücker, I.J.H. (1975): *Pseudohemiodon thorectes*, a new species of mailed catfish from the Rio Mamoré system, Bolivia (Pisces, Siluriformes, Loricariidae).– Beaufortia, 23 (300): 85–92.

Syn.: None.

Hab.: Bolivia. I. Schindler (Berlin) captured the species in the state of Santa Cruz, 6 km west of Puerto Chelo. The *Pseudohemiodon* inhabited the sections with fine sand of this fast-flowing river (water depth between 20 and 80 cm). Water values were: 25°C, 400 µS/cm, pH 7.6, 12° KH. A group of traveling aquarists, Ingo Seidel among them, was able to dig up *Pseudohemiodon thorectes* from the fine sands of the Rio Surutu in Bolivia and bring it back alive to Germany.

M.&B.: *P. thorectes* has requirements similar to those of its congeners. I. Seidel bred the species successfully in tap water at a temperature of 23°–24°C. Approximately 25 young were found the first time in the breeding tank and raised successfully. It is therefore hoped that this species will soon become a staple in the repertoire available to the catfish hobbyist, similar to *P. lamina*. Since the first breeding success with the imported specimens, I. Seidel was able to repeat the feat several more times.

S: A small species which primarily differs from its congeners by having a greater number of interconnected longitudinal scutes on the flanks. The live coloration is another effective identification aid of *P. thorectes*. Viewed from above, two distinct design elements can be observed next to each other on the dorsum, shortly posterior to the head. These two irregular moles, somewhat reminiscent of the rays of a star, can be observed on any live specimen and have a slight variation from individual to individual.

T: 24°–27°C, L: 13 cm, A: 60 cm, R: b

Pseudohemiodon thorectes, portrait. See also next page.

H.-G. Evers

Pseudohemiodon thorectes, egg cluster.

I. Seidel

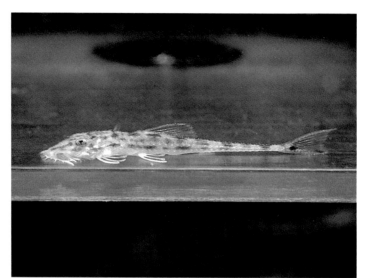

Pseudohemiodon thorectes, 10-day-old juvenile.   I. Seidel

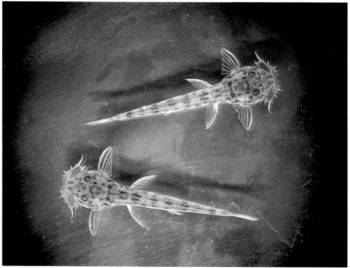

Juveniles of *Pseudohemiodon thorectes* a few days later.   I. Seidel

Río Surutu, Bolivia, Habitat of *Pseudohemiodon thorectes*   I. Seidel

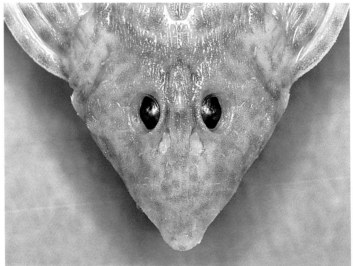

Pyxiloricaria menezesi; head.   I. Seidel

Genus *Pyxiloricaria* IsʙRÜCKER & NıJSSEN, 1984

The monotypic genus *Pyxiloricaria* Is-
BRÜCKER & NıJSSEN, 1984 is another one
that is very similar to the genus *Pseudohemiodon*. Described from the Brazilian
state of Mato Grosso, Rio Cuiabá, *Pyxiloricaria menezesi* lives sympatrically
with *Pseudohemiodon laticeps*. It differs
from the latter especially by having a
seemingly smaller, more pointed, and
therefore more triangular-appearing head,
longer and broader pectoral fins, and
larger eyes. This unorthodox species is
another one of the unknowns of the aquarium hobby.

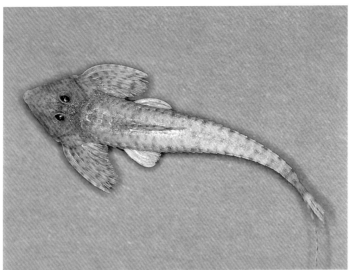

Pyxiloricaria menezesi (ZMA 107.890), preserved specimen.

I. Seidel

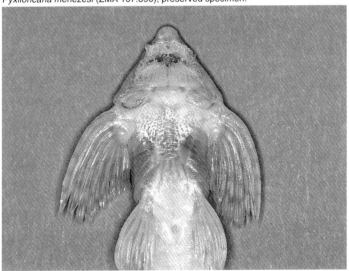

Pyxiloricaria menezesi; ventrum.

I. Seidel

Subtribe Pseudoloricariina Isbrücker, 1981

Genera
Limatulichthys Isbrücker & Nijssen, 1979
Pseudoloricaria Bleeker, 1862

Limatulichthys griseus (Eigenmann, 1909)	Konawaruk, Guyana
Limatulichthys petleyi (Fowler, 1940)	Contamana, Ucayali-System, Peru

These two genera are very similar compared to each other. Isbrücker & Nijssen (1976) published a revision on the genus *Pseudoloricaria* which had been established a long time ago by Bleeker. By including *Pseudoloricaria laeviuscula* (Valenciennes, 1840) and *Pseudoloricaria punctata* (Regan, 1904) into the genus, two species were recognized. Additionally, this publication speaks of the close relationship with *Loricariichthys*, by mentioning the so-called *Loricariichthys* group, the later subtribe Loricariichthyina Isbrücker, 1979.

In *Pseudoloricaria*, too, and in the genus created later for the species *Peudoloricaria punctata, Limatulichthys,* sexually active males have a distinctly larger lower lip than females—it also serves to hold the egg cluster. The dentition of these three genera displays further sex-specific traits. The teeth of adult males are rather round, whereas female teeth have smaller tips. *Pseudoloricaria* and *Limatulichthys* are also very similar to *Loricariichthys* in other aspects, but they differ primarily in the anatomy of the upper lip, which is much more frayed than the upper lip of *Loricariichthys*. Isbrücker & Nijssen (in Isbrücker, 1979) created later the genus *Limatulichthys* with its only species *Limatulichthys punctatus* (Regan, 1904). The main distinguishing characteristic are the small bony platelets anteriorly to the preanal scute of the abdomen. In *Pseudoloricaria* these are numerous (9–15), whereas in *Limatulichthys* less so (3–5). We were able to observe

that the edges of the upper lip of *Limatulichthys* are notched like pinnacles, whereas *Pseudoloricaria* has edges that are more irregular and more frayed, even to the point of speaking of labial barbels. The lower lip of *Limatulichthys petleyi* is frayed, in *Pseudoloricaria laeviuscula* its edge is smooth.

A fish presented in the first [German] edition as *Limatulichthys punctatus* (pp. 600 ff.) must now be called *Limatulichthys petleyi* (Fowler, 1940). The taxon *Limatulichthys petleyi* must be considered a junior homonym, which is why Isbrücker (in Isbrücker et al., 2001) recommends the new name combination for the type species of the genus *Limatulichthys*.

The authors were able to frequently capture specimens of both genera during various trips. In the process, it became clear that both genera always live over sand substrates. The Hamburg aquarist Rolf Schröder was the first to bring a *Pseudoloricaria laeviuscula* specimen to Germany (Evers, 1997b). He captured the species during the night on a sandbank at Itaituba, in the Rio Tapajós. The authors, too, captured *Pseudoloricaria laeviuscula* mostly at night on the sandbanks of the Rio Tefé (see also the chapter "Habitats") together with *Limatulichthys, Hemiodontichthys, Loricariichthys,* and *Furcodontichthys* species. Apparently both genera are distributed throughout the Amazon Basin, and should be quite common at suitable sites (sandbanks). According to ISBRÜCKER & NIJSSEN (1976), *Limatulichthys* has an even much larger area of distribution. Besides inhabiting the Amazon Basin of Brazil, Peru, and Ecuador, it can also be found in the Meta Basin of Colombia, the Essequibo drainage in Guyana (in this case there might be a confusion with *Pseudoloricaria laeviuscula*, which Ingo SEIDEL captured in Guyana), and the Brazilian Parnaiba (state of Piaui). The authors encountered *Limatulichthys petleyi* not only in the Tefé, but also in the upper course of the Negro, and were able to determine later that both variants differ significantly in their head shape. The variant from the Negro River has a much rounder head profile, whereas specimens from the Tefé have a more pointed head. Observing both morphs next to each other, two in-

dependent species could be assumed. ISBRÜCKER mentions in the same publication a second species as valid: *Limatulichthys griseus*, but, unfortunately, does not elaborate.

Male *Pseudoloricaria* and probably also of *Limatulichthys*, carry—in a manner very similar to *Loricariichthys* males—the eggs around in a cluster. In the process, the spawn is provided additional support from below by a small leaf.

H.-G. Evers

L. petleyi from the Rio Tefé. Note the shape of the head. See the following page for text.

Limatulichthys petleyi (FOWLER, 1940)

F.: Fowler, H. W.: A collection of fishes obtained by Mr. William C. Morrow in the Ucayali River basin, Peru.- Proc. Acad. Nat. Sci. Philadelphia, 91: 219-289

Syn.: *Loricaria punctata, Loricariichthys punctatus, Pseudoloricaria punctata, Loricaria grisea, Loricariichthys griseus, Rhineloricaria petleyi, Loricaria petleyi, Loricariichthys parnahybae, Loricaria parnahybae, Limatulichthys punctatus.*

Hab.: Broadly distributed in the Amazon Basin of Peru, Ecuador, and Brazil; Colombia, Meta Basin; Guyana, Essequibo Basin; Brazil, Parnaiba Basin.

M.&B.: Undemanding in its care, *L. petleyi* accepts any standard food. Unfortunately, the species is shy and lives in hiding. A maintenance with sand substrate exclusively requires a large aquarium. The species escapes virtually in panic, but does not burrow. Therefore, in small aquaria it might injure itself easily. By providing hiding places, the panic is somewhat controlled, but still, the fish will be rarely seen. A species for the true catfish specialist. Breeding has not been studied, but it may be assumed to be similar to that described for *Loricariichthys.*

S: There are at least two geomorphs known to us (see genus introduction), something not very surprising, given such an expansive area of distribution.

T: 26°–29°C, **L:** 20 cm, **A:** 120 cm, **R:** b

H.-G. Evers

Limatulichthys petleyi from Rio Tefé. See previous page for additional photo.

Limatulichthys petleyi from the Rio Negro.

H.-G. Evers

L. petleyi from the Rio Tefé. Note the shape of the head.

H.-G. Evers

671

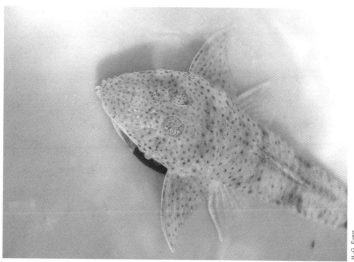

H.-G. Evers

Pseudoloricaria laeviuscula, newly captured ♂ from the Rio Tapajos (sandbank at Alter do Chão) with a spawn on a typical leaf.

Limatulichthys petleyi from the Rio Tefé, previously known as *L. punctatus*.   I. Seidel

Pseudoloricaria laeviuscula from the Rio Tefé. See following pages for more photos.

Pseudoloricaria laeviuscula (VALENCIENNES, 1840)

F.: Valenciennes, A. in Cuvier, G.& A. Valenciennes (1840): Histoire naturelle des poissons (Ch. Pitois, Paris & V. Levrault, Strasbourg)., 15: i–xxxi, 1–540.

Syn.: *Loricaria laeviuscula, Loricariichthys laeviusculus, Loricaria leviuscula.*

Hab.: Brazil, Amazon River and its large tributaries, such as the Madeira, Tapajós, Trombetas, Xingú, and other rivers.

M.&B.: *P. laeviuscula* is also active during the day. So far, only juveniles and subadult specimens have been maintained in aquaria—without problems. A sand substrate and strong filtration are obligatory, ditto for regular water exchanges. This species is not as shy as the similar *Limatulichthys* known to us. Once feed is placed in the aquarium, the loricariids become active and show themselves. Unfortunately, the species grows quite large, a characteristic that markedly reduces its potential popularity. SPRENGER (pers. comm.) could breed this species in captivity. He used a leaf of *Rhododendron* sp. which was accepted by the male as support for the egg cluster. The fry was quite sensitive and not easy to raise.

S: Juvenile *P. laeviuscula* can be distinguished from same-aged *Limatulichthys* with ease up to a length of 10 cm. The ventral half of the caudal fin in *Pseudoloricaria* is dark brown. The lower two thirds of the caudal fin of Tapajós specimens was virtually white, and there was a black spot in the center of the caudal peduncle. As the specimens age, this characteristic fades, until adult specimens only have a somewhat darker inferior caudal fin half.

T: 26°–29°C, L: 30 cm, A: 150 cm, R: b

A spawn of *Pseudoloricaria laeviuscula.* See previous page for text.

I. Seidel

H.-G. Evers

Pseudoloricaria laeviuscula from the Rio Tapajós.

674

Pseudoloricaria laeviuscula from the Tapajós River.   H.-G. Evers

Pseudoloricaria laeviuscula; typical coloration of the caudal fin of a subadult.   H.-G. Evers

Sexual differences of *Pseudoloricaria laeviuscula*: oral lobes of a ♂.

I. Seidel

♀♀ have no enlarged lower lip.

I. Seidel

Pseudoloricaria laeviuscula from the Rio Xingú.

I. Seidel

Pseudoloricaria laeviuscula from the Pirara Creek, Guyana.

I. Seidel

Comparison of the ventrum of *Pseudoloricaria laeviuscula* from Peru...

... with that of a specimen from Guyana.   I. Seidel

Pseudoloricaria laeviuscula, specimen from Guyana (Pirara Creek). Even as juveniles, these animals lack coloration in the lower caudal fin.

Photographs on the previous page:
Comparison of the ventrum of two specimens of *Pseudoloricaria laeviuscula*:
Top: *P. laeviuscula* from Peru. Initially thought erroneously to be a *Loricariichthys.* Only the comparison of the ventrum settled the matter!

Bottom: *P. laeviuscula*, ventrum of a specimen from Guyana. Note the triangular reddish coloration of the ventral area in both specimens!

Pseudoloricaria sp. "Rio Negro," juvenile.

I. Seidel

Pseudoloricaria sp. "Rio Negro"

From the central Río Negro, and in part also from the Río Trombetas, came sporadically individual specimens of a *Pseudoloricaria* species to Germany, which differed distinctly in regards to coloration from the various populations of *Pseudoloricaria laeviuscula*. The specimens, already in their youth, show a coarser spot and dot design on their body. RÖMER & WÖHLER (Aquarium Heute 2/1995, pp. 74–

77) present the photograph of an adult specimen from the Río Negro. The aquarists F. and M. WILHELM (pers. comm.) captured the species repeatedly in the central Río Negro, both in the river proper as well as in its tributaries. A male was captured with his spawn, which did not have a leaf as substrate.

T: 26°–29°C, L: 30 cm, A: 150 cm, R: b

Subtribe Reganellina Isbrücker & Nijssen, 1979

Genus *Reganella* Eigenmann, 1905

With the only representative *Reganella depressa* (Kner, 1854) from the Brazilian Río Negro at Marabitanas, this is another monotypic genus. The very unusually shaped loricariid species was given by Dr. Franke (1985) the German common name "Planarienköpfiger Harnischwels" [=planaria-headed whiptail] in consideration of the shape of its head. The much dorsoventrally compressed catfish is therefore clearly different from all other genera and species. Unfortunately, a first import is still pending.

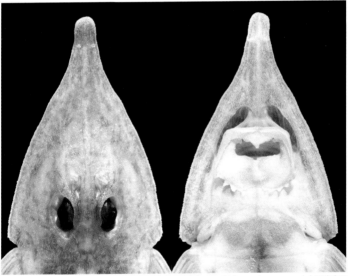

Reganella depressa: dorsal and ventral view of the cephalic region.

L. A. van der Laan

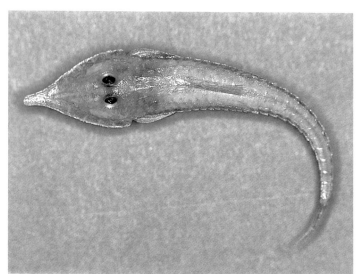

Reganella depressa; preserved specimen.

I. Seidel

Reganella depressa; note the unusual shape of the ventral side of the head.
I. Seidel

Subtribe Ricolina Isbrücker & Nijssen, 1979

Genus *Ricola* Isbrücker & Nijssen, 1978

Ricola macrops (Regan, 1904), from the Río de la Plata Basin, is the only member.

The genus is a close relative of *Loricaria*, but both can be distinguished based on the labial morphology. The many barbels and subbarbels are branched one additional time in *Ricola* in comparison to *Loricaria*. Dentition is rather reminiscent of *Hemiloricaria* species. Aquaristically, *Ricola macrops* has not yet appeared, which is why only preserved specimens can be pictured here. Fishes published to date under this name (e.g., Sands, 1984; Kobayagawa, 1991; C. Schaefer, 1996) are always *Loricaria* species.

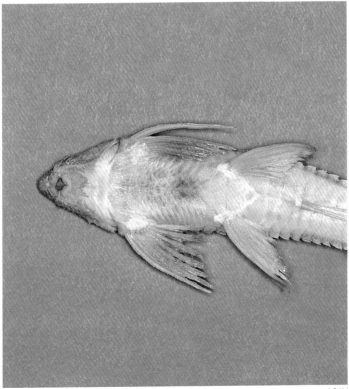

Ricola macrops, ventral view.

I. Seidel

Ricola macrops (ZMA 114.327); preserved specimen.

I. Seidel

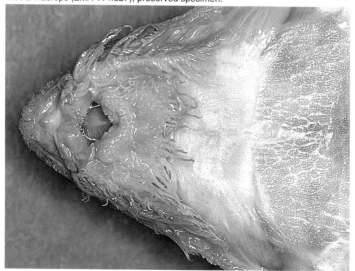

Ricola macrops; view of the oral region.

I. Seidel

Subtribe Rineloricariina ISBRÜCKER, 1979

Genus *Dasyloricaria* ISBRÜCKER & NIJSSEN, 1979

Dasyloricaria capetensis (MEEK & HILDEBRANDT, 1913)	Panama, Tuyra Basin
Dasyloricaria filamentosa (STEINDACHNER, 1878)	Colombia, Magdalena Basin
Dasyloricaria latiura (EIGENMANN & VANCE, 1912)	Colombia, Boca de Certegai
Dasyloricaria seminuda (EIGENMANN & VANCE, 1912)	Colombia
Dasyloricaria tuyrensis (MEEK & HILDEBRANDT, 1913)	Panama, Tuyra Basin

At present, the genus represents five species. These were reclassified from the catchall genus *Loricaria*. Genotype is *Dasyloricaria filamentosa*.

Given the plethora of whiptail loricariine catfishes introduced in the aquarium hobby, it is hard to say, if there ever have been members of the genus *Dasyloricaria* among them. All species grow quite large (20–35 cm total length). The area of distribution extends from southern Panama to northern Colombia, not precisely an area with frequent suckermouth catfish exports.

ISBRÜCKER & NIJSSEN (in ISBRÜCKER, 1979) delineated the genus in front of the related genus *Spatuloricaria*. In contrast to the latter, the bony scutes posteriorly on the body of *Dasyloricaria* are very protruding, making the cover of the entire caudal peduncle very characteristic. *Dasyloricaria* have hardly visible bristles on the sides of the head, likewise in males, where only slightly the head, nape, and the upper side of the pectoral fins are blanketed by a dense cover of small, thin odontodes. Males only develop a small "brush" along the sides of their head, but never as pronounced as is the case in many *Hemiloricaria* species. Such fishes have not yet been pictured in the aquaristic literature. All whiptail catfishes, which here to date have been called *Dasyloricaria filamentosa* in the hobby—upon closer scrutiny—have turned out to be members of the genus *Rineloricaria* or *Hemiloricaria*.

It will probably be necessary for an avid catfish fan to pack up and travel to Panama or the Colombian Magdalena basin to finally make these fishes better known to the aquarium hobby.

Dasyloricaria filamentosa

Drawing from Steindachner, 1878

Dasyloricaria cf. *capetensis*, ZMA 107.937.

I. Seidel

Dasyloricaria cf. *capetensis*, ZMA 107.937.

I. Seidel

Dasyloricaria cf. *capetensis*, ZMA 107.937.

I. Seidel

Dasyloricaria sp. "Orinoco"

I. Seidel

Dasyloricaria sp. "Orinoco"

In the first German edition (p. 733), this fish was presented under the heading of "Unidentified Loricariinae, New Genus LG7." Meanwhile, however, it has become apparent that this is a member of the genus *Dasyloricaria*. A fact which remained obscured, because only poorly-preserved museum specimens had been available to us. This may, however, be an as of yet undescribed member of the genus.

Dasyloricaria is a somewhat close relative to *Spatuloricaria* and has notably large pectoral and ventral fins. Differences can be found especially in the development of the hypertrophied odontodes around the head and pectoral fins of sexually mature males during the spawning season. The odontodes around the snout are signifi-cantly shorter and thinner than those of *Spatuloricaria* and become longer posteriorly. Apparently, there is no distinct broadening of the head with fleshy bulges in *Dasyloricaria*, as is typical for *Spatuloricaria* males; the shape of the head remains pointed. Furthermore, there are short, upward-pointed odontodes on the first pectoral fin rays of adult males. The specimen of the first [German] edition on occasion developed these odontodes under optimal care; however, after some time, these hypertrophied odontodes went into remission.

Sexually mature ♂ of *Dasyloricaria* sp. "Orinoco" with typical whiskers. I. Seidel

Dasyloricaria ♂; with its large pectoral and ventral fins. I. Seidel

Fam.: Loricariidae
Subfam.: Loricariinae

Fonchiiichthys uracanthus (ZMA 114.514) from the Río Frijoles, Panama.   I. Seidel

Genus *Fonchiiichthys* Isbrücker & Michels, 2001

F. uracanthus (Kner & Steindachner, 1863)	Río Chagres, Panama
F. rupestris (Schultz, 1944)	Maracaibo Basin, Venezuela

Isbrücker & Michels (in Isbrücker et al, 2001) described two fishes—previously members of the genus *Rineloricaria*—in honor of the Peruvian ichthyologist Fonchii Chang Matzunga, who drowned August 1999 in the Peruvian section of the Rio Pastaza while capturing fishes. Both species, *F. uracanthus*—now type species of the genus *Fonchiiichthys*—and *F. rupestris,* have been extensively presented in the first [German] edition (pp. 668 and 705) under the old name *Rineloricaria.*

Fonchiiichthys is very similar to *Rineloricaria* and would surely have been maintained as part of it if the geographic separation between the two were not as large. Whereas *Fonchiiichthys* is only known from the Westandean areas of northwestern South America, *Rineloricaria* spp. inhabit primarily the southeastern areas of the continent. In between, only the genera *Hemiloricaria* and *Leliella*—also separated from *Rineloricaria*—can be found.

The body of *Fonchiiichthys* is flat and broad, the ventrum is completely covered by scutes. The upper spine of the caudal fin is proximally thickened and distally filamentously elongated.

Males develop odontodes similar to those of the genus *Rineloricaria.*

Fonchiiichthys rupestris; pair spawning in its natural habitat (Caño El Sapo).   S. Ploeger

Fonchiiichthys rupestris, aquarium specimens.   S. Ploeger

Fonchiiichthys rupestris (Schultz, 1944)

F.: Schultz, L. P. (1944): The catfishes of Venezuela, with descriptions of thirty-eight new forms.– Proc. U. S. nat. Mus., 94: 173–338.

Syn.: *Loricaria uracantha rupestre, Rineloricaria rupestre.*

Hab.: Venezuela, Maracaibo Basin.

M.&B.: In a manner similar to its congeners, breeding has not been successful, but should not present any particular problems. Unfortunately, there are hardly ever any fishes imported to Germany from this area.

S: S. Ploeger (Berlin) observed the spawning of *F. rupestris* in its natural habitat. For this purpose, the pair lays next to each other. A cave was not used during the observed episode.

T: 26°–29°C, **L:** 12 cm, **A:** 80 cm, **R:** b

Fam.: Loricariidae
Subfam.: Loricariinae

Fonchiiichthys uracanthus

Fonchiiichthys uracanthus
(KNER & STEINDACHNER, 1863)

F.: Kner, R. & F. Steindachner in Kner, R. (1863): Hr. v. Siebold legt eine Übersicht der ichthyologischen Ausbeute des Herrn Professors Dr. Mor. Wagner in Central-Amerika von Herrn Professor Rud. Kner in Wien vor. Sber. Königl. Bayer. Akad. Wiss. München, 1863(2): 220–230.

Syn.: *Loricaria uracantha, Rineloricaria uracantha.*

Hab.: Panama, Río Chagres. KEIJMANS (1999, Aquaristik Aktuell Nr. 9–10/99: p. 16–18) reports about the capture of *Fon-chiiichthys uracanthus* in the Panamanian Río Parti. In that article, the species is mistakenly called *Crossoloricaria variegata*. Water values of the Río Parti: temperature 27°C, pH 8.0, and a conductivity of 2300 µs/cm.

M.&B.: Given the water values determined in nature, maintenance and breeding in regular tap water should be no problem. Other aspects of aquarium maintenance are similar to those of *Hemiloricaria* spp.

T: 26°–29°C, **L:** 15 cm, **A:** 80 cm, **R:** b

Genus *Hemiloricaria* BLEEKER, 1862

H. altipinnis (BREEDER, 1925)	Chucunaque Basin, Panama
H. aurata (KNAACK, 2002)	Paraguay
H. beni (PEARSON, 1924)	Beni drainage, Bolivia
H. cacerensis (RIBEIRO, 1912)	Mato Grosso, Brazil
H. caracasensis BLEEKER, 1862	Caracas, Venezuela
H. castroi (ISBRÜCKER & NIJSSEN, 1984)	Trombetas, Brazil
H. eigenmanni (PELLEGRIN, 1908)	Sarare, Venezuela
H. fallax (STEINDACHNER, 1915)	Brazil, Guyana
H. formosa (ISBRÜCKER & NIJSSEN, 1979)	N. Brazil, Colombia
H. hasemani (ISBRÜCKER & NIJSSEN, 1979)	Rio Guamá, Brazil
H. hoehnei (RIBEIRO, 1912)	Paraguay Basin, Brazil
H. jubata (BOULENGER, 1902)	Rio Durango, Ecuador
H. konopickyi (STEINDACHNER, 1879)	Amazon, Brazil
H. lanceolata (GÜNTHER, 1868)	Peru, Ecuador, Brazil
H. magdalenae (STEINDACHNER, 1878)	Magdalena Basin, Colombia
H. melini (SCHINDLER, 1959)	Rio Negro, Manacapuru, Brazil
H. morrowi (FOWLER, 1940)	Ucayali Basin, Peru
H. nigricauda (REGAN, 1904)	Rio de Janeiro, Brazil
H. parva (BOULENGER, 1895)	Mato Grosso, Brazil
H. phoxocephala (EIGENMANN & EIGENMANN, 1889)	Rio Coari, Brazil
H. platyura (MÜLLER & TROSCHEL, 1848)	Rupununi, Guyana
H. sneiderni (FOWLER, 1944)	Rio Jurubida, Colombia
H. stewarti (EIGENMANN, 1909)	Chipoo, Guyana
H. teffeana (STEINDACHNER, 1879)	Rio Tefé, Brazil
H. wolfei (FOWLER, 1940)	Ucayali Basin, Peru

In a recent special publication on loricariid catfishes, Amsterdam ichthyologist Isaäc J.H. ISBRÜCKER declared the synonymity of *Rineloricaria* and *Hemiloricaria* as no longer valid, and the latter again an independent genus (ISBRÜCKER in ISBRÜCKER et al, 2001). Type species is *Hemiloricaria caracasensis* BLEEKER, 1862, pictured here.

The genera *Hemiloricaria* and *Rineloricaria* primarily differ in the degree of cephalic bristling of sexually active males. In *Hemiloricaria*, males have hypertrophied odontodes first between the interorbital and the predorsal region (the "nape," so to speak). These are long, thin, and virtually straight. Second, between the suborbital and the opercular regions, i.e., along the sides of the head. These odontodes are densely clustered, long, and very thin. Additionally, there is a row of less numerous, bent, spinelike odontodes, which are about three times thicker and a quarter as long as the remainder of odontodes in this area. Third, there are odontodes on the pectoral fins. These are numerous, erect, and bent backwards like spines.

On the other hand, *Rineloricaria* has no bristles on the "nape" region. The bristles are densely clustered along the sides of the head. They are long, very thin, and slightly bent. On the pectoral fins they are smallish and numerous, as well as erect, bent backwards, and reminiscent of thorns.

Hemiloricaria stewarti from Suriname.

H.-G. Evers

Hemiloricaria stewarti, head.

H.-G. Evers

Hemiloricaria stewarti (EIGENMANN, 1909): The species is found in Guyana and Suriname. Six crossbands transverse the body, and the cephalic profile is slightly pointed, but not to the extent as that of *H. phoxocephala* (see species description).

Whereas the members of *Hemilorcaria* are always slim whiptails with a ventral area completely covered by scutes, in *Rineloricaria* this is not always the case. ISBRÜCKER, therefore, recommends an urgent revision of the genus *Rineloricaria*. Additionally, in *Hemiloricaria* the upper caudal fin ray is much elongated, something that is not the case in the genus *Rineloricaria*.

694

H. beni, ♂ with a black spot on the relatively tall dorsal fin.

H.-G. Evers

Hemiloricaria beni (Pearson, 1924)
Dwarf whiptail catfish

F.: Pearson, N. E. (1924): The fishes of the eastern slope of the Andes. I. The fishes of the Rio Beni basin, Bolivia, collected by the Mulford Expedition,- Indiana Univ. Stud., 11 (64): 1–83.

Syn.: *Loricaria beni, Rineloricaria beni.*

Hab.: Bolivia, Beni Basin.

M.&B.: An easily maintained and bred species. The males are reliable in their care of the spawn. The tubes used in breeding are narrow (diameter 1.2 cm). Up to 80 orange-brown eggs are laid. The larvae need ca. 10 days at 25°C to hatch and are quite small. Their initial diet consists of rotifers or dust food. Initially, *Artemia* nauplii may be too large, otherwise rearing is uneventful. Males grow small beards, females are always ripe. A group of 6–10 adults produces off- spring in a regular manner. If the males would be somewhat larger, they would be excellent surrogates for the more difficult species.

S: This is the smallest of the maintained whiptail catfishes. Swiss aquarists brought the first specimens in 1997 from Bolivia. Meanwhile, the species is numerously represented in the member aquaria of the VDA-AK BSSW. So, let's watch out that it does not disappear. A very suitable species for the beginning whiptail catfish enthusiast.
Some aquarists have specimens which are identical in coloration, but are 15 cm in total length. This is relatively unusual, because the specimens pictured here are full-grown at a much smaller size.

T: 23°–26°C, L: 8 cm, A: 60 cm, R: b

Hemiloricaria cacerensis (RIBEIRO, 1912), preserved specimen. The species was described from the Brazilian Mato Grosso, Rio Paraguay drainage. The beautiful dots covering its body are eye-catching. The pictured specimen is still relatively small, but the dots do not fade in adults.

Hemiloricaria beni ♀. The black design in the comparatively low dorsal fin is lacking. See previous page for text.

Hemiloricaria aurata Knaack, 2002. The latest described member of the genus *Hemiloricaria*.

Hemiloricaria caracasensis (Bleeker, 1862)

The type locality is listed as being Caracas, the Venezuelan capital. The pictured specimen was captured in northern Colombia. It seems this species inhabits the general area of the Caribbean Andes. In the lowlands of the Llanos it is replaced by other species (e.g., *H. eigenmanni*). Type species of the genus *Hemiloricaria*.

Hemiloricaria caracasensis, Caño Negro, Colombia.

Hemiloricaria castroi, aquarium specimen.

I. Seidel

Hemiloricaria castroi (ISBRÜCKER & NIJSSEN, 1984)
Castro's whiptail catfish

F.: Isbrücker, I. J. H. & H. Nijssen (1984): *Hemiloricaria castroi*, a new species of mailed catfish from Rio Trombetas, Brazil (Pisces, Siluriformes, Loricariidae).- Beaufortia, 34 (3): 93–99.

Syn.: *Rineloricaria castroi*.

Hab.: Brazil, Rio Trombetas.

M.&B.: Medium-large species that requires space. Other aspects of its care are straightforward. Breeding has not been successful, but no major difficulties are expected.

S: *H. castroi* is a close relative of *Hemiloricaria phoxocephala. H. castroi* can be distinguished by having a relatively pointed cephalic profile, two rows of odontodes along the flanks, and typical black bands on the pectoral and ventral fins, which in *H. phoxocephala* are hyaline (transparent).

T: 26°–29°C, L: 18 cm, A: 100 cm, R: b

Hemiloricaria castroi (SL 160 mm), holotype from the Rio Trombetas.

L. A. van der Laan

Hemiloricaria eigenmanni; spawning pair.

H.-G. Evers

Hemiloricaria eigenmanni (PELLEGRIN, 1908)
Eigenmann's whiptail catfish

F.: Description de deux poissons nouveaux de l´Amerique du Sud, de la famille des Loricariidés.- Bull.Soc.zool. Fr., 31: 124–127.

Syn.: *Loricaria eigenmanni, Rineloricaria eigenmanni.*

Hab.: Venezuela, Rio Sarare (type locality). The authors found the species quite commonly in the white-water creeks and rivers of the Venezuelan Llanos. In August (end of the rainy season) the water temperatures were at 28°–30°C. At that time, it was possible to capture specimens of all sizes.

M.&B.: Similar to its congeners, *H. eigenmanni* is easy to maintain. On the other hand, rearing the young is a difficult endeavour only rarely accomplished in a satisfying manner. Up to 150 green eggs are deposited in tubes and guarded by the male. The beard is only slightly developed.

S: This beautiful species has a characteristic black longitudinal stripe design on its ventral side.

T: 25°–29°C, L: 12 cm, A: 80 cm, R: b

699

H. eigenmanni; ventral side showing the characteristic longitudinal black stripes. See previous page for text.

Hemiloricaria eigenmanni ♂

Hemiloricaria eigenmanni ♀

Hemiloricaria eigenmanni, ♂ guarding the spawn.

H.-G. Evers

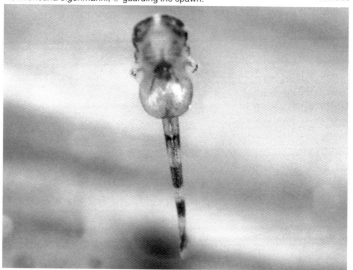

Hemiloricaria eigenmanni; hatchling.

H.-G. Evers

Hemiloricaria fallax, close-up of the head. ♂♂ carry a "mohawk," odontodes dorsally on the head. See next page for text.

Hemiloricaria eigenmanni, fry. See page 699 for text.

Hemiloricaria fallax (Steindachner, 1915)
Delicate whiptail catfish

F.: Steindachner, F. (1915): Das w. M. Hofrat F. Steindachner erstattet einen vorläufigen Bericht über einige neue Süßwasserfische aus Südamerika,..- Anz. Akad. Wiss. Wien, mathem. Naturwiss. Kl., 25 (17): 199–202.

Syn.: *Loricaria fallax, Loricariichthys fallax, Rineloricaria fallax.*

Hab.: Brazil, Rio Branco drainage, Amazon Basin. According to Isbrücker (pers. comm.), the area of distribution is larger than previously thought. The species can be found throughout the entire Amazon Basin. Brazil, Rio Guamá, Rio Tefé; Guyana: Lethem Takutu drainage, the rivers Potaro, Mazaruni, and Essequibo, where their presence was confirmed by I. Seidel.

M.&B.: *H. fallax* is not a demanding charge. Because it grows to a respectable size, the breeding tubes need to be correspondingly dimensioned. The species lays green eggs, the spawns may be comprised of over 200 eggs. Males are particularly nervous while broodcaring, only rarely brooding to term in the authors' aquaria. Rearing the fry, on the other hand, is not difficult as long as the basic rules are respected. The males have a pronounced beard, also the pectoral fins and even the upper head (mohawk) have bristles, which confers a strange image to these fish.

S: This is one of the species with a dark circular spot anterior to the dorsal fin. In *H. fallax* this spot is particularly pronounced and located just anterior to the dorsal fin. Even juveniles a few centimeters in length have this spot. This is a species-identifying criterium, regardless of the design on the remainder of the body —something that changes with its environment.
Hemiloricaria formosa from the upper Rio Negro and Orinoco drainages also has such a spot, but it is located much more anteriorly, just posterior to the head. Under close observation, unusual black pores may be discerned on the head and anterior body of *H. fallax* and some other species (e.g., *H. formosa*). It is unknown whether these are sensory pores or what function they accomplish. The pores of the lateral line are also present in *Rineloricaria,* not black but rather bright and in a symmetrical arrangement along the sides of the body.

T: 25°–29°C, L: 20 cm, A: 100 cm, R: b

Hemiloricaria fallax ♂

H.-G. Evers

Hemiloricaria fallax, spawn in a tube.

H.-G. Evers

Hemiloricaria fallax, pair.

H.-G. Evers

Hemiloricaria fallax, juvenile.

H.-G. Evers

Hemiloricaria formosa from the Rio Uaupés

H.-G. Evers

Hemiloricaria formosa (ISBRÜCKER & NIJSSEN, 1979)

F.: Isbrücker, I. J. H. & H. Nijssen (1979): Three new South American mailed catfishes of the genera *Rineloricaria* and *Loricariichthys* (Pisces, Siluriformes, Loricariidae).– Bijdr. Dierk., 48 (2): 191–211.

Syn.: *Rineloricaria formosa.*

Hab.: Colombia and Venezuela, drainage basin of the upper Orinoco; Brazil, upper Rio Negro, Rio Uaupés. Together with Volker BOHNET and Michael SCHLÜTER, the authors were able to confirm the presence of the species in October 1997 at the upper Rio Negro at São Gabriel da Cachoeira in the black-water-carrying igarapés. The species prefers the faster-flowing biotopes in those areas. The water there is particularly soft and acidic (pH below 5.0), and has a water temperature of 26°–28°C.

M.&B.: More troublesome than species frequenting white- and clear-water. Breeding has not yet been successful, but that may also in part be due to the fact that only few specimens were brought back to Germany. As of yet, none of them have grown whiskers.

S: According to the original describers, *H. formosa* is closely related to *Hemiloricaria morrowi* (remains smaller, lacks a dorsal spot) and *Hemiloricaria melini* (different coloration), both slender, elongated species.
A quite attractive species, which surely would be wanted by one or another catfish hobbyist.

T: 26°–29°C, **L:** 18 cm, **A:** 100 cm, **R:** b

Hemiloricaria hasemani from Tucurui, Tocantins drainage.

H.-G. Evers

Hemiloricaria hasemani
(ISBRÜCKER & NIJSSEN, 1979)
Haseman's whiptail catfish

F.: Isbrücker, I. J. H. & H. Nijssen (1979): Three new South American mailed catfishes of the genera *Rineloricaria* and *Loricariichthys* (Pisces, Siluriformes, Loricariidae).– Bijdr. Dierk., 48 (2): 191–211.

Syn.: *Rineloricaria hasemani.*

Hab.: Brazil, Pará, Rio Guamá Basin. The pictured specimen, here identified as *Hemiloricaria hasemani,* was captured in the central Rio Tocantins at Tucurui. EVERS and P. VALERIO DA SILVA captured this species also in the clear-water streams of the Rio Araguaia drainage at the Ilha do Bananal.

M.&B.: Unproblematic species, although breeding has not been successful. But it is quite possible that there have been unreported successes which, due to erroneous species identification, are not classified correctly.

S: The design elements and the habits of the pictured specimen speak for it being *H. hasemani.* It was captured in the Tocantins River. Guamá and Tocantins are part of the Para drainage, which speaks in favor of the identity of *H. hasemani.*

T: 26°–29°C, L: 15 cm, A: 80 cm, R: b

Hemiloricaria lanceolata, ♂ from the Río Huacamayo, Peru.   I. Seidel

Hemiloricaria lanceolata (GÜNTHER, 1868)
Lanceolate whiptail catfish, chocolate-brown whiptail catfish

F.: Günther, A.(1868): Descriptions of freshwater fishes from Surinam and Brazil.– Proc.zool.Soc.London, 1868: 229–247.

Syn.: *Loricaria lanceolata, Rineloricaria lanceolata.*

Hab.: Brazil, Peru, Ecuador, Bolivia, Paraguay. SEIDEL captured the species in the Peruvian Río San Alejandro, a clear-water biotope. *H. lanceolata* has a very ample area of distribution and inhabits a multitude of lotic biotopes, which, as far as known, all belong to the white- and clear-water types. During two trips to the Araguaia and Tocantins drainages in central Brazil, EVERS captured several interesting whiptail catfishes, which all seemed very similar to *H. lanceolata*. The

two morphs of that region are clearly different in regard to design and are presented separately. SEIDEL was able to capture a morph in Bolivia. Likewise, R. NORMANN (Satow) found the fish in Paraguay. EVERS captured an additional morph with orange whiskers in the drainage of the Rio Madeira and the border area between Brazil and Bolivia. Juveniles captured from among the shore vegetation were brightly colored reddish brown, whereas adults were generally very dark. The morphs captured by SEIDEL in Peru were also quite variable in coloration. Fish from the clear-water-carrying Río Huacamaya had yellow whiskers, were initially red brown, and became darker under aquarium maintenance. Specimens from Yarina Cocha (white-water) were spotted "normal" to dark brown.

709

Hemiloricaria lanceolata from the Río Huacamayo.

H.-G. Evers

M.&B.: This beautiful species is very popular and frequently imported. The 100 and more, orange-colored eggs need up to 12 days to hatch under average temperatures. *H. lanceolata* is a ferocious spawn predator. Any fish eggs are eagerly considered food. It is a rare male that will guard his spawn responsibly. Once such a male has been found, breeding is not a problem. With good water hygiene, rearing the young with *Artemia* nauplii is straightforward.

S: *H. lanceolata* is variable. There are marbled females and such that sport the coloration found in males. Depending on the origin, the species is light brown with a black design to basically black. Some males have white whiskers, others orange/brown ones. The design of the dorsal fin and the numerous cephalic bristles typical of males, allow a good distinction to *L. heteroptera* (see there).

T: 22°–29°C (depending on origin), **L:** 12 cm, **A:** 80 cm, **R:** b

H. lanceolata from Paraguay.

I. Seidel

Rineloricaria from the Rio Madeira drainage.

H.-G. Evers

Aquarium population of *Hemiloricaria lanceolata*, ♂ ...

H.-G. Evers

... and the corresponding ♀.

H.-G. Evers

H. lanceolata, Bolivia.

I. Seidel

Hemiloricaria lanceolata ♂ from a creek at Tarapoa, Ecuador.

H.-G. Evers

Hemiloricaria lanceolata "Rio Cristalino"

The home of this fish is a tributary of the Rio das Mortes, which soon thereafter flows into the Araguaia, Brazil. Here, too, one and the same population may be comprised of individuals of differing coloration. Besides intensely brown specimens, deer-brown individuals were also captured. The latter were highly reminiscent of *Leliella* sp. "red". However, later in the aquarium, these fish, too, became darker and started to display the design typical of *H. lanceolata*.

T: 25°–28°C, L: 12 cm, A: 80 cm, R: b

Hemiloricaria lanceolata "Rio do Peixe"

This polychromic population(?) was captured in a tributary of the Rio Araguaia at the city of Aruaná, the Rio do Peixe, Brazil. There are relatively light individuals and those that are virtually black. Notable in the Rio do Peixe morph is the attractive banding of the pectoral fins, something that clearly distinguishes it from the Rio Cristalino morph. In October 2000, EVERS was able to breed the fish he brought to Germany. A female laid approximately 200 orange-yellow eggs inside a tube. Rearing the fry was uneventful feeding rotifers, *Artemia* nauplii, and commercial fry food.

T: 25°–28°C, L: 12 cm, A: 80 cm, R: b

Hemiloricaria lanceolata from the Rio Cristalino, Brazil.

H.-G. Evers

Hemiloricaria lanceolata from the Rio do Peixe, Brazil.

H.-G. Evers

H. lanceolata, a rather dark specimen, also from the Rio do Peixe.

H.-G. Evers

Hemiloricaria lanceolata, xanthic specimen.

H.-G. Evers

Hemiloricaria cf. *lanceolata*. Aquarium specimen of unknown origin.

H.-G. Evers

Hemiloricaria cf. *lanceolata*

This morph differs somewhat from the others known to us. Given that the origin is ignored because they were acquired in the trade in Germany, there is no additional information available at this time. Maintenance and breeding do not differ from other *Hemiloricaria lanceolata* morphs.

T: 24°–28°C, L: 12 cm, A: 80 cm, R: b

Hemiloricaria melini (SCHINDLER, 1959)
Apache whiptail catfish

F.: Schindler, O. (1959): *Loricariichthys melini* nov. Sp.– Ark. Zool. Stockholm, 12 (2): 387–389.

Syn.: *Loricariichthys melini, Rineloricaria melini*.

Hab.: Type locality is Manacapurú at the Solimões, close to the mouth of the Rio Negro, Brazil. However, dedicated aquarists have been able to repeatedly bring this species to Germany also from the middle Rio Negro drainage.

M.&B.: A black-water species that requires soft, acidic water to spawn. The aquarist V. BOHNET (Oldenburg) has bred *H. melini* successfully. Males practice broodcare, something common to all *Hemiloricaria*. Rearing the young is not as difficult as, for example, rearing those of *Hemiloricaria teffeana*.

This is arguably the most attractive whiptail catfish to reach our aquaria. Juveniles are plain gray brown, but with advancing age, the beautiful coloration appears. To date, individual juvenile specimens reach Germany repeatedly through Manaus. The interested catfish enthusiast should pay particular attention to Manaus imports in search of this species. *H. melini* is a close relative of *Hemiloricaria teffeana* and *Hemiloricaria* sp. "Barcelos." Practically all juveniles have a virtually black caudal fin.

T: 26°–29°C, L: 10 cm, A: 80 cm, R: b

Hemiloricaria melini, portrait.

H.-G. Evers

Hemiloricaria melini, see following pages for additional photos.

I. Seidel

Hemiloricaria melini. Juveniles are gray.

H.-G. Evers

Hemiloricaria melini, egg. See previous page for text.

I. Seidel

Hemiloricaria melini, newly hatched larva with yolk sac.

I. Seidel

Hemiloricaria melini, one month old fry.

I. Seidel

Hemiloricaria melini, central Rio Negro.

H.-G. Evers

Fam.: Loricariidae
Subfam.: Loricariinae

Hemiloricaria morrowi (Fowler, 1940)
Yellow suckermouth catfish

F.: Fowler, H. W. (1940): A collection of fishes obtained by Mr. William C. Morrow in the Ucayali River basin, Peru.– Proc. Acad. Nat. Sci. Philadelphia, 91: 219–289.

Syn.: *Rineloricaria morrowi.*

Hab.: Peru, Ucayali Basin, Contamana. A relatively common inhabitant of Amazonian Peru that is imported with regularity. I. Seidel and travel companions captured the species in 1995 in Peru in clear-water streams near the town of Tierra Roja (southwest of Pucallpa).

M.&B.: Simple to maintain and breed. Sometimes the males do not properly care for their up to 80 orange eggs, but a breeding group usually results in sufficient juveniles so that a sporadically eaten spawn is easily compensated. Males grow slight

bristles on the sides of their head and on the anterior pectoral fin spines. On the head, the medium-long bristles are arranged on the anterior third of the edge into a beard. Additionally, older males have a thin row of bristles superiorly on the head. This is a good identification aid for the species.

S: *H. morrowi* is a longtime staple in the hobby, initially having been offered as *Hemiloricaria sp.* "Peru." After exhaustive analysis, it has become apparent that it is indeed *Hemiloricaria morrowi.*
The beautiful yellow species that has been bred for several years under the name of *Hemiloricaria morrowi* (see also Franke, 1985) is probably a different, still undescribed, species.

T: 25°–29°C, L: 12 cm, A: 80 cm, R: b

Hemiloricaria morrowi, ♂ .

H.-G. Evers

722

Hemiloricaria morrowi

H.-G. Evers

Hemiloricaria morrowi, ♂ guarding a spawn.

I. Seidel

Hemiloricaria nigricauda (REGAN, 1904)
Black-tail whiptail catfish

F.: Regan, C.T. (1904): A monograph of the fishes of the family Loricariidae.– Trans.zool.Soc.London, 17(3): 191–350.

Syn.: *Loricaria nigricauda, Rineloricaria nigricauda.*

Hab.: Brazil, state of Rio de Janeiro, Porto Real. EVERS, LACERDA, and BOHNET were able to capture the species, October 1997, in the Rio Macacu at the town of Papucaia. At the time, the river was very low and carried turbid white-water with a moderate current. The whiptail catfish was captured with a seine and a sturdy dip net among the shore vegetation over sandy substrates.

M.&B.: Unproblematic charge which should be easy to breed. However, reproduction has not yet been successful, probably because of the low number of available specimens.

S: REGAN (1904) pictured a half-grown juvenile (TL 65 mm) as the holotype. At this length, the fish still have the name-giving black coloration of the caudal fin (Lat. *nigricauda* = black tail). Adults usually have crossbands in its stead and only rarely the caudal fin becomes dark.

T: 18°–23°C, L: 12 cm, A: 60 cm, R: b

Hemiloricaria nigricauda, juvenile.

H.-G. Evers

Hemiloricaria nigricauda, ♂

H.-G. Evers

Hemiloricaria nigricauda, typical coloration of the caudal fin of juveniles.

H.-G. Evers

Hemiloricaria phoxocephala, Rio Tefé.

H.-G. Evers

Hemiloricaria phoxocephala
(EIGENMANN & EIGENMANN, 1889)

F.: Eigenmann, C. H. & R. S. Eigenmann (1889): Preliminary notes on South American nematognathi II.– Proc. California Acad. Sci., 2(2): 28–56.

Syn.: *Loricaria phoxocephala, Rineloricaria phoxocephala.*

Hab.: Brazil, Amazon Basin, Rio Coari. The authors captured the species in an Amazon tributary next to the Coari. In the Tefé, the species was captured at night over sand with a seine. Only rarely was the whiptail captured, and only in the main stream, not in its sidearms, which are inhabited by *Hemiloricaria teffeana.*

M.&B.: It is questionable if this species has ever reached the aquarium hobby. At the time (October 1997), the authors only captured adults which were too large to bring along to Germany. However, no particular maintenance problems are anticipated.

S: *H. phoxocephala* has a pointed head and is quite similar to *H. castroi.* However, *H. phoxocephala* lacks a design on the pectoral, ventral, and anal fins, something that makes it readily distinguishable.

T: 26°–29°C, L: 20 cm, A: 120 cm, R: b

Hemiloricaria phoxocephala, ventral side of a recently captured specimen. H.-G. Evers

Hemiloricaria sp. "Amazonia" from the Rio das Mortes drainage, Rio Agua Preta.

Hemiloricaria sp. "Acre"

While searching for interesting sucker-mouth catfishes, October 2000, in the Brazilian state of Acre, EVERS captured in the drainage of the Rio Abuná the pictured species. Unfortunately, the specimens are not attractively colored. They were mainly found in white-water biotopes. Light-colored at the moment of capture, in the aquarium they quickly darkened into the colors depicted. Males have pronounced whiskers.

The species has no special maintenance requirements and is not very shy. All reachable foods are accepted, and a wild-caught female matured after a few weeks of aquarium maintenance.

Hemiloricaria sp. "Acre", ♀   H.-G. Evers

Apparently, *H.* sp. "Acre" has a broad area of distribution, it appears repeatedly as by-catch along fishes from several other areas.

Hemiloricaria sp. "Amazonia"

Hab.: A frequently imported species that is found throughout the Amazon Basin. The authors captured the fish in the Tefé and in the Araguaia and das Mortes drainages; there are further reports from the Guamá. EVERS also captured the species in the Rio Madeira Basin. Guyana is another known origin. *Hemiloricaria platyura* is described from that locality, but this fish doesn't seem to correspond to that species. Consequently, *Hemiloricaria* sp. "Amazonia" inhabits a vast area of distribution. Usually it appears as a by-catch either singly or in small groups among other, attractive species.

M.&B.: Unfortunately, this frequently offered species is a little large. The eggs are orange and are deposited in caves, where they are guarded by the male until they hatch. Successful rearing faces no obstacles.

S: *H.* sp. "Amazonia" has conspicuous rows of odontodes on its flanks. Based on this and its broad distribution, it should be possible to positively identify this species but, unfortunately, for that purpose we lack comparative scientific material from the region, which is why the "generic" name is applied. *H. castroi* and *H. phoxocephala* are likely to be close relatives of this species (?). It is also possible, that the broad area of distribution produces several closely related species—in any case, these are speculations better left to the ichthyologists.

T: 26°–30°C, **L:** 15 cm, **A:** 80 cm, **R:** b

Hemiloricaria sp. "Amazonia" from the Rio Guamá.

Hemiloricaria sp. "Acre", ♂   H.-G. Evers

Hemiloricaria sp. "Amazonia" from the Rio Tefé, see p. 727 for further photo.   H.-G. Evers

729

Hemiloricaria sp. "Barcelos"

In reality, that nomen is misleading. There are several species that call the vicinity of Barcelos home (e.g., *Hemiloricaria melini*). These are species with a notably beautiful design. *Hemiloricaria teffeana* is also part of the group, as is *Hemiloricaria formosa*. All these species are hard to breed and place special demands on the water in the breeding aquarium. It should be as soft and acidic as possible. *Hemiloricaria* sp. "Barcelos" is a shy species which only rarely comes into view. Every once in a while the fish

appears in imports from Manaus. The delicate design makes *H.* sp. "Barcelos" attractive. The caudal fin is virtually black brown and has beautiful light brown spotting. Males only have slight whiskers on the sides and back of the head. In contrast, the bristles on the pectoral fins are well-developed.

T: 26°–29°C, L: 12 cm, A: 80 cm, R: b

Hemiloricaria sp. "Barcelos," subadult with the black caudal fin, typical of all species in this group during their youth.

Hemiloricaria sp. "Crique Balaté"

Jens Gottwald, Hannover, has repeatedly brought this interesting whiptail back to Germany from French Guyana. Its natural habitat is the drainage of the Mana River.
Aquarium care has been sporadic at best, not to mention breeding.

A certain similarity to *Rineloricaria* sp. "French Guyana" is apparent. But under closer scrutiny, it becomes obvious that *Hemiloricaria* sp. "Crique Balaté" has fewer bands covering its body (five, in contrast to *Rineloricaria* sp. "French-Guyana").

T: 25°–28°C, L: 10 cm, A: 80 cm, R: b

Hemiloricaria sp. "Barcelos," full-grown specimen. I. Seidel

Hemiloricaria sp. "Crique Balaté" I. Seidel

Hemiloricaria sp. "French Guyana"

C: L 42 (DATZ 8/89).

Hab.: French Guyana, Mana Basin. The biotope of choice is sandy sections in shallow water.

M.&B.: A prolific species, once it is acclimated. Approximately 100 green eggs are laid in tubes. At 24°C, the fry need 12 days to hatch. Rearing is successful with *Artemia* nauplii and/or frozen rotifers.

S: Although strikingly similar to *H. lanceolata*, there are differences, particularly in regards to coloration. Furthermore, the spawn is colored differently (green, in contrast to the orange eggs of *H. lanceolata*). This species is probably still undescribed.

Hemiloricaria sp. "French Guyana"

T: 25°–28°C, L: 10 cm, A: 80 cm, R: b

Hemiloricaria sp. "yellow"

Throughout this book it has been attempted to designate undescribed species with sensible "working names." Usually these are habitat designations. In the case of *Hemiloricaria* sp. "yellow," we are uncertain of its origin. There is some similarity to *Hemiloricaria* sp. "Rio Madeira," but the yellow coloration is more pronounced in this case. The first specimens appeared in the former GDR and there they were erroneously called *Hemiloricaria morrowi*—a mistake based on a misidentification. FOERSCH & HANRIEDER (1980) reported about their collection trip to Peru and a photograph by FOERSCH had the following caption: "...ISBRÜCKER has posteriorly identified the species as *Hemiloricaria morrowi*. We were the first able to import it alive." As we know today, it was not *Hemiloricaria morrowi*, although it does inhabit the region fished by FOERSCH and HANRIEDER. At the time, only males

were imported; consequently, no breeding was possible. The same photograph is also found in FRANKE (1985). However, it is highly questionable that the fish presented here, more sensibly referred to as *Hemiloricaria* sp. "yellow," are indeed identical to the species pictured by FOERSCH. Klaus ROHLOFF (Berlin) had obtained them at the time from ZOOLOGICA and he numerously reproduced them. At some point in time, Dr. FRANKE also obtained these animals, from which Matthias LAMMEL received bred juveniles. EVERS also obtained young from the breeding efforts by FRANKE, and these are presented here. It is interesting to note that only males acquire the beautiful yellow coloration, females are rather olive green. Reproduction is easy.

This species has an interesting history, and it is a pity that apparently it has disappeared from Germany. In any case, as

Hemiloricaria sp. "French Guyana"

H.-G. Evers

Hemiloricaria sp. "yellow"

H.-G. Evers

part of the research for this book, the authors were unable to find the species. Consequently, the true identity of this fish will remain unknown for some time to come. The head shape of the animals bred in the GDR differs distinctly from that of the specimen presented by FORSCH. KNAACK (2002) recently described a yellow fish with black spots from Paraguay and named it *Hemiloricaria aurata*. Recently a wild caught *Hemiloricaria* sp. came in from Peru which is apparently a yellow form of an undetermined fish (see picture below).

T: 25°–28°C, L: 10 cm, A: 80 cm, R: b

Hemiloricaria sp. "yellow," ventral view.

H.-G. Evers

Hemiloricaria sp. from Peru

H.-G. Evers

Hemiloricaria sp. "km 88"

I. Seidel

Hemiloricaria sp. "km 88"

This whiptail catfish can be found at the famous kilometer 88 on the road that leads through southern Venezuela across the Gran Sabana. There, the species inhabits the drainage of the Rio Venamo, the limiting river to the disputed border region with Guyana. In this area, R. NORMANN (Satow) was able to capture the species. This quite attractive whiptail should be an interesting, but difficult to maintain charge, based on the water characteristics prevalent in the area.
It was not possible to breed the fish that were brought back home.

T: 26°–29°C, L: 12 cm, A: 80 cm, R: b

Hemiloricaria sp. "Colombia" ♀.

H.-G. Evers

Hemiloricaria sp. "Colombia"

This is a conspicuous species which, in the past years every now and then, has reached Germany from Colombia. Initially the fish were thought to be *Hemiloricaria magdalenae* STEINDACHNER. However, under closer scrutiny this idea had to be withdrawn. Based on the well-developed bristles, the fish were also on occasion erroneously considered to be *Rineloricaria latirostris*. Nevertheless, a comparison of the photographs presented here should preclude future confusions.

H. sp. "Colombia" is simple in its care and also breeds without further ado in suitable pipes. It is a fertile species capable of producing one hundred or more offspring per spawn.

In adults, gender can readily be distinguished. The entire anterior body of males is covered in odontodes, especially on the head. Females lack these odontodes and often they are also lighter in color.

T: 26°–29°C, L: 15 cm, A: 100 cm, R: b

Hemiloricaria sp. "Colombia" ♂, portrait.

H.-G. Evers

Hemiloricaria sp. "Colombia" ♂.

H.-G. Evers

Hemiloricaria sp. "Paraguay"

Among the suckermouth catfishes imported from Paraguay, this species can be found every once in a while. But species identification has not yet been possible. *Hemiloricaria* sp. "Paraguay" is less than spectacularly colored and is similar to several other species, which is why it is routinely placed in the same "pile" with several others. This is not to say that many species have been described from the Paraguay Basin, and it seems quite possible that, after a thorough analysis by an interested ichthyologist, additional species will be identified.

H. sp. "Paraguay" is unproblematic in its care, but no breeding data could be confirmed. There is a certain similarity to *Hemiloricaria parva* BOULENGER, a species described from the Brazilian Mato Grosso.

T: 22°–26°C, L: 12 cm, A: 80 cm, R: b

Hemiloricaria sp. "Peru"

The company BERTHOLDS WELSWELT imported this fish in 1996 from Peru. The whiptail is notoriously elongated. An exact area of origin could not be determined.

To our knowledge, *H.* sp. "Peru" has not been reimported too frequently. The lists of Peruvian exporters just explode with fantastic fish descriptions and constantly new names appear. It was therefore not possible to trace the origin of the fish. Maintenance is straightforward, but successful reproduction is not likely to have yet occurred.

T: 25°–28°C, L: 12–15 cm, A: 80 cm, R: b

Hemiloricaria sp. "Paraguay"

H.-G. Evers

Hemiloricaria sp. "Peru"

I. Seidel

Hemiloricaria sp. "Piaui"

Wolfgang STAECK, Berlin, captured the pictured specimen in the drainage of the Rio Parnaiba in the Brazilian state of Piaui. There are insufficient data to aid in species identification.

T: 26°–30°C, L: 12 cm, A: 80 cm, R: b

Hemiloricaria sp. "Puerto Ayacucho"
Pepper catfish

The authors met the pepper whiptail for the first time on a common collection trip to Venezuela. The species inhabits the surroundings of Puerto Ayacucho in the clear-water creeks and rivers of the Orinoco drainage. Subsequently, Bernd SCHMITT (Hamburg) as well as Mike HEMMANN (Gera) found these fish in the vicinity of Puerto Ayacucho and were able to bring them back alive to Germany. The pepper whiptail even appeared in underwater takes during a television documentary about this area!

HEMMANN (pers. comm.) regularly breeds the species. It lays 30–100 grass-green eggs. Breeding is regularly accomplished at 25°C, ca. 15° KH, pH 7.5–8.0, and a conductivity of 520 µS/cm. Growth of the young is said to be slow.

The pepper whiptail is quite compact in body shape, but can devour huge amounts of feed. The specimens captured by the authors in the Pozo Azul near Puerto Ayacucho measured at least 15 cm in total length. These were mostly females which were lying on gravel in shallow water exposed to a strong current. The animals were plump in feed and defecated even the next day long black-green threads. The preserved specimens are presently in a museum awaiting their first description. Besides the compact shape, especially the black dots covering the entire body (common name) are typical for these fish. The species appears to have been sprinkled with pepper, hence our suggestion for this common name.

T: 26°–29°C, L: 15 cm, A: 80 cm, R: b

Hemiloricaria sp. "Piaui"   W. Staeck

Hemiloricaria sp. "Puerto Ayacucho"   H.-G. Evers

Hemiloricaria sp. "Puerto Ayacucho," pair, in front of and in the spawning cave. ♂ outside.

Hemiloricaria sp. "Puerto Ayacucho," sexually active ♂.   M. Hemmann

Hemiloricaria sp. "Puerto Ayacucho," underwater photograph taken in its natural habitat.

Hemiloricaria sp. "Recife"

H.-G. Evers

Hemiloricaria sp. "Recife"

Another import by the company BERT-HOLDS WELSWELT. The batch came from Recife in eastern Brazil. Again, it was not possible to ascertain its origin with more precision. The species grows quite large, and males sport dense, short, orange-brown whiskers. No breeding report has reached the authors, but success should not be difficult.

T: 25°–28°C, L: 16 cm, A: 100 cm, R: b

Hemiloricaria sp. "Rio Abuná"

Marco T. C. LACERDA captured this specimen in the Rio Abuná, a river on the
Brazilian/Bolivian border. Only a single
specimen reached Germany alive and
aquaristic data are therefore sparse and
hardly representative for the species in
general.

T: 26°–29°C, L: 10 cm, A: 60 cm, R: b

Hemiloricaria sp. "Río Huacamayo"

I. SEIDEL and cotravelers collected this species in the Peruvian Huacamayo River,
where it occurs syntopically with *Hemiloricaria lanceolata*. Therefore, its requirements are similar, but breeding has
not yet been successful.
These fish are distinct sand-dwellers,
which only reluctantly settle on other substrates. In the aquarium, as in nature,
*Hemiloricaria s*p. "Río Huacamayo" can
preferentially be found on sand substrates among large rocks.

T: 25°–28°C, L: 12 cm, A: 80 cm, R: b

Hemiloricaria sp. "Rio Abuna"

H.-G. Evers

Hemiloricaria sp. "Río Huacamayo"

H.-G. Evers

745

Hemiloricaria sp. "Rio Juruá I"
Hemiloricaria sp. "Rio Juruá II"

The owner of the import company Mimbon Aquarium (Cologne), Roland Numrich, brought back two interesting *Hemiloricaria* species from the Rio Juruá of western Brazil. The identity of both is still a mystery. Exceptionally, we present both species together.

Given that we only received a single specimen of each, no indications in regard to breeding can be shared. However, these whiptail catfishes should be maintained in a manner similar to the other Amazonian species. The Juruá River is a large white-water carrying stream and most of its tributaries are likewise of the white-water type. Such species are usually straightforward in their aquarium care.

Hemiloricaria sp. "Rio Juruá II"

T: 26°–29°C, L: 12 cm, A: 80 cm, R: b

Hemiloricaria sp. "Rio Madeira"

This whiptail catfish was exported to Germany by Trop Rio from the vicinity of Porto Velho at the Rio Madeira. In time, the individuum, fed well with *Artemia* nauplii in a rearing tank, became progressively more beautiful until it almost acquired an orange hue. The species buries in the substrate, but if *Artemia* are not continuously provided, the orange coloration fades into a beige gray. The pictured specimen is a female which has matured repeatedly, but being alone, naturally there is nothing further to report. Under close observation, certain similarities to *Hemiloricaria* sp. "yellow" become apparent, but the rather olive-green females of *H.* sp. "yellow" remain much smaller and also more slender in shape.

T: 26°–29°C, L: 10 cm, A: 80 cm, R: b

Hemiloricaria sp. "Rio Juruá I"

H.-G. Evers

Hemiloricaria sp. "Rio Madeira"

H.-G. Evers

747

Hemiloricaria sp. "Río Paraguai"

The couple B. and R. Normann (Satow) captured 1999, in the basin of the Rio Paraguay, this quite attractive whiptail catfish and was able to bring some specimens back to Germany alive. The aquaristically unknown species *Hemiloricaria parva* has been described from Paraguay, and there are some similarities to this species, but we stand by the "generic" identification. We were unable to unequivocally confirm the identity with *Hemiloricaria parva*. Since that name has already been used for the most varied misidentified species, we did not want to add to the confusion!

T: 22°–26°C, L: 10 cm, A: 60 cm, R: b

Hemiloricaria sp. "Rio Tocantins"

An unusual species. The cephalic profile is virtually semicircular. The species likes to bury itself and is undemanding in its care.
P. Valerio captured *H.* sp. "Rio Tocantins" in the central Rio Tocantins syntopically with *Loricaria lata*. The few specimens arrived in Germany at the end of 1999, and there are no breeding reports. Although the species differs in regard to head shape, it is clearly a member of the genus *Hemiloricaria*, as could be determined based on the labial structure.

T: 26°–29°C, L: 11 cm, A: 60 cm, R: b

Hemiloricaria sp. "Río Paraguai"   I. Seidel

Hemiloricaria sp. "Rio Tocantins"   H.-G. Evers

Hemiloricaria sp. "Rondônia"

Once again it was Marco T. C. LACERDA who captured this new species in the state of Rondônia and sent a few specimens to Germany. Unfortunately, the pictured individual died soon thereafter and there are hardly any experiences to report. EVERS was able to capture the species in the drainage of the Rio Madeira close to Porto Velho. *Hemiloricaria* sp. "Rondônia" primarily inhabits clear-water biotopes, but can also be found in white-water.

T: 26°–29°C, L: 12 cm, A: 80 cm, R: b

Hemiloricaria sp. "São Gabriel"

This whiptail catfish was captured in the Fall of 1997 by the authors in the vicinity of the city São Gabriel da Cachoeira on the upper Rio Negro. It has so far not been possible to identify the fish further. The species grows relatively large and has an unusual design. It is still an open question whether or not *H.* sp. "São Gabriel" has ever been imported in larger numbers. The authors only captured a few specimens, which so far have failed to breed in the aquarium.

T: 26°–29°C, L: 15 cm, A: 100 cm, R: b

Hemiloricaria sp. " Rondônia" H.-G. Evers

Hemiloricaria sp. "São Gabriel" H.-G. Evers

751

Hemiloricaria sp. "São Gabriel," ventral view.

I. Seidel

H.-G. Evers

On the Rio Negro (l. to r.): Maik BEYER, Ingo SEIDEL, Volker BOHNET, Michael SCHLÜTER, Paulo VALERIO DA SILVA.

Hemiloricaria teffeana from the Rio Tefé.

H.-G. Evers

Hemiloricaria teffeana (STEINDACHNER, 1879)
Tefe whiptail catfish

F.: Steindachner, F. (1879): Über einige neue und seltene Fischarten aus den zoologischen Museen zu Wien, Stuttgart und Warschau.– Anz.Akad.Wiss.Wien, mathem.–naturwiss.Cl., 16(4): 29–34.

Syn.: *Loricaria teffeana*, *Loricaria valenciennesii*, *Rineloricaria teffeana*.

Hab.: Brazil, federal state of Amazonas, tributaries of the Rio Tefé. We were able to capture the species both in clear- as well as black-water igarapés of the Rio Tefé. The fish were found both exposed on sand banks and close to shore as well as—during the extreme dry season—in water remnants on leaf litter where they were surreptitiously captured while in search of *Apistogramma*. In all instances, the water was very warm (29°–34°C at the edge of water remnants), had a pH consistently below 5.5 pH, and low conductivities of approximately 80 µS/cm at the most. *H. teffeana* was only found in the igarapés. In the main stream lives a different *Hemiloricaria* (*H. phoxocephala*). EVERS was able to confirm the experiences of STAECK (written comm.) and also capture the species in the drainage of the Rio Madeira. *Hemiloricaria teffeana* lives in the clear- and black-water biotopes of the drainage of the Rio Preto close to the city of Porto Velho.

M.&B.: The species is shy and sensitive. The daytime hours are spent in hiding places, from were it only emerges at dusk in search of food. With the water values established at the Tefé, it became clear that breeding was not going to be easy. Of the three groups brought back to Germany, the first spawns could be reported after about one year. Unfortunately, no young were obtained. Males are very nervous and quickly cannibalize the green spawn. Michael SCHLÜTER (Hamburg) was able to obtain the first young by artificial rearing, but "something was missing" and the young were very sensitive. Only once virtually pure osmosis water was used for breeding and rearing, was there a modest survival rate to report. That is to say that at least breeding wild-caught specimens is quite difficult. The coincidentally discovered young in the parent tank were also difficult to raise. A strain (?) from the vicinity of Manaus was more willing to breed, but rearing was also not easy. Perhaps the filial generations will be easier to please?

S: One of the most beautiful whiptail catfishes for sure. In FRANKE (1985), a photograph by FOERSCH identifies the species as *H. fallax*, an error which stands corrected on this occasion. Should breeding ever become regular and predictable, this fish for sure will soon become as popular as *L.* sp. "red" and *H. lanceolata*. Unfortunately, the only fishes that come to us from Tefé are discus and dwarf cichlids. But there are indeed other beautiful fishes to be had from there! Apparently, *H. teffeana* has a much more extensive area of distribution than initially suspected. It is said that there have been captures in the vicinity of Manaus. These reached Germany in early 1999.

T: 26°–30°C, L: 12 cm, A: 80 cm, R: b

Hemiloricaria teffeana, front view.

H.-G. Evers

Hemiloricaria teffeana from the Rio Preto at Porto Velho.

H.-G. Evers

Hemiloricaria teffeana, ventral view.

H.-G. Evers

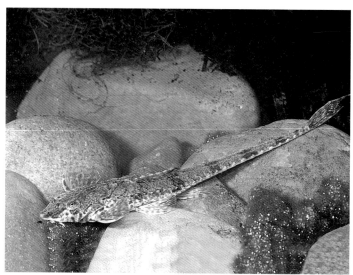

Hemiloricaria wolfei, Yarina Cocha, Peru.   H.-G. Evers

Hemiloricaria wolfei (FOWLER, 1940)

F.: Fowler, H.W. (1940): A collection of fishes obtained by Mr. William C. Morrow in the Ucayali River Basin, Peru.– Proc. Acad.nat.Sci.Philadelphia, 91: 219–289.

Syn.: *Rineloricaria wolfei.*

Hab.: Peru, Ucayali drainage, Contamana. The species is common in the vicinity of Pucallpa, in the Yarina Cocha, and in other white-water carrying waters. The pH is usually around 7, the water temperatures during the dry season around 28°C.

M.&B.: Unproblematic species. The genders can be distinguished even in individuals less than 10 cm in total length. Males grow short whiskers, and short bristles also appear dorsally on the head.

Similar to most of its congeners, this species can be spawned in tubes. Rearing the young is not difficult.

S: The pictured pair hails from the Caño de Paca, a tributary of Yarina Cocha, and corresponds in its significant characteristics to the original description. The ventrum has no design and the caudal fin has dark spots at its base and on the distal end of the lower lobe. The dorsal fin shows little pigmentation, and its tip has a dark zone. The body is transversed by six crossbands. Although the length of the holotype is 15 cm, that size is hardly ever reached in an aquarium.

T: 25°–28°C, L: 12 cm, A: 60 cm, R: b

Genus *Ixinandria*
Isbrücker & Nijssen, 1979

This small genus only contains two species at present, both of which have not yet made their debut on the aquaristic scene.

Ixinandria montebelloi (Fowler, 1940)
Bolivia, Tarija

Ixinandria steinbachi (Regan, 1906)
Northern Argentina, Salta

And that despite the fact that these small whiptails—described from Bolivia and northern Argentina—surely would be good aquarium charges. The entire body is covered by odontodes, which in sexually active males are elongated, giving the fish an unorthodox appearance. Adult males seem as if they are covered by a pelt. The ventrum of *Ixinandria* is naked, lacking the bony scutes which cover the ventral side of *Rineloricaria* spp. to a greater or lesser degree.

If these fishes should ever appear in the trade, they should be cared for under somewhat cooler conditions, because their reported area of distribution is not quite as tropical. B. Schmitt, Hamburg, (pers. comm.) has searched unsuccessfully for *Ixinandria steinbachi* in northern Argentina throughout the vicinity of Salto. The temperatures determined in the local waters at the time (August) were around 12°C!

L. A. van der Laan

Ixinandria steinbachi, lectotype (SL 87.2 mm). ♂ from Salta, Argentina.

Ixinandria steinbachi, lectotype (SL 87.2 mm). ♂ from Salta, Argentina.   L. van der Laan

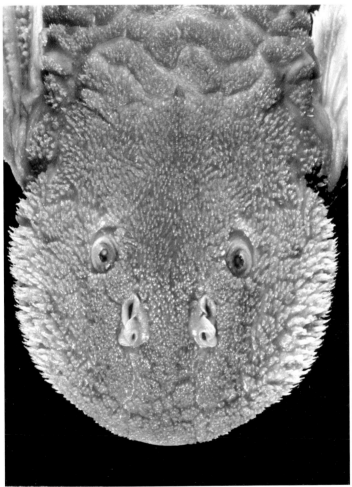

The same specimen; note how densely the head is covered with odontodes. L. van der Laan

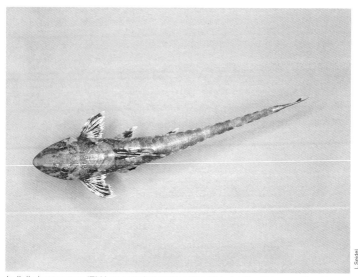

Leliella heteroptera (ZMA 114.506); paratype from the vicinity of Manaus, Brazil.

Genus *Leliella* Isbrücker, 2001

L. heteroptera (ISBRÜCKER & NIJSSEN, 1976)	Manaus, Brazil

In the same publication in which the genus *Fonchiiichthys* is described, and the genus *Hemiloricaria* revalidated, Is-BRÜCKER described the monotypic genus *Leliella* for the only species *Leliella heteroptera* (see 1st ed. [German], p. 642 as *Rineloricaria heteroptera*).

In *Leliella,* the body is thick and the ventrum is completely covered by scutes. The odontodes on the pectoral fins are relatively short. Those on the sides of the head are densely bundled, long and thin, and appear similar to a short brush. The odontodes between the interorbital and the subdorsal regions are broadly scattered, thin, and very short. This arrangement of the odontodes differentiates the *Leliella* both from *Hemiloricaria* and *Rineloricaria* (see there).

As mentioned already in the German first edition, there is a similarity between *Rineloricaria* sp. "red" and *Leliella heteroptera*. If that species is indeed an independent one, it would be safe to assume that it would also be a member of the genus *Leliella*.

Leliella heteroptera (see next page for additional photos)   H.-G. Evers

Leliella heteroptera ISBRÜCKER & NIJSSEN, 1976

F.: Isbrücker, I. J. H. & H. Nijssen (1976): *Leliella heteroptera*, a New Species of Mailed Catfish from Rio Amazonas near Manaus, Brazil (Pisces, Siluriformes, Loricariidae).– Zool.Anz.Jena, 196 (1/2): 109–124.

Syn.: *Rineloricaria heteroptera*.

Hab.: Brazil, Amazon at Manaus. The pictured specimens were captured in the Rio Guamá and were imported to Germany by Jens GOTTWALD, AQUATARIUM HANNOVER.

M.&B.: Unfortunately, this species is a rare presence among our imports. These medium-sized whiptails are well suited for aquarium maintenance. Males develop a slight beard and guard the orange eggs until they hatch. Spawns are small, being comprised by approximately 60–70 eggs at the most. *L. heteroptera* was in the '80s a common charge in the former GDR, but has been progressively displaced by the similar *H. lanceolata*.

S: A beautiful close relative of *H. lanceolata*. *L. heteroptera* males have shorter and more rounded teeth. The number of soft rays in the dorsal fin is variable (5–6), which is constant in *Hemiloricaria*. The larger *H. lanceolata* has a broader area of distribution. Additionally, male *L. heteroptera* have only a slightly developed beard, which extends from the tip of the snout to the opercula, formed by long slender bristles. On the head, the bristles are very short and bent backwards. In *H. lanceolata* these bristles are very long and dense, much more conspicuous. The bristles on the pectorals, too, are much shorter and less pronounced than the long, conspicuously bent backward bristles of *H. lanceolata* males. The popular "red whiptail" ["Roter Hexenwels"], *Leliella* sp. "red" is highly reminiscent of *L. heteroptera* (see there).

Leliella heteroptera ♂, close-up of the head. Notice the beard! I. Seidel

Leliella heteroptera; ventral view. H.-G. Evers

Leliella cf. *heteroptera* from the Tocantins, Tucurui.

H.-G. Evers

Leliella cf. *heteroptera* "Tucurui"

This variant hails from the central Brazilian Tocantins River and was captured in the vicinity of the Tucurui Dam. Its coloration is very similar to that described in the original description of *L. heteroptera*. It seems that *L. heteroptera* does have a somewhat broader area of distribution than previously thought.

T: 26°–29°C, L: 15 cm, A: 100 cm, R: b

Leliella sp. "red"
Red whiptail catfish

Hardly any whiptail catfish is as popular among aquarists as the beautiful red whiptail. Unfortunately, their origin is a mystery. The first juveniles are likely to have seen aquarium lights in the former GDR, i.e., in Leipzig. Supposedly, the parent fish had been imported by the company ZOOLOGICA, but details could not be obtained at the time.

Leliella sp. "red" is somewhat reminiscent of *Leliella heteroptera*, including the design on the dorsal fin. However, if this is an independent species or a bred strain is all the same to the enthusiast aquarist, since the coloration of the animals is an attractive red-brown. The reddish coloration remains visible to an advanced age in purebred specimens. Unfortunately, in the past there have been repeated crosses with another —apparently closely related —species, *Hemiloricaria lanceolata*. As a result, there are hardly any purebred specimens left. The red fish are much less prolific, and that might explain the reason why red males were crossed with large female *Hemiloricaria lanceolata,* which can easily produce 200 eggs. Pure red whiptail catfishes are significantly smaller and on average hardly produce over 50 young. Hybrids can be identified as adults at the latest. They grow much larger than pure reds and darken significantly, in a manner similar to some *Hemiloricaria lanceolata.*

Whereas *Hemiloricaria lanceolata* and its hybrids appreciate cover among wood and close to the substrate, red whiptails often hang among the vegetation to rest— a characteristic behavior which they have in common with *Leliella heteroptera.*

However, we do know that in its natural habitat *Hemiloricaria lanceolata* also hangs among the submersed overhanging shore vegetation. The authors have repeatedly captured the fish in such biotopes. Still, in the aquarium they seem to abandon this behavior. Only a strain from the Rio Huacamayo still hangs among the plants in one of SEIDEL's aquaria.

Males are dependable in their broodcare. The fry hatch after 10–12 days and initially hang with a large yolk sac on the aquarium panes. First feedings with *Artemia* nauplii are readily accepted. But also other crustacea, such as frozen *Cyclops,* are appreciated menu items in later stages. The frequent feeding with crustacea gives the fish a beautiful reddish sheen. A rearing tank with several dozen of this gorgeous fish is a feast for the eyes of the successful breeder!

Bred specimens only turn red with this type of crustacean-centered diet; young raised with other feeds are rather brown and remain far less attractive.

T: 24°–28°C, L: 10 cm, A: 60 cm, R: b

Ten-day-old fry. This specimen already shows an injury. Serious errors were committed during the initial days, such as those shown by the constriction behind the head.

Leliella sp. "red." (see next pages for additional photos)

Leliella sp. "red," ventral view.

H.-G. Evers

Leliella sp. "red," ♂ with his typical whiskers.

H.-G. Evers

Leliella sp. "red," ripe ♀.

H.-G. Evers

Leliella sp. "red," healthy juvenile, three months old.

H.-G. Evers

Leliella sp. "red" x *Hemiloricaria lanceolata* hybrid.

H.-G. Evers

Genus *Rineloricaria* BLEEKER, 1862

Rineloricaria aequalicuspis REIS & CARDOSO, 2001	Brazil, Rio Grande do Sul
Rineloricaria cadeae (HENSEL, 1868)	Southern Brazil
Rineloricaria catamarcensis (BERG, 1895)	Argentina, Catamarca
Rineloricaria cubatonis (STEINDACHNER, 1907)	Southern Brazil, Cubatão
Rineloricaria felipponei (FOWLER, 1943)	Uruguay, Río Santa Lucia
Rineloricaria henselii (STEINDACHNER, 1907)	Southern Brazil, Cubatão
Rineloricaria jaraguensis (STEINDACHNER, 1909)	Southern Brazil, Rio Jaraguá
Rineloricaria kronei (RIBEIRO, 1911)	Southern Brazil, Iporanga
Rineloricaria latirostris (BOULENGER, 1900)	South eastern Brazil, Mogi-Guaçu
Rineloricaria lima (KNER, 1854)	Brazil
Rineloricaria longicauda REIS, 1983	Southern Brazil, Taim
Rineloricaria maquinensis (REIS & CARDOSO, 2001)	Brazil: Rio Grande do Sul
Rineloricaria microlepidogaster (REGAN, 1904)	Southern Brazil
Rineloricaria microlepidota (STEINDACHNER, 1907)	Brazil: Rio Juruá
Rineloricaria misionera RODRIGUEZ & MIQUELARENA, 2005	Argentinia, Misiones
Rineloricaria pareiacantha (FOWLER, 1943)	Uruguay, Río Santa Lucia
Rineloricaria pentamaculata LANGEANI & BRAZ DE ARAUJO, 1994	Southeastern Brazil
Rineloricaria quadrensis REIS, 1983	Southern Brazil, Quadros
Rineloricaria steindachneri (REGAN, 1904)	Brazil, Paraiba Basin
Rineloricaria strigilata (HENSEL, 1868)	Brazil, Santa Cruz
Rineloricaria thrissoceps (FOWLER, 1943)	Uruguay, Río Santa Lucia

Heeding the experiences gathered for other, similarly extensive and broadly distributed genera (e.g., *Ancistrus*), the aquarist should refrain from formulating general maintenance requirements supposedly applicable to all its members. It is very important to know and respect the origins of the charge, which water temperatures prevail in its natural habitat, and which other particular maintenance requirements may need the aquarist's attention. A *Rineloricaria* from cooler waters in Uruguay for sure has different maintenance requirements than a species hailing from the coastal area of southeastern Brazil.

As far as the authors have been able to determine, all species maintained by them have developed a similar reproductive biology. These are broodcaring species in the male gender and the young are nidifugous fry, which are left to their own devices once they have hatched. In nature, it is likely that the interstices between rocks or similar items will provide a suitable spawning substrate. The aquarist may provide various pipes as suitable brooding caves, which are readily accepted. Open, 2.4 cm diameter PVC piping has proven very appropriate, but esthetically more satisfying are the difficult to find bamboo segments. Males, identified in most species by the presence of a "beard," and on occasion by the bristles on the anterior pectoral fin spines and, more rarely, on the dorsal head region, are readily distinguished from females and will soon claim one of the provided tubes. There they wait for ripe females, which will subsequently spawn with the males inside the tight cave. With unexperienced pairs, but also if the tube was chosen too narrow, some eggs roll outside and usually will be lost, if not devoured by other tankmates, not participating in the spawn. After spawning has concluded, the brooding male with his tube are transferred into a dedicated

Rineloricaria lima, (ZMA 120.267), preserved specimen.

I. Seidel

Rineloricaria lima (ZMA 120.267); ventral view of the head.

I. Seidel

Suckermouth Catfishes

aquarium, where the fry will be safe from predators after hatching. Many whiptail males are nervous caretakers, which eat their spawn if disturbed. On the other hand, there are some species that can even be used as surrogates for the more sensitive ones, and it works without a hitch! If it is noticed that a male is eating his spawn because the number of eggs diminishes day after day, the male is shaken out of the tube and returned to the original tank. Good surrogates have been found among the male members of an here to date undescribed related genus (LG 4), which are simply placed into the abandoned tube. In many cases, the males adopt the foreign spawn and spontaneously continue brooding! It seems unimportant if the eggs are green or orange, and a difference in brood time is of no consequence either.

Rineloricaria are often omnivorous, but there are also species which by and large base their diet on vegetable fare. In the aquarium, they readily adapt and accept all the usual fare provided. The initial diet of fry may usually consist of *Artemia* nauplii, but even better are frozen rotifers.

All hints given here for *Rineloricaria* in regards of maintenance and breeding are also to obtain for *Hemiloricaria, Leliella* and *Fonchiiichthys,* just keeping mind that these need somewhat higher temperatures.

The genus *Rineloricaria* long time contained the most species within the subfamily. Its members have a dorsal fin which is based virtually opposite to the base of the pectoral fins. The caudal fin usually follows the formula i/10/I. Most species are small- to medium-sized. The labial anatomy is identical or similar in all species, consisting of a rictal barbel on each side, numerous papillae on the lips, and a short, shinglelike protrusion of the edge of the lips. *Rineloricaria* spp. have bicuspid teeth with pointed tips.

Some of the original descriptions were done in the 19ᵗʰ century. Some type series have been lost, and the descriptions are sometimes quite brief to the point of being imprecise. The latter, for example, in relation to habitat descriptions such as "Rio de Janeiro" or "from the Parnaiba". In such cases, it is hardly possible to make order and classify existing species with certainty. The entire genus is in dire need of a complete revision. Already BLEEKER (1862), in his description of the genus *Rineloricaria,* mentioned the genus *Hemiloricaria*—long considered a synonym. ISBRÜCKER (2001) revalidated the genus *Hemiloricaria* and reclassified a total of 24 species out of the collective genus *Rineloricaria* (see description of the genus *Hemiloricaria*) into it. But also the new genera *Fonchiiichthys* ISBRÜCKER & MICHELS, 2001 and *Leliella* ISBRÜCKER, 2001 have been created, shrinking the heretofore giant genus to presently only 20 species. All *Rineloricaria* species inhabit the southeastern and southern sections of South America—its Amazonian cousins now belong to other genera.

Modern cladistic methods have hardly been applied to this genus, but there will be such an analysis applied for several species inhabiting the Uruguay Basin. There have been announcements in regards to new first descriptions, and the Brazilian ichthyologist Lucia RAPP PY-DANIEL has already raised the question in regard to the evolutionary origin of the *Rineloricaria* ("is *Rineloricaria* monophyletic? Does anyone care about it?," the subject of a presentation in a symposium, published on the Internet).

Some of the taxons listed above might turn up to be synonyms upon closer scrutiny. If, for example, one takes the species from southeastern Brazil ("Iporanga") and compares their habitat descriptions, it becomes apparent that they are inhabiting the same general area. From the collecting experiences of EVERS in that area, we know that in this region indeed there are several different *Rineloricaria* species inhabiting a relatively small area, but a species density to the degree described at present is unlikely. On the other hand, there are other areas from where hardly any *Rineloricaria* have yet been described. For example, from the upper Rio Uruguay drainage, 10 species descriptions are in preparation (GHAZZI, written com.).

Rineloricaria lima (KNER, 1854) is the genotype, and precisely the holotype of this species is considered lost (ISBRÜCKER, 1979). Furthermore, the locality is described precariously in the extreme: "Brazil." The preserved specimen pictured here by and large corresponds to the original description. It was collected in the year 1913 by STEINDACHNER.

We present some identified museum types from various *Rineloricaria*, in order to pos-sibly facilitate the identification of species by interested hobbyists. In conjunction with a specific origin, an identification might become possible. While working on the manuscript, one of our most surprising discoveries was the certainty with which relatively many *Rineloricaria* and *Hemiloricaria* could indeed be determined to species based on existing primary literature and habitat specifications. This is why in this book, for the first time in the aquaristic literature, so many species can be presented with their (presently) correct scientific name. For interested aquarists, this is surely a great help.

Rineloricaria latirostris (BOULENGER, 1900)
Bristly whiptail catfish

F.: Boulenger, G.A. (1900): Descriptions of three new species of siluroid fishes from southern Brazil.– Ann. Mag. nat. Hist., (ser.7), 5, 26: 165–166.

Syn.: *Loricaria latirostris, Loricaria paulina, Rineloricaria paulina.*

Hab.: Brazil, state of São Paulo, Rio Mogi-Guaçu. The catfish lives in the littoral mountain streams of the Atlantic rain forest, in shallow clear-water biotopes with a swift current. Due to its cryptic coloration, even adult specimens are difficult to discern on the similar rubble and gravel substrate. The waters are cool, 16°–22°C, depending on season. The pH is around 6, conductivity is low (below 50 μS/cm).

M.&B.: Despite the rather cool temperatures in its natural habitat, this whiptail readily tolerates water temperatures of around 25°C. However, this should only be the case for a few weeks, months at the most, because under such warm conditions there will be no discernible ripening of the gonads. Breeding has not been successful.

The attractive fish adapt to the coloration of their substrate. The females are smaller and not completely covered with bristles, and usually spend the day buried in the sand, only emerging at twilight in search of food.

S: There are several other species that inhabit southeastern Brazil and which have a similar shape and design. Usually, only specialists are able to successfully tell them apart. EVERS, LACERDA, and BEYER captured at the type locality of *Rineloricaria kronei* (Sao Paulo, Iporanga) specimens, which exteriorly were indistinguishable from *R. latirostris*. *Rineloricaria paulina* from the Mogi-Guaçu is a synonym. It was a *R. latirostris* female which, due to the lack of bristles, was erroneously identified as a different species.

No imports reach Germany from the area of distribution. It is therefore unlikely that this species will become widely distributed in the aquarium hobby there. The bristles appear in males beginning at a length of 10–12 cm. Prior to that, the genders cannot be told apart.

T: 18°–22°C, **L:** 20 cm, **A:** 100 cm, **R:** b

Hemiloricaria cadeae (Hensel, 1968), (ZMA 116.576). The pictured specimen was captured in southern Brazil.

Rineloricaria latirostris, Rio do Azeite, state of São Paulo. H.-G. Evers

Close-up of the above specimen.   H.-G. Evers

Rineloricaria latirostris, juvenile.   H.-G. Evers

Biotope of *Rineloricaria latirostris*. The fish has a length of approximately 20 cm, and is well camouflaged thanks to its cryptic coloration and design.

Rineloricaria sp. aff. *latirostris* ♂ (see next page for additional photos)   H.-G. Evers

Rineloricaria sp. aff. *latirostris*

These fish clearly differ from the true *R. latirostris*. Since these animals are very common in the vicinity of Rio de Janeiro, *Rineloricaria* sp. aff. *latirostris* is often imported, but probably still undescribed scientifically. Aquarium maintenance is unproblematic, and there have been the occasional breeding successes.

Their adult length is approximately 20 cm. They live in clear-water regions of the federal state of Rio de Janeiro and therefore require cool temperatures, with 23°–25°C as a maximum, preferably lower.

The males are entirely covered by dense bristles, females are not. As a consequence, only males are imported as adults, the less attractive females are not. However, there are always subadults being exported, all looking like females. Those who want to acquire the species, are advised to purchase a group of subadults and than patiently wait until some turn out to be males.

T: 20°–24°C, **L:** 20 cm, **A:** 120 cm, **R:** b

Rineloricaria sp. aff. *latirostris*, pair.

Rineloricaria sp. aff. *latirostris* ♀

Rineloricaria pareiacantha, see following page for additional photo.

H.-G. Evers

Rineloricaria pareiacantha (FOWLER, 1943)

F.: Fowler, H. W. (1943): Notes and descriptions of new or little known fishes from Uruguay.– Proc. Acad. Nat. Sci. Philadelphia, 95: 311–334.

Syn.: *Loricaria pareiacantha*.

Hab.: Uruguay, Canelones, Río Santa Lucia.

M.&B.: The streams of Uruguay are relatively cool. Consequently, this species should not be maintained at temperatures above 20°C for extended periods of time. Otherwise, the fish is easy and accepts any kind of feed offered.
There are no breeding reports at present, probably a consequence of the paucity of animals available; there is no regular import of this species.

S: FOWLER described two additional species (*R. felipponei* and *R. thrissoceps*) from the Rio Santa Lucia, also presenting a drawing of each. The specimen pictured here hails from Canelones and by and large coincides with the description of *R. pareiacantha*.
It is quite possible that the claimed three species may be one and the same or only two (male and female *Rineloricaria* sometimes appear different, and it would not be the first time that the sexes would have been described as two independent species). A definitive answer, however, depends on the analysis of the type material.

T: 15°–20°C, **L:** 10 cm, **A:** 80 cm, **R:** b

Rineloricaria pareiacantha, oral disc.

H.-G. Evers

Ancistrus cirrhosus lives together with *R. pareiacantha* in many rivers in Uruguay

Rineloricaria sp. "Argentina"

W. Staeck

Rineloricaria sp. "Argentina"

Rarely does something new reach the German hobby scene from Argentina. But such is the case of a black-brown whiptail catfish captured by Wolfgang STAECK, Berlin, in the Río Paraguay Basin, north of Resistencia. A species which surely would find interested catfish fans. Unfortunately, there has probably not been an import yet. There are certain similarities to *Hemiloricaria lanceolata*, which has a giant area of distribution that allows for such a possibility. However, based on this photograph alone, no positive identification is possible and because of its origin replaced this fish here.

T: 16°–22°C, L. 15 cm, A: 80 cm, R: b

Rineloricaria sp. "Rio Cipo"

H.-G. Evers

Rineloricaria sp. "Rio Cipo"

H.-G. Evers, M. Beyer, M. T. C. Lacerda, and P. Valerio captured this whiptail numerously in the tributaries of the Rio Cipo and the Rio das Velhas (Rio São Francisco Basin) in the state of Minas Gerais, central Brazil.

Rineloricaria sp. "Rio Cipo" prefers somewhat cooler conditions and is more exacting in regard to water quality than its congeners.

Otherwise, it is undemanding in its care. There is no information as far as aquarium breeding is concerned, since only a few specimens were captured for the purpose of photography and no commercial imports reach Germany from the area.

T: 20°–24°C, L: 15 cm, A: 100 cm, R: b

Rio Cipo

H.-G. Evers

H.-G. Evers

Spatuloricaria spp. have extremely elongated first caudal fin filaments, as evidenced by this, probably still undescribed, species captured in the Madeira Basin (Rio Jaci-paraná).

Suckermouth Catfishes

Genus *Spatuloricaria* SCHULTZ, 1944

This genus—established in the '40s by the American ichthyologist Leonard P. SCHULTZ—includes whiptail catfishes of respectable size. The particularity of this genus lies in its dentition. *Spatuloricaria* have bicuspid teeth with spoon-shaped (spatulate) teeth. That characteristic is apparent with the naked eye in adult specimens. On the sides of the head are single rows of odontodes. These are much elongated in adult, sexually active males, and may measure one centimeter or more in length. Initially, the sides of the head of males swell and small odontodes sprout from the fleshy tissue. Later, additional, much longer odontodes emerge. They fall off after the reproductive season, and the tissue is reabsorbed. These are—besides the impressive size of some species, such as *Spatuloricaria euacanthagenys* which grows to over 50 cm in length—the main distinguishing characteristics in relation to the other sux genera in this subtribe.

The main area of distribution is centered in northwestern South America—most species have so far been described from Colombia and western Venezuela. However, in recent years it has become apparent that the large southern clear-water tributaries of the Amazon are also home of *Spatuloricaria* spp., which for sure are not all scientifically described. Species are known from the rivers Tapajós, Xingú, Madeira, Tocantins, and also from a northern Amazon tributary, the Rio Trombetas. The coauthor SEIDEL was able to capture a probably undescribed species in the Peruvian foothills of the Andes, in the Rio Huacamayo and in the Rio San Alejandro (see also the chapter "Habitats"). An additional species was captured by EVERS in the headwaters of the Brazilian Río Xingú. The biotope was always one with a swift current, usually of the clear-water type.

L. A. van der Laan

Spatuloricaria lagoichthys (SCHULTZ, 1944), holotype (USNM 121092); ♀ of 310 mm SL from the Río Palmar, Venezuela.

Fam.: Loricariidae
Subfam.: Loricariinae

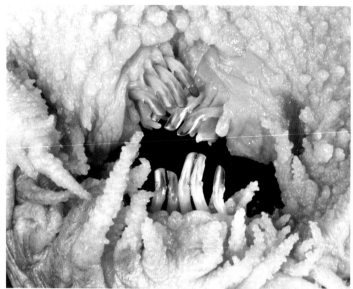

Dentition of the holotype of *Spatuloricaria lagoichthys*.   L. A. van der Laan

In the trade, among the imported larger Loricariinae, sporadically appear members of the genus *Spatuloricaria*, but we were unable to identify them to species. We have therefore opted to present most species with their confirmed geographic origin as part of the identifier, in the same manner other fishes are presented elsewhere in this book.

These large fishes are exacting in their care and require generous quarters besides good water quality and dissolved oxygen concentrations near saturation. Given the high metabolic rate of such large loricariids, to provide such conditions can become a problem, even for experienced hobbyists. There is so far no report for any of the genus' members as far as reproduction is concerned.

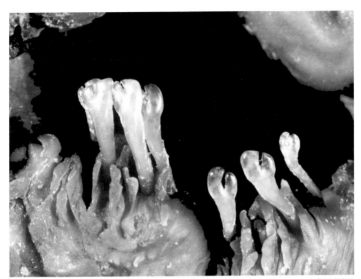

Spatuloricaria euacanthagenys, dentition of the holotype.

L. A. van der Laan

L. A. van der Laan

Holotype (ANSP 71718) of *Spatuloricaria euacanthagenys* from Colombia, Río Caqueta drainage. ♂ of 330 mm SL.

Fam.: Loricariidae
Subfam.: Loricariinae

Spatuloricaria cf. *puganensis,* ventral view of the head of a sexually active ♂. See page 789 for text.

Member species of the genus *Spatuloricaria* (according to ISBRÜCKER, 1980):

Spatuloricaria atratoensis SCHULTZ, 1944	Colombia, Río Atrato
Spatuloricaria caquetae (FOWLER, 1943)	Colombia, Río Orteguasa
Spatuloricaria curvispina (DAHL, 1941)	Colombia, Río Batatal
Spatuloricaria euacanthagenys ISBRÜCKER, 1979	Colombia, Río Caquetá
Spatuloricaria evansii (BOULENGER, 1892)	Brazil, Mato Grosso
Spatuloricaria fimbriata	
(EIGENMANN & VANCE, 1912)	Colombia, Boca de Certegai
Spatuloricaria gymnogaster	
(EIGENMANN & VANCE, 1912)	Colombia, Apulo
Spatuloricaria lagoichthys (SCHULTZ, 1944)	Venezuela, Maracaibo
Spatuloricaria nudiventris (VALENCIENNES, 1840)	Brazil
Spatuloricaria phelpsi SCHULTZ, 1944	Venezuela, Maracaibo
Spatuloricaria puganensis (PEARSON, 1937)	Peru, Río Marañón

Spatuloricaria caquetae, ventral view. Additional photos next page

H.-G. Evers

Spatuloricaria caquetae (FOWLER, 1943)

F.: Fowler, H.W. (1943): A collection of fresh-water fishes from Colombia, obtained chiefly by Brother Nicéforo Maria.– Proc.Acad.nat.Sci.Philadelphia, 95: 223–266.

Syn.: *Loricaria caquetae.*

Hab.: Colombia, Río Orteguasa. The pictured specimen was captured in the Ecuadorian Río Napo, in the vicinity of the city of Coca.

M.&B.: A large species with a healthy appetite. During the spawning season, males develop impressive whiskers, which may become two centimeters long and protrude far from the sides of the head.

Breeding has not yet been successful. It is even unclear if it is a cave-spawner or if there is another form of broodcare.

S: *Spatuloricaria euacanthagenys* is a Colombian congener. It has another corporal design and is even larger (the holotype measures 52 cm in length!). It is unclear if the other Colombian species, i.e., *S. atratoensis, S. curvispina, S. fimbriata,* and *S. gymnogaster* have ever been imported to Germany.

T: 24°–28°C, **L:** 25 cm, **A:** 120 cm, **R:** b

Spatuloricaria caquetae, see previous page for text.

H.-G. Evers

Spatuloricaria caquetae, portrait.

H.-G. Evers

S. cf. *puganensis* ♂ with impressive whiskers. Additional photos next page.

Spatuloricaria puganensis (PEARSON, 1937)

F.: Pearson, N.E. (1937): The fishes of the Atlantic and Pacific slopes near Cajamarca, Peru. Proc. California Acad. Sci. (4th ser.), 23(7): 87–98.

Syn.: *Loricaria puganensis*.

Hab.: Peru, Río Marañón drainage, Pusoc and Tingo de Pauca.

M.&B.: See *S. caquetae. S. puganensis* is somewhat shy and remains hidden during the day. In the evening, the species emerges in the search of food. The next morning, the entire sand substrate in the aquarium appears searched, as can be clearly deduced from the tracks.

S: The pictured specimen was captured in the Huallaga drainage at Tingo María. The design on the body (four crossbands posteriorly) and the fins corresponds to that of the original description given for *S. puganensis*. Of the three species thus far imported from Peru, this fish is the most similar to *S. puganensis*, including the place where it was found.

T: 24°–28°C, **L:** 25 cm, **A:** 120 cm, **R:** b

Spatuloricaria cf. *puganensis* from the Río Huallaga. H.-G. Evers

Spatuloricaria cf. *puganensis*, full-grown pair. ♂ left. I. Seidel

Spatuloricaria sp. "Colombia"

H.-G. Evers

Spatuloricaria sp. "Colombia"

The fuzzy design on the anterior body and the basically yellow-brown coloration of the fish, make this species into an attractive representative of the genus.
In 1995, two specimens were found among imports from Colombia of *Sturisoma* sp., at the company AQUARIUM GROTTE of Hamburg, which after several years of care did not grow larger than 15 cm.

Unfortunately, breeding has not been successful. *Spatuloricaria* sp. "Rio Xingú," is very similar and is also a small species.

T: 26°–29°C, L: 15 cm, A: 120 cm, R: b

Spatuloricaria sp. "Peru"

Unfortunately, there is no exact information available in regard to origin of this
species, eventhough it has been repeatedly imported from Peru.
Maintenance of this large species is similar to that of its congeners.

T: 25°–30°C, **L:** 30 cm, **A:** 150 cm, **R:** b

Spatuloricaria sp. "Rio San Alejandro"

The species has already been mentioned
by FRANKE (1985). SEIDEL and cotravelers
repeatedly captured *Spatuloricaria* sp.
"Rio San Alejandro" on two trips to Peru.
Some specimens were easily 40 cm long.
The species inhabits clear-water rivers,
such as the Río Huacamayo and the Río
San Alejandro, at water temperatures of
up to 30°C (see also the description of
the ancistrine *Panaque dentex*-group
and the chapter "Habitats").
None of the specimens with the attractive design had whiskers.
To date, only a single species—*Spatuloricaria puganensis*—has been described
from the Marañón Basin of Peru. A definitive identification is still pending. Successful import of the species has not
been accomplished in bigger quantities.
It is very sensitive and suffers from all
kinds of bacterial afflictions during the
initial acclimation weeks after transport.
At SEIDEL, a pair almost managed to
spawn. The male had developed stout
whiskers and the female was ventrally
distended. At that stage, the male claimed
a slanted slate plate as shelter and reappeared only to feed. Perhaps it is a
cave spawner?

T: 25°–30°C, **L:** 40 cm, **A:** 150 cm, **R:** b

Spatuloricaria sp. "Peru"

I. Seidel

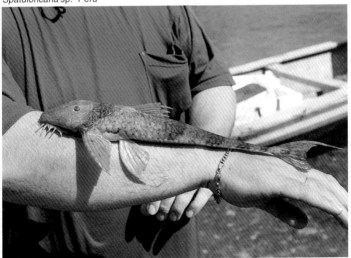

Spatuloricaria sp. "Río San Alejandro," full-grown, shortly after capture. Additional photos next page

I. Seidel

Spatuloricaria sp. "Río San Alejandro," juvenile in an aquarium.   I. Seidel

Spatuloricaria sp. "Río San Alejandro," oral morphology.   I. Seidel

Spatuloricaria sp. "Rio Tapajós"

H.-G. Evers

Spatuloricaria sp. "Rio Tapajós"

The pictured specimen was captured by F. WARZEL (pers. comm.) at the central Rio Tapajós over rocks in raging current. The fish were highly transport sensitive, something common among animals captured in such oxygen-rich biotopes. This animal could not be identified to species either.

T: 26°–29°C, L: 20 cm, A: 120 cm, R: b

View into the mouth of *Spatuloricaria* sp. "Rio Tocantins." This ♂ has a fully developed beard.

Spatuloricaria sp. "Rio Tocantins"

With its approximately 20 cm of total length, *Spatuloricaria* sp. "Rio Tocantins" is readily maintained in an aquarium. Males developed whiskers, but there has not been any success in breeding. It is a pity that this species is not as attractively colored as its Peruvian and Colombian congeners, for example.

T: 26°–29°C, L: 20 cm, A: 120 cm, R: b

Spatuloricaria sp. "Rio Tocantins"   H.-G. Evers

Spatuloricaria sp. "Rio Tocantins" with whiskers that are not yet fully developed.

Spatuloricaria sp. "Rio Trombetas"

This species has been repeatedly imported to Germany by the company MIMBON AQUARIUM, Köln. No *Spatuloricaria* have been described from the region of origin, but there is a certain similarity to *Spatuloricaria evansii* from the Mato Grosso. *S. evansii* is pictured in ISBRÜCKER (1972) (paralectotypes of *Loricaria lata*, fig. 11, p. 184), certain concordances are undeniable.

M.&B.: *Spatuloricaria* sp. "Rio Trombetas" is well suited for aquarium maintenance. Unfortunately, only males have been maintained, because all females imported to Germany died of bacterial complications shortly after arrival, despite attempted treatments. Acclimated males regularly—once or twice each year—develop an impressive beard.

Spatuloricaria sp. "Rio Trombetas," portrait.

S: These fish not grow quite as large as some of its congeners. The tough odontodes that cover their body can be felt when handling *Spatuloricaria* sp. "Rio Trombetas."

T: 24°–28°C, L: 20 cm, A: 120 cm, R: b

Spatuloricaria sp. "Rio Urubamba"

The Peruvian Rio Urubamba is home to this relatively dark species captured by SEIDEL and travel companions. It has not yet been possible to identify the fish to species level.

T: 26°–29°C, L: 20 cm, A: 100 cm, R: b

Spatuloricaria sp. "Rio Trombetas" in an aquarium.

H.-G. Evers

Spatuloricaria sp. "Rio Urubamba," just captured.

I. Seidel

Spatuloricaria sp. "Rio Xingú"

H.-G. Evers

Spatuloricaria sp. "Rio Xingú"

H.-G. Evers was able to only capture juveniles of up to a length of 10 cm in the Rio Suía Missú Basin, a headwater tributary of the Rio Xingú in the Brazilian Mato Grosso. The streams were always of the clear-water type without measurable hardness, a pH around 5.0, and a conductivity below 20 μS/cm. The water temperatures were between 26° and 29°C. It is likely that *Spatuloricaria* sp. "Rio Xingú" is as yet undescribed, because there have been no *Spatuloricaria* spp. described from this area, although it is rich in endemics.

In the Summer of 2000, Jens Gottwald, Garbsen, Germany, imported the same species from the central Rio Xingú. Apparently *Spatuloricaria* sp. "Rio Xingú" is somewhat smaller than its congeners, because the first males developed their whiskers already at a length of 10–12 cm. There is hope, therefore, that this is a *Spatuloricaria* sp. which may also be maintained by nonspecialist aquarists.

T: 26°–29°C, L: 20 cm, A: 100 cm, R: b

Spatuloricaria sp. "Rio Xingú," specimen from the central Rio Xingú at Altamira. I. Seidel

This specimen was imported from the Rio Guamá and is probably also *Spatuloricaria* sp. "Xingú."

H.-G. Evers

Habitat of *Spatuloricaria* sp. "Rio Xingu" in the drainage area of the Rio Suia Missu, a headwater tributary of the Xingú River.

Furcodontichthys novaesi, preserved specimen from the vicinity of the confluence of the rivers Branco and Negro.

L. A. van der Laan

Genus *Furcodontichthys* RAPP PY-DANIEL, 1981

Furcodontichthys is a monotypic genus which has yet to be classified into a subtribe. The division of the labial barbels into two large, further-branched barbels which protrude laterally from below the head, and the pointed head, make these otherwise unremarkably colored fish an attractive addition to our aquarium fauna. In October 1997, the authors were successful during a trip to the Rio Tefé in capturing—and subsequently bringing back to Germany—several of these loricariids.

Furcodontichthys novaesi RAPP PY-DANIEL, 1981

F.: Rapp Py-Daniel, L. (1981): *Furcodontichthys novaesi* n. gen., n. sp. (Osteichthys, Siluriformes: Loricariidae) na bacia amazonica, Brasil.– Bol.Museu Paraense E. Goeldi, Zoologia, 105:1–17.

Syn.: None.

Hab.: Brazil, federal state of Amazonas, Rio Tefé, Lago Tefé; federal state of Acre, Rio Juruá. The authors were able to capture this fish at night at only a single location pulling a seine over a sand bank. The locality (Rio Tefé, approximately at km 85 from the confluence into the Solimões) had a temperature of 29°C. The water in the main channel was black-water rich in sediments. Many sand-dwelling Loricariinae were captured at such biotopes. The *Furcodontichthys novaesi* easily became entangled with their pointed head in the mesh of the net and had to be freed with caution. However, it was unavoidable to injure some to such an extent that they died a short time thereafter.

M.&B.: Only a few specimens reached Germany alive. *F. novaesi* hardly buries itself in the substrate, similar to *Hemiodontichthys*. These catfish are probably mouthbrooders, a criterium based on the morphology of their lips. After an acclimation phase, any suitable fare is eagerly devoured. At the time this book [the German original] went to press, there had not been any success in breeding the species.

T: 26°–30°C, L: 12 cm, A: 80 cm, R: b

Sandbank at the Rio Tefé, habitat of *Furcodontichthys novaesi*.

H.-G. Evers

Furcodontichthys novaesi from the Rio Tefé.   I. Seidel

Furcodontichthys novaesi, portrait.   I. Seidel

Unidentified Loricariinae

Unidentified Genus LG 4

It was uncertain from what South American country this loricariid comes from. The species has been known for several years in the hobby, but when the sellers were asked where the fish came from, the answers included everything from "Brazil" to "Venezuela" and in between. Evers catch this species in the Rio Cuiabá (Pantanal), a big tributary to the Río Paraguai. Already a superficial observation brings into evidence several anatomical peculiarities, which make the classification into a specific genus particularly difficult. First, there is the similarity to some *Hemiloricaria* with a pointed head. And indeed, if the fish lies on the substrate or among the decoration and has its fins closed, it appears like a member of the genus *Hemiloricaria*. However, on the other hand, there are several characteristics which are strongly reminiscent of *Sturisomatichthys* species. The dorsal fin is notably tall, and the pectoral fins are also quite large. Several imported specimens had a strange anal fin morphology. It is huge and the first, thickened ray is very elongated. However, none of our bred specimens showed this characteristic. Besides the fins, the head shape of these catfish is also reminiscent of the genera *Sturisoma* or *Sturisomatichthys*. However, sexually active males do not have pronounced whiskers. Only yellowish bristles of perhaps 1 mm in length appear along the edge of the head.

The reproductive biology, too, is intermediate between *Hemiloricaria* and *Sturisoma*. The fish spawned in the author's aquarium both in offered bamboo segments in the manner of *Hemiloricaria*, as well as also—and preferably so—openly on the aquarium panes. The males guard the spawns, which comprise approximately 40–60 eggs, until they hatch. At 25°–27°C, only 5–6 days are required by the fry to hatch from the green eggs, i.e., much less than the time required by bred *Hemiloricaria* species, and more along the lines of the genera *Sturisoma* and *Sturisomatichthys*.

The juveniles of LG 4 are extremely elongated, much more so than any of the *Hemiloricaria* species bred by the authors. But to the contrary, again, the eggs and the newly hatched fry are clearly reminiscent of *Hemiloricaria* and not the hatchlings of *Sturisoma*, *Sturisomatichthys*, or *Farlowella*. If this species is maintained in a group of 2–4 pairs, there are constantly spawns to see; this is a fertile species.

This interesting suckermouth catfish still has plenty of mysteries to reveal. Britski et al. (1999) mentioned four *Rineloricaria* spp. for the Pantanal of which none meets the characteristica of LG 4. With this information, scientists would be able to describe this apparently undescribed species—possibly even classifying it into a new genus.

For the aquarist, this catfish is a very positive addition, given that maintenance, and also breeding and rearing of the young, are straightforward. In the aquarium trade, there are several erroneous designation for this fish, such as *Sturisoma* "Foerschi" and *Sturisomatichthys* "Foerschi," a nonexisting taxon that must be considered a *nomen nudum*.

T: 25°–29°C, **L:** 10 cm, **A:** 80 cm, **R:** b

LG 4, pair.

H.-G. Evers

LG 4, ♂. See following page for additional photos.

H.-G. Evers

LG 4, ♂ guarding a spawn adhered to one of the aquarium panes.   I. Seidel

LG 4, wild-caught specimens often sport much elongated filaments on the anal fin, something very unusual among suckermouth catfishes.

Unidentified Genus LG 5

Thomas LITZ and Juan REICHERT captured the pictured Loricariinae suckermouth in Uruguay—more precisely, in the Rio Uruguay at Pueblo San Javier.

The pictured specimen measures approximately 10 cm in length. The mouth is slightly pinnate, the body dorsoventrally compressed. The greatest similarities exist to *Rhadinoloricaria* spp. from Peru, but these have a different labial morphology. Until this book went to press [German edition], no additional information to further species identification could be gathered.

T: 16°–22°C, L: 10 cm?, A: 80 cm, R: b

LG 5, the same specimen pictured below, but now preserved. Unfortunately, the fish was dry and the lips stuck together, making it impossible to obtain a better photo depicting the labial anatomy.

LG 5 shortly after capture, in a photo tank.

T. Litz

Family Cetopsidae Bleeker, 1858
Whale Catfishes or Candirús

As of spring 2004, this small, aquaristically virtually unknown family comprises 22 described species with three subspecies classified in seven genera. All species inhabit tropical, and in part also subtropical (São Francisco Basin, Paraná/Paraguay Basin), South America. The area of main presence is located in Amazonia and in the Orinoco Basin. A few species inhabit waters west of the Andes in Ecuador and on the Caribbean side of the northern Andes Mountains (DE PINNA & VARI, 1995). They are found in small rain forest streams (the genus *Helogenes*, for example—as well as other genera—lives both in clear- as well as black-water streams of the rain forest), but also in large clear-water and white-water rivers. The Cetopsidae are called whale catfishes in English-speaking areas, which is a derivation of its scientific name *Cetopsis*. Perhaps just the shape of the head has something in common with these marine mammals, but that is it as far as the similarities are concerned. Truth be said, the behavior of some of these catfish species is reminiscent more of piranhas or even sharks. GOULDING (1980) reports about members of the genera *Cetopsis* and *Hemicetopsis*, describing how they (together with some Trichomycteridae and the pimelodid *Callophysus macropterus*) bite chunks of meat, lightning fast, out of large fishes that have been captured with hook and line. In extreme cases, the captured fish is devoured in large sections. For the Amazonian fishermen, this is a serious nuisance and the "candirús," as they are called in Brazil, are understandably unpopular. The candirús are catfishes with a length between 3 and 35 cm (DE PINNA & VARI, 1995), and both the unorthodox body shape as well as the attractive coloration of some species, can waken the desire to possibly keep these fishes in an aquarium. However, with the exception of the one Peruvian species or another, there are no imports, and so the only effective solution for the seriously interested aquarist is to capture them him or herself on a fishing trip to their natural habitat. Their natural distribution and their nutritional habits are virtual unknowns—besides the rather spectacular comments mentioned above. GOULDING (1980) himself, too, allows that the attack of large fishes captured by hook and line hardly provides an analysis of their "normal" feeding behavior. However, the reports by GOULDING have caused many aquarists to generalize this behavior of only a few representatives of the family and to apply it to the entire group and raise their arms in disgust, when these fishes become a topic of discussion.

Members of the family Cetopsidae are easily identified as such based on their oval body shape. These catfishes are totally void of scales, they are naked. However, the body is protected thanks to a thick mucus layer, something easily noticed when one tries to hold these fishes by hand. Especially the anterior section of the body appears unusually round,

Photo top right:
Large rivers, such as the depicted Araguaia in central Brazil, are the habitat of *Cetopsis* and *Hemicetopsis* species. These catfishes are an especially common presence at the areas of confluence of smaller rivers into the large stream.

Photo bottom right:
A just-captured *Cetopsis* sp. from the Araguaia. The specimen was captured with hook and line and had a total length of approximately 20 cm.

H.-G. Evers

H.-G. Evers

sometimes even longitudinally compressed. This impression is given by a ring of muscles which encircles the entire body. The mouth is usually inferior, although in some species it is terminal. The eyes are very small and covered by a transparent membrane. In the deep-water species *Bathycetopsis oliveirai*, the eyes are totally degenerated. As compensation, so to speak, that species has a hypertrophied (enlarged) olfactory organ. These fish smell their food in the deep, dark channels of the Amazon River (LUNDBERG & RAPP PY-DANIEL, 1994).

The Cetopsidae are cylindrical and, in some genera, the body becomes thinner caudally. The dorsal fin is small and usually triangular in shape. There is no adipose fin (BURGESS, 1989); an exception being the genus *Helogenes*, which includes species both with and without an adipose fin (see SCHINDLER, 1993, for *Helogenes marmoratus*). An additional characteristic is the reduced first ray of the pectoral fins and the dorsal fin, also called a spine. The Cetopsidae have basally stiff pectoral and dorsal fin spines, the following are flexible rays. This characteristic is shared by some other catfishes (Trichomycteridae, Ictaluridae, Amphiliidae, Sisoridae, and by the subfamily Rhamdiinae of the Pimelodidae), but in an evolutionary sense, in these families there seems to have occurred an independent development of this characteristic, which signifies an additional synapomorphy (the common appearance of a derived characteristic within a group of taxa) of the Cetopsidae (DE PINNA & VARI, 1995).

During the maintenance of two *Pseudocetopsis* species from Venezuela and an additional one from northern Brazil, no predation attacks could be observed, although there were other, larger fishes present as tankmates. However, the maintained specimens were small (up to 5 cm) and spent the entire day hidden in cavelike shelters. EVERS (1993) captured

Pseudocetopsis plumbeus orinoco in a swiftly flowing white-water creek in the Venezuelan Llanos. It was a fortuitous capture, i.e., a holey piece of root was lifted from the water and shaken vigorously. Besides the *Pseudocetopsis*, another root inhabitant that fell out was a small trichomycterid of the genus *Ochmacanthus*. In the aquarium, the fish were never observed feeding, but they didn't starve either, as could be confirmed by their distended bellies. The other tankmates were fed with all usual aquarium fare. No injuries on any of the fishes could be detected.

SEIDEL (1997) reports about a *Pseudocetopsis* species with a pronounced sexual dimorphism and dichromatism. Males have flaglike elongate dorsal fins, whereas in females the filament is short. Additionally, in regards to coloration, the brown females are readily told apart from the ventrally bright and dorsally blue-violet males. SEIDEL and travel companions captured these catfish in the Peruvian San Alejandro River, hidden in roots, from where they could only be removed with great effort. These fish, too, are peaceful in the aquarium and do not bother other tankmates. At twilight at most, the candirús emerge from their shelters to feed.

Photo top right:
This *Cetopsis* sp. was captured with hook and line in the central Rio Negro, i.e., in black-water. The distended ventrum seems to indicate a full intestine. In reality, the intestine of this specimen was empty, it did not contain anything but water.

Photo bottom right:
Cetopsidae sp., it may be a member if the genus *Cetopsis* or *Hemicetopsis*, which sporadically has been imported from Peru. Note the beautiful blue coloration this specimen possesses.

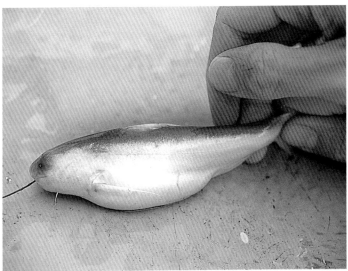

H.-G. Evers

I. Seidel

Fam.: Cetopsidae

The opposite in feeding behavior is represented by *Cetopsis* sp. from Peru. A group of these fish immediately reacted to the presence of food, and even came to the surface of the water to cat the frozen mosquito larvae offered. According to BERTHOLD (pers. comm.), the beautifully blue species which does measure a good 15 cm, also preys on small fishes, which are hunted. At BERTHOLD, these fish lay most of the day on the aquarium substrate in the filter effluent and hardly moved at all until food was introduced into the aquarium. DEBOLD (pers. comm.) maintained, for an extended period of time, a group of *Pseudocetopsis* sp. "Río San Alejandro" with other fish species as tankmates, without ever having an incident to report. Here, too, frozen mosquito larvae were a favorite item.

A family related to the Cetopsidae is the Trichomycteridae—one of the reasons why both families are presented together in this book. The whale catfishes clearly differ in several osteological characteristics from the parasitic catfishes, as the Trichomycteridae (see BURGESS, 1989, pp. 289 ff. and 305 ff.) are misleadingly called. For the aquarist, the most obvious are the differences in head shape. In Cetopsidae the head always appears longitudinally compressed and round, in the trichomycterids the head in most cases is dorsoventrally flattened.

The systematics of this small family, the Cetopsidae, are difficult to sort out. LUNDBERG & RAPP PY-DANIEL (1994) indicate that a modern revision on the genus level is still pending. However, there are two unpublished dissertations which could provide an insight. The classic arrangement of the Cetopsidae is still based on BLEEKER (1862), with the genera *Cetopsis, Hemicetopsis, Pseudocetopsis,* and *Paracetopsis.* The taxon *Cetopsogiton* EIGENMANN, 1910 is considered valid by BURGESS (1989), but is refuted by other authors, who give precedence to *Paracetopsis.* LUNDBERG & RAPP PY-DANIEL (1994)

mention that the phylogenetic analysis of this family is still outstanding, but nevertheless describe the additional genus *Bathycetopsis.*

DE PINNA & VARI (1995) closed a large systematic gap and published the results of their research on the Cetopsidae and the Helogenidae REGAN, 1911, which at the time still had the rank of family. They determined that these are so-called sister groups in the phylogenetic sense, retired the nomenclaturally speaking younger family Helogenidae, and established instead two subfamilies considered monophyletic (Cetopsinae and Helogeninae) within the family Cetopsidae. The difference between the subfamilies are mainly of an osteological and muscular nature; only the presence or absence of an adipose fin can be determined with relative ease by the aquarist. Adult Cetopsinae lack such a fin (an exception are juvenile *Cetopsis coecutiens,* which have a small adipose fin), and in the Helogeninae it is usually present, but very small. Only in the case of *Helogenes marmoratus* there are both specimens with and without an adipose fin (VARI & ORTEGA, 1986; SCHINDLER, 1993). The anal fin of adult Helogeninae is extremely broad (32–49 rays in contrast to 23–34 rays for the Cetopsinae) and the lower caudal lobes are larger than the dorsal fin (in adult Cetopsinae these are of the same size). The base of the dorsal fin of Cetopsinae is at the anterior section of the body, the beginning anterior to the ventral fins, whereas in the Helogeninae it is located on the posterior section, far posterior to the base of the ventral fins.

A revision of the Cetopsinae is actually in preparation and might be published shortly after this book (spring 2004) is finished.

Genera and Species

Family Cetopsidae BLEEKER, 1858

Subfamily Cetopsinae BLEEKER, 1858

Bathycetopsis LUNDBERG & RAPP PY-DANIEL, 1994
– *Bathycetopsis oliveirai* LUNDBERG & RAPP PY-DANIEL, 1994

Cetopsis AGASSIZ, 1829
– *Cetopsis chalmersi* NORMAN, 1926
– *Cetopsis coecutiens* (LICHTENSTEIN, 1823)

Denticetopsis FERRARIS, 1996
– *Denticetopsis royeroi* FERRARIS, 1996
– *Denticetopsis sauli* FERRARIS, 1996

Hemicetopsis BLEEKER, 1862
– *Hemicetopsis candiru* (SPIX & AGASSIZ, 1829)

Paracetopsis BLEEKER, 1862
– *Paracetopsis bleekeri* BLEEKER, 1862
– *Paracetopsis occidentalis* STEINDACHNER, 1880

Pseudocetopsis BLEEKER, 1862
– *Pseudocetopsis amphiloxa* (EIGENMANN, 1914)
– *Pseudocetopsis gobioides* (KNER, 1857)
– *Pseudocetopsis macilentus* (EIGENMANN, 1912)
– *Pseudocetopsis macropteronema* (BOULENGER, 1898)
– *Pseudocetopsis minutus* (EIGENMANN, 1912)
– *Pseudocetopsis morenoi* (FERNANDEZ-YEPEZ, 1971)
– *Pseudocetopsis othonops* (EIGENMANN, 1912)
– *Pseudocetopsis plumbeus motatanensis* SCHULTZ, 1944
– *Pseudocetopsis plumbeus orinoco* SCHULTZ, 1944
– *Pseudocetopsis plumbeus plumbeus* (STEINDACHNER, 1883)
– *Pseudocetopsis praecox* FERRARIS & BROWN, 1991
– *Pseudocetopsis ventralis* (GILL, 1870)

Subfamily Helogeninae REGAN, 1911

Helogenes GÜNTHER, 1863
– *Helogenes castaneus* (DAHL, 1860)
– *Helogenes gouldingi* VARI & ORTEGA, 1986
– *Helogenes marmoratus* GÜNTHER, 1863
– *Helogenes uruyensis* FERNANDEZ-YEPEZ, 1967

Pseudocetopsis macilentus (EIGENMANN, 1912)

F.: Eigenmann, C.H. (1912): The Fresh Water fishes of British Guyana, including a Study of the Ecological Grouping of species and the Relation of the Fauna of the Plateau to That of the Lowlands.– Memoirs of the Carnegie Museum, 5: 1–578.

Syn.: *Hemicetopsis macilentus.*

Hab.: Guyana, Potaro drainage. According to FERNANDEZ-YEPÉZ (1964), this species can also be found in eastern Venezuela. Ingo SEIDEL captured the pictured specimen in August 2000 in a tributary to the Essequibo River in Guyana.

M.&B.: This quite attractively colored fish, too, has probably a cryptic lifestyle. Similar to most of its relatives, this catfish spends most of its time in a shelter, from where it emerges only in darkness to search for food. There is presently scant information available in regard to maintenance, and breeding is unknown due to a lack of available specimens. The pictured fish was photographed at the site, shortly after its capture.

S: The design on the flanks is typical for *Pseudocetopsis macilentus* and it differentiates it clearly from the other *Pseudocetopsis* spp. known to us. In BURGESS (1989), the species is still listed as a member of the genus *Hemicetopsis*. DE PINNA & VARI (1995), however, classify it into the genus *Pseudocetopsis*. We follow the more recent classification.

T: 26°–30°C, **L:** 6.5 cm, **A:** 60 cm, **R:** b

Pseudocetopsis plumbeus orinoco SCHULTZ, 1944
Orinoco whale cat

F.: Schultz, L.P. (1944): The catfishes of Venezuela, with descriptions of thirty-eight new forms.– Proc.U.S.Nat.Mus., Washington, 94(3172): 173–338.

Syn.: None.

Hab.: Venezuela, Orinoco Basin. The authors were able to demonstrate the presence of the species in the Llanos, on the outskirts of the city of Calabozo. A small white-water stream in the Sabanas de Rascamula was fished in August 1992 (28°C water temperature, pH 6.8, conductivity 10 µS/cm). The fish was shaken out of a log that was lying in the current.

M.&B.: *P. p. orinoco* is a nocturnal species which accepts any kind of fish food. It was maintained in a species tank. Therefore, it is not possible to make any comments in regard to its parasitic behavior (or lack thereof).
The reproductive biology is a big unknown here too. The fish spend the day in cavelike shelters and only emerge in darkness.

T: 26°–30°C, **L:** 10 cm, **A:** 80 cm, **R:** b

816

Pseudocetopsis macilentus in a photo tank.

I. Seidel

Pseudocetopsis plumbeus orinoco

H.-G. Evers

Pseudocetopsis praecox FERRARIS & BROWN, 1991

F.: A new species of *Pseudocetopsis* from the Rio Negro Drainage of Venezuela (Siluriformes, Cetopsidae).– Copeia, 1991(1): 161–165.

Syn.: None.

Hab.: Southern Venezuela, northern Brazil, Rio Negro Basin. Black-water igarapés of the Neblina region. According to the original description, it was possible to capture the species at the Neblina base camp at the foot of the Pico Neblina, on the Venezuelan side of the Rio Mawarinuma. The species was captured over gravely/rocky substrates. At night, it was possible to observe the fish swimming in the shallow littoral zone. The black-water had pH values of 4.3 to 5.0.
EVERS & SCHLÜTER captured *P. praecox* on the Brazilian side in the main stream of a small black-water igarapé at the upper course of the Rio Negro near the city of São Gabriel da Cachoeira, which is not far from the Pico Neblina. At km 10 of the northern road, the authors were given permission to fish on the land of a ranch (fazenda). During the day, *P. praecox* remained hidden in roots and overhanging shore vegetation, where they were captured with nets. The black-water was quite acidic and soft, had a temperature of 28°C, and a swift current. The bottom substrates of all these igarapés consisted of fine white quartz sand.

M.&B.: There are presently no breeding experiences to draw on. Only a few specimens were brought back to Germany with the sole purpose of studying them.
The day is spent in caves, and the fish only appears during the most absolute darkness to search for food. The original describers found bloodworms and other insect larvae in the stomachs of recently captured animals, and this diet seems also to satisfy the specimens brought back to Germany.

S: *P. paecox* is closely related to *Pseudocetopsis plumbeus*. The smaller adult size and a lower number of pectoral fin rays in *P. praecox* are appropriate distinguishing characteristics for the aquarist to use. Furthermore, *P. praecox* lacks the dots on the flanks which *P. plumbeus orinoco* sometimes shows. The pictured specimen is larger than the length indicated in the original species description (69.1 mm vs. 47.9 mm SL), but shares the species-typical pectoral fin formula I/7.

T: 26°–30°C, **L:** 7 cm, **A:** 60 cm, **R:** b

Pseudocetopsis praecox, lateral view.

H.-G. Evers

Pseudocetopsis praecox

H.-G. Evers

Pseudocetopsis sp. "Río San Alejandro"

This beautiful species was captured by the coauthor I. Seidel in the Peruvian Río San Alejandro (Ucayali Basin). The fish grow to a length of approximately 12 cm and have a well-defined sexual dimorphism (males have an elongated dorsal fin) and dichromatism (males are dorsally violet, females are simply marbled). *Pseudocetopsis* sp. "Río San Alejandro" is peaceful and feeds on any normal aquarium fare, but there is a distinct preference for foods of animal origin.

Another Peruvian species, which is very reminiscent of the females of *P.* sp. "Río San Alejandro," is also presented in this book. However, throughout the entire shipment there were no animals with a different coloration, although those would have been commercially much more attractive. Are these two independent species?

Pseudocetopsis sp. "Venezuela"

The specimen pictured below was brought to Germany in 1994 by the Hamburger aquarist B. Schmitt from southern Venezuela. It was collected from among wood piles which were lying in the current of small clear-water streams. The moderately attractive flesh tone was always preserved and their final size was around 8 cm.

This species, too, is completely nocturnal and hardly offers any incentive to be ever maintained—or does it?

Pseudocetopsis sp. "Venezuela"   H.-G. Evers

Whale Catfishes and Marbled Catfishes

Pseudocetopsis sp. "Río San Alejandro" ♂ I. Seidel

Pseudocetopsis sp. "Río San Alejandro" ♀ I. Seidel

821

Cetopsidae sp. "Peru"   H.-G. Evers

Cetopsidae sp. "Peru"   H.-G. Evers

Whale Catfishes and Marbled Catfishes

Cetopsidae sp. "Peru." Note the marbled design dorsally.

I. Seidel

Cetopsidae sp. "Peru." The marbled design is missing, the fish is dorsally steel blue.

Helogenes marmoratus GÜNTHER, 1863
Marbled Catfish

F.: Günther, A. (1863): One new Species of Fishes from the Essequibo. Ann.Mag. Nat.Hist.Lond., ser.12(3): 441–443.

Syn.: *Helogenes amazonae*, *Helogenes unidorsalis.*

Hab.: Amazon Basin, Orinoco drainage, Guyana Highlands. The broadly distributed species inhabits forest creeks of the clear- and black-water types. There it is encountered among the leaf litter in shallow sections.

M.&B.: Marbled catfish are nocturnal. At night they swim with a constant speed just below the water's surface, waiting for edibles to fall on it.

An aquarium for these strange fish should not have an excessive current and provide a dense vegetation mat close to the surface. That is their local of choice for the diurnal resting period. After some acclimation time, they will accept food even during the day, as soon as it is given. However, feeding only takes place close to the surface, no food is taken from the bottom. A marbled catfish without a plant group to lean onto, sinks to the bottom and turns sideways to sleep. However, if hiding places in the form of dense vegetation are provided, these small scoundrels will squeeze into it. Caves are not accepted and breeding has not yet been successful.

T: 26°–30°C, L: 5 cm, A: 60 cm, R: t

Helogenes uruyensis FERNÁNDEZ-YÉPEZ, 1967
Venezuelan marbled catfish

F.: Fernández-Yépez, A. (1967): Primera contribución al conocimiento de los peces, con descripción de dos especies y una subespecie nuevas.– Acta Biol. Venez., 5(10): 159–179.

Syn.: *Helogenes marmoratus uruyensis.*

Hab.: Southern Venezuela, federal state of Bolivar, vicinity of the Auyan Tepui, Rio Uruyén, Rio Carrao drainage. SCHINDLER (1993) captured these fish at a depth of 10–50 cm (pH 5.7, conductivity 80 µS/cm, air temperature 33.5°C, water temperature 28.5°C). The water in the surroundings of the Auyan-Tepui is of the black-water type and approximates distilled water in its composition, lacking hardness or conductivity. Coauthor EVERS visited the biotope in April 2001. Unfor-

tunately, the species was not encountered again in the virtually lentic biotope which had dense vegetation.

M.&B.: Nocturnal species which mirrors *H. marmoratus* in regard to surface loitering and specialization towards floating foods.

S: *H. uruyensis* can be distinguished from *H. marmoratus* by having an uniformly colored body, and a lower number of anal fin rays (32–37 vs. >39).

T: 26°–30°C, L: 5 cm, A: 60 cm, R: t

Helogenes marmoratus

H.-G. Evers

Helogenes uruyensis

I. Schindler

Family Nematogenyidae Bleeker, 1862
Genus *Nematogenys* Girard, 1854

The only recent species is *Nematogenys inermis* (Guichenot in Gray, 1848) from Chile. The anatomically quite primitive fish reaches a total length of ca. 25 cm, and its beige-brown body is covered by several irregular black spots on its flanks. The elongated body ends in a strongly laterally compressed caudal peduncle with a rounded caudal fin. The pectoral fins, contrary to most members of the family Trichomycteridae, has a first ray modified into a spine. The small head has three pairs of barbels, the eyes are tiny. For a long time, the genus *Nematogenys* was only classified as the Subfamily Nematogenyinae within the family Trichomycteridae, but today it is considered an independent family. According to DE PINNA (1992b), this family finds its closest relatives within the Trichomycteridae, and is

further removed from the other Loricarioidei. ARRATIA (1983) writes about their natural habitat (see under Trichomycteridae, Subfamily Trichomycterinae). Although these fish will in all likelihood never play a significant role in the aquarium hobby, since there are hardly ever any aquarium fish exports from Chile, they shall be mentioned at this time for completeness sake.

AZPELICUETA & RUBILAR (1998) described a fossil member of the genus. *Nematogenys cuivi* lived in the Miocene, i.e., 25–7 million years ago.

Photo below:
Many loach catfishes live in relatively swift currents. Here, e.g., a clear-water river in the state of Rio de Janeiro in southeastern Brazil: the Canal Mato Grosso.

H.-G. Evers

Family Trichomycteridae Bleeker, 1858
Parasitic catfishes or "loach catfishes"

Hardly any other large family of Neotropical catfishes is aquaristically and scientifically so poorly known as is the case for the loach catfishes. In the aquarium hobby, it is especially the negative and quite spectacular characteristics of a few (!) of its members that have become famous (or infamous, rather), and which have been ingrained in the minds of aquarists. We are speaking of the so-called urinophillic or hematophillic species, which are feared by the local population more than piranha and caiman together. The opinion that these fishes seek nitrogenous wastes lacks any foundation; at least it could never be demonstrated that these fishes reacted in any way to urine. It must be suspected that such an attribute is the result of the negative experiences suffered by naked-bathing persons, which are described in greater detail further below. These parasitic attributes are certainly not promotional assets, but the family has much more to offer than those few black sheep! [It is in this same spirit that here a translation of the German common name for the family, "Schmerlenwelse," is also proposed for the English-speaking hobbyists: loach catfishes.]

In connection to this problem, it would be interesting to analyze how the parasitic catfishes find their way to the gills of other fishes. Fishes excrete ammonium and ammonia through their gills, in a manner similar as mammals do through their urinary tract. In a laboratory experiment it should be possible to determine if, and if indeed that is the case, then in what concentrations, the catfishes can "sniff out" the nitrogenous compounds, and possibly also how they do it.

The members of the family Trichomycteridae are generally elongated, wormlike fishes with a laterally compressed, deep caudal peduncle. The body is naked and protected by a thick mucous layer. Those of us who have held such a fish in our hands know how difficult it is to hold on to one of these slippery "worms." Usually it is them who hold on to us by using small "teeth" which they have on the operculum and the interoperculum to pry into the narrowest of cracks and crevices (or the hand, in this case). These odontodes are readily felt, giving the erroneous impression that these are small spines that are piercing one's hand.

The small head is usually flattened and very mobile thanks to a number of well-developed muscles. The eyes are small and deeply embedded laterally to superiorly. A pair of nasal barbels and two pairs of maxillary barbels are the rule, in some genera there is an additional pair of barbels on the mandible. The mouth is terminal, but in many genera (e.g., the scale-eating genera of the subfamily Stegophilinae) it is inferior and additionally flattened so as to form a disc. Many species have a well-developed dentition.

The dorsal fin is located quite posteriorly, is narrow and usually rounded, and does not have a first ray modified into a spine, as is the case in other catfish families. The anal fin is also rounded and not very broad, and an adipose fin is absent in most genera and species. Also usually lacking is a spine anteriorly on the small pectoral fins, and the caudal fin is likewise short, lacking filamentous elongations or large lobes. It does, however, in conjunction with the strong caudal peduncle, allow for high speeds to escape perceived danger.

Most species are small, only a few exceed 15 cm in total length. On the other end of the spectrum, however, there are dwarfs in their midst.

Fam.: Trichomycteridae

Some species are completely blind; these species live either in cave systems or spend their lives buried in fine sand. The wormlike body shape allows these fishes to live in raging currents, even where no other fish species prevail. With the aid of their spinelike odontodes on opercula and interopercula, the loach catfishes can fasten themselves in the narrowest of crevices and withstand the current. In such biotopes they enjoy relative safety from predators, and the food niche based on a variety of insect larvae (the members of the subfamily Trichomycterinae, for example, do not feed on blood or similar items at all, but rather on "normal" foods) is theirs alone to take advantage of.

The mucus-covered body and the worm shape allow a lightning fast burying, even in coarse gravel.

The family inhabits virtually all of South America. Beginning in the north at Panama and Colombia, the area of distribution extends into the Andean regions of Chile and the temperate climates of Argentina. Some (most members of the subfamily Trichomycterinae) inhabit higher elevations at the headwaters of river systems. The extreme case is *Trichomycterus chungaraensis* from Lake Chungará, northern Chile, a lake at an elevation of 4500

Photo below:
Capture of *Trichomycterus* sp. "Rio Preto" in the Serra das Orgãos, in the back country of Rio de Janeiro. Some loach catfishes inhabit biotopes at even very high altitudes, where there are no other fishes. The water here is cool at 16°–20°C, the current raging during rains. In widened, troughlike areas, the fish hug the rock walls and when feeling threatened also bury in the fine gravel. The capture of these wiggly catfishes is very difficult.

H.-G. Evers

m above sea level. *T. laucaensis* is still encountered at 4390 m above sea level, *T. rivulatus* at approximately 3900 m, *T. roigi* between 3390 and 4300 m elevation, and the just recently described *Trichomycterus catamarcensis* at 3500 m (FERNÁNDEZ & VARI, 2000). However, the Trichomycteridae can also be found in any type of water body of the lowlands. Raging mountain creeks of the "trout zone," lazy rivers or shaded remnant pools, and small igarapés in the rain forest where they dwell among the leaf litter, are all biotopes they inhabit. It is just not possible to lump all these species together, as many aquarists attempt to do with some strange remark in relation to the "parasitic catfishes" (hence our suggestion to also call them loach catfishes, in reference to their body shape). Information is scant in regard to the lifestyle, reproductive biology, and feeding habits. Empirical investigations of complete sections of Neotropical water bodies have only rarely been the subjects of research, although in recent years such efforts have increased notably. Additionally, the Trichomycteridae have always been mentioned only as a by-product of such research. Exceptionally, a study by ARRATIA (1983) has dealt with the living conditions of the Trichomycteridae in nature.

The scientist studied typical Chilean lotic waters and determined where which species of loach catfish lives at what age (species such as *Diplomystes chilensis*, family Diplomystidae, and *Nematogenys inermis*, now family Nematogenyidae). Two *Trichomycterus* species and the closely related *Bullockia maldonadoi* (subfamily Trichomycterinae) as adults prefer regions exposed to swift currents. They are diurnal and live in small groups of two to five individuals. Present over a variety of substrates, from fine sand to gravel, the coloration of the species in question is adapted to the substrate for better camouflage.

The, anatomically speaking, much more primitive *Nematogenys inermis* (the only member of the family Nematogenyidae) inhabits the rather calmer wide and deep sections of these rivers. The smallest juveniles, up to a length of approximately 5 cm, inhabit the immediate shallow littoral rich in plant growth. Larger specimens, up to ca. 18 cm total length, are found at depths of approximately 40–70 cm among plants, and adults live in even deeper zones.

On several trips to South America the authors were able to confirm the presence of several species of loach catfishes in the most varied biotopes. These observations are presented under the corresponding subfamily or species reports.

There is no reason for the Trichomycteridae not to be of any importance in the aquarium hobby. Many tropical species are readily suitable aquarium residents and do not bother tankmates either. But that varies from subfamily to subfamily, which is why indications as to their specific care are also given as part of the introduction of the subfamilies. Due to their cryptic lifestyle and their fast movement, loach catfishes will not be appealing to every aquarist. These characteristics, in the end, have brought them their common name: their similarity to loaches—especially to those of the genus *Pangio*—are readily apparent. Every once in a while, these catfishes appear in the trade, usually with an insufficiently precise indication as to their origin.

The nomenclature of the Trichomycteridae is confusing, and nobody is really certain as to how many species and genera there really are. Scientific papers dealing with the family as a whole are dated (EIGENMANN, 1918b). EIGENMANN assumed mistakenly that the name *Trichomycterus* VALENCIENNES in HUMBOLDT, 1833 had already been used, turning it consequently into a synonym, which is why he chose the next available name, i.e.,

Fam.: Trichomycteridae

Pygidium MEYEN, 1835 as the apparently correct taxon. However, *Trichomycterus* is indeed valid (TCHERNAVIN, 1944). *Pygidium* MEYEN is probably a fish which has not much in common with today's genus *Trichomycterus*. However, since the original description is very vague, and the type material of *Pygidium* is considered lost, that will remain a mystery for the time being (DE PINNA, written comm.). Only in recent years have the efforts by several scientists (MYERS & WEITZMAN, 1966, ARRATIA et al, 1978, DE PINNA, 1989 a and b, DE PINNA & STARNES, 1990, 1992, COSTA & BOCKMANN, 1993 and 1994a, as well as others) increased as a means to clarify the systematics of this family, and some smaller subfamilies have meanwhile been revised in some detail (Sarcoglanidinae, Glanapteryginae), whereas others (Stegophilinae, Trichomycterinae, Vandelliinae) still await their turn to be untangled. A fundamental analysis by BASKIN

(1978) regarding the relationships within the Trichomycteridae is only available as a doctoral dissertation and has, unfortunately, never been published. Consequently, here too, there is little we can say about a definitive species classification of most of the pictured fishes, and so we place a "cf." [= compare with; most likely to be that species, but not certain] in front of the species name.

The 38 genera are presently divided into 8 subfamilies, and the number of species is currently estimated to be over 200, which includes a great number of taxons that are only insufficiently defined.

Trichomycterus sp. "Rio Preto"

H.-G. Evers

Subfamily Copionodontinae DE PINNA, 1992

> *Copionodon* DE PINNA, 1992
> *Glaphyropoma* DE PINNA, 1992

The youngest subfamily, from the state of Bahia in northeastern Brazil, contains the monotypic genus *Glaphyropoma* and the genus *Copionodon* with three species. These catfishes have a long adipose fin which almost extends from the end of the dorsal fin to the base of the caudal fin. The dorsal fin is relatively far anterior. The teeth are spatulate. These characteristics are identifiable with relative ease for the observer versed in the trichomycterids. Additionally, there are several characteristics based on skeletal anatomy which make this subfamily unique. The genus *Trichogenes* is the closest relative, but several synapomorphies, which are typical for the entire family, are lacking.

The species *Copionodon pectens* DE PINNA, 1992 and *Copionodon orthiocarinatus* DE PINNA, 1992, as well as *Glaphyropoma rodriguesi* DE PINNA, 1992 live sympatrically and hail from central Bahia, a mountainous region with an ichthyofauna uninvestigated for a long time, and where it is highly likely that future research—also in relation to other rivers in the region—will uncover further species (genera). For example, just recently the species *Copionodon lianae* CAMPANARIO & DE PINNA, 2001 was described from the national park Chapada Diamantina (Rio Mucujê Basin).

No commercial fish imports are to be expected from the area, although aquarists would surely find interest in these dwarfs that barely reach 5 cm in length.

H.-G. Evers

Small river in the interior of the state of Bahia, northern Brazil.

Subfamily Glanapteryginae MYERS, 1944

Glanapteryx MYERS, 1927
Pygidianops MYERS, 1944
Typhlobelus MYERS, 1944
Listrura DE PINNA, 1988

The dwarf-sized catfishes of this subfamily live hidden among the leaf litter and mud, and even science has hardly any specimens available. The Glanapteryginae often lack a dorsal fin, and the anal fin as well as the pectoral and ventral fins are much reduced or totally lacking. The small head is flattened, and the eyes are either tiny or totally absent.

For a long time, the members of this subfamily were only known from collections taken at the upper Rio Negro, close to the city of São Gabriel da Cachoeira. A second Typhlobelus species was then described from the Rio Tocantins (COSTA & BOCKMANN, 1994b), and the genus Listrura (DE PINNA, 1988) was described from the southeastern states of São Paulo and Rio de Janeiro. EVERS, SEIDEL, SCHLÜTER, and BOHNET were unable, however, to find any of these catfishes during a trip in October 1997, despite an intensive search in the vicinity of São Gabriel.

Glanapteryx anguilla MYERS, 1927 is the only member of the monotypic genus. These eellike fish live in the drainage of the upper Rio Negro and DE PINNA (1989b) described additional material from the Orinoco Basin. These, about six centimeter long, spaghetti-thin fish have three pairs of relatively long barbels and tiny eyes.

Pygidianops eigenmanni MYERS, 1944 has a stouter body and a shovel-like nose. This, the only member of the monotypic genus, lacks eyes, and the largest known specimen measured 2.3 centimeters standard length.

Both species of Typhlobelus are highly reminiscent of Pygidianops, but are more elongated. The roughly 3.5 cm long Ty-phlobelus ternetzi MYERS, 1944 has eyes that are discernible as tiny dots. Typhlobelus macromycterus COSTA & BOCKMANN, 1994 from the Tocantins at Tucurui, on the contrary, is blind.

The genus Listrura is represented by three species, two inhabitants of small swampy areas subjected to severe human influence. DE PINNA (1988) was unable to find L. camposi (RIBEIRO, 1957) at the type locality. LACERDA and EVERS visited, during October 1996, the type locality of Listrura nematopteryx DE PINNA, 1988 and found the only known habitat framed by a constantly expanding sanitary landfill (EVERS, 1998). All species are very slender, eel-like catfishes with much degenerate pectoral fins (four or less rays) and no ventral fins. The rounded, spatulate caudal fin also has a reduced number of rays. LANDIM & COSTA (2002) recently described a third species from a small headwater stream in the state of Rio de Janeiro.

These small fishes are not parasitic and are surely interesting for the so-inclined specialist. However, it is highly unlikely that any of these species will ever be commercially exported to Germany.

Photo top right:
Glanapteryginae sp. This small guy—which we were not able to identify further—was found among the leaf litter of the drainage area of the Rio Tocantins at Cametá. The pictured specimen had a total length of barely 2 cm.

Photo bottom right:
View of the swampy creek in which Listrura nematopteryx was found. The only confirmed habitat of this species is located on the edge of a sanitary land fill and probably will have been destroyed by the time this book is published.

H.-G. Evers

H.-G. Evers

Listrura nematopteryx DE PINNA, 1988
Shoveltail loach catfish

F.: Pinna, M.C.C. de (1988): A new genus of trichomycterid catfish (Siluroidei, Glanapteryginae), with comments on its phylogenetic relationships.– Revue suisse Zool., 95(1): 113–128.

Syn.: None.

Hab.: Brazil, state of Rio de Janeiro. Extremely rare species which has only been found in a swampy creek (EVERS, 1998). The existence of the species is gravely endangered by the destruction of its habitat. *L. nematopteryx* lives in the mud among the bog plants.

M.&B.: The few specimens that have been imported, lived about one year in a small aquarium and occupied tiny caves.

They fed on standard fry foods, such as *Artemia salina* nauplii.

S: Another species of the genus, *L. camposi* (RIBEIRO, 1957), too, inhabits a tiny, similar body of water in the state of São Paulo and has not been found for many years.

T: 20°–25°C, L: 5 cm, A: 50 cm, R: b

Listura nematopteryx, portrait.

H.-G. Evers

Listura nematopteryx   H.-G. Evers

The typical, spatulate caudal fin of *Listura nematopteryx*.   H.-G. Evers

835

In 1996, only little water was in the creek. *Listrura* were in the upper mud zone.

Subfamily Sarcoglanidinae MYERS & WEITZMAN, 1966

> Sarcoglanis MYERS & WEITZMAN, 1966
> Malacoglanis MYERS & WEITZMAN, 1966
> Stauroglanis DE PINNA, 1989
> Stenolicmus DE PINNA & STARNES, 1990
> Microcambeva COSTA & BOCKMANN, 1994
> Ammoglanis COSTA, 1994

If the catfishes of the previous subfamily can already be considered quite small and strange, this subfamily certainly takes the honors. All its members are minifishes which do not grow larger than three centimeters. According to COSTA & BOCKMANN (1994b), the five subfamilies Sarcoglanidinae, Glanapteryginae, Tridentinae, Vandelliinae, and Stegophilinae form a monophyletic group within the Trichomycteridae, based on the expression of a total of four characteristics (synapomorphies).

There is only a small number of specimens in scientific collections, which is not unusual, given the tiny size of the fishes. For example, the only specimen of Sarcoglanis simplex MYERS & WEITZMAN, 1966, from the upper Rio Negro at São Gabriel da Cachoeira, remained for 40 years in the collection of MYERS, without any additional specimens being found.

The fish is broad and deep-bodied, has tiny eyes on a short, stout head, the dorsal fin is small and has only four rays, and a delicate, thin adipose fin extends from the back of the dorsal fin to the base of the caudal fin. The holotype has a standard length of 19.6 mm.

Malacoglanis gelatinosus MYERS & WEITZMAN, 1966 from the Colombian Río Orteguaza is more elongated, its dorsal fin is larger, and the adipose fin also extends from the dorsal fin to the base of the caudal fin, although it is less pronounced. The authors described it as soft and gelatinous with a reddish-brown hue, which is lost under preservation. This species, too, is tiny (2 cm).

Stauroglanis gouldingi DE PINNA, 1989, from the Rio Daraá (Rio Negro drainage), is also a minifish with its 3 cm total length.

The genus shares many characteristics with the subfamily Trichomycterinae, but was classified into the subfamily Sarcoglanidinae based on the predominance of shared characteristics with the genera Malacoglanis and Sarcoglanis.

Stenolicmus sarmientoi DE PINNA & STARNES, 1990 was described from the Rio Mamoré system in Bolivia. A peculiarity are its additional caudal fin rays ("accessory fin rays"), which start at the caudal peduncle (13 dorsally, 11 ventrally). Additionally, the number of pectoral fin rays is reduced (5) and the body is much more elongated than those of its fellow species of the subfamily. This is another very small species.

Recently, COSTA & BOCKMANN (1994a) described Microcambeva barbata, a relatively elongated representative of the subfamily from the Brazilian state of Rio de Janeiro. The Rio São João at Gavioés is, in its upper course, only five meters wide and possibly 40 cm deep at the deepest sections. There is no shore vegetation, and the substrate consists of sand or incrusted rocks. Unfortunately, LACERDA, EVERS, and BOHNET searched in vain during October 1997 for these fishes at that site.

Ammoglanis diaphanus COSTA, 1994 was described from the Araguaia Basin in central Brazil. This species, too, is only two centimeters long as an adult. Besides its skeletal characteristics, which led to its description as a member of a new species and genus, the elongated first rays of the pectoral fins are what catches the eye of even the superficial observer. With Ammoglanis pulex from the Orinoco Basin, DE PINNA & WINEMILLER, 2001 just recently added a second species to the genus. This species is full-grown at a total length of barely 13 mm. Unfortunately, it is virtually impossible that these catfishes will ever be imported for the aquarium hobby. A specialized and interested catfish fan would have a field day with this group!

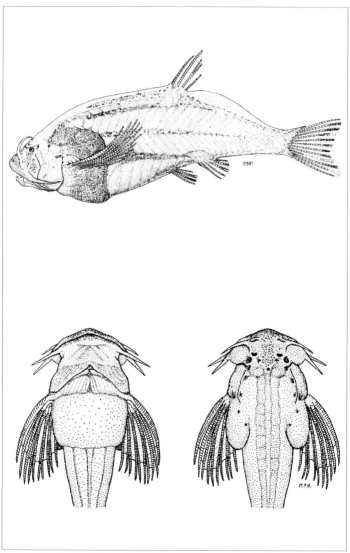

Sarcoglanis simplex, lateral, ventral, and dorsal views. Drawings: J. Zool., Lond. (1966) 149, 277–287

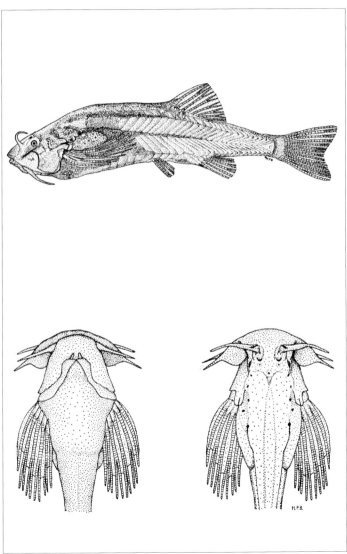

Malacoglanis gelatinosus, lateral, ventral, and dorsal views. Drawings: J. Zool., Lond. (1966) 149, 277–287

Subfamily Stegophilinae Günther, 1864

Pareiodon Kner, 1855
Stegophilus Reinhardt, 1858
Pseudostegophilus Eigenmann &
                              Eigenmann, 1889
Acanthopoma Lütken, 1891
Homodiaetus Eigenmann & Ward, 1907
Ochmacanthus Eigenmann, 1912
Pleurophysus Ribeiro, 1918
Apomatoceros Eigenmann, 1922
Haemomaster Myers, 1927
Parastegophilus Ribeiro, 1946
Schultzichthys Dahl, 1960
Megalocentor Pinna & Britski, 1991

The subfamily Stegophilinae—whose members feed on the mucosas, and in part on scales and the blood of other fishes—contains most of the genera. At first sight, that might appear to be a lot of fishes, but most genera are small, being either monotypic or having 2–8 member species at the most. These fishes, too, do not grow very large—but larger when compared to the Vandelliinae. At least as adults, the Vandelliinae feed exclusively on blood, they are purely hematophagous. In contrast, the Stegophilinae feed on the mucosa (Winemiler & Yan, 1989) and in part also on the scales of other fishes, where they surely also include a piece of flesh on occasion.

The subfamily has an expansive area of distribution and inhabits all major South American river systems: Amazon, Orinoco, São Francisco, Paraná-Paraguay, and the systems of southeastern Brazil. Eigenmann (1918b) reported on the interesting discovery of the branchial parasitism of these catfishes. He quotes Reinhardt (1858), who had spent several years in the central Brazilian state of Minas Gerais and who studied in a more detailed manner the fishes of the Rio das Velhas. Reinhardt had heard the rumor that the large shovelnose catfishes of the genus Pseudoplatystoma, called "soru-

bim" by the Brazilians, carried their young with them in their branchial cavity. Reinhardt offered a reward for anyone who presented him with such a catfish, and indeed, shortly thereafter a commercial fisherman brought him a shovelnose which had a small catfish sitting on its branchial arcs. The small "shovelnose" appeared totally different from the large one, which subsequently was even identified as a male. Reinhardt figured he was being swindled! Only during a further trip to Brazil and the appearance of more shovelnoses with what were supposedly its young, did the truth emerge. The catfishes, previously identified by him as new and rare "Stegophili," were uncovered as what they are: parasites. By the way, the species has been described as Stegophilus insidiosus Reinhardt, 1858. According to de Pinna & Britski (1991), the systematics of this subfamily have received little attention. Therefore, upon closer analysis, there surely will be numerous nomenclatural changes in store for the future.

Typical are the absence of nasal and mandibular barbels. The species have two pairs of maxillary barbels, one of which is much shorter. Both pairs are based at the corner of the mouth. The mouth is pronouncedly inferior, in some genera it gives the impression of being a suctorial disc. The jaws have a great number of small teeth arranged in rows. The anal fin is short.

Pareiodon microps Kner, 1855 is the oldest species of the subfamily. It inhabits the Amazon Basin and is one of the candirús which bite holes into captured large catfishes, or which are found in their branchial cavity. The anatomy differs in many aspects from that of the other Stegophilinae, and the species was earlier classified into its own subfamily—something Burgess (1989) changed by plac-

Parasitic or Loach Catfishes

ing the genus into the Stegophilinae. The club-shaped body with a non-flattened head (only one pair of barbels!), the tiny eyes, and the relatively small mouth are typical for the genus.

The genus *Stegophilus* gave the subfamily its name. These are slim, elongated fishes with a dorsoventrally flattened head profile. The eyes are relatively large and placed superiorly on the head with a small distance between them. In contrast to the similar genus *Ochmacanthus*, the caudal peduncle is not framed by a fin membrane. The approximately eight species inhabit the Guyana Highlands, the Orinoco, Amazon, and São Francisco basins, and southeastern Brazil. They are, like most members of this subfamily, probably mostly nocturnal parasites which attack the gills of large fishes. There are reports, according to which these catfishes spend the remainder of the time buried in muddy sediments, usually in sections with a slight current.

The very similar genus *Homodiaetus* differs from *Stegophilus* in the arrangement of its ventral fins. Three or four species have a broad, discoidal mouth. These fishes feed primarily on the mucosa and the scales of larger fishes which they approach stealthily. There they rasp their food once they have adhered themselves. A *Homodiaetus maculatus* brought back from Bolivia was initially placed into a community aquarium with several sub-adult cichlids, until it became apparent that the cichlids showed more and more injuries on their mucosa. With nocturnal observations, the culprit was quickly identified. The only four-centimeter-long *Homodiaetus* lay motionless on the substrate. Once a victim came close, the

Photo below:
The Rio das Velhas in the Brazilian state of Minas Gerais. This is the location where REINHARDT's story, reported in EIGENMANN (1918b), unfolds.

H.-G. Evers

small beast darted towards its prey, bit part of the mucosa off, and disappeared anew. The bitten fish was startled and twitched sideways. That was the only explanation possible as to how the small catfish stayed in such good condition, even after weeks of aquarium maintenance. Naturally, after the discovery, the small catfish was transferred to a species tank.

The same feeding behavior applies to the approximately five species of the genus *Ochmacanthus*, which can be recognized by their typical fin-fringe framing the caudal peduncle. We were able to bring several specimens of both genera back to Germany. These slowly starved in our aquaria, because they refused to accept any kind of substitute fare. Feeding them mucosa of other fishes was not in the spirit of species protection.

The monotypical genera *Haemomaster, Pleurophysus, Apomatoceros,* and *Par-*

acanthopoma, as well as the genus *Acanthopoma* with two species, have all not appeared in the hobby. The same applies to the recently described genus *Megalocentor.* The status of the also monotypical genus *Schultzichthys* is uncertain, since the only known specimens are considered lost (DE PINNA, written comm.). Only *Pseudostegophilus nemurus* has appeared in the trade, but just in the form of a by-catch of larger characins. SCHREIBER (1992) reports about his experiences with these fish, which at night grazed the mucus of their tankmates, until in the end the host died. There was no other alternative to feed them sufficiently. It is our opinion that such a way to feed a fish constitutes animal torture. So please: keep your hands off these catfishes!

Stegophilinae inhabit waters with a rich ichthyofauna, such as this one: the Río San Julian in Bolivia.

Homodiaetus cf. *maculatus*

I. Seidel

Homodiaetus maculatus (STEINDACHNER, 1879)
Spotted parasitic catfish

F.: Steindachner, F. (1879): Über einige neue und seltene Fischarten aus den k.k. zoologischen Museen zu Wien, Stuttgart und Warschau,– Denkschr. Akad. Wiss. Wien, mathem.–naturwiss. Cl., 41: 1–52.

Syn.: *Stegophilus maculatus, Henonemus maculatus.*

Hab.: The species was described from the Uruguay Basin in Argentina. The pictured fish is very similar in coloration to one in a drawing in Eigenmann (1918b). It was captured by coauthor SEIDEL 1996 in the calmer sections of the Río San Alejandro, Peru. The water had a temperature of 30°C. Just captured, the eight centimeter long catfish were very beautiful and had a yellow coloration. It is impossible to hold these fish by hand. They force their way between the fingers, even if held in a closed fist. This is facilitated by the copious amounts of mucus covering their body.

No indications in regard to aquarium maintenance are given, since this is not an aquarium fish!

Homodiaetus vazferreirai   T. Litz

Homodiaetus vazferreirai DEVINCENZI, 1939

F.: Devicenzi, G. L. in Devincenzi, G. L.
& R. Vaz–Ferreira (1939): Nota preliminar sobre un pygidido hematófago del
Rio Uruguay.– Arch. Soc. Biol. Montevideo, 9 (3): 165–178.

Syn.: None.

Hab.: Uruguay, Río Uruguay drainage.
Thomas LITZ was able to demonstrate the
presence of this species in the basin of
the Río Uruguay during a collection trip
through Uruguay. The streams in the area
are already quite cool, and it is interesting that this hematophagous catfish has
advanced this far into the area.

No indications in regard to aquarium
maintenance are given, since this is not
an aquarium fish!

Homodiaetus sp. "Bolivia"

H.-G. Evers

Homodiaetus sp. "Bolivia"

This fish was captured by SEIDEL, DEBOLD, SCHADE, NORMAN, and others in the Río San Julian, Bolivia, a very swiftly flowing stream of the Guaporé drainage with clear, brown water (pH above 7).
The fish stayed in calmer sections, beneath the floating plant cover, in areas with a plentiful host-fish population. This species, too, has the typical oral disc, but differs significantly from the previous specimen in regard to coloration, and has not been unequivocally identified here.

Ochmacanthus sp.

An *Ochmacanthus* sp. is rasping on the characin *Hyphessobrycon socolofi*. Such "experiments" constitute cruelty to animals and should not be repeated!

Ochmacanthus sp. "Llanos"

This *Ochmacanthus* was captured by EVERS and SEIDEL in the Venezuelan Llanos. The single specimen was shaken out of a root. EVERS (1993) reports about capture and biotope. It is quite possible that all *Ochmacanthus* species pictured here are already scientifically described. However, we were not able to definitively identify these species based on the literature available to us.

The fish is presented as *Ochmacanthus alternus* in the AQUARIUM ATLAS Vol. 5.

Ochmacanthus sp.

H.-J. Franke

Ochmacanthus sp. "Llanos"

H.-J. Franke

Ochmacanthus sp. "Rio Cristalino"

This parasitic catfish lives in the tributaries of the Rio das Mortes in central Brazil (state of Mato Grosso). The species is captured every once in a while on sandbanks, but is rather rare. The Cristalino River is a beautiful clear-water stream. There, this catfish lives syntopically with *Branchioica* cf. *bertoni* and other, non-parasitic catfishes.

Ochmacanthus sp. "Tefé"

EVERS and SEIDEL were able to capture this parasitic catfish several times in the basin of the Brazilian Rio Tefé. Usually they were captured with a seine over sand substrates as they easily became entangled in the mesh with their opercular odontodes. Long-term aquarium maintenance was impossible without suitable host fishes. The specimens brought back died one after the other.

Ochmacanthus sp. "Tefé." Note the dorsoventrally compressed head.

H.-G. Evers

Ochmacanthus sp. "Rio Cristalino" H.-G. Evers

Ochmacanthus sp. "Tefé" H.-G. Evers

Fam.: Trichomycteridae
Subfam.: Stegophilinae

Pseudostegophilus nemurus   U. Schramm

Pseudostegophilus nemurus (GÜNTHER, 1868)

F.: Günther, A. (1868): Descriptions of freshwater fishes from Suriname and Brazil.– Proc.zool.Soc.London, 1868: 229–247.

Hab.: Upper Amazon, Rio Mamoré.

S: *Pseudostegophilus nemurus* has sporadically appeared in the trade as a bycatch. It is readily identified thanks to the distinct crossbands covering its body.

No indications in regard to aquarium maintenance are given, since this is not an aquarium fish!

H.-G. Evers

Stegophilus intermedius shortly after capture, in the photo tank still displaying an intense coloration. See following page for additional photo.

Stegophilus intermedius
EIGENMANN & EIGENMANN, 1889

F.: Eigenmann, C. H. & R. S. Eigenmann (1889): Preliminary notes on South American nematognathi II.– Proc. Calif. Acad. Sci., (2)2: 28–56.

Syn.: None.

Hab.: Brazil, state of Goias, drainage of the Rio Araguaia. EVERS captured the species in the Rio do Peixe (see also the chapter "Habitats"). It was relatively easy to capture the fish with a seine pulled over sandbanks. After capture, the specimens are beautifully yellowish-green; however, after some time in captivity, the color markedly fades until only gray remains. The description of *Stegophilus in-*termedius is solely based on the holotype. It has not been pictured elsewhere either. That is surely not due to being rare or difficult to capture.

The fishermen of the Araguaia know this to be a candirú that feeds on the blood of other fishes and avoid the species, even though it is particularly attractive and would superficially seem interesting for export.

No indications in regard to aquarium maintenance are given, since this is not an aquarium fish!

Fam.: Trichomycteridae

Subfam.: Stegophilinae

Stegophilus intermedius in an aquarium. The yellow-green coloration has disappeared.

H.-G. Evers

Sandbanks of the Rio do Peixe.

H.-G. Evers

Stegophilus cf. *taxistigma* in a photo tank, shortly after capture.

K. Arendt

Stegophilus taxistigma (Fowler, 1914)

F.: Fowler, H.W. (1914): Fishes from the Rupununi River, British Guyana.– Proc. Acad. Nat.Sci. Philadelphia, 66: 229–284.

Syn.: *Ochmacanthus* (*Cobitoglanis*) *taxistigma, Henonemus taxistigmus.*

Hab.: Guyana, Rupununi drainage. Arendt (pers. comm.) captured the species in the Río Orituco, a white-water stream of the Apure system in the Venezuelan Llanos (state of Guarico at Calabozo). The design is strongly reminiscent of a fish depicted in Eigenmann (1918b), a distribution including Venezuela is likely. Notable on freshly caught specimens was the apparent sexual dichromatism present. The slimmer males had greenish overtones, whereas reputed females lacked these.

No indications in regard to aquarium maintenance are given, since this is not an aquarium fish!

Trichogenes longipinnis

R. Wildekamp

Subfamily Trichogeninae ISBRÜCKER, 1986

Trichogenes BRITSKI & ORTEGA, 1983	Brazil, State of São Paulo

This subfamily is monotypic, *Trichogenes longipinnis* BRITSKI & ORTEGA, 1983 is its only member. Fortunately, its small area of distribution is located within a nature preserve of the Brazilian state of São Paulo. This will probably help to insure its continued survival. The free-swimming catfishes have a large anal fin and are reminiscent of the cetopsid genus *Helogenes* (therefore, the genus name is also composed of *Tricho-* from *Trichomycterus* and *-genes* from *Helogenes*). The largest known specimen is 11 cm long.

Subfamily Trichomycterinae BLEEKER, 1858

> Eremophilus HUMBOLDT, 1811 (1805?)
> Trichomycterus VALENCIENNES in
> HUMBOLDT, 1833
> Hatcheria EIGENMANN, 1909
> Scleronema EIGENMANN, 1917
> Rhizosomichthys MILES, 1943
> Bullockia ARRATIA, CHANG, MENU-MARQUE
> & ROJAS, 1978
> Ituglanis COSTA & BOCKMANN, 1993
> Silvinichthys ARRATIA, 1998

The members of this subfamily all have a wormlike elongated body, a cylindrical caudal peduncle, and a comparatively small, flat head with small, superior eyes and three pairs of barbels (one nasal pair and two maxillary pairs). The dentition on the mandible (lower jaw) is particularly pronounced. Various authors (DE PINNA, 1989a; ARRATIA, 1990) have discussed the monophyletic nature (originating from a common line) of the subfamily, and ARRATIA (1990) in the end mentions four skeletal characteristics which are said to confirm the monophyletic nature of the group. When dealing with such a widely distributed subfamily, such research is also very difficult and laborious for various other reasons. The genus Trichomycterus in particular, has hardly been analyzed, even today, as is highlighted by the recent separation of several members into the newly created genus Ituglanis. FERNÁNDEZ & VARI (2000), on the other hand, described the elongated Trichomycterus catamarcensis from Argentina, an additional member. The peculiarities of this species is its total lack of pectoral fins and the absence of the pectoral girdle. The authors also indicate in their publication that the genus Trichomycterus is still not sufficiently revised.
Three of a total of seven genera in this subfamily are monotypic (the possibly extinct Rhizosomichthys, as well as Bullockia and Hatcheria), the genus Scleronema has presently three species (TCHERNAVIN, 1944, ARRATIA, 1990). It differs from all other genera by possessing a dermal lobe on the opercula. After most recent analyses, the genus apparently does indeed include more than three species, a genus revision is in preparation (DE PINNA, written comm.). Bullockia maldonadoi (EIGENMANN, 1927) is a species from Chile. It differs from the closely related genus Trichomycterus by having a lower number of caudal fin rays (< 12 in contrast to >12 for Trichomycterus) and an elongated, relatively thin caudal peduncle. Hatcheria macraei (GIRARD, 1855) has been described from Argentina. ARRATIA & MENU-MARQUE (1981) revalidated the genus and disproved the synonymy to Trichomycterus (see TCHERNAVIN, 1944). There are a total of four synonyms for Hatcheria macraei, the genus is presently considered monotypic. The species is highly variable in design and coloration: there are spotted specimens, those that only exhibit a longitudinal stripe and those with a mixed set of designs. The dorsal fin is quite large and not rounded, the barbels are long. According to RINGUELET et al. (1967), Hatcheria lives in cool clear-water biotopes with strong currents in Argentina. Juveniles of up to two centimeters in length preferably stay among rocks in calm zones on the edge, larger specimens are benthic and face the sometimes raging currents.
Both species of the genus Eremophilus— i.e., E. mutisii from Colombia and E. candidus from southeastern Brazil (state of Espirito Santo)—lack ventral fins, a clear distinguishing characteristic to the other members of the subfamily. E. candidus is a very rare Brazilian export through Rio de Janeiro.
The genus Trichomycterus is the most species-rich of the entire subfamily. A junior synonym is Pygidium MEYEN, 1835.

855

Close to 100 species have been described, most of which are only vaguely diagnosed and very contritely described. DE PINNA (1989a) determined that all likelihood the genus is not monophyletic and in dire need of a taxonomic revision and a phylogenetic analysis. Costa & Bockmann (1993) confirmed this suspicion with the creation of the new genus *Ituglanis*, which differs in skeletal characteristics from the genus *Trichomycterus*. *Ituglanis* COSTA & BOCKMANN, 1993 comprises nine species at present, all originally transferred from the genus *Trichomycterus*. Type species of the genus is *Ituglanis parahybae* (EIGENMANN). ARRATIA (1998) created the monotypic genus, *Silvinichthys*, with a species from the Argentinian Andes. On various trips we were able to confirm the presence of *Trichomycterus* and *Ituglanis* species in Peru and Brazil. The habitats where the fishes were found were always clear streams. The identification of the species was very difficult, and even consulting the most varied primary literature in addition to knowing exactly the origin of the fishes was not sufficient to unequivocally identify them. Therefore, some fishes are listed without a species name, only with the corresponding area of origin and biotope information. It must be noted that especially this subfamily is very successful in South America. These fishes still inhabit bodies of water where other fish species have no chance, and their area of distribution includes both the mountainous regions as well as the lowlands. The members of the subfamily may be maintained long-term and even bred in an aquarium if certain conditions are met. It is important that the maintenance temperatures are not chosen too warm for those species hailing from the mountains, as is the provision of a strong filtration with its associated current. Unfortunately, these little elves might only be seen as they dart out of their hiding places to grab a morsel of food and quickly return

with their bounty to their shelters. Especially animal fare in the form of frozen *Daphnia* and mosquito larvae are accepted, but these are also hunted alive. Even tablet and flake foods are nibbled on after a certain acclimation period. Females can soon be identified by the hobbyist based to their distended bellies. Ripening females have been repeatedly witnessed and in some instances, young were suddenly discovered in the parent's tank a little time thereafter.

As noted above, the maintenance temperature is directly dependant on the origin of the fishes. If origin is ignored, it is best to begin with temperatures between 20° and 22°C and cautiously incrementing them to a maximum of 25°C. Most Trichomycterinae clearly prefer lower temperatures around 20°C and possibly even cooler.

Eremophilus candidus, lateral view. See next page for additional photo.

H.-G. Evers

Eremophilus candidus (RIBEIRO, 1949)

F.: Ribeiro, P. de Miranda (1949): Notas para o estudo dos Pygidiidae Brasileiros (Pisces – Pygidiidae, Pygidiinae) III.– Bol. do Mus.Nac.Zool., 88: 1–3.

Syn.: *Pygidium candidus*.

Hab.: Brazil, Espirito Santo, Rio Claro.

M.&B.: Like all its confamilials, these fish only show themselves at feeding time. Mostly everything, but especially of animal origin, is accepted. *E. candidus* is peaceful and does not bother other fishes.

S: The members of the genus *Eremophilus* lack ventral fins. Given that the fish is imported every once in a while from southeastern Brazil, species diagnosis is relatively certain.

T: 22°–25°C, L: 12 cm, A: 80 cm, R: b

Ituglanis cf. *metae*, head shot. Note the tiny eyes!

H.-G. Evers

E. candidus, dorsal view. See previous page for text.

H.-G. Evers

Ituglanis metae from the Rio Huacamayo, Peru. See next page of add'l photos. I. Seidel

Ituglanis metae (EIGENMANN, 1918)
Rio Meta loach catfish

F.: Eigenmann, C.H. (1918): Eighteen new species of fishes from northwestern South America.–Proc.Amer.phil.Soc., 56(7): 673–689.

Syn.: *Pygidium metae, Trichomycterus metae*.

Hab.: Colombia, Barrigona, Río Meta Basin.

M.&B.: Unproblematic, intraspecifically social species which, unfortunately, hardly ever comes into view. Only at feeding time does it appear on the open sand substrate, otherwise, *I. metae* hides in its cave. When well fed, the females ripen and develop such a distended belly as to virtually burst. Oviposition could not be confirmed, but the females did become "normal" again, although no eggs or young could be discovered.

S: The pictured specimen was imported from Peru, but does coincide quite well in coloration with *I. metae*. In 1993, COSTA & BOCKMANN placed the species into the newly created genus *Ituglanis*.

T: 25°–28°C, **L:** 8 cm, **A:** 60 cm, **R:** b

Ituglanis cf. *metae*, ♂ from Peru with coarser dots and slimmer.   H.-G. Evers

Ituglanis cf. *metae*, ♀ with distinctly distended belly. See previous page for text.   H.-G. Evers

Ituglanis cf. *parahybae*, specimen from Minas Gerais.

H.-G. Evers

Ituglanis parahybae (Eigenmann, 1918)
Paraiba loach catfish

F.: Eigenmann, C.H. (1918): The Pygiidae, a family of South American catfishes.– Mem. Carnegie Mus., 7(5): 259–398.

Syn.: *Pygidium proops parahybae*, *Trichomycterus parahybae*.

Hab.: Southeastern Brazil, drainage of the Rio Paraiba do Sul. In October 1996, the pictured specimen was captured by Evers, Lacerda, and Beyer in a clear-water stream (Corrego Palacio) at the Serra do Cipo, in the Brazilian state of Minas Gerais. The stream is part of the drainage of the Rio Doce and not—as is the case with the rivers on the other side of the watershed—of the Rio São Francisco. The water was quite cool (20°C) and rapid-flowing. The catfishes were hiding in fine sand and difficult to capture.

M.&B.: Maintain like the other members of the subfamily, only somewhat cooler.

S: This is the type species of the genus *Ituglanis*.

T: 17°–22°C, L: 8 cm, A: 60 cm, R: b

Scleronema angustirostris
(DEVINCENZI & TEAGUE, 1942)

F.: Devincenzi, G.J.& G.W. Teague (1942): Ictiofauna del Río Uruguay Medio.– Anales Mus.Hist.Nat. Montevideo: 1–57.

Syn.: *Pygidium angustirostris.*

Hab.: Uruguay, central Rio Uruguay drainage. LITZ (written comm.) captured the species, June 20ᵗʰ '98, at Tacuarembó, approximately 500 m upriver in the Arroyo Cinco Sauces on the bridge of route 26, km 331. The animals were "shoveled" out of the gravel substrate at a sandbank in rapid-flowing water with a temperature of only 13°C!

M.&B.: According to LITZ (written comm.), females grow to a length of 6.5 to 7.0 cm, whereas males remain smaller and slimmer. On a light-brown to beige substrate, both genders display dark spots outside the spawning season. During the spawning season, the female turns dark-brown and her ventral area becomes reddish brown. If maintained with a sand substrate, *S. angustirostris* likes to bury itself. However, after an acclimation phase, it is not shy at all and may also be visible during the day. LITZ (pers. comm.) found, after maintaining the species for a few months in an unheated aquarium (50x20x20 cm) at a temperature between 10 and 25°C, several subadult specimens as he was cleaning out the tank. It may therefore be said that *Scleronema angustirostris* has bred in captivity. A first step to scheduled breeding has been accomplished. The white eggs are readily visible through the abdominal wall of females. LITZ observed shuddering and bowing of the head while the partners were laying next to each other (courtship?).

S. angustirostris feeds mostly on live foods (mosquito larvae, *Daphnia*) and frozen foods in captivity.

S: The correct identification of the pictured catfish is confirmed based on the analysis of preserved specimens. There are strong parallels to *Scleronema operculum.*

T: 18°–22°C, **L:** 7 cm, **A:** 50 cm, **R:** b

Scleronema angustirostris ♀, Arroyo Cinco Sances, Uruguay. T. Litz

Scleronema angustirostris ♂ (top). T. Litz

Trichomycterus alternatus

H.-G. Evers

Trichomycterus alternatus (Eigenmann, 1917)

F.: Eigenmann, C.H. (1917): Description of Sixteen New Species of South American Pygidiidae.– Proc.Amer.Phil.Soc., 16: 690–703.

Syn.: *Pygidium alternatum.*

Hab.: Brazil, Espirito Santo, Rio Doce Basin.

M.&B.: Individual specimens of *T. alternatus* are very sporadically imported. As is the case for all *Trichomycterus* known to date, *T. alternatus* is shy and during the day hides in its shelter. However, it appears lightning fast at feeding time. We are unaware of any breeding reports.

S: This species has been imported together with *Eremophilus candidus* from southeastern Brazil. The design presented in the original description by and large coincides with that of the pictured specimen.

T: 22°–25°C, **L:** 10 cm, **A:** 60 cm, **R:** b

H.-G. Evers

Typical white-water river in the drainage of the Rio Doce, Espirito Santo. This is home to *Trichomycterus alternatus*.

Trichomycterus bahianus COSTA, 1992
Bahia loach catfish

F.: Costa, W.J.E. (1992): Description de huit nouvelles espéces du genre *Tricho-mycterus* (Siluriformes: Trichomycteri-dae) du Brésil oriental.– Revue fr.Aqua-riol., 18(4): 101–110

Syn.: None.

Hab.: Eastern Brazil, Bahia, drainage of the Rio Una.

M.&B.: Aquarium care of *T. bahianus*—a shy species—is not difficult. The water temperature may be maintained at 25°C. A cooler setting, as required for all species from southeastern Brazil, is not needed. The few specimens available to date came from an import by AQUARIUM DIETZENBACH, which received the fish through the company TROP-RIO (Rio de Janeiro). There are no breeding reports.

S: *T. bahianus* is readily distinguished from its congeners by the combination of three longitudinal stripes on the body with coarse spots, especially posteriorly.

T: 23°–26°C, L: 8 cm, A: 60 cm, R: b

Trichomycterus dispar (TSCHUDI, 1845)

F.: Tschudi, J.J. von (1845): Untersu-chungen über die Fauna peruana. Ich-thyologie (Scheitlin & Zollikofer, St. Gal-len): 1–35.

Syn.: *Pygidium dispar*.

Hab.: West Andean species, originally described from Peru. WERNER (written comm.) captured the fish in Ecuador, in the Río Daule drainage, together with *Tri-chomycterus taenia*. It is said the species also exists east of the Andes, but always at higher elevations.

M.&B.: Unknown, probably along the lines of that described for the other species presented.

S: There are similarities to the east Andean species *Ituglanis metae* from Colombia and Peru, but its corporal dots are more delicate.

T: 23°–26°C, L: 10 cm, A: 60 cm, R: b

Trichomycterus bahianus

H.-G. Evers

Trichomycterus dispar

U. Werner

Trichomycterus meridae REGAN, 1903

F.: Regan, C.T. (1903): Descriptions of new south American fishes in the collection of the British Museum.–Ann. Mag. Nat.Hist., ser. 7, 72: 621–630.

Syn.: *Pygidium meridae*.

Hab.: Venezuela, Merida mountain range, probably also at lower elevations.

M.&B.: The pictured specimen is a male. Females are not as slim and elongated, but appear rather plump. *T. meridae* may be maintained without problems at somewhat lower temperatures in an unheated aquarium.

S: The pictured specimen was imported from Venezuela and coincides in regard to coloration and body shape to the description of *T. meridae*. Until the species identification is confirmed, it is preferable to use the designation *Trichomycterus* cf. *meridae*.

T: 18°–22°C, L: 10 cm, A: 60 cm, R: b

Trichomycterus mimonha COSTA, 1992

F.: Costa, W.J.E. (1992): Description de huit nouvelles espéces du genre *Trichomycterus* (Siluriformes: Trichomycteridae), du Brésil oriental.– Revue fr. Aquariol., 18 (4): 101–110.

Syn.: None.

Hab.: Brazil, State of São Paulo, drainage of the Paraiba do Sul, Rio Benfica at Piquete.

M.&B.: The species hails from southeastern Brazil where, especially at higher elevations around São Paulo, temperatures markedly below 20°C routinely occur. This applies in particular to the upper courses of the numerous clear-water streams where, nevertheless, various *Trichomycterus* species can be found. Other aspects of aquarium maintenance follow the suggestions expressed elsewhere for similar species.

S: The holotype pictured in the original description is a female with a short caudal peduncle. The male pictured here was captured by LACERDA and BEYER (written comm.) in the Rio Benfica at the town of Piquete and shows only a slightly expressed longitudinal row of black dots. In the same biotope, both captured an additional (?), highly variable species with a distinctly expressed black longitudinal band. The photographs here show males and females of a species, here preliminarily identified as *Trichomycterus* cf. *mimonha,* as well as an additional male with virtually black flanks. Especially noteworthy in these animals are the golden rows above the black longitudinal band, particularly in males. In the Rio Benfica, and also in neighboring similar rivers, LACERDA and BEYER always captured this community of loach catfishes. The presence of all these transitional color morphs seems to be indicative of a great variability within the species *T. mimonha*, rather than of a syntopic presence of similar species.

T: 16°–22°C, L: 6 cm, A: 60 cm, R: b

Trichomycterus cf. *meridae*

I. Seidel

Trichomycterus mimonha ♂

H.-G. Evers

Trichomycterus cf. *mimonha* ♂   H.-G. Evers

Trichomycterus cf. *mimonha* ♂ with a distinct black longitudinal band. Apparently the species is highly variable in design.

Trichomycterus cf. *mimonha* ♀

H.-G. Evers

H.-G. Evers

The Rio Itabapoana at Espirito Santo, habitat of *Trichymycterus* cf. *nigricans*. The current at this section, called Ilha do Itabapoana, was swift.

Trichomycterus nigricans Valenciennes, 1832

F.: Valenciennes, A. (1832): Nouvelles observations sur le capitan de Bogota, *Eremophilus mutisii*. In: Voyage de Humboldt et Bonpland, deuxième partie. Observations de Zoologie et d'Anatomie comparée. Paris. Vol. 2: 341–348.

Syn.: *Pygidium nigricans*.

Hab.: Brazil, state of Santa Catarina.

M.&B.: Unknown, since it has not yet been imported alive [to Germany].

S: The pictured specimen was captured much further north, in the Rio Itabapoana, at the border between the states of Rio de Janeiro and Espirito Santo. Size, coloration, and its constitution allow the conclusion that this indeed is *T. nigricans*. Evers, Lacerda, and Beyer captured the species in April 1995 in the raging currents of small cachoeiras at the Ilha do Itabapoana and were surprised about the size of this loach catfish. The whitewater had a relatively warm temperature of 27°–28°C, a pH of 7.3, and a conductivity of 44 µs/cm. *T. nigricans* is the type species of the genus *Trichomycterus*. Arratia (1998) describes very vividly how, due to the very incomplete original description, for a long time only little was known about the species. Additionally, *T. nigricans* was only known from a single specimen from Santa Catarina. Arratia (1998) studied the holotype and was then able to split the new genus *Silvinichthys* from *Trichomycterus*.

T: 24°–27°C, L: 15 cm, A: 80 cm, R: b

Trichomycterus regani (Eigenmann, 1917)
Regan's loach catfish

F.: Eigenmann, C.H. (1917): Description of Sixteen New Species of Pygidiidae.– Proc.Amer.Phil.Soc., 16: 690–703.

Syn.: *Pygidium regani*.

Hab.: Colombia, Río San Juan. The pictured specimen was captured by Seidel in the Peruvian Tulumayo River. Biotope information can be found in the chapter "Habitats" in the section on loricariids.

M.&B.: Breeding is unknown. The species appreciates swiftly flowing water and lives the entire day hidden among rocks and plant roots.

S: The pictured individual agrees by and large in design with a drawing of *T. regani* in Eigenmann (1918b). However, it was captured in Peru, outside its reputed area of distribution, and so we prefer to presently call it *Trichomycterus* cf. *regani*.

T: 22°–26°C, L: 10 cm, A: 60 cm, R: b

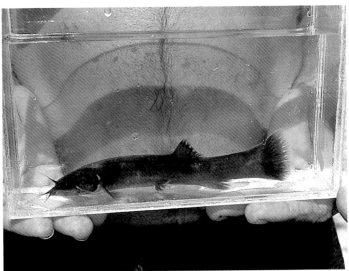

Trichomycterus nigricans, shortly after capture, in a photo tank.

H.-G. Evers

Trichomycterus cf. *regani*

I. Seidel

Trichomycterus taenia KNER, 1863
Striped loach catfish

F.: Kner, R. (1863): Eine Übersicht der ichthyologischen Ausbeute des Herrn Professor Dr. Mor. Wagner in Central-Amerika. – Sber. Kön. Bayer. Akad. Wiss., München, 2:220–230.

Syn.: *Pygidium taenium.*

Hab.: Ecuador, west of the Andes. WERNER (1992 and written comm.) captured the species in the Daule River Basin at Vinces, together with an additional *Trichomycterus* species (*T. dispar*). The clear water had a temperature of 25°C and flowed swiftly over a gravel substrate. The loach catfishes were captured with sturdy dip nets from the gravel with a technique that might be more accurately described as sieving.

M.&B.: According to WERNER (written comm.), the specimens brought home remained in good condition for an extended period of time but, as expected, were hardly ever seen. *T. taenia* is, like its congeners, unaggressive and does not bother its tankmates.

S: The typical corporeal stripes make this catfish attractive and allows for an unequivocal species determination when used in conjunction with information on its natural area of distribution.

T: 23°–26°C, L: 8 cm, A: 60 cm, R: b

Trichomycterus zonatus (EIGENMANN, 1918)

F.: Eigenmann, C.H. (1918): The Pygidae, a family of South American catfishes.– Mem.Carnegie Mus., 7(5): 259–398.

Syn.: *Pygidium zonatum.*

Hab.: Brazil, state of São Paulo, Agua Quente at Santos.

M.&B.: Dietrich RÖSSEL (pers. comm.) maintained a group of this species for a while. The animals were quite shy, but felt at home in an aquarium with vegetation and normal feeding. Every so often the females appeared ripe, but young were never detected.

S: The characteristic design readily identifies the species. Five or more variably pronounced crossbands cover dorsally, prior to the dorsal fin base, the body. The remainder of the pigmentation is highly variable, even within the same population. Two different morphs which belong to the same species, are presented here.

T: 20°–25°C, L: 8 cm, A: 60 cm, R: b

Trichomycterus zonatus in an aquarium.

D. Rössel

Trichomycterus taenia

U. Werner

Trichomycterus zonatus, a somewhat deviating morph.

U. Werner

Trichomycterus sp. "Bermejo"

Bolivian loach catfishes hardly ever have reached our aquaria. The pictured species was captured close to the town of Bermejo, approximately one hour by car southwest of Santa Cruz de la Sierra, in a clear-water creek that empties into the Rio Bermejo. The water temperature was 18°C at the time and fluctuates in the course of one year between 16 and 24°C. The species was found in large numbers above some waterfalls. The daytime hours are spent among the leaf litter and the night is spent feeding. The largest specimens measured about 25 cm in total length, a respectable size for a loach catfish. *Trichomycterus* sp. "Bermejo" is unlikely to ever play a significant role in the aquarium hobby.

Trichomycterus sp. "Campo Grande"

M. BEYER captured this loach catfish in the upper basin of the Rio Tietê at the city of Campo Grande (Brazil, state of São Paulo). The only species, to date, described from the Tietê is *T. paolence* EIGENMANN, 1917. That fish, however, has three longitudinal stripes, something *Trichomycterus* sp. "Campo Grande" clearly does not. The biotope consists of the typical small rivers of the area. They carry clear water and have a swift current. The water temperature is usually below 20°C.

Trichomycterus sp. "Bermejo"   I. Seidel

Trichomycterus sp. "Campo Grande"   H.-G. Evers

Trichomycterus sp. "Canal Mato Grosso"

During an October 1996 trip to the Brazilian state of Rio de Janeiro, EVERS and LACERDA captured in the Canal Mato Grosso, a sidearm of the Rio Capivari, this catfish in shallow water flowing with a swift current over a sand/gravel substrate. An identification to the species level has not yet been possible.

Trichomycterus sp. "Kavac"

In August 1994, this small—approximately three centimeters long—loach catfish was captured by EVERS at the foot of the Auyan Tepui at the town of Kavac (southern Venezuela) in a swiftly flowing stream directly below some submersed rocks. The black-water had such low values that the instruments did not register correctly. These dwarfs swam without problems in the roiling waters against the current and were easily captured using a diving mask. The only species known from the area is *Trichomycterus guianensis* (see FERNÁNDEZ-YÉPEZ, 1967). That species, however, has uniform dots covering its body and no stripes whatsoever. *Trichomycterus* sp. "Kavac" is very likely a new species.

Trichomycterus sp. "Canal Mato Grosso"

Trichomycterus sp. "Kavac"

Trichomycterus sp. "Rio Itapemerim"

This loach catfish with its unusual design was captured by H.-G. Evers and M. Beyer in the Brazilian state of Espirito Santo. The swiftly flowing, clear-water carrying Rio Itapemerim flows directly into the Atlantic and is therefore home to a distinctly different ichthyofauna than that present in the Rio Doce Basin. We were unable to determine if this species had already been scientifically described.

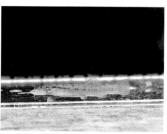

H.-G. Evers

Trichomycterus sp. "Itapemerim," shortly after capture, in a photo tank.

The Rio Kavac drains the Auyan Tepui of southern Venezuela.

H.-G. Evers

Trichomycterus sp. "Peru"

With its four centimeters, this is a relatively small loach catfish. In regard to its design, certain similarities to *T. zonatus*, from southeastern Brazil, become evident, especially in regard to the dorsal crossbands, anterior to the base of the dorsal fin.

The pictured specimen, however, was a by-catch of characins in a shipment from Peru. A species determination was not possible.

Trichomycterus sp. "Peru"　　H.-G. Evers

Trichomycterus sp. "Rio Preto," lateral view. See also the following pages.　　H.-G. Evers

Trichomycterus sp. "Rio Preto"

This fish, too, hails from the Brazilian state of Rio de Janeiro. LACERDA and EVERS captured several of these very attractively patterned fish in a tributary of the Rio Preto (a tributary of the Paquequer), called Pozo Fundo. The water was cool and had a swift current.

Especially noteworthy are the golden dots on the caudal peduncle and on the dorsum. Although several species have been described from the area (*T. florensis, T. paquequerensis*), their coloration differs from that of *T.* sp. "Rio Preto." Is this possibly an undescribed species?

Trichomycterus sp. "Rio Vermelho"

EVERS, LACERDA, and BEYER captured this unidentified catfish in the small, white-water carrying Rio Vermelho, a tributary of the Rio das Velhas (Rio São Francisco Basin) in the Brazilian state of Minas Gerais.

This, at five centimeters, small species was maintained with no problems for almost two years in an aquarium with other loach catfishes as tankmates.

Trichomycterus sp. "Rio Preto"

H.-G. Evers

Trichomycterus sp. "Rio Vermelho"

H.-G. Evers

883

Subfamily Tridentinae Eigenmann, 1918

Tridens Eigenmann & Eigenmann, 1889
Miuroglanis Eigenmann &
Eigenmann, 1889
Tridentopsis Myers, 1925
Tridensimilis Schultz, 1944

Whereas the genera *Tridens* and *Miuroglanis* are monotypic, *Tridensimilis* and *Tridentopsis* only contain two species each. Main distinguishing characteristic to other subfamilies is the presence of a long and wide anal fin with 15–25 rays, which begins anteriorly (!) to the base of the dorsal fin. The eyes are situated laterally and are readily visible, in contrast to those of many other confamilials. The body is crystalline and makes the fishes virtually invisible over sand substrates. It is likely that these small catfishes mingle in schools of other fishes and swim in the open water.

The opinions on the social interaction of these dwarfs with their tankmates are varied. *Tridensimilis brevis* is a regular by-catch of *Corydoras pygmaeus* and, with a little luck, a small school can be established. Both authors have, on several occasions, maintained these fish together—for over a year—with small characins and corydoras. The fish were untiringly moving about the aquarium all day long, eating small livefoods such as *Artemia* nauplii and *Cyclops,* and never bothered their tankmates. Other hobbyists experienced that a group of *T. brevis* attacked their tankmates and bit their mucosa. Whatever the situation, the interested aquarist is advised to initially maintain a small group in a species tank. The second *Tridensimils* sp. is *T. venezuelae* Schultz, 1944 from the Maracaibo Basin. The genus *Tridentopsis*—with the two species *T. pearsoni* Myers, 1925 (Bolivia) and *T. tocantinsi* La Monte, 1939 (Rio Tocantins, Brazil)—is physically more compact than *Tridensimilis* and has a greater number of opercular and interopercular odontodes.

Similarly, *Tridens melanops* Eigenmann & Eigenmann, 1889, from the border region Brazil/Peru, has not yet made its appearance in the hobby. The species is very elongated and has an inferior mouth and lateral eyes which, in a manner similar to the suckermouth catfish genus *Hypoptopoma,* can also detect what is happening below the fish. Barbels are present, but they are highly vestigial.

The last species in the subfamily is *Miuroglanis platycephalus* Eigenmann & Eigenmann, 1889, also an aquaristically unknown entity. The body shape is similar to the genus *Tridentopsis,* the large eyes are lateral. An important difference to *Tridentopsis* is the arrangement of the odontodes on the opercula and interopercula. However, hardly ever will an aquarist be in such a bind as to have to observe these up close.

Tridensimilis brevis, see next page for additional photos.

H.-G. Evers

Tridensimilis brevis (EIGENMANN & EIGENMANN, 1889)

F.: Eigenmann, C.H.& R.S. Eigenmann (1889): Preliminary notes on South American Nematognathi.– Proc. California Acad. Sci., 2(2): 28–56.

Syn.: *Tridens brevis.*

Hab.: Brazil, Peru, Amazon Basin. Probably a white-water inhabitant.

M.&B.: Very suitable for aquarium maintenance. In a species tank, there are no problems in feeding small livefoods such as *Artemia* nauplii, *Cyclops,* and *Daphnia.* In community aquaria experiences vary (see introduction to subfamily). HOFFMANN & HOFFMANN (1998) were able to obtain first experiences with the breeding of *T. brevis.* A group of these free-swimming catfish was maintained with various characins. A pair separated and swam around each other in circles. Oviposition proper could not be observed, but as the substrate was siphoned, several eggs of 3 mm diameter with a vitreous nucleus were found. They were reminiscent of frog spawn. The hatchlings were quite large and accepted *Artemia* nauplii already 72 hours later. Unfortunately, the young did not survive much longer. Although unsuccessful in the end, this partial success does entice the aquarist to try breeding this interesting catfish.

S: *T. brevis* is an occasional by-catch of the massive imports of *Corydoras pygmaeus* and *Corydoras hastatus.*

T: 26°–30°C, **L:** 3 cm, **A:** 50 cm, **R:** m, t

Tridensimilis brevis, recently hatched larva. See previous page for text.   P. Hoffmann

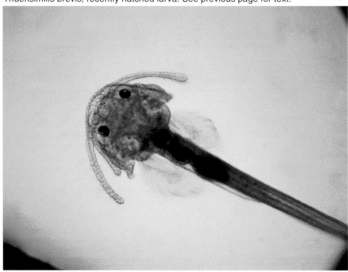

Tridensimilis brevis, fry after feeding on *Artemia*.   P. Hoffmann

Tridensimilis venezulae, lateral view. See next page for additional photo.

E. Schraml

Tridensimilis venezuelae SCHULTZ, 1944
Venezuelan parasitic catfish

F.: Schultz, L.P. (1944): The catfishes of Venezuela, with descriptions of thirty–eight new forms.– Proc. U. S. Nat. Mus., 94: 173–338.

Syn.: None.

Hab.: Venezuela, Maracaibo Basin.

M.&B.: Due to a paucity of imported specimens, maintenance experience in regard to this species is even sparser than with that of its congener, *T. brevis.* However, it stands to reason that the maintenance requirements of *T. venezuelae* are similar.

S: *T. venezuelae* inhabits an area from where rarely any fishes reach Germany. However, since there are many parallels between the piscine fauna of the Maracaibo Basin and that of the Colombian Magdalena Basin, it may be that this species has a more expansive area of distribution and that it will therefore be imported as a by-catch. The species is more elongated than *T. brevis* and, consequently, the eyes appear proportionally larger.

T: 25°–28°C, **L:** 3 cm, **A:** 50 cm, **R:** m, t

887

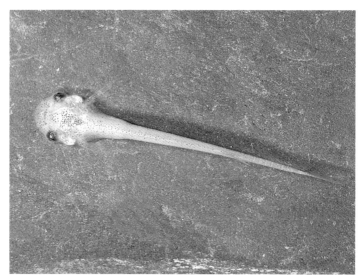

Tridensimilis venezulae, dorsal view. Note the slender body.

E. Schraml

I. Seidel

The rivers of the Llanos, home to *T. venezuelae*, flood severely during the rainy season.

Subfamily Vandelliinae BLEEKER, 1862

Vandellia VALENCIENNES, 1846
Paravandellia RIBEIRO, 1912
Plectrochilus RIBEIRO, 1917
Branchioica EIGENMANN, 1918
Paracanthopoma GILTAY, 1935

The stories about small, blood sucking fishes which parasitize the gills of large fishes and even do not fear entering the urethra of humans are so well-known in the hobby that the entire family fell victim to this stigma. But in reality—based on present observations—it is only the members of this subfamily which actually feed on blood.

The Vandelliinae are catfishes without nasal nor mandibular barbels. The broad, inferior mouth has small pointed teeth. These catfishes are very slender and only a few centimeters long. They are, therefore, readily able to enter tiny openings. There have been repeated reports where these small beasts have entered the nose, ear, anus, vagina, or urethra of the penis. It could not be ascertained, if they ended up there because they were in search of food or if they were reacting to countercurrents. There will hardly be an aquarist whose "eagerness to know" will lead to self-experimentation in the home aquarium.

In any case, the suspicion does come to mind, that much might be an exaggeration in regard to those reports. Although, indeed, minor surgery is needed to remove the fish which has wedged itself into a tight spot with its opercular odontodes, an amputation is not going to be necessary anymore, contrary to what has been reported in older reports. Nowadays, medicine has progressed far enough, even in remote areas. The natives and caboclos in Brazil call this fish candirú (in eastern Peru "canero"). As a protective measure from these beasts, the natives use tubes and similar items as barriers or tie closed their penis when they bath. This keeps these parasites from searching for food in the wrong places if given the chance.

During their search for food, the caneros (or candirús) usually attack large fishes, such as shovelnose catfishes of the family Pimelodidae. As described in the chapter introduction on the family Cetopsidae, when fishing for these huge catfishes with hook and line, the caneros often appear and bite pieces of flesh out of the defenseless fish. Besides the Cetopsidae, especially the parasitic catfishes of the subfamily Stegophilinae are found in such situations. The Vandellinae usually swim into the brachial cavity to parasitize the richly vascularized gills. MACHADO & SAZIMA (1983) reported impressively on field observations in the Rio Cuiabá, Mato Grosso, central Brazil. Large, captured *Pseudoplatystoma fasciatum* (LINNAEUS, 1766) were pulled alive towards the shallow water at a sandbank. After only 4–10 minutes, hundreds, if not thousands, of catfishes of the species *Branchioica bertoni* came swimming and entered straight into the gill chambers, from where they emerged after 1–3 minutes with full bellies. Stomach contents analyses performed on the parasites revealed the presence of large quantities of red blood cells (erythrocytes). One of the fishes in the study was left for six hours at the site and served as a feeding station for thousands of candirús, which gladly took advantage of the helplessness of the victim.

EVERS was repeatedly able to capture members of this subfamily in the Rio Araguaia and its tributaries, central Brazil. It became apparent that these wormlike fishes were captured more numerously when the sandbanks were seined during twilight. Both *Vandellia* and *Branchioica* were to be taken to Germany for photography. Unfortunately, the intermediate holding during transit, in a well-aerated maintenance tank, was not survived after 7–9 days. Although no intent was made to let the fish parasitize others, starvation can be excluded, since it is virtually certain that longer periods of hunger can be withstood.

Besides the genus *Branchioica* (synonym *Parabranchioica*) with 4 species, the monotypic genus *Paravandellia* and the three species of the genus *Plectrochilus* have hardly become known, although for them, too, gill parasitism is also probable. *Plectrochilus* (synonym *Urinophilus*) is eellike-elongated and might be placed into the genus *Vandellia* after a more detailed analysis. The genus *Vandellia*, with presently seven species, is the best-known genus in the subfamily. KELLY & ATZ (1964) reported about an experiment performed in the CLEVELAND-AQUARIUM, where the "vampire behavior" of a *Vandellia* species on a goldfish was documented photographically. The three to six centimeter long eellike fishes are difficult to identify.

The area of distribution includes the Guyana Highlands and the Amazon Basin. These fishes are hardly suitable for aquarium maintenance. The *Vandellia cirrhosa,* captured in the Araguaia, lightning fast sucked themselves onto the hand when they were carefully removed from the net. Fortunately, they were unable to break the skin. *Vandellia* are by far the strangest parasitic catfishes of all, having a long body and a tiny head with far superiorly placed "knob eyes."

Photograph top right:
Members of the subfamily feed on blood and parasitize the gill rakers of large fishes, such as *Phractocephalus hemiolopterus.* The fishes also excrete their nitrogenous wastes over the gills, which might possibly explain why the small fishes also react to urinating mammals, where they enter the urethra and become stuck.

Photograph bottom right:
It is often relatively easy to capture members of the Vandellinae at twilight on sandbanks, such as here at the Rio Vermelho, a tributary of the Araguaia.

H.-G. Evers

H.-G. Evers

Branchioica bertoni Eigenmann, 1917

F.: Eigenmann, C. H. (1917): Descriptions of sixteen new species of Pygiidae.– Proc. Am. Philos. Soc., 56 (4): 690–703.

Syn.: None.

Hab.: Described from Paraguay, Asuncion. However, the species seems to have a much more extensive area of distribution. The pictured specimen hails from the Araguaia region in central Brazil. *B. bertoni* is common there, both in clear- as well as white-water, anywhere sandbanks are found.

No indications in regard to aquarium maintenance are given, since this is not an aquarium fish!

H.-G. Evers

Branchioica cf. *bertoni* shortly after capture. The full intestine can be discerned on the ventral side.

Plectrochilus erythrurus (Eigenmann, 1922)

F.: Eigenmann, C.H. (1922): The Fishes of the Western South America, Part I. The fresh-water fishes of northwestern South America, including Colombia, Panama, and the Pacific slopes of Ecuador and Peru, together with an appendix upon the fishes of the Rio Meta in Colombia.– Memoires of the Carnegie Museum, 9(1): 1–346.

Syn.: *Urinophilus erythrurus*.

Hab.: Peru, Río Morona, Ucayali drainage. The species can probably be found in the entire Ucayali Basin. Occasionally, it has appeared as by-catch in shipments of various other fishes. Naturally, such slender fishes are immediately noted, and this is how Kai Arendt was able to acquire such a rare specimen for photographic purposes.

No indications in regard to aquarium maintenance are given, since this is not an aquarium fish!

H.-G. Evers

Branchioica cf. *bertoni* from the Araguaia region. Note the beautiful dot design on the transparent body.

K. Arendt

Plectrochilus erythrurus in an aquarium.

Vandellia cirrhosa
VALENCIENNES in CUVIER & VALENCIENNES, 1846

F.: Valenciennes, A. in G. Cuvier & A. Valenciennes (1846): Histoire naturelle des poissons, tome 18.– Strasbourg.

Syn.: None.

Hab.: Amazonia, Orinoco Basin. The pictured specimen was captured by EVERS in the drainage of the Rio Araguaia (Brazil). During the day, *V. cirrhosa* is easily captured on sandbanks with a seine. Recently captured specimens usually have a very distended gastrointestinal tract and can handle several weeks without feeding.

No indications in regard to aquarium maintenance are given, since this is not an aquarium fish!

Vandellia cirrhosa shortly after capture. As can be readily seen at the ventrum, the intestine is bursting full.

Vandellia sanguinea EIGENMANN, 1918

F.: Eigenmann (1918): Eighteen new species of fishes from northwestern South America.– Proc.Amer.phil.Soc., 56(7): 673–689.

Syn.: None.

Hab.: Brazil, Madeira drainage. The pictured specimen was captured by WERNER (written comm.) in the Rio Abuná at Foraleza in the Madeira drainage.

M.: *V. sanguinea* does not belong in an aquarium!

"Feeding" them with large host fishes is cruelty to animals. In nature, these catfish find many hosts and do not abuse a single specimen as would be the case in the reduced confines of an aquarium.

S: The species in this genus are difficult to distinguish one from the other.

No indications in regard to aquarium maintenance are given, since this is not an aquarium fish!

Vandellia cirrhosa in the aquarium.

H.-G. Evers

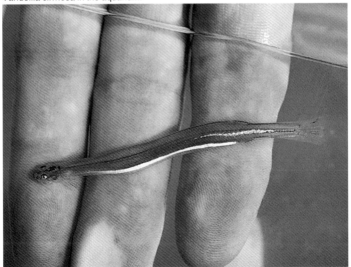

Vandellia sanguinea

U. Werner

Glossary

Glossary

Abdomen: The "stomach." Body cavity containing the viscera. In arthropods, the section behind the thorax or cephalothorax (the "tail").

Aberrant: Deviating from "normal."

Accessory Breathing: In fishes, having ways of obtaining oxygen from the air in addition to their normal gas exchange through the gills in the water.

Acclimatization: Adaptation of a species to a new environment.

Acidic: Said of water having a pH below neutral (7.0). Contrary to alkaline.

Adaptation: Adjusting to particular conditions prevalent in a biotope. The change can be physiological (e.g., tanning of the skin in response to sunlight) as well as genetic in response to natural selection.

Adhesive Spawner: Mode of reproduction where the eggs are adhered randomly among plants.

Adipose Fin: The small fin located dorsally and behind de dorsal fin and in front of the caudal (tail) fin.

Adult: Full-grown, with sufficient age to reproduce

Aerobic: A condition where oxygen is present. Organism which requires oxygen to survive.

Albinism: Lack of body pigments due to genetic causes (inability to form melanin).

Albino: Individual that lacks pigments (red eyes).

Alkaline: Water with a basic reaction (pH above 7). Contrary to acidic.

Allochthonous: An organism that originated at a different (eco)system of where it is found. Contrary to autochthonous.

Allopatric: Populations or species occurring in different geographical areas.

Anaerobic: Place where no oxygen is present. Organism which does not require the presence of oxygen to live.

Anagram: A word that is formed by changing the order of the letters of a different word.

Anal fin: Single fin located ventrally, posterior to the anus and in front of the caudal (tail) fin.

Anatomy: Structure and form of animals and plants.

Anorganic: Part of nonliving nature (e.g., rocks).

Antibiotic: Chemical compound produced by microorganisms or synthetically that has the capacity to inhibit the growth of, or destroy, other microorganisms (e.g., bacteria, but not viruses).

Aposematic: Colors or structures on organisms meant to deter potential predators (e.g., bright colors on poison arrow frogs).

Artemia: Genus of small, saltwater crustaceans used worldwide in aquaculture to feed the fry of cultured fishes (using just hatched cysts, the nauplii). Adults (usually frozen or freeze-dried) are fed to larger fishes. The eggs of these crustacea (cysts) are harvested from the beaches of the Salt Lake in Utah, USA, for example. Also called brine shrimp.

Aufwuchs: Biocover. Largely, the layer of filamentous algae growing on hard substrates and the associated tiny invertebrates living within. Many fishes have specialized morphological adaptations that allow them to efficiently feed upon this layer.

Autochthonous: An organism that originated at the same (eco)system of where it is found. Contrary to allochthonous.

Bactericide: An agent that destroys bacteria.

Barbels: A slender, almost threadlike tactile appendage near the mouth in certain fishes (e.g., catfishes).

Base: A solution with a pH above 7.

Benthic: Associated with or living on the bottom of bodies of water.

Bicuspid: Having two points. A quality of teeth and of importance in the characterization of the dentition ion fishes.

Biotope: The specific habitat of a particular (fish) species.

Black-water: Brown, transparent water rich in humic acids which is very acid and soft. It originates from severely weathered areas. Chemically it approaches distilled water and is even slightly germicidal.

Body Width: Distance between the outer edges of the clavicles.

Body Depth: Height of the body measured anteriorly of the base of the first dorsal fin ray.

Bosmids, *Bosmina*: A genus of water flea (Cladocera). Used as feed for small fish fry, in a manner similar to the artemia.

Brackish Water: Water with a salinity between that of freshwater and seawater, i.e., with a salinity between 0.05% and 1.7 %. It is still undrinkable. This type of water is mostly found in estuaries and in general close to the sea.

Branchia: The gills.

By-catch: Fishes inadvertently packed with shipments of other (usually similar) species.

Carbonate Hardness (°KH or °dKH): The German scale to measure carbonate hardness or the quantitative amounts of carbonate or bicarbonate. One degree of German hardness is equivalent to 17 ppm $CaCO_3$.

Carnivorous: Eating flesh, having a diet based on animal constituents.

Glossary

Cascudinhos: "Small armored fishes." Common name given in Brazil to the small suckermouth catfishes of the subfamily Hypoptopomatinae.

Cave Spawner: A species that lays its eggs inside a cave or similarly protected site. The eggs are typically adhered by their pole or side, colorful, relatively large, and few in number.

Caudal fin: The tail fin.

Chloroplast: A type of cell plastid occurring in green plants. It contains chlorophyll and is the site of photosynthesis and protein synthesis.

Chironomids: A family of flies (Diptera) commonly called midges and on occasion mistaken for mosquitoes.

Chromosomes: Threadlike structures that carry the linearly arranged genes.

Cisandinean: On the same side of the Andes Mountains. From an European point of view this is the eastern side (in contrast to transandinean).

Cleithrum: Bone external and adjacent to the clavicle in certain fishes.

Cloaca: A common cavity into which the intestine and the urinary and generative tracts open.

Coexistence: Living together.

Commensalism: A relationship between two different species, whereby one is benefited and the other is neither benefited nor harmed.

Concave: Curved inward, i.e., away from the observer, towards the opposite plane of the object.

Conductivity: Electrical conductivity is the unit of measurement of conducting elements in water, by and large proportional to the dissolved hardness factors contained in this water sample.

Convergence (Convergent Development): Development of similarities between animals or plants of different groups resulting from adaptation to similar habitats. Erroneously, a close systematic relationship is often implied.

Convex: Curved outward, i.e., towards the observer, away from the opposite plane of the object.

Copepods: Largest class of small crustacea, with over 7500 described species (Copepoda). There are predators among them which may be a danger for young fishes. In freshwater, the genus *Cyclops* is of importance.

Courtship: The wooing of a sexual partner preceding spawning.

Cryptic: Camouflaged in agreement with the background. Hard to see or otherwise notice.

Cyclops: A fish food (crustacean) to be used with caution for small fry. See under copepods above.

Glossary

Daphnia: Genus of the water fleas (Cladocera). An important fish food usually given frozen or freeze-dried.

Detritus: Sediment consisting of settled and decomposed animal and plant remains.

Diatom: Common name applied to algae composing the class Bacillariophyceae. Noted for the symmetry and sculpturing of the siliceous cell walls. Used as a white powder in "polishing" water filters for aquaria, retaining very small suspended particles, including suspended ectoparasitic agents.

Dichromatism: Within a same species, the occurrence of two forms distinct in coloration but similar in other aspects, particularly gender related (sexual dichromatism). See also polychromatism, below.

Diffuser: Porous terminal section of an air line to break the continuous air stream into small bubbles to increase the air-water interface and contact time.

Dimorphism: The occurrence of two forms distinct in structure, coloration, etc. among animals of the same species, particularly due to sex (sexual dimorphism).

Diptera: Insect order characterized by possessing two wings, e.g., flies, mosquitoes, etc.

Disjunct: Not contiguous. Two distribution areas of a species that have no border in common.

Diverticulum: A sac or outpocketing on the wall of a hollow organ.

Domesticated: An animal or plant adapted through breeding in captivity to a life intimately associated with humans.

Dorsal: Pertaining to the back, located on the back.

Dorsal fin: Vertical fin located on the back of a fish.

Dorsoventral: Extending from the dorsum ("back") to the ventrum ("stomach").

Dorsoventrally Flattened: The dorsum and the ventrum are closer together than the left and the right of the fish. Like a stingray.

Ectoparasite: External parasite (e.g., *Ichtyophthirius multifillis* = white spot).

Endemic: Indigenous. Particular to a certain, relatively restricted, geographical range (e.g., endemic to a particular lake).

Endoparasite: Internal parasite (e.g., tape worm).

Epidermis: The outer, nonsensitive, nonvascular portion of the skin comprised of two strata of cells. The outermost layer of cells of an animal or plant.

Epithelium: A primary animal tissue, distinguished by having tightly packed cells with little intercellular substance; covers free surfaces and lines body cavities and ducts.

Glossary

Erythrocyte: Red blood cell, carrier of hemoglobin and, consequently, the transporter of oxygen in the blood stream.

Ethmoid bone: An irregularly shaped cartilage bone of the skull, forming the medial wall of each orbit and part of the roof and lateral walls of the nasal cavities.

Etymology: The derivation (origin and meaning) of a word.

Eucaryote: All organisms where the cells have a definitive nucleus.

Eutrophic: Pertaining to a body of water containing a high concentration of dissolved nutrients.

Euryecological: Designation given to organisms which tolerate broad fluctuations of vital environmental factors (e.g., pH, salinity).

Evolution: The processes of biological and organic change in organisms by which descendants come to differ from their ancestors.

Eye diameter: Diameter of the fish eye measured horizontally. An important component of taxonomic studies.

Facultative: Not required, optional. In an aquarium, where dissolved oxygen concentrations are optimal, many catfishes will not need to come to the surface to gulp air.

Family: A taxonomic category below order, grouping related genera (ending -idae).

Fauna: The animals present in a habitat.

Filament: Threadlike elongation (in this book: of the fin rays).

Filial Generation: Direct offspring of the parents.

Fin Formula: The representation of the number and characteristic of the fin rays of fins (e.g., D I/7). It is composed out of the initial of the scientific fin name, followed by Roman (hard rays = spines) and Arabic numbers (soft, terminally divided rays), separated by a slash, comma, or not at all. In this particular case, we are dealing with a dorsal fin that has one spine and seven soft rays.

Flagellate: An organism that has flagella. A member of the protozoan superclass Mastigophora.

Flora: The plants present in a habitat.

Fossil: The organic remains, traces, or imprint of a specimen preserved for some geological time. There is no living individual of this species in present time.

Fright Coloration: A color pattern adopted by animals when feeling threatened or when exposed to inadequate environmental conditions.

Genus: A taxonomic category below family, grouping related species. It is written in *italics*.

Gene: Functional section on chromosomes carrying particular hereditary information.

Genital Papilla: Tube protruding from the genital opening for the release of eggs or sperm cells.

Genotype: 1. The type species of a genus. 2. The genetic makeup of an organism.

Gonads: Glands responsible for producing the reproductive cells.

Habitus: General appearance of an organism.

Half-life: The time it takes for something to be present only by half the amount, concentration, etc. For example, the time that passes before a therapeutic concentration in the aquarium water has fallen to half its initial value.

Hematophagous: Feeding on blood.

Herbivore: Feeding on vegetable matter.

Hermaphrodite: An individual with both male and female reproductive organs.

Heterogenous: Not uniform.

Holotype: A single specimen of a species, stored in a museum, from which the characteristics of the species for its description were derived.

Homogenous: Uniform.

Host Specific: A parasite which has specialized to infest a particular host species and which, consequently, will not infest others.

Humic Acid: Any of various complex organic acids obtained from humus.

Hyaline: Crystalline, transparent.

Hybrid: The offspring of the cross of two different species.

Hylaea: Tropical rain forest.

Hypertrophy: Enlarged, overdeveloped.

Ichthyology: The science that deals with fishes.

Ichthyophagous: Feeding on fishes.

Immunity: The ability of a living organism to resist and overcome an infection or a disease.

Inferior Mouth: Oral opening directed towards the lower plane of the fish.

Infusoria: Any of various microscopic organisms found in infusions of decaying organic matter. They are motile and feed on bacteria, microscopic algae, and microorganisms. The hobbyist can produce his or her own infusions at home with banana peels, lettuce, or hay. Infusoria represent a necessary first food for tiny fry, which cannot yet feed on ground flake foods or brine shrimp nauplii.

Incubation Period: Period of time required for the appearance of symptoms of a disease after infection.

Glossary

Interorbital Distance: The shortest distance between the eyes. A measurement used in taxonomy.

Interspecific: Interaction between different species.

Intraspecific: Interaction among the members of one species.

Lateral Line: A line along the body of most fishes, often distinguished by different-colored scales, which marks the lateral line organ. It detects vibrations in the water.

Larva: Early, immature developmental stage of certain fish species. It still has to undergo a series of changes before it resembles the parent.

Latent: Present but not visible or apparent. Existing in concealed or dormant form, but potentially able to achieve expression.

Lectotype: A specimen in a collection, selected as the type of a species or subspecies if the type was not designated by the author of the description.

Length of Head: Distance between the ethmoid bone and the posterior edge of the operculum.

Lentic: Of or pertaining to still waters such as lakes, reservoirs, ponds, and bogs. Opposite of lotic.

Littoral Zone: Shore area of bodies of water (lake, sea, or ocean).

Limnology: The scientific study of bodies of freshwater.

Locus Typicus: Site where the type material of a species was collected.

Lotic: Pertaining to or living in flowing waters. Opposite of lentic.

Membrane: A thin layer of tissue, e.g., between the fin rays.

Meristic Values: Measurements or geometric relations of parts of an organism.

Metamorphosis: A change of form (tadpoles into frogs).

Metanauplius: A primitive intermediate larval stage of certain decapod crustaceans. Follows the nauplius stage.

Microorganism: A plant or animal organism, invisible to the unaided eye, with a size that makes it readily visible under a microscope.

Mimesis: Imitation of living organisms or inanimate objects.

Mimicry: A system of protection gained through adaptation when one species resembles another in behavior and appearance. The species being mimicked generally has an unpleasant, protective property in the face of predators—e.g., venom, spines, or an unpalatable flavor. Hence, the mimic is avoided because of the attributes of the species it is mimicking.

Modification: A nonhereditary change in appearance in response to environmental conditions.

Mollusk: Snails, mussels, octopuses, squids, and other members of the order Mollusca.

Monophyletic: Descending from a common ancestor.

Monophyletic Group: All members of the group are descendents of a common ancestor. Conversely, no descendent of this ancestor may be classified into another group.

Monotypic: A taxon whose immediate subordinate taxon is not divided (i.e., a monotypic genus is only made up of one species.

Morph: Form. A group of individuals within a species that share common characteristics—such as a particular coloration pattern—but generally are separated from other morphs by geographic barriers and not genetics. The differences are not relevant enough to confer the state of subspecies to the population.

Morphology: Science that deals with structure and form of an organism.

Mutant: Individual changed in its genetic makeup from the parent generation.

Mutation: Hereditary change in the genetic makeup of an organism.

Narine: Nasal opening.

Nauplius (*pl.* nauplii): The first free-swimming larval stage of some crustacea.

Neotropical: A zoogeographic region that includes Mexico south of the Mexican Plateau, the West Indies, Central America, and South America.

Neotype: A specimen selected as type specimen subsequent to the original description, when the holotype, lectotype, or syntype are known to be destroyed.

Niche: 1. The role or position of an organism in an ecosystem. 2. A cranny or crevice.

Nitrate: A salt of nitric acid, any compound containing the NO_3^- radical. Not a serious health threat in the aquarium as long as regular water exchanges are respected.

Nitrification: Formation of nitrates. Oxidation of ammonium salts to nitrite and oxidation of nitrites into nitrate by the bacteria *Nitrosomonas* and *Nitrobacter*.

Nitrite: NO_2^-, a very toxic intermediate step in nitrification. The hemoglobin is affected, and death is by asphyxiation.

Nomenclature: Systematic arrangement of identifying names.

Nomen Novum: A new name, given in exchange of another one that has become invalid.

Glossary

Nomen Nudum: A taxonomic name invalid because the accompanying description of the taxon cannot be interpreted satisfactorily.

Odontodes: Bristlelike, calcareous appendages found on the body scutes and fin spines of many fishes, especially the suckermouth catfishes.

Olfactory: Related to smell.

Oligophagous: Eating only a limited variety of foods.

Oligotrophic: Of a lake, lacking plant nutrients and usually containing plentiful amounts of dissolved oxygen without marked stratification.

Omnivorous: Feeding on both animal and vegetable matter.

Ontogeny: The origin and development of an organism from conception to adulthood.

Oodinium: Ectoparasitic alga. A dangerous pathogen of fishes.

Open Spawner: A species which adheres its eggs onto an exposed substrate or among plants (sometimes also called substrate spawner). The eggs are relatively small, cryptically colored, and numerous.

Operculum: Gill cover.

Order: Taxonomic unit to classify families (termination -iformes).

Osteological: Pertaining to bones.

Paraphyletic: A group (taxon) containing some, but not all, descendents of a common ancestor.

Parasite: Organism which lives on or in another organism (host) to its detriment. An organism that generally derives its nutrients from another organism.

Paratype: A specimen other than the holotype which is before the author at the time of the description and which is designated as such or is clearly indicated as being one of the specimens upon which the original description was based.

Pathogen: A disease-producing agent.

Pectoral fins: Paired fins, usually just posterior to the gill covers (opercula).

Periphyton: Sessile biotal components of a freshwater ecosystem.

pH: Measurement of the concentration of hydrogen ions in water (pH 7 = neutral water; pH < 7 = acidic water; pH > 7 = alkaline water).

Phenotype: The observable characteristics of an organism.

Photosynthesis: The manufacture of organic compounds (primarily carbohydrates) from carbon dioxide and a hydrogen source (i.e., water), with simultaneous release of oxygen, by chlorophyll-containing plant cells exposed to light.

Phylogeny: The evolutionary history of organisms.

Glossary

Pigment: Any coloring matter in animal and plant cells.

Plankton: Organisms that drift or weakly swim in oceanic or freshwater currents. They are incapable of any but the most nominal directional mobility.

Plesiomorph: The original character found in the ancestral forms.

Polychromatism: Presence of several color schemes displayed by one and the same species at a given habitat.

Polyphyletic: Taxon whose members are not all descendents of the same ancestor.

Postdorsal: Located behind the dorsal fin.

Premaxilla: Either of two bones of the upper jaw of vertebrates located in front of and between the maxillae. Toothed section of the upper jaw.

Preserve: Place a fish in a such a solution as to maintain its integrity after death without refrigeration, e.g., with formaldehyde or alcohol.

Prophylaxis: The prevention of disease.

Protandry: An animal which initially is a functional male and later a functional female. (Protandric hermaphrodite)

Protozoa: Unicellular animals.

Quarantine: Isolation of fishes suspected of harboring pathogens for a period of time equal to the incubation period of possible diseases.

Rheophilous: Quality of organisms which appreciate current-swept biotopes.

Rictal Barbels: Barbels which grow from the edge of the mouth.

Rostrum: A beaklike elongation of the head.

Rotifers: Very small, multicellular organisms used as initial food for very small fish fry.

Salinity: Salt content of the water. It is expressed by weight in parts per thousand.

School: A group of fish of a single species swimming in a similar direction all at once.

Secretion: A substance produced by a gland which has particular biochemical functions.

Secondary Sexual Characteristics: All sex-linked morphological differentiating characteristics (e.g., fin development, size, cephalic tentacles) besides the primary sexual characteristics (ovaries, testes).

Secondary Infection: An opportunistic infection that appears due to a weakened defense system of the host organism that suffers from an earlier affliction (injury, compromised immune system due to another disease, etc.).

Sexual Dichromatism: See dichromatism above.

Glossary

Sexual Dimorphism: See dimorphism above.

Sensu: Lat. "in the sense of."

Sensu Lato: Lat. "in the broader sense."

Sensu Stricto: Lat. "in the narrow sense," strictly speaking.

Sessile: Permanently attached to a substrate.

Spawn: The fertilized eggs released into the water or adhered onto a substrate. The end product of spawning.

Spawning: The synchronized release of eggs and sperm to perpetuate a species.

Species: A taxonomic category immediately below genus which includes closely related, morphologically similar individuals which can interbreed.

Standard Length: Length measured from the tip of the snout to the caudal peduncle. See total length.

Stenoic: Said of organisms which are not tolerant of wide variations in their environmental characteristics.

Sterile: 1. Free of microbial activity. 2. Unfecund, unable to reproduce.

Subadult: Virtually full-grown individual which has not attained sexual maturity.

Subfamily: Systematic unit below family and above genus. Ending is -inae.

Suborbital: Below the eye.

Subspecies: Geographic race of a species. It is indicative of the momentarily occurring segregation of the species.

Substrate: Bottom. A surface.

Subtribe: A systematic taxon below the tribe. It is not required. Termination is -ina.

Supraorbital: Above the eye.

Sympatric: Different species living together in nature, but not interbreeding.

Synapomorphy: Any derived morphological characteristic in common. When two or more species coincide in a particular characteristic and it can be excluded that the characteristic is a plesiomorph (found in the ancestral form), it may be concluded, based on this characteristic, that the two species are related.

Synonym: A taxonomic name that is rejected as being incorrectly applied to a previously described species. It can also be incorrect in form, or not representative of a natural genetic grouping.

Synthesis: Formation of complex compounds by the union of simpler compounds or elements.

Syntopic: Occurring in a particular habitat together with another species.

Glossary

Syntype: Any specimen in a group used to describe a species when no specimen was designated as the holotype by the original describer. It has the same rank nomenclaturally speaking.

Systematics: The science of animal and plant classification.

Taxon: (pl. taxa.) A level (group) within the systematic classification of organisms (e.g., species, genus, family).

Taxonomy: The study aimed at producing a hierarchical system of classification of individuals which best reflects all similarities and differences.

Tentacle: Flexible process with tactile, prehensile, or other function borne on the head or mouth region of many animals.

Terminal Mouth: Oral opening directed forward.

Terra Typica: Area of distribution of the type material of a species.

Territory: A specific area occupied by a species or individuals and defended against others (intruders).

Topoparatype: A paratype found at the same location as the holotype.

Topotype: An individual of a species not of the original type series collected at the type locality.

Total Hardness: Measure of the sum of all hardeners contained in a water sample, especially calcium and magnesium ions.

Total Length: Length of the fish measured from the tip of the head to the posterior end of the caudal fin. For scientific purposes, the inclusion of the length of the caudal fin in the total measurement brings with it a series of problems. See standard length.

Toxic: Poisonous. Of harmful effect on the organism.

Transandinean: Across the Andes. From an European point of view, on the western side of the mountains (in contrast to cisandenean).

Tribe: Systematic group below the subfamily which may unite similarly related genera. It is not obligatory. (Termination –ini.)

Trichoptera: Order of insects; the caddies flies.

Trophozoite: A parasite located on the host (e.g., ich or _Oodinium_)

Type Species: The species which served as basis for the definition of a higher taxon (the type species of a genus).

Unpaired Fins: In fishes the dorsal, adipose, anal, and caudal fins.

Urinophile: Said of a fish that seeks urine (like some of the parasitic catfishes).

Variant: A somewhat deviant morph or form from what is considered normal for a species.

Ventral: On the side of the ventrum, stomach. Opposite to the back.

Glossary / Abreviations

Ventral Fins: Paired fins on the ventral (inferior) side of fishes, usually located opposite the dorsal fin, posterior to the pectoral fins and anterior to the anal fin.

Ventrorostral: On the lower side of the rostrum.

Yolk Sac: Larval organ which contains the yolk for the growing embryo. It is connected through the umbilicus to the midgut.

Xanthism: A color variation in which an animal's normal coloring is largely replaced by yellow pigments. Also called xanthochroism.

Abreviations

aff.: (Lat. *affinis* = close to, affinity) The pictured specimen is very similar to the named species, but in all likelyhood it is a different, not yet described species.

cf.: (Lat. *confero* = compare) It is most likely the pictured specimen corresponds to this species, but there is no certainty, because there are some discrepancies.

sp.: (Lat. *species*) Designation for an undescribed species.

spp.: Plural of species.

ssp.: Subspecies.

TL: Total length

SL: Standard length (no caudal fin)

° C: Degrees Celsius (°C = [°F - 32]÷1.8; °F = °C x 1.8 + 32)

° KH: Degrees carbonate hardness.

° GH: Total hardness.

General Bibliography and for the Family Loricariidae

Andrews, C., A. Exell & N. Carrington (1990): Gesunde Zierfische. Grundlagen, Vorbeugung, Heilung.- Tetra Verlag, Melle

Almirón, A. E., M. de las Mercedes Azpelicueta & J. R. Casciotta, 2004: A new species of Epactionotus (Siluriformes : Loricariidae : Otothyrini) from the río Iguazú basin, Argentina.- Zoologische Abhandlungen (Dresden), 54: 137-144

Aquino, A. E. (1996): Redescripción de *Otocinclus flexilis* Cope, 1894 (Siluriformes, Loricariidae, Hypoptopomatinae) con un nuevo sinónimo.- Iheringia, ser. Zool., 81: 13-22

— (1997): Las especies de Hypoptopomatinae (Pisces, Siluriformes, Loricariidae) en la Argentina.- Revista de Ictiologia, 5 (1-2): 5-21

—& S. A. Schaefer & A. M. Miquelarena (2001): A new Species of *Hisonotus* (Siluriformes, Loricariidae) of the Upper Río Uruguay Basin.- Amer. Mus. Novitates, 3333: 1-12

Armbruster, J. W. (1997): Phylogenetic relationships of the sucker-mouth armored catfishes (Loricariidae) with particular emphasis on the Ancistrinae, Hypostominae, and Neoplecostominae.- Unpubl. Ph.D. dissertation. University of Illinois, Urbana-Champaign. 409 pp.

— (1998a): Phylogenetic Relationships of the Suckermouth Armored Catfishes of the *Rhinelepis* Group (Loricariidae: Hypostominae).- Copeia, 1998(3): 620-636

— (1998b): Modifications of the Digestive Tract for Holding Air in Loricariid and Scoloplacid Catfishes.- Copeia, 1998(3): 663-675

— (1999): "Loricariid Home Page",- Auburn University, USA. URL: http://george. cosam.auburn.edu/usr/key_to_loricariidae/lorhome/lorhome.html

Bailey, R. M. & J. N. Baskin (1976): *Scoloplax dicra*, a new armored catfish from the Bolivian Amazon.- Occ. Pap. Mus. zool. Univ. Michigan, 671: 1-14

Barzanti, J. M. & N. O. Oldani (1976): *Lamontichthys filamentosa* (La Monte, 1935) (Pisces, Loricariidae). Una nueva cita para la fauna de peces de la Republica Argentina.- Physis, seccion B, 35(91): 131-137

Baskin, J. N. (1978): Structure and relationships of the Trichomycteridae.- Unpublished pH.D. dissertation, City University of New York, published by Univ. Microfilms Intern., Ann Arbor, London, i-xxi, 1-389

Bassleer, G. (1983): Bildatlas der Fischkrankheiten.- Verlag Neumann-Neudamm, Melsungen

Bibliography

Bauer, R. (1991): Erkrankungen der Aquarienfische. Tierärztliche Heimtierpraxis 4.- Verlag Paul Parey, Berlin

Bergleiter, S. (1999): Zur ökologischen Struktur einer zentralamazonischen Fischzönose.- Zoologica, Schweizerbart´sche Verlagsbuchhandlung, Stuttgart: 1-191

Bhatti, H. (1938): The integument and dermal skeleton of Siluroidei.- Trans. Zool. Soc. London, 24(1): 1-102

Bilke, E. (1992): "Eichhörnchen" im Aquarium: *Otocinclus notatus*.- D. Aqu. u. Terr. Z. (DATZ), 45(10): 625-627

Bleeker, P. (1858): Ichthyologiae archipelagi Indici prodomus I. Siluri. De visschen van den Indischen Archipel beschreven en toegelicht. I. Siluri (Lange & Co., Batavia): v-viii, 1-370

— (1862): Atlas ichthyologique des Indes orientales néerlandaises, publié sous les auspices du Gouvernement colonial néerlandaises: Siluroides, Chacoides et Hétérobranchoides 2: 1-112, pls. 49-101

— (1863): Systema silurorum revisum.- Ned. Tijdschr. Dierk., 1: 77-122

Boeseman, M. (1953): Scientific results of the Surinam Expedition 1948-1949. Part II. Zoology. No. 2. The fishes (I).- Zool. Meded. Leiden, 32(1): 1-24

— (1971): The comb-toothed Loricariinae of Surinam, with reflections on the phylogenetic tendencies within the family Loricariidae (siluriformes, Siluroidei).- Zool. Verh. Leiden, 116: 1-56

— (1974): On two Surinam species of Hypoptopomatinae, both new to science (Loricariidae, Siluriformes, Ostariophysi).- Proc. Koninkl. Nederl. Akad. Wetenschapen, Amsterdam, Ser. C, 77(3): 257-271

Bohnet, V., M. Wilhelm & I. Seidel (2001): Prachthexenwelse - Systematik und Ökologie, Aquarienhaltung und Vermehrung der wohl schönsten Hexenwelse.- DATZ-Sonderheft "Harnischwelse 2": 36-42

Bonaparte, C. L. J. L. (1831): Saggio di una distribuzione metodica degli animali vertebrati.- G. Arcadico Sci., 49: 1-77

Bowser, P. R. (1999): Diseases of Fish.- Ph.D. thesis. Department of Microbiology and Immunology, College of Veterinary Medicine, Cornell University, New York

Bremer, H. (1999): Die Epidermis der Fische. Dynamischer Schutz und Rolle bei der Brutpflege.- In: "Die Fortpflanzung der Aquarienfische". Tagungsband vom 3. VDA-Süßwasser-Symposium, Fulda 1998: 33-37

Bibliography

Britski, H. A. (1997): Descricão de um novo gênero de Hypoptopomatinae, com duas espécies novas (Siluriformes, Loricariidae).- Papeis Avulsos de Zool., São Paulo, 40 (15): 231-255

— & J. C. Garavello (1984): Two new southeastern brazilian genera of Hypoptopomatinae and a redescription of *Pseudotocinclus* Nichols, 1919 (Ostariophysi, Loricariidae).- Papéis Avulsos de Zool., São Paulo, 35(21): 225-241

— & J. C. Garavello (2002): *Parotocinclus jumbo*, a new Species of the subfamily Hypoptopomatinae from northeastern Brazil (Ostariophysi: Loricariidae).- Ichthyol. Explor. Freshwaters, 13(3): 279-288

— & J. C. Garavello (2003): *Hisonotus insperatus*: New Species, from the Upper Rio Paraná Basin (Pisces: Ostariophysi: Loricariidae).- Copeia, 2003 (3): 588-593

Britto, M. R. & C. R. Moreira (2002): *Otocinclus tapirape*: A New Hypoptopomatine Catfish from Central Brazil (Siluriformes: Loricariidae).- Copeia, 2002 (4): 1063-1069

Buck, S. & I. Sazima (1995): An assemblage of mailed catfishes (Loricariidae) in southeastern Brazil: distribution, activity and feeding.- Ichthyol. Explor. Freshwaters, 6(4): 325-332

Burgess, W. E. (1989): An Atlas of Freshwater and Marine Catfishes. A Preliminary Survey of the Siluriformes.- T.F.H. Publications, Neptune City

Burkard, H. (2000): Der Inkubator für Fische! BSSW-Report, 12(2): 24-28

Casatti, L. & R. M. C. Castro (1998): A fish community of the São Francisco River headwater riffles, southeastern Brazil.- Ichthyol. Explor. Freshwaters, 9(3): 229-242

Castro, R. M. C. & L. Casatti (1997): The fish fauna from a small forest stream of the upper Paraná River basin, southeastern Brazil.- Ichthyol. Explor. Freshwaters, 7(4): 337-352

Chang, F. & E. Castro (1999): *Crossoloricaria bahuaja*, a new loricarid fish from Madre de Dios, southeastern Peru.- Ichthyol. Explor. Freshwaters, 10(1): 81-88

Cuvier, G. & A. Valenciennes (1840): Histoire naturelle des poissons (Ch. Pitois, Paris & V. Levrault, Strasbourg), 15: i-xxxi, 1-540 (Paris edition), : i-xxiv, 1-397, ii (Strasbourg edition), pls. 421-455

Dittmar, H. & H.-G. Evers (2000): Zur Fischfauna einiger Fließgewässer im südostbrasilianischen Küstenbereich und zum Nahrungsspektrum ausgewählter Fischarten.- Z. Fischk., 5(2): 45-70

Bibliography

Dorn, E. (1983): Über die Atmungsorgane einiger luftatmender Amazonas-fische.- Amazoniana, 4: 375-395

Drachenfels, E. von (1989): Harnischwelse aus Französisch-Guyana.- D. Aqu. u. Terr. Z. (DATZ), 42(8): 495-496

Eigenmann, C. H. (1910): Catalogue and bibliography of the fresh water fishes of the Americas south of the tropic of Cancer. Catalogue of the fresh-water fishes of tropical and South temperate America.- Rep. Princeton Univ. Exped. Patagonia, 1896-1899, 3 (Zool. 4): 375-511

— (1912): The freshwater fishes of British Guiana, including a study of the ecological grouping of species and the relation of the fauna of the plateau to that of the lowlands.- Mem. Carnegie Mus. 5: 1-578

— & W. R. Allen (1942): Fishes of western South America.- Univ.Kentucky, Lexington, 1-494

— & R. S. Eigenmann (1888): Preliminary notes on the South American nematognathi.- Proc. California Acad. Sci., (2)1: 119-172

— & — (1889): Preliminary notes on the South American nematognathi II.- Proc. California Acad. Sci., (2) 2: 28-56

— & — (1890): A revision on the South American nematognathi, or cat-fishes.- Occ. Pap. California Acad. Sci., 1: 1-508, 1 map

— & — (1891): A catalogue of the fresh-water fishes of South America.- Proc. U.S. nation. Mus., 14: 1-81

Elsholz, K. D. & W. Elsholz (1992): Ohrgitter- und Saugwelse - *Parotocinclus* cf. *maculicauda*, ein Saugwels aus dem Tribus [sic] Otocinclini.- Wels-Jahrbuch 1993, Kollnburg: 90-93

— & — (1994): Zwei selten importierte Arten aus der Unterfamilie Hypopto-pomatinae: *Hypoptopoma* sp. und *Parotocinclus* cf. *cristatus*.- BSSW-Report, 6(1): 14-19

Evers, H.-G. (1991): Anmerkungen zur Haltung und Zucht von *Farlowella*-Arten.- Das Aquarium, 262: 12-14

— (1992a): Zur Identifizierung der "neuen" Art.- D. Aqu. u. Terr. Z. (DATZ), 45(2): 76

— (1992b): Kreuzungen bei *Sturisoma*-Arten.- D. Aqu. u. Terr. Z. (DATZ), 45(9): 558-559

— (1992c): Harnischwelse aus der Unterfamilie Hypoptopomatinae.- D. Aqu. u. Terr. Z.(DATZ), 45(10): 623-624

Bibliography

— **(1993):** Die Sabanas de Rascamula - ein venezolanisches Wels-"Traum-Biotop".- Wels-Jahrbuch 1994, Kollnburg: 12-16

— **(1996a):** Der Hummel-Harnischwels *Otocinclus gibbosus* Ribeiro, 1908 - ein außergewöhnlicher Wels. - TI Magazin, 128: 24-26

— **(1996b):** Der Nasenharnischwels *Hemiodontichthys acipenserinus*.- Aquarium Heute, 14(4): 417-419

— **(1997a):** Zur Kenntnis einiger aquaristisch bislang unbekannter Salmler aus dem brasilianischen Bundesstaat Minas Gerais. 1.Teil: *Hysteronotus megalostomus* Eigenmann, 1911.- BSSW-Report, 9(2): 18-20

— **(1997b):** *Pseudoloricaria laeviuscula* (Valenciennes, 1840).- BSSW-Report, 9(2): 5-7

— **(1997c):** Einer meiner Lieblingsfische: Rote Hexenwelse.- Aquarium Heute, 15(3): 583-586

— **(1997d):** *Hypostomus* aus dem Rio-São-Francisco-Becken.- D. Aqu. u. Terr. Z. (DATZ), 50(8): 493

— **(1998a):** Gar nicht so einfach: Die Nachzucht von *Sturisomatichthys* sp.- Aquarium Heute, 16(3): 140-143

— **(1998b):** In der Heimat der Kupfersalmler.- Aquaristik Aktuell, 6(7-8): 34-39

— **(1998c):** Ein interessanter *Otocinclus* aus Zentralbrasilien.- D. Aqu. u. Terr. Z. (DATZ), 51(11): 689

— **(2000a):** Harnischwelse aus São Paulo.- D. Aqu. u. Terr. Z. (DATZ), 53(3): 16-19

— **(2000b):** Neu importiert: Ein *Parotocinclus* aus Peru.- D. Aqu. u. Terr. Z. (DATZ), 53(9): 54

— **(2000c):** Harnischwelse aus dem Rio São Francisco.- D. Aqu. u. Terr. Z. (DATZ), 53(10): 34-38

— **(2001):** Erste Erfahrungen mit *Apistoloricaria condei*.- DATZ-Sonderheft "Harnischwelse 2": 43-45

— **& I. Seidel (1996):** Maulbrütende Harnischwelse.- BSSW-Spezial. Sonderheft des BSSW-Report. 70 S.

— **& — (2002):** Wels Atlas Band 1; 1. Auflage,- Melle

Foersch, W. & A. Hanrieder (1980): Wir fanden Welse – Erlebnisse im peruanischen Urwald.- Aquarien Magazin, 14(12): 686-693

Bibliography

Forshey, J. (1996): A Visit to Brazil´s Xingu River.- Tropical Fish Hobbyist (#483), 44(9): 22-28

Fowler, H. W. (1941): A collection of fresh-water fishes obtained in eastern Brazil by Dr. Rodolpho von Ihering.- Proc. Acad. Nat. Sci. Philadelphia, 93: 123-199

— (1954): Os peixes de água doce do Brasil.- Arq. zool. São Paulo, 9: i-ix, 1-400

Franke, H.-J. (1961): Erstzucht von *Otocinclus* cf. *maculipinnis* Regan, 1912, dem Zwergsaugwels.- Aquarien Terrarien, 8(3): 67-70

— (1985): Handbuch der Welskunde.- Landbuch-Verlag, Hannover

— (1999): Blickfänge im Aquarium: Störwelse (*Lamontichthys* und *Pterosturisoma*).- D. Aqu. u. Terr. Z. (DATZ), 52(2): 20-23

Freihofer, W. C. & E. H. Neil (1967): Commensalism between midge larvae (Diptera: Chironomidae) and catfishes of the families Astroblepidae and Loricariidae.- Copeia, 1967(1): 39-45

Galvis, G., J. I. Mojica & M. Camargo (1997): Peces del Catatumbo.- Santa Fé de Bogota, D. C., ISBN-958-96378-0-9

Garavello, J. C. (1977): Systematics and geographical distribution of the genus *Parotocinclus* Eigenmann & Eigenmann, 1889 (Ostariophysi, Loricariidae).- Arq. Zool. São Paulo, 28(4): 1-37

— (1988): Three new species of *Parotocinclus* Eigenmann & Eigenmann, 1889 with comments on their geographical distribution (Pisces, Loricariidae).- Naturalia (São Paulo) 13: 117-128

— , H. A. Britski & S. A. Schaefer (1998): Systematics of the Genus *Otothyris* Myers, 1927, with Comments on Geographic Distribution (Siluriformes: Loricariidae: Hypoptopomatinae).- Amer. Mus. Novitates, 3222: 1-19

— & H. A. Britski (2003): *Parotocinclus* planicauda, a new species of the subfamily Hypoptopomatinae from southeastern Brazil (Ostariophysi: Loricariidae).- Braz. J. Biol., 63(2): 253-260

Gee, J.H. (1976): Buoyancy and aerial respiration: factors influencing the evolution of reduced swim bladder volume of some Central American catfishes (Trichomycteridae, Callichthyidae, Loricariidae, Astroblepidae).- Can. J. Zool., 54: 1030-1037

Geisler, R. & S. Bolle (1956): Nahrungsuntersuchungen bei nordargentinischen Wildfischen.- D. Aqu. u. Terr. Z. (DATZ), 9(8): 208-213

Bibliography

George, U. (1991): Inseln in der Zeit. Venezuela-Expeditionen zu den letzten weißen Flecken der Erde.- GEO, Hamburg

Gery, J. (1969): The freshwater fishes of South America. In: Biogeography and ecology in South America 2.- The Hague: 828-848

Gibbs, R. J. (1971): Amazon River: environmental factors that control its dissolved and suspended load.- Science, 56: 1734-1736

Gill, T. N. (1872): Arrangement of the families of fishes, or classes Pisces, Marsipobranchii and Leptocardii.- Smithsonian Miscellaneous Collections, 11(247): xiv + 49 pp.

Gosline, W. A. (1945): Catálogo dos nematognathos de água-doce da América do Sul e Central.- Bol. Mus. nac. Rio de Janeiro, (n.s.), Zool., 33: 1-138

— (1947): Contributions to the classification of the loricariid catfishes.- Arq. Mus. nac. Rio de Janeiro, 41: 79-134, 9 pls

Goulding, M., M. L. Carvalho & E. G. Ferreira (1988): Rio Negro. Rich Life in Poor Water.- The Hague

Günther, A. (1864): Catalogue of the Physostomi, containing the families Siluridae, Characinidae, Haplochitonidae, Sternoptychidae, Scopelidae, Stomiatidae, in the collection of the British Museum. Catalogue of the fishes in the British Museum, London 5: i-xxii, 1-455

— (1868): Diagnoses of some new freshwater fishes from Surinam and Brazil, in the collection of the British Museum.- Ann. Mag. Nat. Hist. (Ser. 4), 1(6): 475-481

Hartl, A.(1996): Nadelwelse - Meister der Anpassung.- D. Aqu. u. Terr. Z. (DATZ), 49(12): 769-772

Haseman, J. D. (1911): Descriptions of some new species of fishes and miscellaneous notes on others obtained during the expedition of the Carnegie Museum to Central South America.- Ann. Carnegie Mus., 7(3-4): 315-328

Hassur, R. L. (1970): Rediscovery of the loricariid catfish, *Acestridium discus* Haseman, near Manaus, Brazil.- Proc. California Acad. Sci., ser. 4, 38(9): 157-162

Holota, K. (1992): Ein neuer *Sturisomatichthys*.- D. Aqu. u. Terr. Z. (DATZ), 45(2): 75-76

Howes, G. J. (1983): The cranial muscles of loricarioid catfishes, their homologies and value as taxonomic characters (Teleostei: Siluroidei).- Bull. Br. Mus. nat. Hist. Zool., 45(3): 309-345

Bibliography

Husmann, R. (1999): Internet-Seite "Rotbraune Flecken bei 'Hypostomus punctatus' = Liposarcus pardalis und LDA25". URL: http://www. rhusmann. de/aqua/flecken.htm

Ihering, R. von (1911): Algumas especies novas de peixes d´agua doce (Nematognatha) (Corydoras, Plecostomus, Hemipsilichthys).- Rev. Mus. Paul., 8: 380-404

Isbrücker, I. J. H. (1971a): A redescription of the South American catfish Loricariichthys maculatus (Bloch, 1794), with designation of the lectotype and restriction of its type locality (Pisces, Siluriformes, Loricariidae).- Bijdr. Dierk., 41(1): 10-18

— (1971b): Scientific results of the Peru-Bolivia-Expedition Dr. K.H. Lüling, 1966. Pseudohemiodon (Planiloricaria) cryptodon, a new species and subgenus from Peru.- Bonner Zool. Beitr., 21(314): 274-283

— (1972): The identity of the South American catfish Loricaria cataphracta Linnaeus, 1758, with redescriptions of the original type specimens of four other nominal Loricaria species (Pisces, Siluriformes, Loricariidae).- Beaufortia, 19(255): 163-191

— (1975): Pseudohemiodon thorectes, a new species of mailed catfish from the Rio Mamoré system, Bolivia (Pisces, Siluriformes, Loricariidae).- Beaufortia, 23(300): 85-92

— (1979): Description préliminaires de nouveaux taxa de la famille des Loricariidae, Poisson-Chats cuirassés néotropicaux, avec un catalogue critique de la sous-famille nominale (Pisces, Siluriformes).- Rev. fr. Aquariol. Herpétol., 5(4): 86-116

— (1980): Classification and catalogue of the mailed Loricariidae (Pisces, Siluriformes).- Versl. Techn. Geg., Inst. Taxon. Zoöl. (Zoöl. Mus.), Univ. Amsterdam, 22: 1-181

— (1981): Revision of Loricaria Linnaeus, 1758 (Pisces, Siluriformes, Loricariidae).- Beaufortia, 31(3): 51-96

— (1992): Überblick über die gültigen (Unter-) Gattungsnamen der Harnischwelse (Loricariidae) und ihre Synonyme.- DATZ-Sonderheft "Harnischwelse", Stuttgart: 71-72

— (2001): Nomenklator der Gattungen und Arten der Harnischwelse, Familie Loricariidae Rafinesque, 1815 (Teleostei, Ostariophysi).- D. Aqu. u. Terr. Zeitschr. DATZ-Sonderheft: Harnischwelse 2: 25-32

— (2002): Nomenklatur 2001 - ein Update.- Aqu. u. Terr. Z. DATZ, 55 (5): 49

Bibliography

— , H. A. Britski, H. Nijssen & H. Ortega (1983): *Aposturisoma myriodon*, une espéce et un genre nouveaux de Poisson-Chat cuirassé, tribu Farlowellini Fowler, 1958 du Bassin du Rio Ucayali, Perou (Pisces, Siluriformes, Loricariidae).- Rev. fr. Aquariol. Herpét., 10(2): 34-43

— & H. Nijssen (1974a): *Rhadinoloricaria* gen.nov. and *Planiloricaria*, two genera of South American mailed catfishes (Pisces, Siluriformes, Loricariidae).- Beaufortia, 22(290): 67-81

— & — (1974b): *Hemiodontichthys acipenserinus* and *Reganella depressa*, two remarkable mailed catfishes from South America (Pisces, Siluriformes, Loricariidae).- Beaufortia, 22 (294): 193-222

— & — (1976): The South American mailed catfishes of the genus *Pseudoloricaria* Bleeker, 1862 (Pisces, Siluriformes, Loricariidae).- Beaufortia, 25(325): 107-129

— & — (1978a): Two new species and a new genus of neotropical mailed catfishes of the subfamily Loricariinae Swainson, 1838 (Pisces, Siluriformes, Loricariidae).- Beaufortia, 27(339): 177-206

— & — (1978b): The neotropical mailed catfishes of the genera *Lamontichthys* P. de Miranda Ribeiro, 1939 and *Pterosturisoma* n. gen., including the decription of *Lamontichthys stibaros* n. sp. from Ecuador (Pisces, Siluriformes, Loricariidae).- Bijdr. Dierk., 48(1): 57-80

— & — (1979): Three new South American mailed catfishes of the genera *Rineloricaria* and *Loricariichthys* (Pisces, Siluriformes, Loricariidae).- Bijdr. Dierk., 48(2): 191-211

— & — (1984): *Pyxiloricaria menezesi*, a new genus and species of mailed catfish from Rio Miranda and Rio Cuiaba, Brazil (Pisces, Siluriformes, Loricariidae).- Bijdr. Dierk., 54(2): 163-168

— & — (1986a): New records of the mailed catfish *Planiloricaria cryptodon* from the upper Amazon in Peru, Brazil and Bolivia, with a key to the genera of the Planiloricariina.- Bijdr. Dierk., 56(1): 39-46

— & — (1986b): *Apistoloricaria condei*, nouveau genre et nouvelle espèce de Poisson-Chat cuirassé, tribu Loricariini Bonaparte, 1831, du bassin du Rio Napo, haute Amazone, Equateur (Pisces, Siluriformes, Loricariidae).- Rev. fr. Aquariol. Herpét., 12(4): 103-108

— & — (1988): Trois nouvelles espèces du genre *Apistoloricaria* de Colombie et du Perou, avec illustration du dimorphisme sexuel secondaire des lèvres de *A. condei* (Pisces, Siluriformes, Loricariidae).- Rev. fr. Aquariol. Herpét., 15(2): 33-38

Bibliography

— & — (1992): Sexualdimorphismus bei Harnischwelsen (Loricariidae).-
DATZ-Sonderheft "Harnischwelse", Stuttgart: 19-33

—, I. Seidel, J. P. Michels, E. Schraml & A. Werner (2001): Diagnose vierzehn
neuer Gattungen der Familie Loricariidae Rafinesque, 1815 (Teleostei,
Ostariophysi).- D. Aqu. u. Terr. Zeitschr. DATZ-Sonderheft: Harnischwelse
2: 17-24

Keijman, M. C. W. (1999): Loricariiden aus Panama.- Aquaristik aktuell, 7(9-
10): 16-18

Kner, R. (1853a): Die Panzerwelse des k. k. Hof-Naturalien-Cabinetes zu
Wien.- Sber. Akad. Wiss. Wien, mathem.-naturw. Cl., 10(1): 113-116

— (1853b): Die Hypostomiden, oder die zweite Hauptgruppe der Panzer-
fische.- Sber. Akad. Wiss. Wien, mathem.-naturw. Cl., 10(3): 279-282

— (1854a): Die Panzerwelse des k. k. Hof-Naturalien-Cabinetes zu Wien. I.
Abtheilung: Loricariinae.- Denkschr. Akad. Wiss. Wien, mathem.-naturw.
Cl., 6: 65-98, 8 pls.

— (1854b): Die Hypostomiden. Zweite Hauptgruppe der Familie der Pan-
zerfische (Loricata vel Goniodontes).- Denkschr. Akad. Wiss. Wien,
mathem.-naturw. Cl., 7: 251-286, 5 pls.

Knaack, J.: 2002: Ein neuer Prachthexenwels aus Paraguay: *Hemiloricaria
aurata* n. sp. (Pisces, Siluriformes, Loricariidae).- Aquaristik Aktuell, 1/2003:
56-61

Kobayagawa, M. (1991): Faszination Welse.- Bede Verlag, Kollnburg

Kramer, D. L., C. C. Lindsey, G. E. E. Moodie & E. D. Stevens (1978): The
fishes and the aquatic environment of the central Amazon basin, with particular reference to respiratory patterns.- Canadian J. of Zoology, 56(4),
Part 2: 717-729

Lacerda, M. T. C. (1994a): *Aspidoras* im Nordeste - Himmel und Hölle
Brasiliens (Teil 1).- Aquaristik Aktuell, 2(2): 20-22

— (1994b): *Aspidoras* im Nordeste - Himmel und Hölle Brasiliens (Teil 2).-
Aquaristik Aktuell, 2(3): 22-23

— & H.-G. Evers (1996): *Parotocinclus*-Arten aus Brasilien.- D. Aqu. u. Terr.
Z. (DATZ), 49(2): 88-95

Lammel, M. (1993): Ein hübscher Hexenwels: *Rineloricaria morrowi*.- D. Aqu.
u. Terr. Z. (DATZ), 46(5): 287-288

La Monte, F. R. (1935): Fishes from Rio Jurua and Rio Purus, Brazilian Amazonas.- Amer. Mus. Novit., 784: 1-8

Langeani, F. (1991): Revisão do genero *Neoplecostomus* Eigenmann & Eigenmann, 1888, com a descrição de quatro novas espécies do sudeste brasileiro (Ostariophysi, Siluriformes, Loricariidae).- Comm. Mus. Ciênc. PUCRS, sér. Zool., Porto Alegre, 3(1): 3-31

—, O. T. Oyakawa & J. I. Montoya-Burgos (2001): New Species of *Harttia* (Loricariidae, Loricariinae) from the Rio São Francisco Basin.- Copeia, 2001(1): 136-142

Lopez, R. B. (1970): Viejas del Rio de la Plata.- Rev. Museo Argentino Cienc. Naturales "Bernadino Rivadavia", 10(8): 113-129

Lowe Mc Connell, R. H. (1964): The fishes of the Rupununi savanna district of British Guiana, South America. Part 1. Ecological groupings of fish species and effects of the seasonal cycle on the fish.- J. Linn. Soc. (Zool.), 45(304): 103-144

— (1991): Natural history of fishes in Araguaia and Xingu Amazonian tributaries, Serra do Roncador, Mato Grosso, Brasil.- Ichthyol. Explor. Freshwaters, 2: 63-82

Lüling, K.H. (1971): Wissenschaftliche Ergebnisse der Peru-Bolivien-Expedition Dr. K.H. Lüling 1966: *Aequidens vittata* (Heckel) und andere Fische des Rio Huallaga im Übergangsbereich zur Hylaea.- Zool. Beitr., N.F., 17(2/3): 193-226

— (1975): Wissenschaftliche Ergebnisse der Peru-Bolivien-Expedition Dr. K.H. Lüling 1966 und Peru-(Amazonas-Ucayali-) Expeditionen 1959/60 und 1970: Ichthyologische und gewässerkundliche Beobachtungen und Untersuchungen an der Yarina Cocha, in der Umgebung von Pucallpa und am Rio Pacaya (mittlerer und unterer Ucayali, Ostperu).- Zool. Beitr. N.F. Bd., 21(1): 29-96

— (1978): Südamerikanische Fische und ihr Lebensraum. Engelbert Pfriem Verlag, Wuppertal-Elberfeld

— (1979): Wissenschaftliche Ergebnisse der Peru-Bolivien-Expedition Dr. K. H. Lüling 1974: Weitere ichthyologische und gewässerkundliche Untersuchungen und Beobachtungen an der Yarina Cocha (mittlerer Ucayali, Ostperu).- Zool. Beitr. N.F. Bd., 24(3): 417-436

— (1980): Das Fischparadies Yarina Cocha – Exkursion zum mittleren Ucayali in Ostperu.- Aquarien Magazin, 14(5): 248-254

Lundberg, J. G. et. al. (1996): Homepage "Fishes of the Río Orinoco Basin, South America".- URL: http://eebweb. arizona. edu/fish/Orinoco. html

Bibliography

—, L. G. Marshall, J. Guerrero, B. Horton, M. C. S. L. Malabarba & F. Wesselingh (1998): The Stage for Neotropical Fish Diversification: A History of Tropical South American Rivers.- In: L. R. Malabarba, R. E. Reis, R. P. Vari, Z. M. S. Lucena & C. A. S. Lucena, Eds, Phylogeny and Classification of Neotropical Fishes. Edipucrs, Porto Alegre, Brasil: 13-48

Machado-Allison, A. & H. Moreno (1993): Estudios sobre la comunidad de peces des Rio Orituco, Estado Guarico, Venezuela. Parte 1 Inventario, abundancia relativa y diversidad.- Acta Biol. Venez., 14(4): 77-94

Martin Salazar, F. J.(1964): Las especies del genero *Farlowella* de Venezuela (Piscis-Nematognalhi-Loricariidae) [sic] con descripcion de 5 especies y 1 sub-especie nuevas.- Mem. Soc.Cienc. Nat. La Salle, 69(25): 242-260

Mayland, H. J. (1988): Diskusfieber.- Landbuch Verlag, Hannover

Meek, S. E. & S. F. Hildebrand (1916): The fishes of the fresh waters of Panama. Field Mus. Nat. Hist. zool. ser., Chicago, 191, 10 (15): 217-385

Menezes, R. S. de (1949a): Incubação labial de ovos pelo macho de „*Loricaria typus*" Bleeker, da Lagoa de peixe, Piauí, Brasil (Actinopterygii, Loricariidae, Loricariinae).- Rev. Brasil. Biol., 9(3): 381-387

— (1949b): Alimentacão de car chicote, "*Loricaria typus*" Bleeker, da bacia do Rio Parnaiba, Piauí.- Rev. Brasil. Biol., 9(4): 479-484

Moeller, R. B. Jr. (1996): Internet-Seite "Diseases of Fishes".- Armed Forces Institute of Patology. Washington. URL: http://www. afip.org/vetpath/POLA/POLA96/fish.txt

Montoya-Burgos, J.-I., S. Muller, C. Weber & J. Pawlowski (1997): Phylogenetic relationships between Hypostominae and Ancistrinae (Siluroidei: Loricariidae): first results from mitochondrial 12S and 16S rRNA gene sequences.- Rev. Suisse Zool., 104(1): 185-198

—,—, —, & — (1998): Phylogenetic relationships of the Loricariidae (Siluriformes) based on mitochondrial rRNA gene sequences.- In: L. R. Malabarba, R. E. Reis, R. P. Vari, Z. M. S. Lucena & C. A. S. Lucena, Eds, Phylogeny and Classification of Neotropical Fishes. Part 3 - Siluriformes. Edipucrs, Porto Alegre, Brasil: 363-374

Moreno M., H. & H.-J. Franke (1996): Portrait eines venezolanischen Flusses: Der Río Orituco bei Calabozo.- D. Aqu. u. Terr. Z. (DATZ), 49 (9): 599-604

Myers, G. S. (1927): Descriptions of new South American fresh-water fishes collected by Dr. Carl Ternetz.- Bull. Mus. Comp. Zool. Harvard College, 68(3): 107-135

— (1942): Studies on South American fresh-water fishes I.- Stanford ichth. Bull., 2(4): 89-114

Nelson, J. A., D. A. Wubah, M. E. Whitmer, E. A. Johnson & D. J. Stewart (1999): Wood-eating catfishes of the genus *Panaque*: gut microflora and cellulolytic enzyme activities.- Journal of Fish Biology, 54(5): 1069-1082

Nichols, J. T. (1919): Brazilian catfishes of the genus *Plecostomus* from the Museu Paulista.- Revta. Mus. Paul., 11: 3-8

Nijssen, H. & I. J. H. Isbrücker (1987): *Spectracanthicus murinus*, nouveaux genre et espèce de Poisson-Chat cuirassé du Rio Tapajós, Est. Pará, Brésil, avec des remarques sur d´autres genres de Loricariidés (Pisces, Siluriformes, Loricariidae).- Rev. fr. Aquariol. Herpét., 13(4): 93-98

Oyakawa, O. T. (1993): Cinco espécies novas de *Harttia* Steindachner, 1876 da região sudeste do Brasil, e commentários sobre e gênero (Teleostei, Siluriformes, Loricariidae).- Comm. Mus. Ciênc. PUCRS, sér. zool., Porto Alegre, 6: 3-27

Patrick, R., F. A. Aldrich, J. Cairns Jr., F. Drouet, M. H. Hohn, S. S. Roback, H. Skuja, P. J. Spangler, Y. H. Swabey & L. A. Whitford (1966): The Catherwood Foundation Peruvian Amazon expedition: limnological and systematic studies.- Monogr. Acad. Nat. Sci. Phil., 14.: 1-495

Peyer, B. (1922): Über die Flossenstacheln der Welse und Panzerwelse, sowie des Karpfens.- Morph. Jahrb., 51: 493-554

Power, M. E. (1984a): Habitat quality and the distribution of algae-grazing catfish in a panamanian stream.- Journ. Animal Ecol., 53: 357-374

— (1984b): Depth distributions of armoured catfish: predator induced resource avoidance?- Ecology, 65(2): 523-528

— (1984c): The importance of sediment in the grazing ecology and size class interactions of an armoured catfish, *Ancistrus spinosus*.- Environmental Biology of Fishes, 10(3): 173-181

Rapp Py-Daniel, L. (1981): *Furcodontichthys novaesi* n. gen., n.sp. (Osteichthys, Siluriformes, Loricariidae) na bacia Amazonica,- Brasil. Bol. Mus. Paraense E. Goeldi, Zool., 105: 1-17

— (1991): *Chaetostoma jegui*, a new mailed catfish from Rio Uraricoera, Brazil (Osteichthyes: Loricariidae).- Ichthyol. Explor. Freshwaters, 2(3): 239-246

— , L. H. & E. C. Oliveira (2001): Seven new species of Harttia from the Amazonian-Guyana region (Siluriformes: Loricariidae).- Ichtyol. Explor. Freshwaters, 12(1): 79-96

Bibliography

Reed, P. & R. Francis-Floyd (1993): Internet-Seite "Red Sore Disease in Game Fish".- University of Florida, Gainesville. URL: http://edis.ifas.ufl. edu/VM059

Regan, C. T. (1904): A monograph of the fishes of the family Loricariidae.- Trans. Zool. Soc. London 17(3): 191-350, pls. 9-21.

— (1912): Descriptions of new fishes of the family Loricariidae in the British Museum collection.- Proc. Zool. Soc. London, 1912: 666-670, pls. 75-77.

Reichenbach-Klinke, H.-H. & W. Körting (1993): Krankheiten der Aquarienfische. 4. überarbeitete Auflage.- Eugen Ulmer Verlag, Stuttgart

Reis, R. E. & E. H. L. Pereira (2000): Three New Species of the Loricariid Catfish Genus *Loricariichthys* (Teleostei: Siluriformes) from Southern South America.- Copeia, 2000(4): 1029-1047

— & S. A. Schaefer (1992): *Eurycheilus pantherinus* (Siluroidei: Loricaridae), a New Genus and Species of Hypoptopomatinae from Southern Brazil.- Copeia, 1992(1): 215-223

— & — (1993): *Eurycheilichthys* nom. Nov., a substitute name for *Eurycheilus* Reis and Schaefer, 1992 (Siluroidei: Loricariidae).- Copeia, 1993(3): 894

— & — (1998): New Cascudinhos from Southern Brazil: Sytematics, Endemism, and Relationships (Siluriformes, Loricariidae, Hypoptopomatinae).- Amer. Mus. Novitates, 3254: 1-25

Retzer, M. E. & L. M. Page (1997): Systematics of the Stick Catfishes, *Farlowella* Eigenmann & Eigenmann (Pisces, Loricariidae).- Proc. Acad. Nat. Sci. Philadelphia, 147: 33-88

—, L. G. Nico & F. Provenzano R. (1999): Two new species of *Acestridium* (Siluriformes, Loricariidae) from southern Venezuela, with observations on camouflage and color change.- Ichthyol. Explor. Freshwaters, 10(4): 313-326

Ribeiro, A. de Miranda (1907): Peixes do Iporanga – S. Paulo. Resultados de excursões do Sr. Ricardo Krone, Membro Correspondente do Museu Nacional do Rio de janeiro.- A Lavoura, Soc. Nac. Agric., 11: 185-190

— (1908): Peixes da Ribeira. Resultados des excursão do Sr. Ricardo Krone, Membro Correspondente do Museu Nacional do Rio de Janeiro.- Kosmos, Rio de Janeiro, 2: 1-5

Ribeiro, P. de Miranda (1939): Um *Parotocinclus* do nordeste brasileiro (Peixes - Loricariidae - Hypoptopomatinae).- Bol. Biol. São Paulo (n. s.), zool., 104: 1-3, i, 4 pls.

Bibliography

Rocha, A. A. & R. Linsker (1995): Brasil Aventura 2.- São Paulo, Terra Virgem ISBN 85-85981-02-4

Römer, U. & M. Wöhler (1995): Ein neuer Harnischwels aus NW-Brasilien. Beobachtungen im Gebiet des mittleren Rio Negro.- Aquarium Heute, 13(2): 74-77

Rudolph, D. & G. Rauer (1999a): Vergleichende Untersuchungen an vier Tieflandflüssen.- D. Aqu. u. Terr. Z. (DATZ), 52(4): 30-38

— & — (1999b): Vergleichende Untersuchungen an vier Tieflandflüssen. Fortsetzung.- D. Aqu. u. Terr. Z. (DATZ), 52(6): 44-51

Salazar, F. J. M., I. J. H. Isbrücker & H. Nijssen (1982): *Dentectus barbamatus*, a new genus and species of mailed catfish from the Orinoco basin of Venezuela (Pisces, Siluriformes, Loricariidae). Beaufortia, 32 (8): 125-137

Sands, D. D. (1984): Catfishes of the world. Volume 4: Aspredinidae, Doradidae & Loricariidae.- Dunure Publications, Dunure

Schaefer, C. (1994): Tagebuch vom Tapajós.- DATZ-Sonderheft "Amazonas", Stuttgart: 60-65

— (1996): Das Große Buch der Welse mit L-Nummern Register.- Bede Verlag, Ruhmannsfelden

Schaefer, S. A. (1988): A new species of the loricariid genus *Parotocinclus* from southern Venezuela (Pisces: Siluroidei).- Copeia, 1988(1): 182-188

— (1991): Phylogenetic analysis of the loricariid subfamily Hypoptopomatinae (Pisces: Siluroidei: Loricariidae), with comments on generic diagnoses and geographic distribution.- Zool. Journ. of the Linn. Soc., 102: 1-41, 19 figs.

— (1993): A remarkable occurrence of isopod parasitism on an armoured catfish, *Microlepidogaster maculipinnis*.- Journal of Fish Biology, 42: 307-310

— (1996a): *Nannoptopoma*, a new genus of Loricariid Catfishes (Siluriformes: Loricariidae) from the Amazon and Orinoco River basins.- Copeia, 1996(4): 913-926

— (1996b): Type designations for some Steindachner Loricariid material (Siluriformes: Loricariidae) in the Natural History Museum, Vienna.- Copeia, 1996(4): 1031-1035

— (1997): The neotropical cascudinhos: systematics and biogeography of the *Otocinclus* catfishes (Siluriformes: Loricariidae).- Proc. Acad. Nat. Sci. Philadelphia, 149: 1-120

923

Bibliography

— (1998): Conflict and Resolution: Impact of New Taxa on Phylogenetic Studies of the Neotropical Cascudinhos (Siluroidei: Loricariidae).- In: Phylogeny and Classification of Neotropical Fishes. Part 3: Siluriformes: 375-400

— & C. J. Ferraris (1985): A new species of *Parotocinclus* (Pisces: Loricariidae) from Guyana.- Proc. Biol. Soc. Wash., 98: 341-346

— & F. Provenzano R. (1993): The Guyana shield *Parotocinclus*: Systematics, biogeography, and description of a new Venezuelan species (Siluroidei: Loricariidae).- Ichthyol. Explor. Freshwaters, 4(1): 39-56.

— & — (1998): *Niobichthys ferrarisi*, a new genus and species of armored catfish from southern Venezuela (Siluriformes: Loricariidae).- Ichthyol. Explor. Freshwaters, 8 (3): 221-230

— & D. J. Stewart (1993): Systematics of the *Panaque dentex* species group (Siluriformes: Loricariidae), wood-eating armored catfishes from tropical South America.- Ichthyol. Explor. Freshwaters, 4(4): 309-342

Schliewen, U. & R. Stawikowski (1989): *Teleocichla*.- D. Aqu. u. Terr. Z. (DATZ), 42(4): 227-231

Schmidt, R. E. & C. J. Ferraris Jr. (1985): A new species of *Parotocinclus* (Pisces: Loricaridae) from Guyana.- Proc. Biol. Soc. Wash., 98(2): 341-346

Schramm, U. (1991a): Welse mit "Trommelfell": *Otocinclus* & Co. Teil I: Einführung - Ernährung.- Das Aquarium, 268: 14-16

— (1991b): Welse mit "Trommelfell": *Otocinclus* & Co. Teil II: Wasser, Technik und Beckeneinrichtung.- Das Aquarium, 270: 5-6

— (1992): Welse mit „Trommelfell": *Otocinclus* & Co. Teil III: Zucht und Aufzucht.- Das Aquarium, 272: 7-9

Schubart, O. (1964): Sôbre algumas Loricariidae da bacia do Rio Mogi Guaçu. Bol. Mus. Nac.- Rio de Janeiro, zool. (n. s.), 251: 1-19

Seidel, I. (1993): Über Haltung und Zucht von *Sturisomatichthys* sp. - BSSW-Report, 5(4): 89-95

— (1994): Erfahrungen mit dem Flunder-Harnischwels.- D. Aqu. u. Terr. Z. (DATZ), 47(5): 292-295

— (1995): Der Nasenharnischwels - Ein Maulbrüter der Zwergenklasse.- D. Aqu. u. Terr. Z. (DATZ), 48(2): 78-81

— (1997): *Loricaria cataphracta* Linnaeus, 1758 und *Loricaria simillima* Regan, 1904. Zwei maulbrütende Harnischwelse aus Südamerika.- Aquaristik Aktuell, 5(3): 22-2

924

Bibliography

— (2000a): Nützliche Schwarmfische aus Südamerika: Zwergharnischwelse der Gattung *Otocinclus*.- Aquaristik Aktuell, 8(7-8): 16-21

— (2000b): Zwergharnischwelse der Gattung *Otocinclus*. Aquaristik Aktuell, 8(11-12): 25-29

Sioli, H. (1967): Studies in Amazonian Waters.- Atas Simp. Biota Amazônica. Limnologia, Rio de Janeiro 3: 9-50

Stawikowski, R. (1989): Harnischwelse aus dem Rio Xingú.- D. Aqu. u. Terr. Z. (DATZ), 42(3): 173-175

— & U. Werner (1998): Die Buntbarsche Amerikas.- DATZ Aquarienbücher, Stuttgart

Steindachner, F. (1900): Das w. M. Hofrat F. Steindachner erstattet im Auftrage Ihrer königlichen Hoheit Frau Prinzessin Therese von Bayern einen vorläufigen Bericht über einige von Ihrer königlichen Hoheit während einer Reise nach Südamerika 1898 gesammelte neue Fischarten, [...].- Anz. Akad. Wiss. Wien, mathem.-naturwiss. Cl., 37(18): 206-208

— (1902): Herpetologische und ichthyologische Ergebnisse einer Reise nach Südamerika, bearbeitet von Dr. Franz Steindachner, W. M. K. Akad., mit einer Einleitung von Therese Prinzessin von Bayern. - Denkschr. Akad. Wiss. Wien, mathem.-naturwiss. Cl., 72: 89-148

Swainson, W. (1938): The natural history and classification of fishes, amphibians, & reptiles, or monocardian animals.- London. 1: i-vi + 1-368

Szidat, L. (1955): Beiträge zur Kenntnis der Reliktfauna des La Plata-Stromsystems.- Arch. Hydrobiol., 1: 209-260

Taphorn, D. C.& C. G. Lilyestrom (1984): *Lamontichthys maracaibero* y *L. llanero*, dos especies nuevas para Venezuela (Pisces, Loricariidae).- Revista Unellez de Cienc. Tecnol., 2(2): 93-99

Taylor, J. N. (1983): Field observations on the reproductive ecology of three species of armored catfishes (Loricariidae: Loricariinae) in Paraguay.- Copeia, 1983(1): 257-259

Thatcher, V. E. (1991): Amazon fish parasites.- Amazoniana, 11: 263-572

— & I. Schindler (1999): *Artystone bolivianensis* n. sp. (Isopoda, Cymothoidae) from a loricariid catfish of the Bolivian Amazon.- Amazoniana, 15 (3/4): 183-191

Tschudi, J. J. von (1846): Ichthyologie. Pp. ii-xxx + 1-35, Pls. 1-6.- In: Untersuchungen über die Fauna Peruana. Scheitlin & Zollikofer, St. Gallen. 1844-46, in 12 parts. Fauna Peru

Bibliography

Untergasser, D. (1989): Krankheiten der Aquarienfische.- Kosmos-Verlag, Stuttgart

Val, A. L. & V. M. F. de Almeida-Val (1995): Fishes of the Amazon and their environment.- Zoophysiology. Vol. 32. Springer-Verlag, Berlin

Vierke, J. (1983): Yarinacocha – ein Paradies für Salmler und Welse.- Aquarien Magazin, 17(8): 437-443

Weidner, T. (1994): Neue Loricariiden aus Venezuela.- D. Aqu. u. Terr. Z. (DATZ), 47(12): 755-756

— & C. Zölch (1994): *Pseudohemiodon laticeps*.- D. Aqu. u. Terr. Z. (DATZ), 47(5): 295-297

Weitzman, S. H. & M. Weitzman (1982): Biogeography and Evolutionary Diversification in Neotropical Freshwater Fishes, with Comments on the Ruge Theory.- In: Biological diversification in the tropic. Colombia University Press, New York: 403-422

Wendenburg, H.(1993): *Otocinclus* cf. *notatus*, klein und empfehlenswert.- Wels-Jahrbuch 1994, Kollnburg: 83-85

— (1996): Eine *Otocinclus*-Art aus den venezolanischen Llanos.- D. Aqu. u. Terr. Z. (DATZ), 49(3): 148-150

— (1997): "Trommelfell-Welse". Auf der Suche nach *Otocinclus* im Departement Ucayali, Peru.- Das Aquarium, 341: 22-26

Werner, U. (1992): Harnischwelse einer selten gepflegten Gattung: *Loricariichthys*.- DATZ-Sonderheft "Harnischwelse", Stuttgart: 39-41

Bibliography for the Families Cetopsidae, Nema-togenyidae, and Trichomycteridae

The pertinent literature cited for the families Cetopsidae, Nematogenyidae, and Trichomycteridae is listed below. We have chosen to divide the bibliography, in order to give the interested aquarist a better overview of the specialized literature of these catfishes in particular.
General lists, as well as standard references of the Neotropical ichthyological fauna, are given in the bibliography pertinent to suckermouth catfishes.

Arratia, G. (1983): Preferencias de habitat de peces siluriformes de aguas continentales de Chile (Fam. Diplomystidae y Trichomycteridae).- Stud. Neotrop. Fauna Environm., 18(4): 217-237

— (1990): The South American Trichomycterinae (Teleostei: Siluriformes), a problematic group.- In: Vertebrates in the tropics (ed. Peters & Hutterer), Mus. A. König, Bonn

— (1998): *Silvinichthys*, a new genus of trichomycterid catfishes from the Argentinian Andes, with redescription of *Trichomycterus nigrican*s.- Ichthyol. Explor. Freshwaters, 9(4): 347-370

—, A. Chang, S. Menu-Marque & G. Rojas (1978): About *Bullockia* gen. nov., *Trichomyterus mendozensis* n. sp. and a revision of the family Trichomyteridae (Pisces, Siluriformes). - Studies on Neotropical Fauna, 13 (1978): 157-194

— & S. Menu-Marque (1981): Revision of the Freshwater Catfishes of the Genus *Hatcheria* (Siluriformes, Trichomycteridae) with Comments on Ecology and Biogeography.- Zool. Anz.Jena, 207 (1/2): 88-111

Mercedes Azpelicueta, de las, M. &. A. Rubilar (1998): A miocene *Nematogenys* (Teleostei: Siluriformes: Nematogenyidae) from south-central Chile. - Journ. Vertebr. Paleontology, 18 (3): 475-483

Baskin, J. N. (1978): Structure and relationships of the Trichomycteridae. - Unpublished ph. D. dissertation, City University of New York, published by Univ. Microfilms Intern., Ann Arbor, London, i-xxi, 1-389

Bibliography

—, T. M. Zaret & F. Mago-Leccia (1978): Feeding of Reportedly Parasitic Catfishes (Trichomycteridae and Cetopsidae) in the Rio Portuguesa Basin, Venezuela.- Biotropica, 12(3): 182-186

Bleeker, P. (1862): Atlas ichthyologique des Indes Orientales Néelandaises. Tome II. Silurodes, Chacoides et Heterobranchoides.- J. Smith and Gide, Amsterdam

Burgess, W. E. (1989): An atlas of Freshwater and Marine catfishes. A preliminary survey of the Siluriformes.- Neptune City

Campanario, C. M. & M. C. C. de Pinna (2001): A new species of the primitive trichomycterid subfamily Copionodontinae from northeastern Brazil (Teleostei: Trichomycteridae).- Ichthyol. Explor. Freshwaters, 11(4): 369-375

Costa, W. J. E. M. (1992): Description de huit nouvelles espèces du genre *Trichomycterus* (Siluriformes: Trichomycteridae) du Brèsil oriental.- Rev. fr.Aquariol., 18(4): 101-110

— (1994): A new genus and species of Sarcoglanidinae (Siluriformes: Trichomycteridae) from the Araguaia basin, central Brazil, with notes on subfamilial phylogeny.- Ichthyol. Explor.Freshwaters, 5(3): 207-216

— & F.A. Bockmann (1993): Un nouveau genre néotropical de la famille des Trichomycteridae (Siluriformes: Loricarioidei).- Rev.fr.Aquariol., 20(2): 4346

— & — (1994a): A new genus and species of Sarcoglanidinae (Siluriformes: Trichomycteridae) from southeastern Brazil, with a re-examination of subfamilial phylogeny.- Journ.Nat.Hist., 28: 715-730

— & — (1994b): *Typhlobelus macromycterus*, a new blind glanapterygine fish (Siluriformes Trichomycteridae) from the Rio Tocantins, Brazil.- Tropical Zoology, 7: 67-72

Devincenzi, G. L. & R. Vaz-Ferreira (1939): Nota preliminar sobre un pygidido hematófago del Rio Uruguay.-Arch. Soc. Bio. Montevideo, 9 (3): 165-178

Eigenmann, C. H. (1912): The Fresh Water fishes of Britisch Guiana, Including a Study of the Ecological Grouping of species and the Relation of the Fauna of the Plateau to That of the Lowlands. - Memoirs of the Carnegie Museum, 5: 1-578

Bibliography

— **(1917):** Description of Sixteen New Species of Pygidiidae.- Proc. Amer. Phil.S oc., 16: 690-703

— **(1918a):** Eighteen new species of fishes from northwestern South America.- Proc. Amer. phil.Soc., 56(7): 673-689

— **(1918b):** The Pygidiidae, a Family of South American Catfishes.- Mem. Carnegie Mus., 7 (5): 159-373

— **& R. S. Eigenmann (1889):** Preliminary Notes on South American Nematognathi.- Proc. Calif. Acad. Sci., 2: 28-56

— **& — (1890):** A Revision of the South American Nematognathi or Cat-Fishes.- Occ.Pap. Calif. Acad. Sci., 1: 1-508

Evers, H.-G. (1993): Die Sabanas de Rascamula. Ein venezolanisches Wels-"Traum-Biotop".- Welsjahrbuch 1994, Kollnburg: 12-16

— **(1998):** Beobachtungen an Welsen im Südosten Brasiliens.- D.Aqu. u.Terr.Z., DATZ, 51(10): 620-622

Fernandez, L. & R. P. Vari, (2000): New Species of *Trichomycterus* (Teleostei: Siluriformes: Trichomycteridae) Lacking a Pelvic Fin and Girdle from the Andes of Argentina.- Copeia, 2000 (4): 990-996

Fernandez-Yepez, A. (1964): El genero *Hemicetopsis* Bleeker, 1863 (Cetopsidae) en Venezuela. - In Lagena, Cumana, 1964

Ferraris, C. J., Jr. (1996): *Denticetopsis*, a new genus of South American whale catfishes (Siluriformes: Cetopsidae, Cetopsinae), with two new species.- Proc. Calif. Acad.Sci, 49(6): 161-170

Ferraris, C .J., Jr.& B. A. Brown (1991): A new Species of *Pseudocetopsis* from the Rio Negro Drainage of Venezuela (Siluriformes: Cetopsidae). Copeia, 1991 (1): 161-165

Goulding, M. (1980): The fishes and the forest. Explorations in Amazonian Natural History.- Univers.Cal., Berkeley, U.S.A.

Hoffmann, P. & M. Hoffmann (1998): Erste Beobachtungen zur Fortpflanzung von Schmerlenwelsen.- D.Aqu. u. Terr. Z., DATZ, 51(7): 429-431

Isbrücker, I. J. H. (1986): Trichomycteridae, mysterieuze meervallen.- Het Aquarium, 56: 274-279

Bibliography

Kelly, W. E. & J. W. Atz (1964): A pygidiid catfish that can suck blood from goldfish.- Copeia, 1964(4), 702-703

Landim, M.I. & W.J.E.M. Costa (2002): *Listura tetraradiata* (Siluriformes: Trichomycteridae): A New Glanapterygine Catfish from the Southeastern Brazilian Coatal Plain.- Copeia, 2002 (1): 132-156

Lüling, K. H. (1984): Über einige bemerkenswerte Welse Amazoniens.- Natur und Museum, 114(11): 323-327

Lundberg, J. G. & L. Rapp Py-Daniel (1994): *Bathycetopsis oliveirai*, Gen.et Sp.Nov., a Blind and Depigmented Catfish (Siluriformes: Cetopsidae) from the Brazilian Amazon.- Copeia, 1994(2): 381-390

Machado, F. A. & I. Sazima (1983): Comportamento alimentar dp peixe hematófago *Branchioca bertonii* (Siluriformes, Trichomycteridae).- Ciencas e Cultura, 35(3): 344-348

Manriquez, A., L. Huaquin, M. Arellano & G. Arratia (1988): Aspectos Reproductivos de *Trichomycterus areolatus* Valenciennes, 1846 (Pisces: Teleostei: Siluriformes) en Rio Angosturo, Chile.- Stud. Neotrop. Fauna Environm., 23(2): 89-102

Myers, G. S. & S. H. Weitzman (1966): Two remarkable new trichomycterid catfishes from the Amazon basin in Brazil and Colombia.- J. Zool., London, 149: 277-287

Nico, L. G. & M. C. C. de Pinna (1996): Confirmation of *Glanapteryx anguilla* (Siluriformes, Trichomycteridae) in the Orinoko river basin, with notes on the distribution and habitats of the Glanapteryginae.- Ichthyol. Explor. Freshwaters, 7(1): 27-32

Pinna, M. C. C. de (1988): A new genus of trichomycterid catfish (Siluroidei, Glanapteryginae) with comments on its phylogenetic relationships.- Revue suisse Zool., 95(1): 113-128

— (1989a): A new Sarcoglanidine Catfish, Phylogeny of Its Subfamily, and Appraisal of the Phyletic Status of the Trichomycterinae (Teleostei, Trichomycteridae).- Amer.Mus. Novitates, 2950: 1-39

— (1989b): Redescription of *Glanapteryx anguilla*, with Notes on the Phylogeny of Glanapteryginae (Siluriformes, Trichomycteridae).- Proc. Acad.Nat.Sci. Philadelphia, 141: 361-374

— **(1992a)**: *Trichomycterus castroi*, a new species of trichomycterid catfish from the Rio Iguacu of Southeastern Brazil (Teleostei: Siluriformes).- Ichthyol.Explor. Freshwaters, 3(1): 89-95

— **(1992b)**: A new subfamily of Trichomycteridae (Teleostei, Siluriformes), lower loricarioid relationships and a discussion on the impact of additional taxa for phylogenetic analysis.- Zool.Jour. Linnean Soc., 106: 175-229

— **& H. A. Britski (1991)**: *Megalocentor*, a new genus of parasitic catfish from the Amazon basin: the sister group of *Apomatoceros* (Trichomycteridae: Stegophilinae).- Ichthyol. Explor. Freshwaters, 2(2): 113-128

— **& W. Starnes (1990)**: A new genus and species of Sarcoglanidinae from the Rio Mamoré, Amazon Basin, with comments on subfamilial phylogeny (Teleostei, Trichomycteridae).- J. Zool.Lond., 222: 75-88

— **& R. P. Vari (1995)**: Monophyly and Phylogenetic Diagnosis of the Family Cetopsidae, with Synonymization of the Helogenidae (Teleostei: Siluriformes). - Smiths. Contrib. Zool., 571: 1-26

— **& K. O. Winemiller (2001)**: A new species of *Ammoglanis* (Siluriformes: Trichomycteridae) from Venezuela.- Ichthyol. Explor. Freshwaters, 11(3): 255-264

Reinhardt, J. T. (1958): *Stegaphilus insidiosus*, en ny Mallefish fra Brasilien of dens Levemaade.- Vidensk. Medd. Dansk Naturh. Foren. Kjob. Aaret 1858: 79-97, pl.2

Ribeiro, P. de Miranda (1949): Notas para o estudo dos Pygidiidae Brasileiros (Pisces - Pygidiidae, Pygidiinae) III.- Bol.do Mus.Nac. Zool., 88: 1-3

Ringuelet, R., R. Alonso de Aramburu & R. Aramburu (1967): Los peces de agua dulce de la República Argentina.- Com. Nac. Inv.Cient. Buenos Aires: 1-602

Schindler, I. (1993): Die Fähnchenwelse - Helogenidae. Arten-Ökologie-Aquarienhaltung.- Wels-Jahrbuch 1994: 68-76. Kollnburg

Schreiber, R. (1992): Nichts für sanfte Gemüter: *Pseudostegophilus nemurus*.- Welsjahrbuch 1993: 64-65, Kollnburg

Seidel, I. (1997): Vier aquaristisch neue Welse aus dem Einzugsgebiet des Rio Ucayali in Ostperu.- BSSW-Report, 9(1): 6-12

Bibliography

Tchernavin, V. V. (1944): A Revision of some Trichomycterinae based on material preserved in the British Museum (Natural History).- Proc. Zool.Soc.Lond., 114: 234-275

Trajano, E. & M. C. C. de Pinna (1996): A new cave species of Trichomycterus from Eastern Brazil (Siluriformes, Trichomycteridae).- Rev. fr. Aquariol., 23(3-4): 85-90

Ufermann, A. (1991): Ernährung durch Hautschleim bei Schmerlenwelsen.- D. Aqu. u.Terr.Z., DATZ, 44(9): 552-553

Vari, R. P. & H. Ortega (1986): The Catfishes of the Neotropical Family Helogenidae (Ostariophysi: Siluroidea):- Smithsonian Contrib. Zool., 442: 1-20

Vaz-Ferreira, R. & C. Rios-Parodi (1975): Trichomycteridae y otros peces que ocupan el piso de las corrientes de agua dulce.- Rev.Biol. Uruguay, 3(2): 87-102

— & B. Sierra de Soriano (1959): Relacion entre las longitudes antedorsal y anteventral y la longitud del cuerpo en dos Trichomycteridae (Pisces, Siluroidei). Arch. Soc. Biol. Montevideo, 24-81

Werner, U. (1992): Fischfangabenteuer Südamerika. Reisen in Sachen Aquaristik.- Landbuch, Hannover

Winemiller, K. O.& H. Y. Yan (1989): Obligate Mucus-feeding in a South American Trichomycterid Catfish (Pisces, Ostariophysi).- Copeia 1989 (2): 511-514

Index

Currently valid scientific names and "working names" for new species are in **bold**. Species and genera additionally are in *italics*.
Synonyms are in *italics* and light. Common names are listed in normal, light font.

Index

Index

Index

Index

Index

940

Index

DR. UWE RÖMER
1311 pages, ca. 1400 color photos, 150 drawings, 12.5 x 19 cm

This CICHLID ATLAS is a must-have for every enthusiast of South American dwarf cichlids. All of the described *Apistogramma* species, many of which are novelties, are presented. An original key to identify *Apistogramma* spp. has been included as well as explanations on maintenance, breeding, and factors determinig sex. Species identification of juvenile and female *Apistogramma* spp. gives aquarists assurance that he/she is maintaining pure blood lines. Numerous drawings, distribution charts, and the most extensive bibliography ever assembled for the genus complete this reference.

ISBN 3-88244-056-2 (hardcover)